THE CHRISTIAN BED & BREAKFAST DIRECTORY

2003–2004 Edition

BARBOUR BOOKS

An Imprint of Barbour Publishing, Inc.

Published by Barbour Books, an imprint of Barbour Publishing, Inc., P.O. Box 719, Uhrichsville, Ohio 44683, www.barbourbooks.com

 Member of the
Evangelical Christian
Publishers Association

Printed in the United States of America.

Table of Contents

How to Use This Book

Have you ever dreamed of spending a few days in a rustic cabin in Alaska? Would you like to stay in an urban town house while taking care of some business in the city? Would your family like to spend a weekend on a Mid-western farm feeding pigs and gathering eggs? Maybe a romantic Victorian mansion in San Francisco or an antebellum plantation in Mississippi is what you've been looking for. No matter what your needs may be, whether you are traveling for business or pleasure, you will find a variety of choices in the 2003–2004 edition of *The Christian Bed & Breakfast Directory*.

In the pages of this guide you will find over 1,200 bed and breakfasts, small inns, and homestays. All of the information has been updated from last year's edition, and many entries are listed for the first time. Although not every establishment is owned or operated by Christians, each host has ex-pressed a desire to welcome Christian travelers.

The directory is designed for easy reference. At a glance, you can determine the number of rooms available at each establishment and how many rooms have private (PB) and shared (SB) baths. You will find the name of the host or hosts, the price range for two people sharing one room, the kind of breakfast that is served, and what credit cards are accepted. There is a "Notes" section to let you know important information that may not be included in the description. These notes correspond to the list at the bottom of each page. The descriptions have been written by the hosts. The publisher has not visited these bed and breakfasts and is not responsible for inaccuracies.

General maps are provided to help you with your travel plans. Included are the towns where our bed and breakfasts are located, some reference cities, and major highways. Please use your road map for additional assistance and details when planning your trip.

It is recommended that you make reservations in advance. Many bed and breakfasts have small staffs or are run single-handedly and cannot easily accommodate surprises. Also ask about taxes, as city and state taxes vary. Remember to ask for directions, and if your special dietary needs can be met, and confirm check-in and check-out times. Whether you're planning a honeymoon, family vacation, or business trip, *The Christian Bed & Breakfast Directory* will make any outing out of the ordinary.

Log on to www.christianbedbreakfast.com for the latest information on Christian bed and breakfast lodgings. . . .
• Search geographically by zip code, area code, or state. . .search according to nearby attractions (such as tennis, golf, or skiing).
• Check out "Today's Featured Inn," and find some great ideas for future trips.
• Enjoy the exclusive "B & B Cookbook," recipes from many of our featured inns.

www.christianbedbreakfast.com also provides a direct link to E-mail listed B & Bs and to state tourism bureaus. Along with the directory, it's the one-stop resource you need to plan your next adventure.

ALABAMA

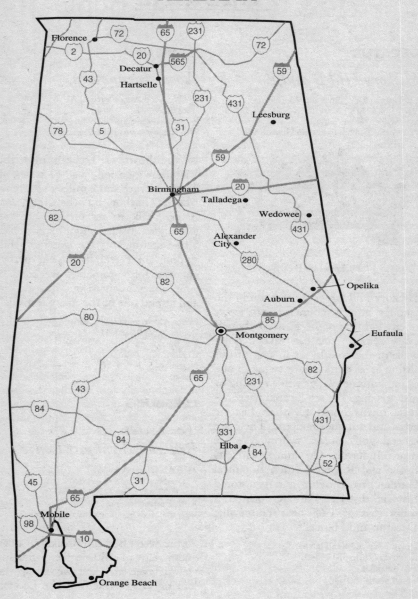

Alabama

DECATUR

Hickory Hill B and B

224 Hagood Dr., Somerville, AL 35670
(256) 584-6972
E-mail: kkjh1@aol.com
Web site: www.bbonline.com/al/hickoryhill

Hickory Hill B & B

Hickory Hill is a very quiet inn in the country, atop a mountain with views of city lights at night. Flowers abound every season. You can take a quiet walk in the woods, sit in one of our sitting areas outdoors, or swing in one of our antique swings while reading or just relaxing. We are located near historic towns noted for their historic areas and antique shopping. There are several golf courses nearby. We are near Huntsville (20 min.), with its Space and Rocket Center, Botanical Garden, Art Museum, and its restored historic district. We are located 5 miles east of I-65 near Huntsville, Decatur, and Hartselle.

Hosts: Joyce and Ken Helphand
Rooms: 3 (2PB;1SB) $75–85
Full Breakfast
Credit Cards: A B D
Notes: 2 5 7 8 9 10

FLORENCE

Wood Avenue Inn

658 N. Wood Ave., Florence, AL 35630-4608
(256) 766-8441
E-mail: woodaveinn@aol.com
Web site: www.woodavenueinn.com

In the heart of Dixie stands this Victorian mansion, just 13 miles off Natchez Trace and 2 miles to Florence Marina harbor on the Tennessee River. Walk to restaurants, art galleries, and antique shopping; or enjoy bird-watching on the porches while sipping mint tea! Plan your perfect getaway for a romantic weekend or your honeymoon in our historic city and attend one of the many festivals!

Hosts: Alvern and Gene Greeley
Rooms: 4 (4PB) $80–115
Full Breakfast
Credit Cards: A B D
Notes: 4 5 7 8 9 10

LEESBURG

The Secret Bed and Breakfast Lodge

2356 AL Highway 68 W.
   Leesburg, AL 35983-4000
(256) 523-3825; Fax (256) 523-6477
E-mail: secret@tds.net
Web site: www.bbonline.com/al/thesecret

At the Secret Bed and Breakfast Lodge, guests have a 180-degree panoramic view of seven cities and two states, overlooking Weiss Lake from the Lookout

---

NOTES: Credit cards accepted: A Master Card; B Visa; C American Express; D Discover; E Diners Club; F Other; 2 Personal checks accepted; 3 Lunch available; 4 Dinner available; 5 Open all year;

Mountain Parkway. Rooftop pool. Vaulted ceiling in lodge area and bedrooms. The lodge offers king/queen beds, TVs, VCRs, private baths, Jacuzzis, fireplace, and balconies. AAA star rating. A special place—a secret with a view as spectacular in the day as it is enchanting at night. Come. Discover. Enjoy!

The Secret Bed and Breakfast Lodge

Hosts: Carl and Diann Cruickshank
Rooms: 8 (8PB) $95–145
Full Breakfast
Credit Cards: A B
Notes: 2 5 8 9 10 11 12

MONTGOMERY

Red Bluff Cottage

551 Clay St., Montgomery, AL 36104
(334) 264-0056; (888) 551-2529
    Fax (334) 263-3054
E-mail: redblufbnb@aol.com
Web site: www.redbluffcottage.com

Everyone has heard about Southern hospitality, but at Red Bluff Cottage, we invite you to experience true Alabama hospitality. Our spacious and airy cottage, filled with family antiques, is located high above the Alabama River in the downtown historic Cottage Hill

District. Relax after a day of travel or work in our clean, comfortable, and cozy rooms; or just unwind from your day's activities in our peaceful gazebo. Our large veranda gives a panoramic view of the river plain and downtown Montgomery, including a unique view of the state capitol. Start your next morning off with a bountiful and sumptuous breakfast. Find out why we have become known as Montgomery's premier B & B, and experience for yourself what we mean when we say you will "Arrive as guests, depart as friends."

Hosts: Barry and Bonny Ponstein
Rooms: 4 (4PB) $90
Full Breakfast
Credit Cards: A B C D
Notes: 2 5 7 10

Red Bluff Cottage

ORANGE BEACH

The Original Romar House

23500 Perdido Beach Blvd.
    Orange Beach, AL 36561-3007
(251) 974-1625; (800) 847-6627
    Fax (251) 974-1163
E-mail: original@gulftel.com
Web site: www.bbonline.com/al/romarhouse

Wake up to rediscover romance in a charmingly historic atmosphere, as the sun streams through the stained-glass windows of your art deco-furnished

---

6 Pets welcome; 7 Children welcome; 8 Tennis nearby; 9 Swimming nearby; 10 Golf nearby; 11 Skiing nearby; 12 May be booked through travel agent

room. After breakfast, take a morning swim or stroll along the beach collecting seashells, curl up in a cypress swing or hammock and read a book, or relax in the hot-tub whirlpool spa. You are only minutes by car to gift shops, golf courses, seafood restaurants, and entertainment. Break away from your everyday world. Come, be a part of the history at the Original Romar House bed and breakfast inn.

Hosts: Darrell Finley, Mgr.
    Jerry Gilbreath, Owner
Rooms: 7 (7PB) $79–129
Full Breakfast
Credit Cards: A B C
Notes: 2 5 8 9 10

ALASKA

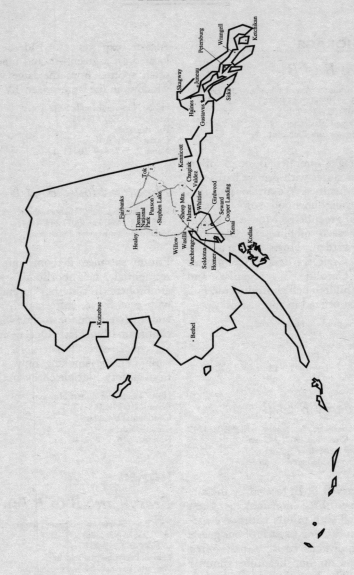

Petersburg
Wrangell
Ketchikan
Skagway
Juneau
Haines
Sitka
Gustavus
Kennicott
Tok
Chugiak
Valdez
Girdwood
Fairbanks
Paxson
Stephen Lake
Sheep Mtn.
Whittier
Seward
Cooper Landing
Denali
National
Park
Palmer
Kenai
Kodiak
Healey
Wasilla
Anchorage
Willow
Soldotna
Homer

Kotzebue

Bethel

Alaska

ANCHORAGE

Camai B & B

3838 Westminster Way, Anchorage, AK 99508
(907) 333-2219; (800) 659-8763
   Fax (907) 337-3959
E-mail: camai@alaska.net
Web site: www.camaibnb.com

Anchorage's premier B & B offers spacious suites with private baths and many amenities. We are located in a quiet neighborhood on Chester Creek's greenbelt. Moose are frequently seen nibbling in Caroline's flower garden. Hosts are active in church. Craig is Missions Committee chair. Caroline is organist and youth/children bell choir director. Full breakfast offered in summer only.

Hosts: Craig and Caroline Valentine
Rooms: 3 (3PB) $45–110
Full Breakfast
Credit Cards: F
Notes: 2 5 7 8 9 10 11 12

Elderberry B & B

8340 Elderberry St., Anchorage, AK 99502-4245
(907) 243-6968 ; Fax (907) 243-6968
E-mail: elderberry-b-b@gci.net
Web site: www.elderberrybb.com

Elderberry B & B, located by the airport, has three nonsmoking guest rooms, all with private baths. We specialize in catering to each of our guests on an individual basis. Guests often comment on our beautiful summer flowers. The hosts love to share their Alaska experiences. Elderberry is located on a greenbelt, and moose are often spotted from the large viewing windows in the large-screen TV room.

Hosts: Norm and Linda Seitz
Rooms: 3 (3PB) $75–95
Full Breakfast
Credit Cards: A B
Notes: 2 5 7 8 9 10 11 12

Houston House B & B

9041 Amanda Circle, Anchorage, AK 99502
(907) 248-4454; Fax (907) 248-4454
Web site: www.houstonshouse.com

Private entrance, 2-room suite, quiet residential neighborhood. Family atmosphere. In suite hot beverage cart with microwave, coffeemaker, toaster, and small refrigerator stocked with nice continental breakfast. Queen-size bed and queen-size sleeper sofa. Private bath. Outside smoking only. 4 miles from airport. Flexible check-in time.

Hosts: Linda and Robert Houston
Rooms: 1 (1PB) $65–95
Continental Breakfast
Credit Cards:
Notes: 2 5 6 7 8 9 10 11

HOMER

Beary Patch B & B Inn

P. O. Box 1544, 664 Soundview, Homer, AK 99603
(907) 235-2483; (888) 977-2327
   Fax (907) 235-2327
E-mail: bearybb@ptialaska.net
Web site: www.alaska-beary-patch.com

Homer's only gourmet breakfast and complimentary evening desserts. If you want beautiful decor, wonderful hospitality, while enjoying our pristine hamlet, come and stay at the Beary Patch! Our beds are so comfy that you won't want to get up in the morning. But the tantilizing aromas coming from the kitchen will entice you to get to the table first. Mmm, fresh-roasted, rich coffee; sizzling Alaskan sausages on the grill; hot, mouthwatering homemade breads.

Hosts: Raymond and Coletta Walker
Rooms: 4 (2PB;2SB) $79–119
Full Breakfast
Credit Cards: A B
Notes: 2 5 8 9 10 12

Spruce Acre Private Cabins

910 Sterling Hwy, Homer, AK 99603-8301
(907) 235-8388; (877) 500-7404
   Fax (907) 235-0636
E-mail: sprucea@ptialaska.net
Web site: www.spruceacrecabins.com

Wonderful view of mountains and Kachemak Bay and glaciers, cozy, comfortable country Victorian decor, squeaky   clean.   Private   baths. Kitchenettes,   satellite   TV/VCR. Phones, laundry facilities, freezer space.   Mocha,   coffee,   and   tea. Homemade breads. Outside smoking only. Reasonable rates. RV parking. Est. 1987.

Hosts: John and Joyce Williams
Rooms: 6 (4PB;2SB) $65–105
Continental Breakfast
Credit Cards: A B D
Notes: 2 5 6 7 8 9 10 11

Three Moose Meadow Wilderness B & B

P. O. Box 15291, Homer, AK 99603-6291
(907) 235-0755; (1-8) 777-0930
   Fax (907) 235-0755
E-mail: 3moose@xyz.net
Web site: www.threemoose.com

Spirit-filled couple invites you to enjoy your own log cabin in a serene wilderness setting. Your private cabin overlooks beautiful, snowcapped mountains and glaciers. All are fully equipped with kitchen, bath, living room, and a bedroom with a queen bed. All have fireplaces and porch swing.

Hosts: Jordan and Jennie Hess
Rooms: 5 (5PB) $95–165
Continental Breakfast
Credit Cards: A B
Notes: 5 7 10 11

JUNEAU

A Cozy Log Bed and Breakfast

8668 Dudley St., Juneau, AK 99801
(907) 789-2582 ; Fax (907) 789-3617
E-mail: cozylog@alaska.net
Web site: www.cozylog.net

Imagine sitting on the porch of your Alaskan log home in the heart of Juneau's recreation area, just 5 minutes from the airport and shopping and 15 minutes from the city. The quiet of the forest and majesty of the Mendenhall Glacier are only heartbeats away. From cozy beds to all the little extras, your stay will be a relaxed and memorable one.

Hosts: Bruce and Judy Bowler

---

6 Pets welcome; 7 Children welcome; 8 Tennis nearby; 9 Swimming nearby; 10 Golf nearby; 11 Skiing nearby; 12 May be booked through travel agent

Rooms: 2 (2SB) $65–99
Full Breakfast
Credit Cards: A B C D
Notes: 2 5 6 7 8 9 10 11 12

KENAI

Eldridge Haven B & B

2679 Bowpicker Ln., Kenai, AK 99611-8835
(907) 283-7152 ; Fax (907) 283-7152
E-mail: lridgebb@ptialaska.net
Web site: www.ptialaska.net/~lridgebb

Eldridge Haven B & B is hospitality at its best: peaceful, clean, friendly! Excellent food includes giant Alaskan pancakes, steaming gingered bananas, stuffed scones, and more. It's in a wooded area surrounded by prime habitat for moose, caribou, bald eagles, and waterfowl. You can walk to the beach. Cross-country skiing is convenient. The lodging is close to all Peninsula points, including Seward and Homer. So eliminate packing and unpacking; stay with the best and visit the rest. Children are treasured; guests are pampered. Eldridge Haven B & B is open year-round. We've been serving satisfied guests since 1987.

Host: Marta Eldridge
Rooms: 2 (1PB;1SB) $65–80
Full Breakfast
Credit Cards: A B
Notes: 2 5 7 10 11 12

PALMER

Hatcher Pass B & B

HC05 Box 6797D, Palmer, AK 99645-9611
(907) 745-6788 ; Fax (907) 745-6787
E-mail: cabins@hatcherpassbb.com
Web site: www.hatcherpassbb.com

Stay at Hatcher Pass Bed and Breakfast, where you will experience Alaska's finest log cabins with all the modern conveniences of private bath, kitchenette, phone, and TV/VCR. Nestled at the base of beautiful Hatcher Pass, Alaska—home to a variety of outdoor activities in any season—only 50 miles north of Anchorage and 8 miles from Palmer. Relax in the comfort and beauty that is yours at Hatcher Pass Bed and Breakfast.

Hosts: Dan and Liz Hejl
Rooms: 5 (5PB) $70–125
Full Breakfast
Credit Cards: A B
Notes: 2 5 6 7 8 9 10 11 12

SEWARD

Bell–in–the–Woods B & B

P. O. Box 345, Seward, AK 99664
(907) 224-7271; Fax (907) 224-7271
E-mail: bellwoodbnb@juno.com
Web site: www.bellinthewoodsbnb.com

A full, hot breakfast awaits you when you stay in one of our five guest bedrooms or two family suites during your visit to the pristine Kenai Peninsula in the heart of south central Alaska. Nature cruises out of Seward and hiking and fishing are nearby.

Hosts: Jerry and Peggy Woods
Rooms: 7 (7PB) $109–170
Full Breakfast
Credit Cards: A B C D
Notes: 2 5 7 12

NOTES: Credit cards accepted: A Master Card; B Visa; C American Express; D Discover; E Diners Club; F Other; 2 Personal checks accepted; 3 Lunch available; 4 Dinner available; 5 Open all year;

SITKA

Alaska Ocean View Bed and Breakfast

1101 Edgecumbe Dr., Sitka, AK 99835-7122
(904) 747-8310; Fax (907) 747-3440
E-mail: alaskaoceanview@gci.net
Web site: www.sitka-alaska-lodging.com

This popular lodging is rated one of "Alaska's Best!" Drift to sleep on an exceptionally comfortable king/queen bed under a fluffy down comforter after a relaxing soak in the patio Jacuzzi. Wake to the wonderful aroma of a delicious, generous breakfast. In-room TV/VCR/DVD, stereo, refrigerator, microwave, coffeemaker, and phone are provided. Enjoy the extensive library, beautiful fireplaces, lush rock gardens, magnificent view, and gracious, genuinely warm, cheerful hospitality. Centrally located, all non-smoking, outstanding concierge.

Hosts: Carole and Bill Denkinger
Rooms: 3 (3PB) $89–179
Full Breakfast
Credit Cards: A B C D E
Notes: 2 5 7 8 9 10 12

SOLDOTNA

Longmere Lake Lodge B & B

P. O. Box 1707, Soldotna, AK 99669
(907) 262-9799; Fax (907) 262-5937
E-mail: bblodge@ptialaska.net
Web site: www.longmerelakelodge.com

Longmere Lake Lodge is located on the Kenai Peninsula 6 miles from the town of Soldotna and the Kenai River. Five bedrooms all with private baths plus a large apartment is decorated in Alaskan artifacts collected by longtime Alaskan hosts, Tom and Pat. A picturesque lake setting, immaculate facilities, and warm service have given Longmere Lake Lodge B & B a strong reputation.

Hosts: Tom and Pat Dwinnell
Rooms: 5 (5PB) $75–135
Full Breakfast
Credit Cards: A B
Notes: 2 5 7 9 10 12

STERLING

J C's Bed and Breakfast

P. O. Box 1761; 36885 Beau Circle
   Soldotna, AK 99669
(907) 260-3856
E-mail: jcbb@ptialaska.net
Web site: www.ptialaska.net/~jcbb

Master suite with private bath w/king or twin beds. Shared bath, queen suite w/lakeview. Beautiful B & B on Whisper Lake just 7 miles to Soldotna and Kenai River, where king salmon fishing is awesome!

Hosts: Jack and Cheryl Page
Rooms: 2 (1PB;1SB) $140–180
Full Breakfast
Credit Cards: A B
Notes: 2 5 7 9 10

WASILLA

Alaska's Snowed Inn

495 S. Begich Dr., Wasilla, AK 99654
(907) 376-7495; (866) 799-5169
E-mail: snowedinn@gci.net

Snowed Inn is located in pristine Matanuska Valley just 40 minutes north of Anchorage. The inn offers two large suites with private balconies and spectacular views. Relax on our Victorian porch in a quiet, secluded setting. Enjoy a hearty Alaskan sourdough breakfast. Book a salmon excursion on the Little Susitna River. Experience the Iditarod Race Headquarters, walk on the Matanuska Glacier, go flight-seeing from Talkeetna for awesome views of Denali. Experience Alaska at its best from our comfortable inn.

Hosts: David and Charlotte Crockett
Rooms: 2 (1PB;1SB) $100–125
Full Breakfast
Credit Cards: A B
Notes: 5   7 8 9 10 11 12

Alaska's Snowed Inn

ARIZONA

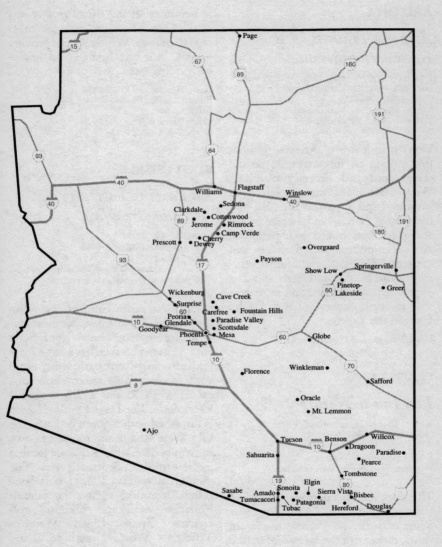

Arizona

Arizona Trails B & B Reservation Service

P. O. Box 18998, Fountain Hills, AZ 85269-8998
(480) 837-4284; (888) 799-4284
  Fax (480) 816-4224
E-mail: aztrails@arizonatrails.com
Web site: www.arizonatrails.com

Don't plan a trip to Arizona without first calling us for statewide central reservations and itinerary planning. We offer accommodations at inspected and approved B & Bs, historic inns, hotels, and ranches. Ask about our customized tour packages, golf vacations, romance packages, and car rental discounts. Additional services available in San Diego and Las Vegas. Arizona's largest and most reliable reservation service. Your Grand Canyon star experts.

Hosts: Roxanne and Hank Boryczki

FLAGSTAFF

Fall Inn to Nature

8080 N. Colt Dr., Flagstaff, AZ 86004
(928) 714-0237; (888) 920-0237
  Fax (928) 714-0237
E-mail: fallinn@infomagic.com
Web site: www.bbonline.com/az/fallinn/

The place with the personal touch like visiting old friends! One-story cedar home sits on 2½ acres, mountain views, pines with the sounds of nature in a country setting. Small group tours to the Grand Canyon, in-house massage therapists. Winter special January –April. Hot tub, hiking, and horseback riding close by.

Hosts: Annette and Ron Fallaha
Rooms: 3 (2PB;1SB) $65–95
Full Breakfast
Credit Cards: A B C
Notes: 5 7 8 10 11 12

SCOTTSDALE

La Paz in Desert Springs Bed and Breakfast

Scottsdale, AZ 85254
(408) 922-0963; (888) 922-0963
  Fax (480) 219-5251
E-mail: lapaz-desertsprings@juno.com
Web site: www.lapazindesertsprings.com

Come enjoy peace, comfort, and warm hospitality. Three guest accommodations are offered. The Arizona Suite with private entrance has a large master bedroom, private bath, living room with a comfortable queen sleep sofa, cable TV/VCR, and a fully equipped kitchenette. The Desert Spring Room is furnished with a queen bed, and the Old West Room accommodates two in twin beds. La Paz is ideally located in beautiful N. Scottsdale near fine dining, museums, hiking, horseback riding, historical sights, the famous Phoenix Open and Kierland golf courses, Frank Lloyd Wright's Taliesen West, Rawhide, and

---

NOTES: Credit cards accepted: A Master Card; B Visa; C American Express; D Discover; E Diners Club; F Other; 2 Personal checks accepted; 3 Lunch available; 4 Dinner available; 5 Open all year;

WestWorld. A gourmet continental-plus breakfast including fresh fruit, homemade yogurt and granola, baked breads or muffins. A full SW breakfast is served on weekends. Complimentary refreshments are offered. Reservations required. No smoking. On-site pool open April–October and hot tub open year-round.

Hosts: Luis and Susan Cuevas
Rooms: 3 (1PB;2SB) $65–175
Full Breakfast
Credit Cards: A B C
Notes: 2 5 7 8 9 10 12

SEDONA

Apple Orchard Inn

656 Jordan Rd., Sedona, AZ 86336-3534
(928) 282-5328; (800) 663-6968
   Fax (928) 204-0044
E-mail: appleorc@sedona.net
Web site: www.appleorchardbb.com

Nestled in the heart of Sedona, on the site of the historic Jordan Apple Orchard. Though secluded on nearly 2 acres of wooded property, our unparalleled location allows easy access to "uptown" galleries, shops, and trails. The inn features king beds, whirlpool tubs, TV/VCRs, private patios, fireplaces, and a massage room. Smoke-free environment. Walk to shops and Sedona Heritage Museum. Enjoy spectacular views of Sedona's Red Rocks, with hiking off the property.

Hosts: Jean McDonald and Stephanie Sherwin
Rooms: 7 (7PB) $135–235
Full Breakfast
Credit Cards: A B C
Notes: 2 5 7 8 9 10 11 12

The Lodge at Sedona

125 Kallof Pl., Sedona, AZ 86336-5566
(928) 204-1942; (800) 619-4467
   Fax (928) 204-1942
E-mail: info@lodgeatsedona.com
Web site: www.lodgeatsedona.com

The Lodge at Sedona

Elegantly rustic and newly renovated luxury Mission-style B & B Inn on 2½ acres of seclusion in the Heart of Sedona. Awarded #1 Arizona B & B (2001). Red Rock views, gardens, sculptures, labyrinth. Romantic fireplaces, double spa tubs, private decks and entrances, massages. Full gourmet breakfast and snacks. Several guest areas—fireplace lounges, lodge shop, outdoor celebration terrace. Executive meetings and receptions. Was originally home to Sedona's first doctor, later owned by Rev. Don Roberts.

Hosts: Shelley and Ronald Wachal
Rooms: 14 (14PB) $150–290
Full Breakfast
Credit Cards: A B D
Notes: 2 5 8 9 10 11 12

TEMPE

Mi Casa Su Casa B & B Reservation Service

P. O. Box 950, Tempe, AZ 85280-0950
(480) 990-0682; (800) 456-0682
   Fax (480) 990-3390
E-mail: micasa@azres.com
Web site: www.azres.com

---

6 Pets welcome; 7 Children welcome; 8 Tennis nearby; 9 Swimming nearby; 10 Golf nearby; 11 Skiing nearby; 12 May be booked through travel agent

Founded in 1981, our name, Mi Casa Su Casa (Spanish for "My House (is) Your House"), describes our service, for our intent is to help visitors feel at home in the Southwest. Our friendly, helpful hosts have host homes, guest cottages, inns, ranches, and condos. (We list condos only in Arizona.) Some hosts have accommodations with kitchenettes and are available for long-term stays. You can choose from 250 historic-to-contemporary accommodations in four states. (See our listings under New Mexico, Utah, and Nevada.) A few of the cities where we list in Arizona are: Ajo, Benson, Bisbee, Cave Creek, Clarkdale, Flagstaff, Globe, Mesa, Page, Patagonia, Phoenix, Portal, Prescott, Scottsdale, Sedona, Sonoita, Tempe, Tombstone, Tucson, and Williams. We also represent two luxury villas, one in Puerto Vallarta, Mexico, and the second in the Costa Brava area of Spain, and a few B & Bs in southern California. The rates range from modest (one at $45) to luxurious (one at $350) for double occupancy.

Host: Ruth Young (coordinator)

TUCSON

Casa Alegre B & B

316 E. Speedway Blvd., Tucson, AZ 85705-7429
(520) 628-1800; (800) 628-5654
    Fax (520) 792-1880
E-mail: alegre123.aol.com
Web site: www.casaalegreinn.com

Casa Alegre is a sprawling 1915 Arts and Crafts bungalow where your comfort is foremost and where you always

feel welcome. Whether you want to be a part of lively conversation with other guests or curl up with your favorite book, your wishes will be fulfilled. Our serene gardens, pool, and hot tub make "an oasis of comfort in central Tucson" just minutes from the University of Arizona. Looking forward to seeing you at Casa Alegre.

Host: Phyllis Florek
Rooms: 4 (4PB) $80–135
Full Breakfast
Credit Cards: A B D
Notes: 2 5 12

Copper-Bell B & B Inn

25 N. Westmoreland Ave., Tucson, AZ 85745
(520) 629-9229; Fax (520) 629-9229

Copper-Bell B & B Inn

Copper-Bell B & B is a unique turn-of-the-century lava stone home, built in 1907, and listed in the National Register of Historical Places. Four of the eight rooms have ground-level entry, private bath, and TV. A/C and heater; a honeymoon suite is available; homemade German breakfast. Rooms uniquely decorated, stained-glass windows, 1 mile from downtown. This is your home away from home. Come celebrate the inn's 12th-year anniversary.

NOTES: Credit cards accepted: A Master Card; B Visa; C American Express; D Discover; E Diners Club; F Other; 2 Personal checks accepted; 3 Lunch available; 4 Dinner available; 5 Open all year;

Host: Gertrude M. Eich
Rooms: 8 (5PB;3SB) $89–98
Full Breakfast
Credit Cards:
Notes: 2 5 8 9 10

Hacienda B & B

5704 E. Grant Rd., Tucson, AZ 85712-2235
(520) 290-2224; (888) 236-4421
     Fax (520) 721-9066
E-mail: info@tucsonhacienda.com
Web site: www.tucsonhacienda.com

Disconnect from the world in this peaceful B & B. Enjoy quiet time in the patio, pool, spa, or large sitting rooms where you can sit and listen to music while you visit or read. Jetted tubs. Unwind in the exercise room. Make some memories while swimming in the pool and waiting for the stars to make their appearance. Relax awhile before that important meeting. The central location provides easy access for any schedule. Handicapped accessible.

Hosts: Barbara and Fred Shamseldin
Rooms: 6 (6PB) $95–145
Full Breakfast
Credit Cards: A B C D E
Notes: 2 5 7 8 9 10 12

Jeremiah Inn B & B, Ltd.

10921 E. Snyder Rd., Tucson, AZ 85749-9066
(520) 749-3072; (888) 750-3072
E-mail: info@jeremiahinn.com
Web site: www.jeremiahinn.com

"Oh, that I had in the desert a lodging place for travelers" (Jeremiah 9:2). This Santa Fe-style contemporary sits on 3.3 tranquil desert acres in the foothills of the Catalina Mountains.

Spectacular mountain views, spacious accommodations, delightful breakfasts, inn-baked cookies, pool, and spa will welcome you. Hike, bird, golf, visit Kartchner Caverns, and be refreshed.

Jeremiah Inn B & B, Ltd.

Hosts: Robert and Beth Miner
Rooms: 5 (5PB) $90–125
Full Breakfast
Credit Cards: A B C
Notes: 2 5 7 8 9 10 11 12

La Posada del Valle B & B Inn

1640 N. Campbell Ave., Tucson, AZ 85719-4313
(520) 795-3840; (888) 404-7113
E-mail: laposadabandbinn@hotmail.com
Web site: www.bbhost.com/laposadadelvalle

La Posada del Valle, surrounded by orange trees and lush gardens, is an elegant inn built in 1929. Five guest rooms with private baths and private entrances are furnished with antiques from the 1920s and '30s. Breakfast is served in the dining room with its glorious Catalina Mountain views. Guests gather for afternoon tea. The University of Arizona, University Medical Center, shops, restaurants, etc., are all within walking distance. Wir sprechen Deutsch. La Posada del Valle is AAA 3-diamond-rated. All

---

6 Pets welcome; 7 Children welcome; 8 Tennis nearby; 9 Swimming nearby; 10 Golf nearby; 11 Skiing nearby; 12 May be booked through travel agent

rooms have TVs, and three rooms have phones. Private, off-street parking.

Host: Karin Dennen
Rooms: 5 (5PB) $75–149
Full Breakfast
Credit Cards: A B
Notes: 2 5 7 8 9 10 11 12

La Posada del Valle B & B Inn

ARKANSAS

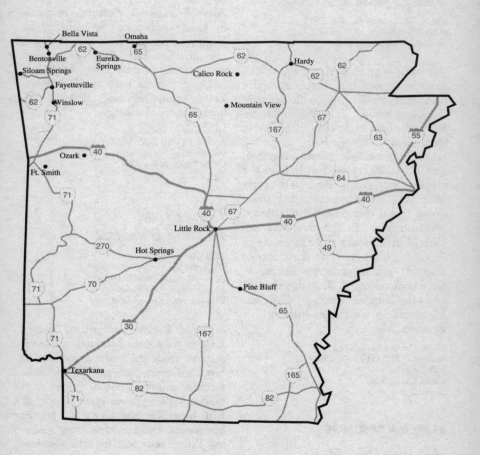

Arkansas

BENTONVILLE

Tudor House at the Oak

806 N. W., Bentonville, AR 72712
(479) 273-2200
Web site: www.tudorplace.com

We pamper you! Feel the warmth of genuine friendship, savor specialty breakfasts, stroll through flower gardens and woods. The Tudor House features guest bedrooms in a private wing, shared luxury bath, gathering room with a classic movie collection, and a quartz crystal fireplace in the elegant living room. Built in the early '20s, this recently remodeled stone home is full of international artifacts and antiques. In the area, visit the Wal-Mart museum and University of Arkansas, shop at craft fairs, choose from 21 golf courses, go fishing or horseback riding. A short drive brings you to Eureka Springs, Precious Moments in Carthage, Missouri, or Branson, Missouri.

Hosts: Lee and Linda Long
Rooms: 3 (2PB;1SB) $100–130
Full Breakfast
Credit Cards: A B
Notes: 2 5 8 9 10

EUREKA SPRINGS

Angel at Rose Hall

46 Hillside Ave.
   Eureka Springs, AR 72632-3133
(479) 253-5405; (800) 828-4255
   Fax (479) 253-5405

E-mail: info@eurekaspringsangel.com
Web site: www.eurekaspringsangel.com

AAA 4-diamond Victorian mansion in historic district. Specializing in weddings, honeymoons, anniversaries, romantic getaways. King honeymoon suites with Jacuzzi tubs, fireplaces, balcony, private bath with showers. Designer linens, fresh flowers, full breakfast, free beverages.

Host: Sandy Latimer
Rooms: 5 (5PB) $155–185
Full Breakfast
Credit Cards: A B C D
Notes: 2 5 9 10 12

Beaver Lake Bed and Breakfast

1234 Cty. Rd. 120
   Eureka Springs, AR 72631-8958
(479) 235-9210; (888) 253-9210
E-mail: elaine@beaverlakebb.com
Web site: www.beaverlakebb.com

Secluded 9 acres on pristine Beaver Lake in the Ozark Mountains. Fifteen minutes from the many attractions in historic Eureka Springs. Casual, comfortable country home decorated with unique antiques. Four guest rooms, all with incredible lake views and private bathrooms. Full breakfast every morning. Private boat dock for fishing, swimming, and snorkeling. Abundant wildlife and nature trails. Knowledgeable, friendly innkeepers. Sorry, no smoking, children, or pets permitted.

Hosts: David and Elaine Reppel
Rooms: 4 (4PB) $85–105
Full Breakfast
Credit Cards: A B D
Notes: 2 9 10

Bonnybrooke Farm atop Misty Mountain

361 Cty. Rd. 117
  Eureka Springs, AR 72631
(479) 253-6903
Web site: www.bonnybrooke.com

Bonnybrooke Farm
atop Misty Mountain

If your heart's in the country—or longs to be—we invite you to share the sweet quiet and serenity that await you in your place to come home to. We offer five cottages, each distinctly different in its tempting pleasures. Fireplace and Jacuzzi for two, full glass fronts and mountaintop views, shower under the stars, wicker porch swing in front of the fireplace. . .you're gonna love it! In order to preserve privacy, the location is given to registered guests only. Bonnybrooke Farm was featured as the most romantic accommodation in Arkansas (*Country Heart Magazine*).

Hosts: Bonny and Josh
Rooms: 5 (5PB) $135–185

Continental Breakfast
Credit Cards:
Notes: 2 5 9 12

The Brownstone Inn

75 Hillside Ave.
  Eureka Springs, AR 72632-3120
(479) 253-7505; (800) 973-7505
  Fax (479) 253-2285
Web site: www.eureka-usa.com/brownstone

A present part of Eureka's past is this historic limestone building, located on the trolley route to historic downtown and an easy, short drive to the Great Passion Play. Victorian accommodations, private outside entrances, private baths, and gourmet breakfasts with coffee, tea, or juice at your doorstep before breakfast. Featured in *Best Places to Stay in the South*. Closed January and February.

Hosts: Marvin and Donna Shepard
Rooms: 4 (4PB) $95–135
Full Breakfast
Credit Cards: A B D
Notes: 2 5 10 12

1884 Bridgeford House Bed and Breakfast

263 Spring St., Eureka Springs, AR 72632
(479) 253-7853; (888) 567-2422
  Fax (479) 253-5497
E-mail: henry@bridgefordhouse.com
Web site: www.bridgefordhouse.com

Where beauty and hospitality exceed expectations! Short, relaxing stroll to shops, spas, restaurants, galleries. Antiques, Jacuzzis, horse-drawn carriage/trolley route, queen/king beds, fireplaces, great packages, Southern-

6 Pets welcome; 7 Children welcome; 8 Tennis nearby; 9 Swimming nearby; 10 Golf nearby; 11 Skiing nearby; 12 May be booked through travel agent

style breakfast, and romantic weddings. Our "Secret Garden" was recently honored with Garden of the Season. Southern hospitality combined with Victorian charm awaits you. Children over 8 welcome.

Hosts: Linda and Henry Thornton
Rooms: 5 (5PB) $95–250
Full Breakfast
Credit Cards: A B C D
Notes: 2 5 9 10 12

11 Singleton House B & B

11 Singleton St., Eureka Springs, AR 72632-3026
(479) 253-9111; (800) 833-3394
E-mail: info@singletonhouse.com
Web site: www.singletonhouse.com

This old-fashioned Victorian house is whimsically decorated and has an eclectic collection of treasures and antiques. All rooms include private baths, cable TV, and air-conditioning. Some suites have two beds. Breakfast is served on the balcony overlooking stony paths, fragrant wildflower gardens, and a lily-filled pond. Guests walk one block down a scenic wooded footpath to historic district shops and cafes. Passion Play and Holy Land tour reservations can be arranged. Two free tickets to Passion Play for liscensed card carrying clergy. Ask about our Gardener's Cottage at a separate private location with its treetop porch, hammock, swing, Jacuzzi-for-two, and gas-log fireplace. The 11 Singleton House has been featured in more than sixteen B & B guidebooks. We are currently celebrating our 20th year as a B & B in Eureka.

Host: Barbara Gavron

Rooms: 5 (5PB) $69–125
Full Breakfast
Credit Cards: A B C D F
Notes: 2 9 10 11

Gardener's Cottage

11 Singleton St., Eureka Springs, AR 72632-3026
(479) 253-9111; (800) 833-3394
E-mail: info@singletonhouse.com
Web site: www.singletonhouse.com

Tucked away in a wooded historic district valley close to the Passion Play, the Gardener's Cottage features country decor with romantic touches, cathedral ceilings, skylight, full kitchen, gas-log fireplace, and Jacuzzi-for-two. The treetop porch with its hammock and swing is perfect for relaxing moments. Great for honeymooners or a long, peaceful stay. Ask about optional breakfast.

Host: Barbara Garvon
Rooms: 1 (1PB) $125–145
Credit Cards: A B C D F
Notes: 2 9 10 11

Heartstone Inn B & B Cottages

35 Kings Highway
    Eureka Springs, AR 72632-3534
(479) 253-8916; (800) 494-4921
    Fax (479) 253-5361
E-mail: heartinn@ipa.net
Web site: www.heartstoneinn.com

An award-winning inn with all private baths, private entrances, king and queen beds, and cable TV. Furnished with antiques galore, the inn offers a renowned gourmet breakfast, in-house

---

NOTES: Credit cards accepted: A Master Card; B Visa; C American Express; D Discover; E Diners Club; F Other; 2 Personal checks accepted; 3 Lunch available; 4 Dinner available; 5 Open all year;

massage therapy studio, and golf privileges. You'll find large decks and a gazebo under the trees—great for bird-watching. Recommended by the *New York Times, Country Home Magazine, America's Wonderful Little Hotels and Inns, Recommended Inns of the South,* and many more. Closed Christmas through January.

Heartstone Inn B & B Cottages

Hosts: Rick and Cheri Rojek
Rooms: 12 (12PB) $75–134
Full Breakfast
Credit Cards: A B C D
Notes: 2 10 12

1908 Ridgeway House B & B

28 Ridgeway Ave., Eureka Springs, AR 72632
(479) 253-6618; (800) 477-6618
E-mail: rheureka@ipa.net
Web site: www.ridgewayhouse.com

1908 Ridgeway House B & B

Just the right combination of pampering and privacy. Historic district, luxurious rooms, antiques, wonderfully quiet street within walking distance of the shops, incredible full breakfasts, and desserts. Trolley just 1 block away, porches, decks, private Jacuzzi suites, packages available, will build custom package.   Small weddings, complimentary cold and hot beverages. All of our guests are VIPs!

Hosts: Gayla and Keith Hubbard
Rooms: 5 (5PB) $99–149
Full Breakfast
Credit Cards: A B D F
Notes: 5 7 12

MOUNTAIN VIEW

Happy Lonesome Log Cabins

1444 Forest Home Ln.
   Calico Rock, AR 72519-9102
(870) 297-8764; (501) 626-4237
E-mail: hlcabins@centurytel.net
Web site: www.bbonline.com/ar/hlcabins

Unhosted, secluded comfort and charm, surrounded by Ozark National Forest. Each cabin has a comfortable sleeping loft, kitchenette, including microwave, downstairs living area, bath, hide-a-bed, wood stove, and air-conditioning. Outside is a covered porch with swing or rockers and outdoor grill nearby. Cabins are on a 200-foot bluff overlooking the White River. Relax on the porch swing and take delight in the panoramic view of the river valley, forest, and ever-present wildlife.

Rooms: 4 (4PB;6SB) $72.50

---

6 Pets welcome; 7 Children welcome; 8 Tennis nearby; 9 Swimming nearby; 10 Golf nearby; 11 Skiing nearby; 12 May be booked through travel agent

Continental Breakfast
Credit Cards: A B C F
Notes: 2 7 8 9 10 12

OMAHA

Aunt Shirley's Sleeping Loft

7250 Shirley Ln. N, Omaha, AR 72662
(870) 426-5408
E-mail: shirleys@omahaweb.net
Web site: www.auntshirleysloft.com

Quiet, relaxed atmosphere. Rustic country setting with the convenience of home. Air-conditioning, private bath, clean. Beautiful view with walkways, patio. Gas grill, campfires available. Swings under the trees. Big country breakfast, lots of Southern hospitality. Children welcome. Located 10 miles north of Harrison, 24 miles south of Branson, Missouri. Near Eureka Springs, Buffalo River, Tablerock Lake, Bull Shoals Lake. Member of Harrison Chamber of Commerce.

Hosts: Buddy and Shirley Lebleu
Rooms: 3 (3PB) $60
Full Breakfast
Credit Cards: A B
Notes: 2 5 6 7 9 10

WINSLOW

Sky-Vue Lodge

22822 N. Highway 71
   Winslow, AR 72959-9212
(479) 634-2003; (800) 782-2003
E-mail: skyvue@valuelinx.net
Web site: www.bbinternet.com/sky-vue

Enjoy mountain vistas from Sky-Vue. Located 23 miles from Fayetteville, AR, on Boston Mountains Scenic

Byway 71. Activities include fishing, playground, hiking, and movies on our 83 acres. Near state parks, horseback riding, antiques, battlefields, and other attractions. Five cute cottages equipped with modern amenities and swings on covered porches. Two cabins also include kitchens and fireplaces. Two new lodge rooms. New conference room for your meeting, party, or retreat. AV equipment. Facility seats 65. Sky-Vue can accommodate your vacation, honeymoon, retreat, seminar, or reunion. Property is alcohol-free. Smoking permitted on porches.

Hosts: Glenn and Janice Jorgenson
Rooms: 9 (9PB) $45-65
Full Breakfast
Credit Cards: A B C D
Notes: 2 5 7 8 9

NOTES: Credit cards accepted: A Master Card; B Visa; C American Express; D Discover; E Diners Club; F Other; 2 Personal checks accepted; 3 Lunch available; 4 Dinner available; 5 Open all year;

CALIFORNIA

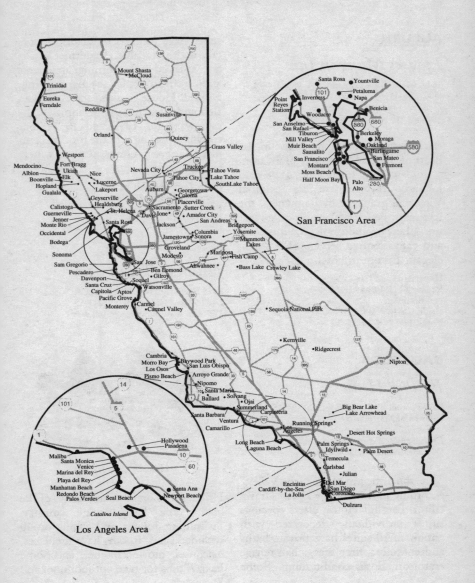

California

AUBURN

Power's Mansion Inn

164 Cleveland Ave., Auburn, CA 95603-4801
(530) 885-1166; Fax (530) 885-1386
E-mail: powerinn@westsierra.net
Web site: www.vfr.net/~powerinn/

An elegant Bed and Breakfast in the heart of the Gold Country. Built from a gold-mining fortune in 1898 and lovingly restored to its original Victorian grandeur by its owners, the landmark Power's Mansion offers visitors the hospitality of a country inn and the attentive service of a small, elegant European hotel.

Hosts: Arno and Jean Lejnieks
Rooms: 13 (13PB) $89–169
Full Breakfast
Credit Cards: A B C
Notes: 2 5 7 8 10 11 12

CALISTOGA

Foothill House

3037 Foothill Blvd., Calistoga, CA 94515-1225
(707) 942-6933; (800) 942-6933
    Fax (707) 942-5692
E-mail: gus@calicom.net
Web site: www.foothillhouse.com

"The romantic inn of the Napa Valley," according to the *Chicago Tribune* travel editor. Foothill House offers spacious suites individually decorated with antiques. All suites have private baths and entrances, fireplaces, small refrigerators, and air-conditioning. Some suites have Jacuzzis. A luxurious cottage is also available. A gourmet breakfast is served each morning; appetizers and refreshments each evening. Foothill House received the American Bed and Breakfast Association's highest award for 1997 and 1998 (four crowns—placing it in the top 5 percent in U.S.). Spas, restaurants, and wineries are nearby.

Hosts: Doris and Gus Beckert
Rooms: 4 (4PB) $175–400
Full Breakfast
Credit Cards: A B C D
Notes: 2 5 10 12

Hillcrest Country Inn

3225 Lake Cty. Hwy., Calistoga, CA 94515-9738
(707) 942-6334; Fax (707) 942-3955
Web site: www.bnbweb.com/hillcrest

Hillcrest Country Inn

Hillcrest has breathtaking views of the lush Napa Valley wine country. Swimming, hiking, and fishing on 40 secluded acres. Rooms have fireplaces, balconies, movie channel, and some Jacuzzi tubs for two, outdoor pool and

Jacuzzi. Home is filled with heirlooms from family mansion, which burned to the ground in 1964. The land has been in the family since 1860. Nearby wineries, spas, biking, horseback riding, balloon and glider rides. Old Faithful Geyser and Petrified Forest. Continental breakfast included on weekends and holidays.

Hosts: Debbie O' Gorman and Matt Hickerson
Rooms: 6 (4PB;2SB) $69–175
Continental Breakfast
Credit Cards: A B F
Notes: 2 5 6 7 8 9 10 11 12

Scarlett's Country Inn

3918 Silverado Trail, Calistoga, CA 94515
(707) 942-6669; Fax (707) 942-6669
E-mail: scarletts@aol.com
Web site: http://members.aol.com/scarletts

Three exquisitely appointed suites set in the quiet mood of green lawn and tall pines overlooking the famed Napa Valley vineyards. Seclusion, romance, queen beds, private baths, antiques, fireplace, air-conditioning, secluded woodland swimming pool. Phone and television available in rooms on request. Home-baked breakfast and afternoon refreshments served in rooms or under the apple trees by the pool. Close to wineries and spas. Children welcome at no charge.

Host: Scarlett Dwyer
Rooms: 3 (3PB) $135–205
Full Breakfast
Credit Cards:
Notes: 2 5 7 8 9 10 12

CAMBRIA

J. Patrick House B & B Inn

2990 Burton Dr., Cambria, CA 93428
(805) 927-3812; (800) 341-5258
    Fax (805) 927-3812
E-mail: jph@jpatrickhouse.com
Web site: www.jpatrickhouse.com

J. Patrick House B & B Inn

Authentic log home and carriage house nestled in the woods surrounded by country gardens. A quiet, wooded location, yet the ocean and town are minutes away. All rooms with woodburning fireplaces and private baths. The decor is pure country elegance. Jerry Hulse, retired travel editor of the *L. A. Times* wrote: "Without question, the prettiest bed and breakfast on the entire Central California coast." A great locale, near internationally recognized wine country and Hearst Castle.

Hosts: Ann and John
Rooms: 8 (8PB) $145–200
Full Breakfast
Credit Cards: A B D
Notes: 5 10

CARMEL

Green Lantern Inn

Seventh and Casanova; P. O. Box 1114
    Carmel, CA 93921
(831) 624-4392; (888) 414-4392
    Fax (831) 624-9591
E-mail: info@greenlanterninn.com
Web site: www.greenlanterninn.com

Charming, historic property, a country garden inn by the sea with 18
guest rooms, all with private
entrances and baths. An easy five-
minute walk to White Sand Beach;
renowned Ocean Avenue with shops,
galleries, and restaurants one short
block away. Delicious buffet-style
breakfast and afternoon tea included.
TVs and VCR in all rooms; some
rooms with fireplaces.

Host: Bill Fowler
Rooms: 18 (18PB) $89–229
Continental Breakfast
Credit Cards: A B C D
Notes: 5 7 9 10 12

Wayfarer Inn

4th and Mission, P. O. Box 1896, Carmel, CA 93921
(831) 624-2711; (800) 533-2711
    Fax (831) 625-1210
E-mail: info@carmelwayfarerinn.com
Web site: www.carmelwayfarerinn.com

Charming bed and breakfast in downtown Carmel. Offering an expanded
buffet breakfast and afternoon tea and
refreshments. Newly renovated rooms
with fireplaces, views, and kitchenettes.

Host: Roman Padilla
Rooms: 15 (15PB) $89–209
Continental Breakfast
Credit Cards: A B C D E
Notes: 5 7 10 12

EUREKA

Carter House Inns

301 L St., Eureka, CA 95501-0571
(707) 444-8062; (800) 404-1390
    Fax (707) 444-8067
E-mail: reserve@carterhouse.com
Web site: www.carterhouse.com

Carter House Victorians is an enclave
of four gracious inns bordering
Humboldt Bay in Eureka, California's
historic Old Town. Each Victorian
unites contemporary good taste and
luxurious amenities with the timeless
elegance of a bygone era. The inn's
Restaurant 301 offers guests artfully
prepared regional, seasonal dining,
replete with produce harvested from
the inn's own organic gardens. The
301 wine list has been acknowledged
by many to be one of the finest in the
world and has been awarded *Wine
Spectator's* Grand Award, the publica-
tion's highest honor. Together, our
wine cellar, garden-fresh cuisine, and
luxurious accommodations create the
Redwood Coast's most unforgettable
hospitality experience.

Hosts: Mark and Christi Carter
Rooms: 32 (32PB) $125–495
Full Breakfast
Credit Cards: A B C D E
Notes: 2 4 5 7 8 9 10 12

FELTON

Felton Crest Inn B & B

780 El Solyo Heights Dr., Felton, CA 95018-9307
(831) 335-4011; (800) 474-4011
E-mail: hannapeters@mymailstation.com
Web site: www.feltoncrestinn.com

NOTES: Credit cards accepted: A Master Card; B Visa; C American Express; D Discover; E Diners
Club; F Other; 2 Personal checks accepted; 3 Lunch available; 4 Dinner available; 5 Open all year;

The most beautiful and unique B & B nestled in the majestic mountain on 1 acre of sunny redwoods. Very quiet and soothing. Fifteen minutes from the beach and boardwalk in Santa Cruz. Each room comes with a bottle of champagne, a bowl of fresh fruit, cheese tray, chocolate kisses, fresh flower, and continental breakfast.

Host: Hanna Peters
Rooms: 4 (4PB) $140–275
Continental Breakfast
Credit Cards: A B C
Notes: 5

GEORGETOWN

American River Inn

Orleans and Main, P. O. Box 43
  Georgetown, CA 95634-0043
(530) 333-4499; (800) 245-6566
  Fax (530) 333-9253
E-mail: ariinnkeeper@aol.com
Web site: www.americanriverinn.com

American River Inn

The innkeepers carry on the century-old tradition of graciousness in a setting far removed from the fast pace of modern living. Cool off in a beautiful mountain pool or relax in the spa. Choose a day of bicycling amid the colorful, breathtaking daffodils, irises, and yellow-gold scotch broom; bicycles are provided. The historic Queen Anne inn specializes in ladies' and couples' retreats and seminars and corporate meetings of fifteen to forty people. We will arrange white-water rafting and kayaking trips.

Hosts: Will and Maria and Betty
Rooms: 15 (7PB;8SB) $90–125
Full Breakfast
Credit Cards: A B C D
Notes: 2 5 7 8 9 10 11 12

GRASS VALLEY

Elam Biggs B & B

220 Colfax Ave., Grass Valley, CA 95945
(530) 477-0906
Web site:
  www.virtualcities.com/ons/ca/g/cag1601.htm

This beautiful, 1892 Queen Anne Victorian is set amidst a large yard surrounded by grand shade trees and a rose-covered picket fence. It's just a short stroll from historic downtown Grass Valley. In the morning, enjoy brewed coffee and a hearty breakfast served in the lovely dining room or outside on the private porch.

Hosts: Barbara and Peter Franchino
Rooms: 5 (5PB) $85–120
Full Breakfast
Credit Cards: A B C
Notes: 2 5 7 8 9 10 11 12

HALF MOON BAY

Old Thyme Inn

779 Main St., Half Moon Bay, CA 94019-1924
(650) 726-1616; (800) 720-4277
  Fax (650) 726-6394
E-mail: innkeeper@oldthymeinn.com
Web site: www.oldthymeinn.com

---

6 Pets welcome; 7 Children welcome; 8 Tennis nearby; 9 Swimming nearby; 10 Golf nearby; 11 Skiing nearby; 12 May be booked through travel agent

Old Thyme Inn

Spend enchanted nights in 1898 Victorian B & B. Fragrant herb and flower garden provides tranquil setting for romance, rest, and relaxation. Inn is furnished in antiques and innkeepers' collection of fine art. Seven uniquely decorated guest rooms, each featuring queen bed with featherbed and down comforter, cable TV/VCR, data port, and private bath. Jacuzzi and/or fireplace rooms available. Afternoon hors d'oeuvres and delectable full breakfast served daily. Walk to beach, shops, galleries, and fine restaurants.

Hosts: Rick and Kathy Ellis
Rooms: 7 (7PB) $130–300
Full Breakfast
Credit Cards: A B C D E
Notes: 2 5 7 9 10 12

JAMESTOWN

Palm Hotel Bed and Breakfast

10382 Willow St., Jamestown, CA 95327-9761
(209) 984-3429; (888) 551-1852
    Fax (209) 984-4929
E-mail: innkeeper@palmhotel.com
Web site: www.palmhotel.com

More home than hotel, this Gold Country Victorian offers eight guest rooms with private bath, lacy curtains, fresh flowers, claw-foot tubs, marble showers, and robes. Air-conditioning, in-room TV, and handicapped accessibility. A full breakfast along with the Palm's special blend of coffee is served daily in the parlor. The Palm is located 2½ hours from San Francisco and about an hour from Yosemite Park's north entrance and is within walking distance of Main Street shops, restaurants, and Railtown State Park.

Guest comment from journal: *"The simple elegance of our room and ambience of the Palm in general was a balm for our souls."*

Hosts: Rick and Sandy Allen
Rooms: 8 (8PB) $95–155
Full Breakfast
Credit Cards: A B C
Notes: 5 7 10 11 12

JULIAN

Butterfield's Bed and Breakfast

2284 Sunset Dr., P. O. Box 1115
    Julian, CA 92036-9447
(760) 765-2179; (800) 379-4262
    Fax (760) 765-1229
E-mail: butterfield@abac.com
Web site: www.butterfieldbandb.com

Enjoy yourself and relax on our 3-acre country garden setting in the quiet hills of Julian. Rest under the oaks, walk among the dozens of roses and bonsai, and retreat to your unique room each night. Five rooms are offered; three with fireplaces or wood-

---

NOTES: Credit cards accepted: A Master Card; B Visa; C American Express; D Discover; E Diners Club; F Other; 2 Personal checks accepted; 3 Lunch available; 4 Dinner available; 5 Open all year;

stove. Gourmet breakfast is served in the gazebo every morning during the warmth of summer and by a crackling fireplace in winter.

Hosts: Ed and Dawn Glass
Rooms: 5 (5PB) $130–180
Full Breakfast
Credit Cards: A B C
Notes: 2 5 7 12

KERNVILLE

Kern River Inn
Bed and Breakfast

119 Kern River Dr., P. O. Box 1725
   Kernville, CA 93238-1725
(760) 376-6750; (800) 986-4382
   Fax (760) 376-6643
E-mail: kernriverinn@lightspeed.net
Web site: www.kernriverinn.com

A charming, classic country riverfront bed and breakfast located on the wild and scenic Kern River in the quaint little town of Kernville within the Sequoia National Forest in the southern Sierra Mountains. We specialize in romantic getaways. All guest rooms have private baths and feature river views; some have fireplaces and whirlpool tubs. A full breakfast is served. Within walking distance of restaurants, shops, parks, and the museum and just a short drive to giant redwood trees. This is an all-year vacation area with white-water rafting, hiking, fishing, biking, skiing, and Lake Isabella water activities.

Hosts: Jack and Carita Prestwich
Rooms: 6 (6PB) $99–109
Full Breakfast
Credit Cards: A B C D
Notes: 2 5 7 9 10 11

LONG BEACH

Lord Mayor's B & B Inn

435 Cedar Ave., Long Beach, CA 90802-2245
(562) 436-0324; Fax (562) 436-0324
E-mail: innkeepers@lordmayors.com
Web site: www.lordmayors.com

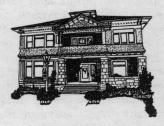

Lord Mayor's B & B Inn

Rest and relax in our 1904 award-winning historic landmark with meticulously restored rooms, private baths, and sundeck access. Two recently restored 1906 cottages provide alternative space in the B & B Collection. You'll find warm hospitality enhanced by home-cooked specialty breakfasts. Within walking distance of shops and Convention Center, Aquarium of the Pacific, and Tall Ships. Driving distance to Disneyland, Universal Studio, and Getty Museum. A gateway to Catalina Island by ferry.

Hosts: Laura and Reuben Brasser
Rooms: 12 (10PB;2SB) $85–140
Full Breakfast
Credit Cards: A B C D E
Notes: 2 5 7 9 12

The Turret House B & B

556 Chestnut Ave., Long Beach, CA 90802
(562) 983-9812; (888) TURRET
   Fax (562) 437-4082

---

6 Pets welcome; 7 Children welcome; 8 Tennis nearby; 9 Swimming nearby; 10 Golf nearby; 11 Skiing nearby; 12 May be booked through travel agent

E-mail: innkeepers@turrethouse.com
Web site: www.turrethouse.com

Indulge in Victorian hospitality and antique finery in an elegant, restored 1906 home in historic downtown residential Long Beach. Five romantic guest rooms with private baths, savory gourmet candlelit breakfasts, and relaxing afternoon tea and treats offer guests a peaceful retreat to a time when gracious hospitality and gentle manners were a way of life. Pleasant walk to ocean, Aquarium, Convention Center, theaters, fine dining, antique and specialty shops. Convenient to all southern California attractions.

Hosts: Nina and Lee Agee
Rooms: 5 (5PB) $100–150
Gourmet Breakfast
Credit Cards: A B C D
Notes: 2 5 8 9 10 12

MENDOCINO

Antioch Ranch

39451 Comptche Rd., Mendocino, CA 95460
(707) 937-5570; Fax (707) 937-1757
E-mail: cbbd@antiochranch.com
Web site: www.antiochranch.com

A Christian atmosphere of peace, this is a place for refreshment and renewal. Located just 5 miles inland from the picturesque town of Mendocino, the ranch features four guest cottages on 20 acres of rolling hills, redwoods, and apple orchards. Each cottage has its own style and ambience. Rustic, yet comfortable, each cottage features a woodstove, complete kitchen with microwave, two bedrooms, bath, and

open living/dining room.

Hosts: Jerry and Pat Westfall
Rooms: 4 (4PB) $75–95
No Breakfast Served
Credit Cards:
Notes: 2 5 7 8 9 10

Dehaven Valley Farm

39247 N. Hwy. One, Westport, CA 95488
(707) 961-1660; (877) DEHAVEN
    Fax (707) 961-1677
E-mail: info@dehaven-valley-farm.com
Web site: www.dehaven-valley-farm.com

This 1875 Victorian farmhouse sits amid 20 acres of meadows and hills, just a two-minute walk to the beach. The cozy parlor offers a crackling fire, piano, and VCR movies. The upstairs deck overlooks the ocean, perfect for reading or dozing. A hot tub on the hill offers spectacular daytime views and evening stargazing. Entertainment is provided by the resident goats, donkey, horses, sheep, cat, and dog. Close to Mendocino Village, the Lost Coast, and giant redwoods. The owner is a minister and will perform wedding ceremonies and other services if desired.

Host: Christa Stapp
Rooms: 8 (6PB;2SB) $89–144
Full Breakfast
Credit Cards: A B C D
Notes: 2 4 5 7 9 10 12

MONTEREY

Grand View Inn

557 Ocean View Blvd.
    Pacific Grove, CA 93950-2653
(831) 372-4341
Web site: www.pginns.com

NOTES: Credit cards accepted: A Master Card; B Visa; C American Express; D Discover; E Diners Club; F Other; 2 Personal checks accepted; 3 Lunch available; 4 Dinner available; 5 Open all year;

Built in 1910, the Grand View Inn is situated at the very edge of Monterey Bay overlooking the Pacific Ocean. Completely restored by the Flatley family, the Grand View Inn has unsurpassed views of Monterey Bay from each room. Guest rooms enjoy the comfort of beautiful antique furnishings, beautifully appointed marble bathrooms, patterned hardwood floors, and lovely grounds. Easily accessible to Monterey Aquarium, Cannery Row, 17-Mile Drive, Carmel, and Highway 1 to Big Sur. Children welcome over 12 years old.

Hosts: Susan and Ed Flatley
Rooms: 11 (11PB) $175–385
Full Breakfast
Credit Cards: A B F
Notes: 5 8 9 10 12

Seven Gables Inn

555 Ocean View Blvd.
  Pacific Grove, CA 93950-2934
(831) 372-4341
Web site: www.pginns.com

Crashing waves, rocky shorelines, sea otters, whales, and beautiful sunsets are the images seen from each guest room at the Victorian-style Seven Gables Inn. Such a romantic setting on the edge of Monterey Bay is enhanced by a dazzling display of fine European antiques, a sumptuous breakfast, afternoon tea, the comfort of all private baths, and excellent guest service. Nearby attractions include the Monterey Bay Aquarium, Pebble Beach, Carmel, and Highway 1 to Big Sur. Children welcome over 12 years old.

Hosts: Susan and Ed Flatley
Rooms: 14 (14PB) $175–385
Full Breakfast
Credit Cards: A B F
Notes: 5 8 9 10 12

MOUNT SHASTA

Mount Shasta Ranch B & B

1008 W. A. Barr Rd., Mount Shasta, CA 96067
(530) 926-3870; Fax (530) 926-6882
E-mail: alpinere@snowcrest.net
Web site: www.travelassist.com/reg/cal2s.html

The inn is situated in a rural setting with a majestic view of Mt. Shasta and features a main lodge, carriage house, and cottage. Group accommodations are available. Our breakfast room is ideally suited for seminars and retreats, with large seating capacity. The game room includes piano, Ping-Pong, pool table, and board games. Nearby recreational facilities include Alpine and Nordic skiing, fishing, hiking, mountain bike rentals, surrey rides, and museums. Call for pastor's discount.

Hosts: Bill and Mary Larsen
Rooms: 10 (5PB;5SB) $55–115
Full Breakfast
Credit Cards: A B C D
Notes: 2 5 7 8 9 10 11 12

NAPA

The Napa Inn Bed and Breakfast

1137 Warren St., Napa, CA 94559-2302
(707) 257-1444; (800) 435-1144
  Fax (707) 257-0251
E-mail: info@napainn.com
Web site: www.napainn.com

---

6 Pets welcome; 7 Children welcome; 8 Tennis nearby; 9 Swimming nearby; 10 Golf nearby; 11 Skiing nearby; 12 May be booked through travel agent

The Napa Inn Bed and Breakfast

The Napa Inn is comprised of two historic, Victorian buildings, adjacent to each other. Here you will find the romance and relaxed pace of a bygone era and all the conveniences of home. Rooms with fireplaces, whirlpool tubs, balconies, and gardens are available.

Hosts: Brooke and Jim Boyer
Rooms: 14 (14PB) $140–300
Full Breakfast
Credit Cards: A B C D E
Notes: 2 5 6 7 10 12

The Old World Inn

1301 Jefferson St., Napa, CA 94559-2412
(707) 257-0112; (800) 966-6624
    Fax (707) 257-0118
E-mail: oldworldinn@aol.com
Web site: www.oldworldinn.com

This 1906 home is an eclectic combination of architecture, detailed with wood shingles, shady porches, leaded and beveled glass. Each romantic room is adorned in bright, welcoming colors and features canopy beds, clawfoot tubs, fireplaces, and Jacuzzis. You'll be pampered with an afternoon tea, early evening wine and cheese, and a chocolate lovers' dessert buffet

after dinner. In the morning, awaken to the aroma of freshly brewed coffee and a gourmet breakfast. Enjoy the outdoor spa under the stars. Eight rooms plus a cottage. Romance spoken here.

Host: Sam Van Hoeve
Rooms: 9 rooms + cottage (10PB) $145–265
Full Breakfast
Credit Cards: A B C D
Notes: 5 7 8 9 10 12

NEVADA CITY

Deer Creek Inn

116 Nevada St., Nevada City, CA 95959-2604
(530) 265-0363; (800) 655-0363
    Fax (530) 265-0980
E-mail: deercreek@gv.net
Web site: www.deercreek.com

Romance and elegance abound as you wander through this lovely Queen Anne Victorian home. She sits high above the gardens with the sound of Deer Creek to lull you to sleep each night. The guest rooms are appointed with period furniture, and several have private verandas or patios. A large gourmet breakfast is in store for you, and Nevada City is but a few steps away.

Hosts: Elaine and Chuck Matroni
Rooms: 6 (6PB) $105–179
Full Breakfast
Credit Cards: A B C
Notes: 2 5 8 9 10 11 12

The Parsonage B & B Inn

427 Broad St., Nevada City, CA 95959
(530) 265-9478; (877) 265-9499
    Fax (530) 265-8147
Web site: www.theparsonage.net

NOTES: Credit cards accepted: A Master Card; B Visa; C American Express; D Discover; E Diners Club; F Other; 2 Personal checks accepted; 3 Lunch available; 4 Dinner available; 5 Open all year;

The Parsonage B & B Inn

In the little blue house on Broad St. that was once the home of the Methodist minister, Deborah Dane has created a cozy bed and breakfast inn full of family heirlooms and memories of days gone by. The inn's six guest rooms all have private baths and antique furniture that dates back to the Dane family history in the Gold Country. A full breakfast is offered each morning of your stay. Children are welcome in the Mouse House.

Host: Deborah Dane
Rooms: 6 (6PB) $100–150
Full Breakfast
Credit Cards: A B F
Notes: 2 5 7 9 10 11 12

OJAI

Theodore Woolsey House

1484 E. Ojai Ave., Ojai, CA 93023-9623
(805) 646-9779; Fax (805) 646-4414
E-mail: twhouse@mindspring.com
Web site: www.theodorewoolseyhouse.com

The 7 acres belonging to the Woolsey estate are shaded by ancient oak trees and guarded by the Chinese stone wall built centuries ago to keep the land from flooding. As you wander the grounds, you'll discover a rushing waterfall emptying into a fish pond, a putting green, a horseshoe-throwing pit, a volleyball court, and croquet area, all among the many flowering gardens and ornamental trees.

Host: Ana Cross
Rooms: 5 (5PB) $95–175
Continental Breakfast
Credit Cards: A B
Notes: 2 5 7 8 9 10

PACIFIC GROVE

Gatehouse Inn

225 Central Ave., Pacific Grove, CA 93950
(831) 649-8436; (800) 753-1881
　Fax (831) 648-8044
E-mail: lew@redshift.com
Web site: www.sueandlewinns.com

Gatehouse Inn

Built in 1884 as a summer retreat for Sen. Langford, the inn features nine thematic guest rooms. Journey through the past in rooms such as the Steinbeck, Langford, or Victorian, all with Victorian elegance. For a different feel, try the Cannery Row, Turkish, or Italian rooms. Sumptuous food, breathtaking views, romantic elegance.

Host: Ruby Rustan

Rooms: 9 (9PB) $125–195
Full Breakfast
Credit Cards: A B C D
Notes: 2 5 7 8 9 10 12

Old St. Angela Inn

321 Central Ave., Pacific Grove, CA 93950
(831) 372-3246; (800) 748-6306
    Fax (831) 372-8560
E-mail: lew@redshift.com
Web site: www.sueandlewinns.com

Built in 1910, this inn reminds you of a day on Cape Cod. Guest rooms are decorated in antiques and provide ocean views, Jacuzzis, fireplaces, and cast-iron stoves. Add New England hospitality, a garden hot-tub spa, and a warm, homey feeling, and you have our inn. Bring your appetites!

Hosts: Lewis Shaefer and Susan Kuslis
Rooms: 9 (9PB) $110–210
Full Breakfast
Credit Cards: A B D
Notes: 2 5 7 8 9 10 12

Pacific Grove Inn

581 Pine Ave., Pacific Grove, CA 93950-3315
(831) 375-2825; (800) 732-2825
    Fax (831) 375-0752
E-mail: info@pacificgrove-inn.com
Web site: www.pacificgrove-inn.com

Theodore Woolsey House

Historic Victorian bed and breakfast inn with 16 rooms, fireplaces, TV/VCR, private bath with heated towel racks, some views of the bay. Scrumptious homemade breakfasts and hors d'oeuvres. Five blocks from ocean, two blocks from shopping and dining. Close to aquarium, golf courses, Pebble Beach, Monterey, and Carmel. This is "your home away from home."

Host: Joan M. Hamlett
Rooms: 16 (16PB) $99–229
Continental Breakfast
Credit Cards: A B C D E
Notes: 5 7 10 12

PALM DESERT

Tres Palmas B & B

73135 Tumbleweed Ln.
    Palm Desert, CA 92260-4207
(760) 773-9858; (800) 770-9858
    Fax (760) 776-9159
Web site: www.innformation.com/ca/trespalmas

Tres Palmas is located just 1 block south of El Paseo, the "Rodeo Drive of the Desert," where you will find boutiques, art galleries, and many restaurants. Or you may choose to stay "home" and enjoy the desert sun in and around the pool and spa. The guest rooms feature queen- or king-size beds, climate controls, ceiling fans, and color cable televisions and are uniquely decorated in southwestern style. Lemonade and iced tea are always available for guests. Snacks are served in the late afternoons. Tres Palmas is AAA 3-diamond rated; Mobil 3-star rated.

NOTES: Credit cards accepted: A Master Card; B Visa; C American Express; D Discover; E Diners Club; F Other; 2 Personal checks accepted; 3 Lunch available; 4 Dinner available; 5 Open all year;

Tres Palmas B & B

Hosts: Karen and Terry Bennett
Rooms: 4 (4PB) $90–200
Continental Breakfast
Credit Cards: A B C
Notes: 2 5 8 9 10 12

PALM SPRINGS

Casa Cody Country Inn

175 S. Cahuilla Rd.
  Palm Springs, CA 92262-6331
(760) 320-9346; (800) 231-2639
  Fax (760) 325-8610
E-mail: casacody@aol.com
Web site: www.palmsprings.com/hotels/casacody

Casa Cody Country Inn

Romantic, historic hideaway nestled against the spectacular San Jacinto Mountains in the heart of Palm Springs village. One-story California adobe hacienda-style buildings surrounded by lovely gardens of bougainvillea and citrus. Completely

redecorated in Santa Fe decor. Our 23 units include hotel rooms, studio suites, one- and two-bedroom suites with private patios, fireplaces, and kitchens. Cable TV and private phones. Two pools and secluded, tree-shaded whirlpool spa.

Hosts: Frank Tysen and Therese Hayes
Rooms: 23 (23PB) $59–359
Continental Breakfast
Credit Cards: A B C D E
Notes: 2 5 6 7 8 9 10 12

POINT REYES STATION

The Tree House B & B

P. O. Box 1075; 73 Drake Smt.
  Point Reyes Station, CA 94956-1075
(415) 663-8720
Web site: www.treehousebnb.com

A secluded and peaceful getaway in legendary West Marin. Located on the tip of Inverness Ridge with a view of Point Reyes Station and rolling hills. Enjoy the breathtaking views of the surrounding countryside, picture post-card perfect with every season, while relaxing on the deck with wine, oysters, and barbeque. Only one hour from San Francisco or Santa Rosa, a truly beautiful drive at any time of the year.

Host: Lisa Patsel
Rooms: 3 (3PB) $125–155
Full Breakfast
Credit Cards: A B C
Notes: 6 7

6 Pets welcome; 7 Children welcome; 8 Tennis nearby; 9 Swimming nearby; 10 Golf nearby; 11 Skiing nearby; 12 May be booked through travel agent

RIDGECREST

Bevlen Haus Bed and Breakfast

809 N. Sanders St., Ridgecrest, CA 93555-3529
(760) 375-1988; (800) 375-1989
    Fax (760) 375-6871
E-mail: blh_b&b@iwvisp.com

"Once a guest, always a friend."
Gracious, quiet, safe, and comfortable;
your "secret high desert hideaway."
Nearly 2,000 square feet, furnished
with antiques, handmade quilts, and
comforters in winter! Paved parking.
Cooling air in summer. Old-fashioned
kitchen has antique cast-iron cook-
stove and a hand-hammered copper
sink. Year-round hot tub spa. In a full-
service community close to Sierra
Nevada, Death Valley, Naval Air
Warfare Center, China Lake, ghost
towns, movie sites, and ancient Indian
cultural sites. Wildflowers in spring.
No smoking.

Hosts: Bev and Len De Geus
Rooms: 3 (3PB) $55–75
Full Breakfast
Credit Cards: A B C D
Notes: 2 5 8 9 10 12

SAN ANDREAS

The Robin's Nest

247 W. St. Charles St., P. O. Box 1090
    San Andreas, CA 95249-1408
(209) 754-1076; (888) 214-9202
    Fax (209) 754-3975
E-mail: info@robinest.com
Web site: www.robinest.com

A traditional, yet informal Victorian
bed and breakfast country inn in the
heart of the Gold Country. Eight hun-
dred square feet of interior common
space make it ideal for group gatherings. The 1⅓ acres of gardens and fruit
orchards have several seating areas.
Central heat and air-conditioning, hot
spa, and five-course gourmet breakfast.
Lunch is available by reservation, minimum of 4.

The Robin's Nest

Hosts: Karen and Bill
Rooms: 9 (7PB;2SB) $85–150
Full Breakfast
Credit Cards: A B C D
Notes: 5 7 8 9 10 12

SAN DIEGO

Carole's B & B Inn

3227 Grim Ave., San Diego, CA 92104-4656
(619) 280-5258; (800) 975-5521

Built in 1904 by Mayor Frary, this historic site displays the handsome style
and craftsmanship of its time. It has
been restored by the present owners,
who live on-site, giving it constant
loving care. The decor is of its period,
with antiques and comfort as the
focus. Amenities include a spa, black-
bottom pool, and rose garden. Carole's

Bed and Breakfast is within walking distance of Balboa Park, an assortment of small shops, and restaurants. Also available: Charming 1-bedroom cottage $129.00 and a spacious 2-bedroom apartment $189.00.

Hosts: Carole Dugdale and Michael O' Brien
Rooms: 10 (4PB;6SB) $89–159
Continental Breakfast
Credit Cards: A B C D E
Notes: 5 7 8 9 10 12

Seabreeze Bed and Breakfast

121 N. Vulcan Ave., Encinitas, CA 92024
(760) 944-0318
Web site: www.seabreeze-inn.com

Seabreeze Bed and Breakfast Inn is a clean, comfortable home away from home and a private, romantic retreat. Five guest rooms all have their own entries and baths. All have cable TV; two with VCR and phone access. They are individually decorated with one-of-a-kind custom furnishings. Downstairs there is a common sitting room with a fireplace and kitchenette. The upstairs Penthouse Shangri-La, has a private, 8-ft. hot tub on an ocean-view balcony. The private upstairs apartment has a fireplace, kitchen, double tub and shower bath, and ocean-view balcony.

Host: Kirsten Richter
Rooms: 5 (5PB) $89–175
Continental Breakfast
Credit Cards: A B
Notes: 5 7 8 9 10

SAN FRANCISCO

Garratt Mansion

900 Union St., Alameda, CA 94501
(510) 521-4779
E-mail: garrattm@pacbell.net
Web site: www.garrattmansion.com

Garratt Mansion

Fifteen minutes from San Francisco, the quiet island of Alameda is convenient and unique. We can offer touring ideas or privacy to regroup. Whether you're on business or vacation, we love to anticipate and meet your needs with fresh flowers, down comforters, afternoon cookies, fresh orange juice, and direct-line phones. Twenty-four-hour beverages and other amenities are provided.

Hosts: Royce and Betty Gladden
Rooms: 7 (5PB;2SB) $95–175
Full Breakfast
Credit Cards: A B C
Notes: 5 8 9 10

The Grove Inn

890 Grove St., San Francisco, CA 94117-1712
(415) 929-0780; (800) 899-0780
    Fax (415) 929-1037
E-mail: grovinn@jps.net
Web site: www.grovinn.com

Victorian inn at Alamo Square historic site. The inn is managed by the

---

6 Pets welcome; 7 Children welcome; 8 Tennis nearby; 9 Swimming nearby; 10 Golf nearby; 11 Skiing nearby; 12 May be booked through travel agent

owners. It is centrally located.

Hosts: Klaus and Rosetta Zimmermann
Rooms: 19 (12PB;4SB) $90–110
Continental Breakfast
Credit Cards: A B C
Notes: 2   7 8 9 10 12

The Monte Cristo

600 Presidio Ave., San Francisco, CA 94115
(415) 931-1875; Fax (415) 931-6005
Web site: www.virtualcities.com

The Monte Cristo has been part of San Francisco since 1875, located 2 blocks from elegantly restored Victorian shops, restaurants, and antique stores on Sacramento Street. Convenient transportation to downtown San Francisco and to the financial district. Each room is elegantly furnished with authentic period pieces.

Host: George
Rooms: 14 (11PB;3SB) $83–118
Continental Breakfast
Credit Cards: A B C D
Notes: 5 7

SANTA BARBARA

Prufrock's Garden Inn by the Beach

600 Linden Ave., Carpinteria, CA 93013-2040
(805) 566-9696; (8PR) UFR-OCKS
    Fax (805) 566-9404
E-mail: innkeepers@prufrocks.com
Web site: www.prufrocks.com

Prufrock's Garden Inn by the Beach

A "Most Romantic Getaway" (*Santa Barbara Independent*) by the "Best Beach in the West" (University Beach rating service), voted "Reader's Favorite" (*L. A. Times*), photographed for (*Land's End Catalog*). Jacuzzis, fireplaces, in-room fresh flowers, sunset hors d'oeuvres, bedtime chocolates. Best Santa Barbara B & B beach location, State beach park one block. Restaurants, boutiques, antique stores. Tucked between the ocean and the mountains in a community known for orchards and flower fields. AMTRAK, beach amenities, wharf lunches.

Hosts: Judy and Jim Halvorsen
Rooms: 7 (7PB) $89–229
Full Breakfast
Credit Cards: A B D
Notes: 5 7 8 9 10 11

Secret Garden Inn and Cottages

1908 Bath St., Santa Barbara, CA 93101
(805) 687-2300; (800) 676-1622
    Fax (805) 687-4576
E-mail: garden@secretgarden.com
Web site: www.secretgarden.com

The Secret Garden is one of Santa Barbara's oldest inns, formerly called the Blue Quail. The inn consists of a main house, four cottages, and a house. Ideal for vacation rentals. All are set among lush jasmine, jacaranda, and camellia interwined with branches of persimmon, avocado, lemon and pecan trees. High hedges, private lawns add to the secrecy of the gardens. Rooms have private bathrooms, and five of the suites have private outdoor hot tubs.

NOTES: Credit cards accepted: A Master Card; B Visa; C American Express; D Discover; E Diners
Club; F Other; 2 Personal checks accepted; 3 Lunch available; 4 Dinner available; 5 Open all year;

Host: Dominique Hannaux
Rooms: 12 (12PB) $121–300
Full Breakfast
Credit Cards: A B C D
Notes: 2 4 5 8 9 10

Tiffany Country House

1323 De la Vina, Santa Barbara, CA 93101
(805) 963-2283; (800) 999-5672
    Fax (805) 963-2825
E-mail: upham.hotel@verizon.net
Web site: www.tiffanycountryhouse.com

Circa 1898. This Victorian house features a steep front gable and balcony
accentuating the entrance. Colonial
diamond-paned bay windows and a
front veranda welcome guests to an
antique-filled inn. All seven rooms
have private bathrooms with three
rooms with spa tubs. Daily amenities
include a full breakfast, afternoon fruit,
wine and cheese, and cookies in the
evening. Located in the heart of Santa
Barbara, the Tiffany Country House is
within walking distance to museums,
restaurants, shops, and galleries.

Host: Jan Martin Winn
Rooms: 7 (7PB) $150–300
Full Breakfast
Credit Cards: A B C E F
Notes: 5 8 9 10 12

Upham Hotel and Garden Cottages

1404 De La Vina St.
    Santa Barbara, CA 93101-3057
(805) 962-0058; (800) 727-0876
    Fax (805) 963-2825
E-mail: upham.hotel@verizon.net
Web site: www.uphamhotel.com

The Upham Hotel, established in
1871, is the oldest continuously operating hotel in southern California. With
50 guest rooms including garden cottages and suites, the Upham is located
in beautiful downtown Santa Barbara
and is easy walking distance to shopping, restaurants, and cultural attractions. Louie's, the hotel's on-site
restaurant, offers modern California
cuisine.

Host: Jan Martin Winn
Rooms: 50 (50PB) $160–425
Continental Breakfast
Credit Cards: A B C E
Notes: 3 4 5 7 8 9 10 12

SEQUOIA NATIONAL PARK

Plantation Bed and Breakfast

33038 Sierra Hwy. #198, Lemon Cove, CA
    93244-1700
(559) 597-2555; (800) 240-1466
    Fax (559) 597-2551
E-mail: relax@plantationbnb.com
Web site: www.plantationbnb.com

Plantation Bed and Breakfast

Nestled in the foothills of the Sierra
Nevada Mountains among acres of
orange groves, only 16 miles from
Sequoia National Park. "Gone with
the Wind" theme rooms; heated
swimming pool in spring and fall;

Jacuzzi hot tub located in orange groves for privacy—open 24 hours. A full gourmet breakfast is served, including orange juice made from oranges picked fresh each morning. Fireplaces, verandas, gazebos, fountains, and many gardens.

Hosts: Scott and Marie Munger
Rooms: 7 (7PB) $129–209
Full Breakfast
Credit Cards: A B C D E
Notes: 2 5 9 10 11 12

SONORA

Barretta Gardens Inn B & B

700 S. Barretta St., Sonora, CA 95370
(209) 532-6039; (800) 206-3333
    Fax (209) 532-8457
E-mail: barrettagardens@hotmail.com
Web site: www.barrettagardens.com

Situated atop a terraced hillside, surrounded by an acre of landscaped gardens, this Victorian-era inn is a ten-minute walk to the center of Sonora. Enjoy relaxing in two open-air porches and three guest parlors. The five guest rooms, each with private bath (two with whirlpool tubs), have been elegantly decorated in period antiques. A full breakfast is served (including fresh French pastries baked daily in the on-site bakery) in the formal dining room or screened breakfast porch.

Hosts: Bruno and Sally Trial
Rooms: 5 (5PB) $95–250
Full Breakfast
Credit Cards: A B C D
Notes: 2 5 9 10 11 12

Lavender Hill B & B

683 S. Barretta St., Sonora, CA 95370
(209) 532-9024; (800) 466-1333, x29
E-mail: lavender@sonnett.com
Web site: www.lavenderhill.com

Come home to a 1900 Victorian overlooking the historic Gold Rush town of Sonora. The inn is situated in a quiet country setting with year-round gardens and a wrap-around porch with swing. Inside there are four guest rooms, an antique dining room, sitting room, and library. Cable TV and a video library are available for guest use. A home-cooked, hearty country breakfast and afternoon refreshments are included. State and federal parks, wine tasting, skiing, outdoor activities, and antiquing are all close by.

Host: Gail Golding
Rooms: 4 (4PB) $85–105
Full Breakfast
Credit Cards: A B C D
Notes: 2 5 7 8 9 10 11

TRINIDAD

The Lost Whale Bed and Breakfast Inn

3452 Patricks Point Dr.
    Trinidad, CA 95570-9782
(707) 677-3425; (800) 677-7859
    Fax (707) 677-0284
E-mail: lmiller@lostwhaleinn.com
Web site: www.lostwhale.com

Beautiful inn set on a bluff overlooking the rugged north coast. Four acres with private beach, tidepools, outdoor hot tub, large gourmet breakfast, and afternoon tea. Families welcome. "One of the top ten vacation spots in

California. . .a divine place." (*San Francisco Chronicle*)

Rooms: 8 (8PB) $140–210
Full Breakfast
Credit Cards: A B C D
Notes: 2 7 10 12

UKIAH

Vichy Hot Springs Resort and Inn

2605 Vichy Springs Rd., Ukiah, CA 95482
(707) 462-9515
E-mail: vichy@vichysprings.com
Web site: www.vichysprings.com

Vichy Springs is a delightful, two-hour drive north of San Francisco. Historic cottages and rooms await you with delightful vistas from all locations. Vichy Hot Springs features naturally sparkling, 90-degree mineral baths, a communal 104-degree pool, and an Olympic-size pool. Guests can explore 700 private acres with trails and roads for hiking, jogging, picnicking, and mountain bicycling. Vichy's idyllic setting provides a quiet, healing environment for travelers. This is California State Landmark No. 980. A Historic Inns member.

Hosts: Gilbert and Marjorie Ashoff
Rooms: 26 (26PB) $150–245
Full Breakfast
Credit Cards: A B C D E
Notes: 2 5 7 8 9 10 12

VENTURA

La Mer Bed and Breakfast

411 Poli St., Ventura, CA 93001-2614
(805) 643-3600; Fax (805) 653-7329

E-mail: lamerbb@aol
Web site: www.lamerbnb.com

La Mer Bed and Breakfast

Nestled in a green hillside, the Cape Cod-style Victorian house overlooks the heart of historic San Buenaventura and the spectacular California coastline. Each guest room has been individually furnished to capture a particular European country. A bottle of wine and a sumptuous Bavarian breakfast.

Hosts: Gisela and Michael Baida
Rooms: 5 (5PB) $95–185
Full Breakfast
Credit Cards: A B C F
Notes: 2 5 7 8 9 10 12

WESTPORT

Howard Creek Ranch

P. O. Box 121; 40501 N. Hwy. One
   Westport, CA 95488
(707) 964-6725; Fax (707) 964-1603
E-mail: howardcreekranch@mcn.org
Web site: www.howardcreekranch.com

Howard Creek Ranch is a historic, 60-acre, oceanfront farm dating to 1867, bordered by miles of beach and mountains in a wilderness area. Award-winning flower gardens, antiques, fireplaces, redwoods, a 75-foot swinging footbridge over Howard

Creek, cabins, comfortable beds, hot tub, sauna, pool, nearby horseback riding, and excellent restaurants are combined with hospitality and a full ranch breakfast. Termed "one of the most romantic places to stay on the planet" by the *San Francisco Examiner.* Children are welcome by arrangement.

Howard Creek Ranch

Hosts: Charles and Sally Grigg
Rooms: 15 (13PB;2SB) $75–160
Full Breakfast
Credit Cards: A B C D
Notes: 2 5 9

WILLITS

Beside Still Waters Farm B & B

30901 Sherwood Rd., Willits, CA 94590
E-mail: besidestillwatersfarm@yahoo.com
Web site: www.besidestillwatersfarm.com

Opening in Spring 2003! Beside Still Waters Farm lies 8 miles outside of the town of Willits, 2½ hours north of San Francisco. Perched upon the hillside are four luxurious private cottages boasting whirlpool baths, gas fireplace/stoves, king-sized beds, and high-end linens. Three cottages have steam showers, and one can accommodate families. A full breakfast is deliv-

ered each morning, and guests can join the innkeepers for wine, tea, and appetizers at the farmhouse each evening. Enjoy organic fruits and veggies from the garden and orchard. Many special packages available. Escape to the not-so-far-away country life!

Hosts: Earl and Christy Collins
Rooms: 4 (4PB) $350–450
Full Breakfast
Credit Cards: A B C D
Notes: 4 6 7 10

YOSEMITE

Karen's Yosemite B & B Inn

1144 Railroad Ave., P. O. Box 8
   Fish Camp, CA 93623-0008
(559) 683-4550; (800) 346-1443
   Fax (559) 683-8127
E-mail: karenbnb@sierratel.com
Web site: www.karensyosemitebnb.com

Yosemite National Park is only 2 miles away. Nestled among the towering pines and whispering cedars at 5000 feet, Karen's offers a unique blend of contemporary living. Each room, delicately decorated, has a full ensuite bath, individual temperature control, and a woodland view. Afternoon refreshments, compatible with the season, are served each afternoon. A bountiful breakfast is offered each morning by candlelight in the dining room. Many adventures await you depending on the season.

Host: Karen Bergh
Rooms: 3 (3PB) $100
Full Breakfast
Credit Cards:
Notes: 2 5 7 8 9 10 11 12

NOTES: Credit cards accepted: A Master Card; B Visa; C American Express; D Discover; E Diners Club; F Other; 2 Personal checks accepted; 3 Lunch available; 4 Dinner available; 5 Open all year;

COLORADO

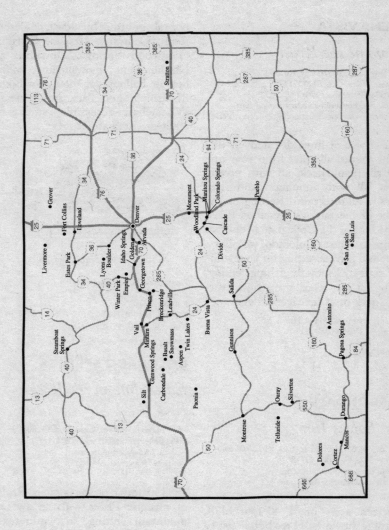

Colorado

BUENA VISTA

Room at the River

P. O. Box 1133; 30670 Cty. Rd. 371
  Buena Vista, CO 81211-1133
(719) 395-8599; Fax (970) 668-3038
E-mail: riverhouse@meistermarketing.com
Web site: www.meistermarketing.com/riverhouse

Your choice of three distinctively different rooms; all enter from your private riverbank deck, all with private baths, all with mountain and river views in all directions! Resting on the banks of the famous Arkansas River, at the foot of the Collegiate Mountain Range in central Colorado, we offer a quiet and private setting for your summer retreat. Enjoy fly fishing, hiking, biking, or just relaxing on your riverbank deck or at the river's edge.

Hosts: Barbara and Frank Hofmeister
Rooms: 3 (3PB) $125–135
Full Breakfast
Credit Cards:
Notes: 2 7 8 9 10 11 12

CARBONDALE

Mt. Sopris Inn

P. O. Box 126, Carbondale, CO 81623-0126
(970) 963-2209; (800) 437-8675
E-mail: mt.soprisinn@juno.com
Web site: www.mtsoprisinn.com

Fourteen acres on a 40-foot bluff, magnificent views. Three buildings; 13 guest rooms with private bath, TV, telephone, A/C, fireplaces. Outdoor hot tub, gourmet breakfast, conference room. Central to Aspen, Redstone, Glenwood Springs. Downhill and Nordic skiing, snowshoeing, golfing, hot air ballooning, mountain biking, fly fishing, horseback riding nearby. Wheelchair accessible, smoke-free adult-oriented atmosphere.

Mt. Sopris Inn

Host: Barbara Fasching
Rooms: 13 (13PB) $100–250
Full Breakfast
Credit Cards: A B C
Notes: 8 9 10 11 12

COLORADO SPRINGS

Eastholme in the Rockies B & B

4445 Hagerman Ave., Cascade, CO 80809
(719) 684-9901; (800) 672-9901
E-mail: info@eastholme.com
Web site: www.eastholme.com

1885 Victorian on the National Register of Historic Places with an awesome mountain setting, just minutes to Colorado Springs and all Pikes Peak attractions. Quiet area among tall

---

pines, the inn features a 40-foot porch and balcony, stone patio, gazebo (great for weddings). Spacious rooms boast original antiques (1885) and queen beds. Two honeymoon cottages are available with Jacuzzis and fireplaces.

Host: Terry Thompson
Rooms: 8 (6PB;2SB) $75–150
Full Breakfast
Credit Cards: A B C D
Notes: 2 5 7 8 9 10

Holden House–1902 Bed and Breakfast Inn

1102 W. Pikes Peak Ave.
   Colorado Springs, CO 80904-4347
(719) 471-3980; (888) 565-3980
   Fax (719) 471-4740
E-mail: mail@holdenhouse.com
Web site: www.holdenhouse.com

Discover a Pikes Peak treasure! These 1902 storybook Victorians are filled with antiques and family heirlooms. Each guest suite boasts feather pillows, period furnishings, queen bed, in-room fireplace, and oversized bubble bathtub-for-two. Centrally located in a residential area near historic Old Colorado City. You can enjoy shopping, restaurants, and attractions nearby. Experience "the romance of the past with the comforts of today." Inn cats "Mingtoy" and "Muffin" are in residence. AAA/Mobil awards.

Hosts: Sallie and Welling Clark
Rooms: 5 (5PB) $130–145
Full Breakfast
Credit Cards: A B C D E
Notes: 5 8 9 10 12

DENVER

Castle Marne— a Luxury Urban Inn

1572 Race St., Denver, CO 80206-1308
(303) 331-0621; (CAS) TLEMARNE
   Fax (303) 331-0623
E-mail: info@castlemarn.com
Web site: www.castlemarne.com

Castle Marne

Chosen by *Country Inns Magazine* as one of the "Top 12 Inns in North America." Fall under the spell of one of Denver's grandest historic mansions. Your stay here combines old-world elegance with modern convenience and comfort. Each guest room is a unique experience in pampered luxury. All rooms have private baths. Two suites have Jacuzzis-for-two. Three rooms have private balconies and hot tubs. Afternoon tea and a full gourmet breakfast are served in the cherry-paneled dining room. Castle Marne is a certified Denver Landmark and is on the National Register of Historic Structures.

Hosts: The Peiker Family
Rooms: 9 (9PB) $105–255
Full Breakfast
Credit Cards: A B C D E
Notes: 2 3 4 5 8 9 10 11 12

---

6 Pets welcome; 7 Children welcome; 8 Tennis nearby; 9 Swimming nearby; 10 Golf nearby; 11 Skiing nearby; 12 May be booked through travel agent

Queen Anne Bed and Breakfast Inn

2147 Tremont Pl., Denver, CO 80205-3132
(303) 296-6666; (800) 432-4667
  Fax (303) 296-2151
E-mail: travel@queenannebnb.com
Web site: www.queenannebnb.com

Queen Anne Bed and Breakfast Inn

Facing quiet Benedict Fountain Park in downtown Denver are two side-by-side National Register Victorian homes with fourteen guest rooms, including four gallery suites. Flowers, chamber music, phones, period antiques, and private baths are in all rooms. Seven rooms have special tubs; two have a fireplace. Air-conditioning, free parking. Located within walking distance of the capitol, 16th Street Pedestrian Mall, the Convention Center, Larimer Square, retaurants, shops, and museums. Among its many awards: Best 12 B & Bs Nationally, Ten Most Romantic, Best of Denver, and Best 105 in Great American Cities. Now in its fourteenth year, it is inspected and approved by major auto clubs and Distinctive Inns of Colorado.

Hosts: The King Family
Rooms: 14 (14PB) $75–175
Full Breakfast
Credit Cards: A B C D E
Notes: 2 5 12

DIVIDE

Silver Wood B & B

463 Cty. Rd. 512, Divide, CO 80814-9731
(719) 687-6784; (800) 753-5592
E-mail: silver1007@aol.com
Web site: www.silverwood.com

Mountain serenity and western beauty. Brilliant sunsets, starry nights. World-class views of the Continental Divide mountains to the west and Pikes Peak to the southeast. Modern home, private baths, quality comfort. Guests stay here for the quietness, the superb breakfasts, the world-class views, and the hosts. Breakfast is served next to the large windows of the great room. Quiet country get-away only 45 minutes from downtown Colorado Springs. Hiking, fishing, sightseeing nearby.

Hosts: Bess and Lawrence Oliver
Rooms: 2 (2PB) $62–95
Full Breakfast
Credit Cards: A B D
Notes: 2 5 7 11 12

ESTES PARK

The Quilt House Bed and Breakfast

P. O. Box 339, Estes Park, CO 80517-0339
(970) 586-0427
E-mail: hgraetzer@aol.com

A beautiful view can be enjoyed from every window of this sturdy mountain home. It is just a 15-minute walk from downtown Estes Park and only 4 miles from the entrance of Rocky Mountain National Park. There are

NOTES: Credit cards accepted: A Master Card; B Visa; C American Express; D Discover; E Diners Club; F Other; 2 Personal checks accepted; 3 Lunch available; 4 Dinner available; 5 Open all year;

three bedrooms upstairs, plus a lounge where guests can read, look at the mountains, and have a cup of coffee or tea. A guest house beside the main house has a kitchenette. The hosts gladly help with information concerning hiking trails, car drives, wildlife viewing, shopping, etc. No smoking.

Hosts: Hans and Miriam Graetzer
Rooms: 4 (4PB) $60–75
Full Breakfast
Credit Cards:
Notes: 2 5 8 9 10 11

Romantic River Song Inn

P. O. Box 1910, Estes Park, CO 80517-1910
(970) 586-4666; Fax (970) 577-0699
E-mail: romanticriversong@earthlink.net
Web site: www.romanticriversong.com

Secluded on 27 wooded acres, River Song has been voted Colorado's Most Romantic B & B. Rooms with fireplaces and tubs for two, styled in country elegance, await guests celebrating a special getaway. After a day in the National Park, enjoy a candlelight dinner for two or a specially prepared picnic basket for your hike. The inn is the place to elope!

Hosts: Gary and Sue Mansfield
Rooms: 9 (9PB) $150–295
Full Breakfast
Credit Cards: A B D
Notes: 2 4 5 10 11 12

LEADVILLE

The Ice Palace Inn

813 Spruce St., Leadville, CO 80461-3555
(719) 486-8272; (800) 754-2840
Fax (719) 486-0345

E-mail: icepalace@bwn.net
Web site: http://icepalaceinn.com

The Ice Palace Inn

This gracious Victorian inn was built at the turn of the century using lumber from the famous Leadville Ice Palace. Romantic guest rooms are elegantly decorated with antiques, feather beds, and quilts. Each has an exquisite private bath and is named after an original room of the Ice Palace. Begin your day with a delicious gourmet breakfast served at individual tables in this historic inn. Afternoon teas and goodies are available every day. Turn-down service in the evening. Fireplaces and TV/VCRs. Hot tub.

Hosts: Giles and Kami Kolakowski
Rooms: 8 (8PB) $89–159
Full Breakfast
Credit Cards: A B C D E
Notes: 2 5 7 8 9 10 11 12

MANITOU SPRINGS

Spring Cottage Bed and Breakfast

113 Pawnee Ave., Manitou Springs, CO 80829
(719) 685-9395; (888) 588-9395
Fax (719) 685-1248
E-mail: lancaster@springcottage.com
Web site: www.springcottage.com

6 Pets welcome; 7 Children welcome; 8 Tennis nearby; 9 Swimming nearby; 10 Golf nearby; 11 Skiing nearby; 12 May be booked through travel agent

"A time and a place to count as your own." Two private cottages. 1885 family-friendly Spring Cottage accommodates 7. Intimate Spring Cottage Two, accommodates two only for a personal holiday, honeymoon or anniversary, retreat. Breakfast privately in the cottage. Fully equipped kitchens, TV, VCR, phone. One block to town center. Pets welcome outdoors only.

Hosts: Ron and Judy Lancaster
Rooms: 2 (2PB) $110
Full Breakfast
Credit Cards: A B F
Notes: 2 5 6 7 8 9 10 12

PAGOSA SPRINGS

Davidson's Country Inn

P. O. Box 87, Pagosa Springs, CO 81147-0087
(970) 264-5863; Fax (970) 264-5492
E-mail: dcibb@aol.com
Web site: www.davidsonsinn.com

Davidson's, est. 1986, continues to be "home away from home" to people from all over the world. We are located 2 miles east of town on Hwy. 160. Nancy and Gilbert invite you to come sit on the porches and enjoy our peaceful setting and magnificent view of Pagosa Peak. Come inside to comfortable rooms decorated with antiques and heirlooms and experience our warmth, hospitality, humor, and famous country breakfasts. Groups welcome. Cabin available.

Hosts: Gilbert and Nancy Davidson
Rooms: 8 (4PB;4SB) $75–100
Full Breakfast
Credit Cards: A B C D
Notes: 2 5 7 8 9 10 11 12

PINE

Meadow Creek B & B

13438 Hwy. 285; Berry Hill Ln. @ Douglass
  Ranch, Pine, CO 80470
(303) 838-4167; Fax (303) 838-0360
E-mail: info@meadowcreekbb.com
Web site: www.meadowcreekbb.com

Meadow Creek

Nestled among 34 acres of pine and aspen, this restored 1929 historic stone lodge offers a luxurious, relaxing, romantic getaway. Start your day with our full, gourmet breakfast—and then decide—hiking, biking, art galleries, or just curl up with a good book after a relaxing massage. Three deluxe suites feature private hot tubs and gas fireplaces. Four standard suites access a generous outdoor hot tub where guests can soak while enjoying the mountain sky.

Hosts: Loren and Ivan Fuentes
Rooms: 7 (7PB) $110–205
Full Breakfast
Credit Cards: A B C
Notes: 2 4 5 8 10

SALIDA

The Tudor Rose
Bed and Breakfast

6720 Cty. Rd. 104, Salida, CO 81201-0089

NOTES: Credit cards accepted: A Master Card; B Visa; C American Express; D Discover; E Diners Club; F Other; 2 Personal checks accepted; 3 Lunch available; 4 Dinner available; 5 Open all year;

(719) 539-2002; (800) 379-0889
  Fax (719) 530-0345
E-mail: info@thetudorrose.com
Web site: www.thetudorrose.com

The Tudor Rose

Stately elegance and homelike comfort are combined tastefully at this majestic country manor. Nestled in the pines on 37 acres and surrounded by three mountain ranges, the inn commands views of the Rocky Mountains by day and starry skies by night. Overly large guest rooms, spacious common areas. Wildlife, native landscape, sunken hot tub, and a hiking trail enrich the surrounding grounds.

Hosts: Jon and Terré Terrell
Rooms: 6 (6PB) $75–165
Full Breakfast
Credit Cards: A B D
Notes: 2 5 7 8 9 10 11 12

WOODLAND PARK

The Woodland Inn

159 Trull Rd., Woodland Park, CO 80863
(719) 687-8209; (800) 226-9565
  Fax (719) 687-3112
E-mail: woodlandinn@aol.com
Web site: www.woodlandinn.com

Guests enjoy the relaxing, homelike atmosphere and fantastic views of Pikes Peak from this cozy country inn in the heart of the Rocky Mountains. Peacefully secluded on 5 private acres of woodlands, the Woodland Inn is 18 miles west of Colorado Springs. Guests enjoy our beautiful hot tub nestled among the aspen trees. Nearby attractions include Pikes Peak, Manitou Springs, hiking, biking, horseback riding, golf, cross-country skiing, and limited-stakes gambling in Cripple Creek. We welcome small retreats and seminars.

Hosts: Frank and Susan Gray
Rooms: 7 (7PB) $89–99
Full Breakfast
Credit Cards: A B C D
Notes: 2   5 7   10 11

The Woodland Inn

CONNECTICUT

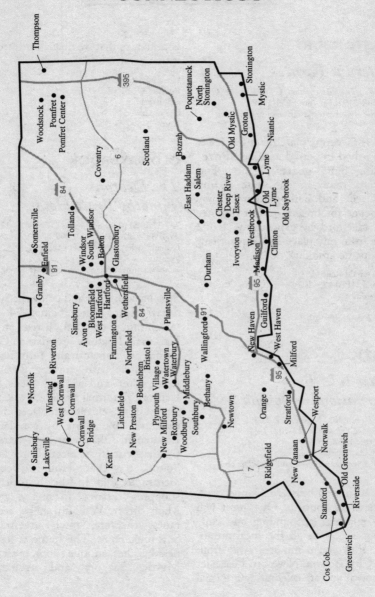

Connecticut

GLASTONBURY

Butternut Farm

1654 Main St., Glastonbury, CT 06033-2962
(860) 633-7197; Fax (860) 659-1758
Web site: www.butternutfarmbandb.com

This 18th-century architectural jewel is furnished in period antiques. Prize-winning dairy goats, pigeons, and chickens roam in an estate setting with trees and herb gardens. Enjoy fresh eggs for breakfast. Ten minutes from Hartford by expressway; 1 1/2 hours from any place in Connecticut. No pets, no smoking.

Host: Donald Reid
Rooms: 4 (4PB) $85–105
Full Breakfast
Credit Cards: C
Notes: 2 5 7 8 9 10 11

MYSTIC

Butler B & B International—Joshua 24:21

202 Shewville Rd., Mystic, CT 06355
(860) 536-6497; (800) 522-1077
Fax (860) 536-0304
E-mail: mkbutlerbb@aol.com
Web site: www.butler-bed-and-breakfast.com

Located in southeastern Connecticut, the heart of tourism. Our guest will enjoy relaxing; surrounding and convenient access to all the local attractions. Plus you're minutes away from N.Y. City, Boston, Newport. Please let us know if you are celebrating a special occasion, so that we may afford you our extra personal butler touch.

Host: Mildred Butler
Rooms: 3 (3PB) $90–155
Full Breakfast
Credit Cards:
Notes: 2 5 7 8 9 10

OLD SAYBROOK

The Deacon Timothy Pratt House

325 Main St., Old Saybrook, CT 06475-2375
(860) 395-1229; Fax (860) 395-4748
E-mail: shelley.nobile@snet.net
Web site:
    www.connecticut-bed-and-breakfast.com

Step back in time and enjoy the splendor of this magnificent circa 1746 center-chimney colonial, listed on the National Historic Register. Guest rooms are romantically furnished in period style with working fireplaces, four-poster and canopy beds, and Jacuzzis. A formal fireside breakfast is served in the elegant fireplaced dining room on fine china by candlelight. Located in Old Saybrook, where the Connecticut River meets Long Island Sound, the Pratt House is conveniently located in the historic and shopping district on pretty, gas-lit Main Street. Walk to shops, restaurants, theaters, town green, and Saybrook Point. The home is located near beaches, antique shops, museums, Mystic Seaport and Aquarium,

---

NOTES: Credit cards accepted: A Master Card; B Visa; C American Express; D Discover; E Diners Club; F Other; 2 Personal checks accepted; 3 Lunch available; 4 Dinner available; 5 Open all year;

Foxwoods and Mohegan Sun Casinos, Goodspeed musicals, factory outlet malls, Essex Steam Train, Connecticut River and Long Island Sound cruises, Gillette Castle State Park, and lots more! Beach passes, maps, and advice provided. Picturesque grounds. Bicycle loop. Nonsmoking. Two-night minimum stay on weekends; three-night minimum on holiday weekends. Massage therapy on premises. Cable TV, phone/modem lines, stereo/CD players in all rooms.

Host: Shelley Nobile
Rooms: 7 (7PB) $90–225
Continental Breakfast
Credit Cards: A B C
Notes: 2 5 8 9 10 11 12

OLD WETHERSFIELD

Chester Bulkley House B & B

184 Main St., Old Wethersfield, CT 06109-2340
(860) 563-4236; Fax (860) 257-8266
E-mail: chesterbulkley@aol.com

Chester Bulkley House

Nestled in the historic village of Old Wethersfield, minutes from downtown Hartford, the Chester Bulkley

House offers a uniquely comfortable haven for travelers. The Greek Revival structure from 1830 provides five luxurious guest rooms. Wide pine floors, hand-carved woodwork, working fireplaces, and period pieces enhance the ambience of this warm and gracious Bed and Breakfast.

Host: Tom Aufiero
Rooms: 5 (3PB;2SB) $90–105
Full Breakfast
Credit Cards: A B C D
Notes: 2 5 7 8 9 10

PLYMOUTH

Shelton House
Bed and Breakfast

663 Main St. # 6, Plymouth, CT 06782-2212
(860) 283-4616; Fax (860) 283-4616
E-mail: sheltonhbb@prodigy.net

Shelton House

Greek Revival (1825) nominated for the Historic Register, elegantly furnished with antiques and period furniture. Parklike grounds, perennial flower garden, and pineapple fountain. Spacious guest parlor with fireplace and TV. Full breakfast is served. Afternoon tea available. Convenient to I-84 and just 1 mile from Rte. 8, Exit 39. Twenty minutes to historic Litchfield—30 minutes to state capi-

6 Pets welcome; 7 Children welcome; 8 Tennis nearby; 9 Swimming nearby; 10 Golf nearby; 11 Skiing nearby; 12 May be booked through travel agent

tol. Antique centers, restaurants, vineyards, nature preserves, museums, and skiing are all nearby.

Hosts: Pat and Bill Doherty
Rooms: 4 (2PB;2SB) $80–95
Full Breakfast
Credit Cards:
Notes: 2 5 9 10 11

NOTES: Credit cards accepted: A Master Card; B Visa; C American Express; D Discover; E Diners Club; F Other; 2 Personal checks accepted; 3 Lunch available; 4 Dinner available; 5 Open all year;

DELAWARE

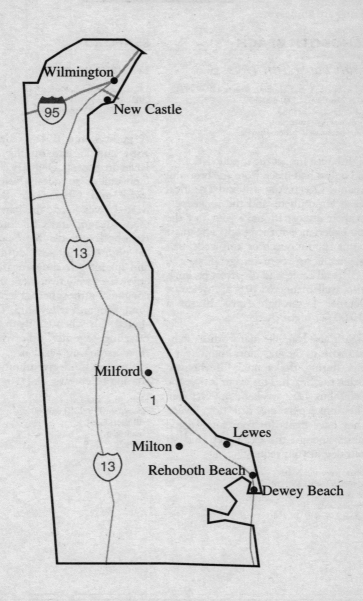

Delaware

REHOBOTH BEACH

Lighthouse Inn B & B

20 Delaware Ave., Rehoboth Beach, DE 19971
(302) 226-0407; (800) 600-9092
    Fax (302) 226-3385
E-mail: skijo@erols.com
Web site: www.lighthouseinn.net

Lighthouse Inn, at the ideal location. . . and only a half block from the beautiful Atlantic Ocean. You will find a nautical beach atmosphere, and the innkeepers do their utmost to make your stay the best experience at the beach. The guest rooms feature queen or king beds, private baths, in-room refrigerators, TV, VCR, and cable, and off-street parking. Also, well-mannered pets are welcome October 1 through April 30 for a $10.00 per night charge.

Lighthouse Inn, like many other establishments in the area, host hounds for 3 days during the annual Greyhounds Reach the Beach. This event is over the Columbus Day weekend in October. The innkeepers are real dog lovers. They have treats for your four-legged babies and go the extra step and sit your dog at your request.

Hosts: Jerry and Matt
Rooms: 6 (6PB) $50–185
No Breakfast Served
Credit Cards: B
Notes: 2 5 6 7 8 9 10

SEAFORD

Nanticoke House

121 S. Conwell St., Seaford, DE 19973-3905
(302) 628-1331
E-mail: bdse3235@aol.com

A guest home B & B dating from 1881 and located on the Nanticoke River in central Delmarva Peninsula. Convenient to ocean beaches, Delaware and Chesapeake Bays, Cape May–Lewes Ferry, the barrier islands of Assateague and Chincoteague, also Rehoboth outlet stores. Many historical points of interest, antique shops, and quaint gift shops nearby. Guests enjoy the lovely river view and relaxed, congenial atmosphere. Plenty of good food, fun, and fellowship. The bath is shared only when family or friends are traveling together, otherwise private. A nonsmoking residence, Nanticoke House is a God-given home we enjoy sharing (Hebrews 13:2).

Hosts: Bob and Dianne Seiler
Rooms: 2 (0PB;2SB) $50–60
Full Breakfast
Credit Cards:
Notes: 2 5 7 9 10

NOTES: Credit cards accepted: A Master Card; B Visa; C American Express; D Discover; E Diners Club; F Other; 2 Personal checks accepted; 3 Lunch available; 4 Dinner available; 5 Open all year;

DISTRICT OF COLUMBIA

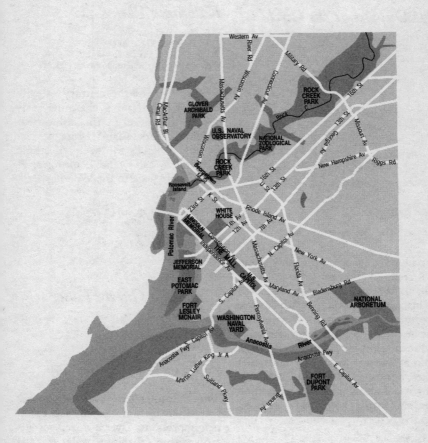

District of Columbia

WASHINGTON

The Dupont at the Circle

1606 19th St., NW, Washington, D.C. 20009
(202) 332-5251; (888) 412-0100
  Fax (202) 332-3244
E-mail: inn@dupontatthecircle.com
Web site: www.dupontatthecircle.com

The Dupont at the Circle

The Dupont at the Circle is housed in two restored Victorian townhomes, built in 1885. Our eight guest rooms are luxuriously appointed with antique furniture and sumptuous linens with private baths. Tasteful decor and original features like gas lamps and ornate moldings give a cozy ambience that belies our urban setting. Breakfast consists of fresh muffins and scones, seasonal fruits, homemade granola, and the best coffee around!

Hosts: Alan and Anexora Skvirsky
Rooms: 8 (8PB) $150–320
Continental Breakfast
Credit Cards: A B C D E
Notes: 2 5 8 9 10 12

Kalorama Guest House at Kalorama Park

1854 Mintwood Pl., NW
  Washington, D.C. 20009
(202) 667-6369; Fax (202) 319-1262
Web site: www.washingtonpost.com/yp/kgh

Three turn-of-the-century townhomes situated on a charming residential side street in the fashionable Kalorama Park/Adams Morgan area. Only two blocks to dozens of ethnic restaurants, cafes, and bookstores. A ten-minute walk to the Woodley Park Metro Stop.

Hosts: Michael, Katy and Lauranne
Rooms: 30 (16PB;14SB) $60–120
Continental Breakfast
Credit Cards: A B C D E
Notes: 5 12

Kalorama Guest House/ Woodley Park

2700 Cathedral Ave., NW
  Washington, D.C. 20009
(202) 328-0860; Fax (202) 328-8730
Web site: www.washingtonpost.com/yp/kgh

Two charming Victorian townhouses located in one of the city's choicest neighborhoods. Over a dozen restaurants within a 5-minute walk, as is the National Zoo. Only 2 blocks to the Woodley Park Metro Stop. The guesthouse's quaint, turn-of-the-century atmosphere has been attracting guests for over 17 years.

Hosts: Karin, Lynn and Carol
Rooms: 18 (6PB;12SB) $50–110
Continental Breakfast
Credit Cards: A B C D E
Notes: 5 12

Swiss Inn

1204 Massachusetts Ave., NW
    Washington, D.C. 20005-4501
(202) 371-1816; (800) 955-7947
    Fax (202) 371-1138
E-mail: swissinndc@aol.com
Web site: www.theswissinn.com

The Swiss Inn is a charming turn-of-the-century Victorian townhouse located in Washington, D.C. Amenities include bay windows, high ceilings, and fully equipped kitchenettes. The small, family-owned-and-operated inn is within walking distance of the White House, FBI, National Geographic, Chinatown, Convention Center, Smithsonian Museums, Ford's Theater, Women in the Arts Museum, subway, and many other attractions. We are also just 2 blocks from the main business district. Grocery stores are within walking distance, as are many noted churches, including St. Matthew's Cathedral.

Rooms: 7 (7PB) $59–118
No Breakfast Served
Credit Cards: A B C D E
Notes: 5 6 7 12

FLORIDA

Florida

AMELIA ISLAND

Bailey House

28 S. 7th St., Amelia Island, FL 32034-3960
(904) 261-5390; (800) 251-5390
  Fax (904) 321-0103
E-mail: baileyhs@bellsouth.net
Web site: www.bailey-house.com

Bailey House

Bailey House is a picturesque Queen Anne style B & B with Victorian decor. Built in 1895, it is listed in the National Register. Features include a wrap-around porch, turrets, gables, beautiful stained-glass windows, a magnificent staircase, pocket doors, ten fireplaces, and much more. The house is located in the historic district of Fernandina Beach on Amelia Island. You will be able to walk to restaurants, shops, and historic facilities. A delicious full breakfast is included.

Hosts: Tom and Jenny Bishop
Rooms: 10 (10PB) $129–189
Full Breakfast
Credit Cards: A B C D
Notes: 2 5 8 9 10 12

ARCADIA

Historic Parker House

427 W. Hickory St., Arcadia, FL 34266-3703
(863) 494-2499; (800) 969-2499
E-mail: parkerhouse@desoto.net
Web site: www.historicparkerhouse.com

Step back in time at the Historic Parker House. This lovely two-story 1895 home is full of period antiques, old clocks, and bits of Florida history. Four elegantly appointed guest rooms are located on the second floor. Larger rooms feature private baths, cable TV, and in-room phones. Breakfast in the formal dining room is a real treat. Children over 10 welcome.

Hosts: Bob and Shelly Baumann
Rooms: 4 (3PB;2SB) $69–85
Continental Breakfast
Credit Cards: A B C
Notes: 2 5 8 10 12

BRANDON

Behind the Fence B & B

1400 Viola Dr. at Countryside
  Brandon, FL 33511
(813) 685-8201; (800) 448-2672

Behind the Fence

NOTES: Credit cards accepted: A Master Card; B Visa; C American Express; D Discover; E Diners Club; F Other; 2 Personal checks accepted; 3 Lunch available; 4 Dinner available; 5 Open all year;

Retreat into the simplicity and tranquility of a bygone era with the conveniences of today's world. Choose your accommodations from a cottage by our pool to a private room in our antique-filled New England saltbox house. Nearby parks and river canoeing offer lots of opportunities for family activities. Homemade Amish sweet rolls are featured, and "relaxing" is the word most guests use to refer to their stay "behind the fence." Country furniture is for sale. Tours are available upon request. AAA, 3-star approved. Some pets are welcome by prior arrangements.

Hosts: Larry and Carolyn Yoss
Rooms: 5 (3PB;2SB) $79–89
Continental Breakfast
Credit Cards:
Notes: 2 5 6 7 8 9 10

DUNEDIN

J. O. Douglas House

209 Scotland St., Dunedin, FL 34698
(727) 735-9006
E-mail: lorrainepelosi@msn.com

Built in 1878, the J. O. Douglas House is the oldest in historic Dunedin and is listed on the National Register. This Victorian beauty was carefully restored for authenticity and enjoyment. Visitors are warmly welcomed and quickly feel comfortable as honored guests. Here one can enjoy the old-fashioned amenities along with the best of Florida: swimming, fishing, boating, and cycling. Shopping in historic Dunedin is filled with arts, crafts, antiques, boutiques, and tantalizing gourmet food.

J. O. Douglas House

Hosts: Andy and Lorraine Pelosi
Rooms: 6 (6PB) $90–165
Full Breakfast
Credit Cards: A B C D
Notes: 2 8 9 10

KEY WEST

Center Court Historic Inn and Cottages

915 Center St., Key West, FL 33040-7437
(305) 296-9292; (800) 797-8787
Fax (305) 294-4104
E-mail: ccinn@bellsouth.net
Web site: www.centercourtkw.com

Center Court Historic Inn and Cottages offers affordable, elegant, Historic Preservation award-winning accommodations nestled in quiet, tropical gardens just one-half block off Duval! We have 24 rooms, suites, villas, and cottages with queen and king beds (many with private Jacuzzis), TVs, phones, VCRs, air-conditioning, fans, private baths, hair dryers, beach towels, and beach bags. Enjoy breakfast each morning overlooking one of our two heated pools, Jacuzzi, exercise pavilion, and fishpond with its waterfall. Be pampered in our secret paradise! Center Court Historic Inn and Cottages is 3-diamond AAA rated. Pets stay for $10 per night.

Host: Naomi van Steelandt
Rooms: 24 (24PB) $98
Continental Breakfast
Credit Cards: A B C D
Notes: 5 6 7 8 9 10

Whispers Bed and Breakfast

409 William St., Key West, FL 33040-6853
(305) 294-5969; (800) 856-7444
    Fax (305) 294-3899
E-mail: info@whispersbb.com
Web site: www.whispersbb.com

Whispers sits in the heart of Olde Town Key West, within view of the Gulf Harbor and surrounded by a 30-block historic district of distinctive 19th-century homes. Ceiling fans whirl above rooms filled with antique furnishings. Guests enjoy the cool porches and lush garden. Take advantage of our complimentary membership at the local state park beaches, pool, and full health club facilities. Enjoy our tropical fish, birds, and gourmet breakfast creations. Come to paradise. Come home to Whispers.

Host: John Marburg
Rooms: 7 (7PB) $99–175
Full Breakfast
Credit Cards: A B C D
Notes: 5 6 8 9 10 12

LAKE WALES

Chalet Suzanne Inn and Restaurant

3800 Chalet Suzanne Dr., Lake Wales, FL
    33853-7060
(863) 676-6011; (800) 433-6011
    Fax (863) 676-1814
E-mail: info@chaletsuzanne.com
Web site: www.chaletsuzanne.com

Chalet Suzanne Inn

Listed on the National Register of Historic Places, the "folkloric" village that is Chalet Suzanne lies on the shore of Lake Suzanne surrounded by fragrant central Florida orange groves. Since 1931, the Hinshaw family has welcomed guests to the 30-room inn and five-star restaurant, which serves breakfast, lunch, and dinner daily. Visit the gift shop, ceramic studio, Chapel Antiques, swim, tour the soup cannery, home of the soups that went to the moon.

Host: Vita Hinshaw
Rooms: 30 (30PB) $169–229
Full Breakfast
Credit Cards: A B C D E
Notes: 2 3 4 5 7 10 12

MIAMI

Miami River Inn

118 S. W. South River Dr., Miami, FL 33130
(305) 325-0045; (800) HOTEL89

NOTES: Credit cards accepted: A Master Card; B Visa; C American Express; D Discover; E Diners Club; F Other; 2 Personal checks accepted; 3 Lunch available; 4 Dinner available; 5 Open all year;

Fax (305) 325-9227
E-mail: miamihotel@aol.com
Web site: www.miamiriverinn.com

Fresh-squeezed paradise! Looking for something completely different? You'll find it at this restored turn-of-the-century hotel on the banks of the Miami River. Restored in the 1980s by preservationist Sallye Jude, the inn provides all the necessary amenities in a tropical setting. Rooms have hardwood floors and are individually decorated with antiques. You'll also find a pool and Jacuzzi, a croquet green, and a garden courtyard where an expanded continental breakfast is served to guests.

Hosts: Sallye Jude and Jane Caporelli
Rooms: 40 (38PB;2SB) $69–199
Continental Breakfast
Credit Cards: A B C D E
Notes: 5 6 7 9 12

ORLANDO

Meadow Marsh B & B

940 Tildenville School Rd.
  Orlando/Winter Garden, FL 34787-3027
(407) 656-2064; (888) 656-2064
  Fax (407) 654-0656
E-mail: cavelle5@aol.com
Web site: meadowmarshbb.com

Meadow Marsh

Peace and tranquility embrace you as God's beauty unfolds in 12 acres of ol' Florida. You'll enjoy the 1877 Victorian farmhouse, where cozy fireplaces, hardwood floors, and lace curtains enhance the warmth and beauty of this country estate. The spacious lawn invites a romantic picnic or hand-in-hand walk through the meadow to the adjacent rails-to-trails path. Old-fashioned porch swings add to the feeling of yesteryear. After a busy day at central Florida's many attractions, relive the genteel era that whispers faintly through Meadow Marsh.

Hosts: Cavelle and John Pawlack
Rooms: 5 (5PB) $119–229
Full Breakfast
Credit Cards: A B
Notes: 5 8 9 10 12

PerriHouse Acres Estate Bed and Breakfast Inn

10417 Vista Oaks Court, Orlando, FL 32836
(407) 876-4830; (800) 780-4830
  Fax (407) 909-1294
E-mail: birds@perrihouse.com
Web site: www.perrihouse.com

PerriHouse is a quiet, country estate inn secluded on 2 acres of land adjacent to the Walt Disney World Resort. Surrounded by trees, grassy fields, and golf courses, the estate is a voluntary bird sanctuary. Five minutes to Disney, Pleasure Island, Seaworld Discovery, and EPCOT. Upscale continental breakfast. Eight guestrooms with private bath and entrances.

Hosts: Mark and Becky Manganella
Rooms: 8 (8PB) $89–145

Continental Breakfast
Credit Cards: A B C D E
Notes: 2 5 7 8 9 10 11 12

PALATKA

The Azalea House

220 Madison St., Palatka, FL 32177
(386) 325-4547
E-mail: azaleahouse@gbso.net
Web site: www.theazaleahouse.com

A 125-year-old Queen Anne Victorian Painted Lady. Located in quiet North Historic District—28 miles west of St. Augustine. Double parlors with fireplaces; a three-story curly pine staircase leads up to six guest rooms. This B & B has over 200 pieces of needlework on display, and a small counted cross stitch shop is available to guests. All rooms have queen beds. Lower rates weekdays with continental breakfast. Full breakfast on weekends. Pastry chef owner.

Hosts: Doug and Jill de Leeuw
Rooms: 6 (4PB;2SB) $75–135
Continental Breakfast
Credit Cards: A B C
Notes: 5 9 10

Ferncourt B & B

150 Central Ave., San Mateo, FL 32187-8785
(386) 329-9755
E-mail: ferncourt@gbso.net
Web site: www.ferncourt.com

Ferncourt

Ferncourt is a Victorian farmhouse built in 1889. Seventeen rooms allow lots of common area for guests plus large veranda. Hens on site provide basis for many delightful breakfast entrees. St. Augustine is a short 25 miles through farm country. Drive a little, save a lot. Large, comfortable rooms await you at the end of the day. Home is furnished in antiques and collectibles for your pleasure.

Hosts: Jack and Dee Dee Morgan
Rooms: 6 (5PB;1SB) $65–85
Full Breakfast
Credit Cards: A B
Notes: 2 4 5 10
Notes: 2 5 8 10 12

ST. AUGUSTINE

Carriage Way B & B

70 Cuna St., St. Augustine, FL 32084-3684
(904) 829-2467; (800) 908-9832
   Fax (904) 826-1461
E-mail: bjohnson@carriageway.com
Web site: www.carriageway.com

Built in 1833, this Victorian home is located in the heart of the historic district amid unique and charming shops, museums, and historic sites. The atmosphere is leisurely and casual, in keeping with the general attitude and feeling of Old St. Augustine. All guest rooms have a private bath with a clawfoot tub or shower. Rooms are furnished with antiques and reproductions including brass, canopy, or four-poster beds. A full home-baked breakfast is served. Children over 8 are welcome.

Hosts: Bill Johnson and son, Larry
Rooms: 11 (11PB) $85–190

NOTES: Credit cards accepted: A Master Card; B Visa; C American Express; D Discover; E Diners Club; F Other; 2 Personal checks accepted; 3 Lunch available; 4 Dinner available; 5 Open all year;

Full Breakfast
Credit Cards: A B C D
Notes: 2 5 7 8 9 10 12

Castle Garden Bed and Breakfast

15 Shenandoah St.
  St. Augustine, FL 32084-2817
(904) 829-3839; Fax (904) 829-9049
E-mail: castleg@aug.com
Web site: www.castlegarden.com

Stay at a castle and be treated like royalty! Relax and enjoy the peace, quiet, and "royal treatment" at our newly restored, 100-year-old castle of Moorish Revival design. The only sounds you'll hear are the occasional roar of a cannon shot from the old fort 200 yards to the south or the creak of solid wood floors. Awaken to the aroma of freshly baked goodies as we prepare a full, mouthwatering, country breakfast just like "Mom used to make." The unusual coquina stone exterior remains virtually untouched. The interior of the former Castle Warden Carriage House boasts three beautiful bridal rooms complete with soothing, in-room Jacuzzis and sunken bedrooms! Amenities include complimentary wine, chocolates, bikes, and private parking. Packages and gift baskets are available. We believe every guest is a gift from God.

Hosts: Bruce and Brian Kloeckner
Rooms: 7 (7PB) $65–179
Full Breakfast
Credit Cards: A B C D
Notes: 2 3 5 7 8 9 10 12

The Cedar House Inn

79 Cedar St., St. Augustine, FL 32084-4311
(904) 829-0079; (800) 233-2746
  Fax (904) 825-0916
E-mail: cbb@cedarhouseinn.com
Web site: www.cedarhouseinn.com

The Cedar House

Capture romantic moments at our 1893 Victorian home in the heart of the ancient city. Escape into your antique-filled bedroom with private whirlpool bath or clawfoot tub; enjoy the comfortable parlor with its fireplace, player piano, and antique Victrola; or sit on the shady veranda. Elegant full breakfast, evening snack, parking on premises, Jacuzzi spa, and bicycles. Walk to historical sites or bicycle to the beach. AAA-approved, 3-diamond rated. Smoke-free home; midweek discounts. Children over 10 welcome.

Hosts: Russ and Nina Thomas
Rooms: 6 (6PB) $89–205
Full Breakfast
Credit Cards: A B C D
Notes: 2 3 4 5 7 8 9 10 12

St. Francis Inn

279 St. George St.
  St. Augustine, FL 32084-5031
(904) 824-6068; (800) 824-6062
  Fax (904) 810-5525
E-mail: innceasd@aug.com
Web site: www.stfrancisinn.com

---

6 Pets welcome; 7 Children welcome; 8 Tennis nearby; 9 Swimming nearby; 10 Golf nearby; 11 Skiing nearby; 12 May be booked through travel agent

St. Francis Inn

Built in 1791, the St. Francis Inn is a beautiful Spanish Colonial building. The courtyard garden provides a peaceful setting for traditional hospitality. Our accommodations range from double rooms and suites to a five-room cottage, all with private bath, cable television, and central air/heat; many have fireplaces. The inn is centrally located in the historic district within easy walking distance of restaurants, shops, and sites.

Host: Joe Finnegan
Rooms: 17 (17PB) $99–199
Full Breakfast
Credit Cards: A B C D F
Notes: 2 5 7 8 9 10 12

Victorian House B & B

11 Cadiz St., St. Augustine, FL 32084-4431
(904) 824-5214; (877) 703-0432
    Fax (904) 824-7990
E-mail: vhouse@victorianhousebnb.com
Web site: www.victorianhouse-inn.com

The Victorian House, built in 1897, has been lovingly restored and furnished in period antiques. Enjoy canopy beds, quilts, stenciled walls, and heart pine floors. We are located in the historic district within walking

distance of fine restaurants, the waterfront, shops, museums, and the plaza. Breakfast is served in the dining room from 8:30 until 10:00 A.M. and features homemade granola, sweet breads, muffins, fruit, juice, hot entree, coffee, and tea.

Hosts: Ken and Marcia Cerotzke
Rooms: 8 (8PB) $90–175
Full Breakfast
Credit Cards: A B C D F
Notes: 5 7 8 9 10 12

ST. PETERSBURG

Mansion House B & B
The Courtyard on Fifth

105 5th Ave., NE
    St. Petersburg, FL 33701-3015
(727) 821-9391; (800) 274-7520
    Fax (727) 821-6906
E-mail: mansion1@ix.netcom.com
Web site: www.mansionbandb.com

Mansion House

Historic property, 1901–1912, features 13 rooms in two mansions and a carriage house surrounding a courtyard garden and swimming pool. Delicious breakfast, complimentary wine, soft drinks, and snacks, plus ten common areas provide the ultimate inn experience for business and leisure travelers. "Preferred Hotel" Bank of America, InnPoint Travel Rewards; AB & BA

NOTES: Credit cards accepted: A Master Card; B Visa; C American Express; D Discover; E Diners Club; F Other; 2 Personal checks accepted; 3 Lunch available; 4 Dinner available; 5 Open all year;

3-Crowns for Excellence; AAA, Superior Small Lodging; FH/MA, PAII. Expect the unexpected! "Mansion House, The Best!"— Michael and Kevin, Bacon Bros. Band.

Hosts: Robert and Rose Marie Ray
Rooms: 13 (13PB) $90–220
Full Breakfast
Credit Cards: A B C D E
Notes: 3 4 5 7 8 9 10 12

ST. PETERSBURG BEACH

Island's End Resort

1 Pass A Grille Way,
    St. Petersburg Beach, FL 33706-4326
(727) 360-5023; Fax (727) 367-7890
E-mail: jzgpag@aol.com
Web site: www.islandsend.com

Island's End, an oasis of real peace and quiet, where the crystal blue waters of the Gulf of Mexico meet the Intracoastal Waterway. Experience the brilliant sunrises while sipping freshly squeezed orange juice. Hunt for the shells along our private beach, stroll out to the end of our fishing dock, and watch dolphins playfully swimming by. Island's End features five well-appointed one-bedroom cottages and a fantastic three-bedroom home with a private solar-heated pool. Continental breakfast served Tuesday, Thursday, and Saturday.

Hosts: Jane and Millard Gamble
Rooms: 6 (6PB) $87–235
Continental Breakfast
Credit Cards: A B
Notes: 2 5 7 8 9 10

SANFORD

The Higgins House Victorian B & B

420 S. Oak Ave., Sanford, FL 32771-1826
(407) 324-9238; (800) 584-0014
    Fax (407) 324-5060
E-mail: reservations@higginshouse.com
Web site: www.higginshouse.com

Enjoy the romance of a bygone era at this 108-year-old Queen Anne Victorian bed and breakfast. Three guest rooms and a cottage all have private baths. Enjoy the Victorian gardens and hot tub. The Higgins House Bed and Breakfast is located in historic Sanford near beautiful Lake Monroe and the St. Johns River. Antique shops are nearby.

Hosts: Walter and Roberta Padgett
Rooms: 4 (4PB) $100–135
Full Breakfast
Credit Cards: A B C D

TARPON SPRINGS

East Lake B & B

421 Old East Lake Rd.
    Tarpon Springs, FL 34688-8401
(727) 937-5487
E-mail: littleflower@prodigy.net
Web site: www.bbonline.com/fl/eastlake

East Lake Bed and Breakfast is a private home on 2 1/2 acres situated on a quiet road along Lake Tarpon, close to the Gulf of Mexico. The hosts are retired businesspeople who enjoy new friends and are well informed about the area. The room and adjoining bath are at the front of the house, away from the family quarters. The room

---

6 Pets welcome; 7 Children welcome; 8 Tennis nearby; 9 Swimming nearby; 10 Golf nearby; 11 Skiing nearby; 12 May be booked through travel agent

has central air-conditioning, color TV, and telephone. Breakfast includes fresh fruit, juice, entree, and homemade breads and jams. Located close to many Florida attractions. Smoking on porch/deck only.

Hosts: Dick and Marie Fiorito
Rooms: 1 (1PB) $45
Full Breakfast
Credit Cards:
Notes: 2 5 8 9 10

VENICE

Banyan House

519 S. Harbor Dr., Venice, FL 34285
(941) 484-1385; Fax (941) 484-8032
E-mail: relax@banyanhouse.com
Web site: www.banyanhouse.com

Banyan House

Experience the Old World charm of one of Venice's historic Mediterranean homes, circa 1926, on the Gulf Coast. Relax in the peaceful atmosphere of our lovely courtyard dominated by a huge banyan tree. This provides an unusual setting for the garden patio, pool, and Jacuzzi. The Banyan House is central to shopping, beaches, restaurants, and golf. Complimentary bikes. No smoking. Minimum two-night stay on weekends. Continental deluxe breakfast is served.

Hosts: Chuck and Susan Mccormick
Rooms: 10 (10PB) $99-139
Full Breakfast
Credit Cards: A B
Notes: 2 8 9 10

VERO BEACH

Redstone Manor Bed and Breakfast

806 43rd Ave., Vero Beach, FL 32960
(772) 562-8082

Enjoy this Florida ranch-style home on 2 1/2 acres of beautifully landscaped grounds. There are four tastefully decorated bedrooms with four private baths. The common areas consist of a great room, library, dining room, large screened porch, pool, and hot tub. A full breakfast and afternoon refreshments are served in gracious style. Just minutes from beaches, shopping mall, Prime Outlet, golf, tennis, and many fine restaurants. Local activities include: Center for the Arts, Riverside Theater, Vero Beach Dodgers, Environmental Learning Center, Mel Fisher Treasure Museum, and Harbor Branch Oceanographic Institution. Nearby attractions include: Disney World and Wet and Wild in Orlando and Cape Kennedy at Cocoa Beach.

Hosts: Butch and Joyce Redstone
Rooms: 4 (4PB) $85-120
Full Breakfast
Credit Cards:
Notes: 2 5 8 9 10

NOTES: Credit cards accepted: A Master Card; B Visa; C American Express; D Discover; E Diners Club; F Other; 2 Personal checks accepted; 3 Lunch available; 4 Dinner available; 5 Open all year;

WHITE SPRINGS

White Springs B & B

P. O. Box 403, White Springs, FL 32096
(386) 397-1665; (888) 412-1665
E-mail: kgavronsky@aol.com
Web site: www.whitesprings.org

A 1905 boardinghouse located in picturesque White Springs just 2 blocks from the Stephen Foster Folk Center and the romantic Suwannee River. Features four woodburning fireplaces, front porch, heart of pine floors, and original stained-glass window. Renovated in 2000, offering four guest rooms decorated in Country Cottage and traditional furnishings. Listed in the National Registry of Historic Places and 90% original, including the original tin roof and original windows.

White Springs

Hosts: Kerry and Jake
Rooms: 4 (2PB;2SB) $65–95
Full Breakfast
Credit Cards: A B   F
Notes: 2 5 9

---

6 Pets welcome; 7 Children welcome; 8 Tennis nearby; 9 Swimming nearby; 10 Golf nearby; 11 Skiing nearby; 12 May be booked through travel agent

GEORGIA

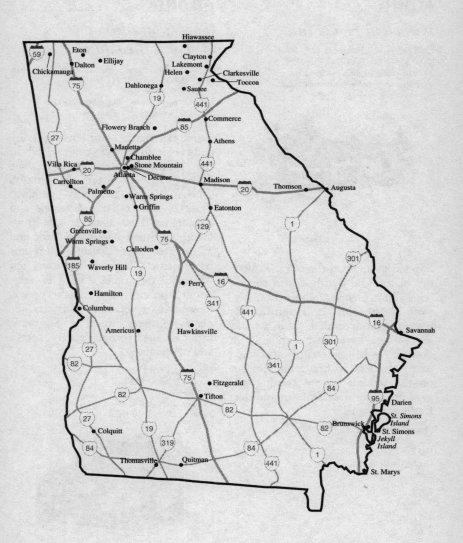

Georgia

ATHENS

Nicholson House Inn

6295 Jefferson Rd., Athens, GA 30607-1714
(706) 353-2200; Fax (706) 353-7799
E-mail: 1820@nicholhouseinn.com
Web site: www.nicholsonhouseinn.com

Nicholson House

Slip back quietly in time to the splendor of the Old South in this elegant antebellum Georgia home. This historic 1820 inn is magnificently restored and decorated, set in a relaxing 34-acre haven just 5 miles from downtown. It is splendidly appointed with antiques and fine prints. Join us on the veranda in the evening and gaze upon the friendly fawn and deer feeding in the yard.

Hosts: Celeste and Harry Neely
Rooms: 9 (9PB) $99–129
Full Breakfast
Credit Cards: A B C D F
Notes: 2 5 10

ATLANTA

The Village Inn Bed and Breakfast

992 Ridge Ave., Stone Mountain, GA 30083-3676
(770) 469-3459; (800) 214-8385
   Fax (770) 469-1051
E-mail: reservations@villageinnbb.com
Web site: www.villageinnbb.com

Come experience Southern hospitality and classic antebellum charm. Built in the 1820s, restored in 1995, the Village Inn is Stone Mountain's ONLY historic bed and breakfast. Walk to over 60 unique shops and restaurants. Less than 1 mile from Georgia's Stone Mountain Park and 15 minutes east of Atlanta. All rooms have private baths with oversized whirlpool tub, cable TV/VCR, telephone, and individual climate control. Several have verandas and gas fireplaces. Guests enjoy a Southern breakfast and complimentary snacks and beverages.

Hosts: Earl and Christy Collins
Rooms: 6 (6PB) $149–219
Full Breakfast
Credit Cards: A B C D
Notes: 5 7 8 9 10 12

The Village Inn

NOTES: Credit cards accepted: A Master Card; B Visa; C American Express; D Discover; E Diners Club; F Other; 2 Personal checks accepted; 3 Lunch available; 4 Dinner available; 5 Open all year;

FLOWERY BRANCH

Whitworth Inn

6593 McEver Rd., Flowery Branch, GA 30542-3860
(770) 967-2386; Fax (770) 967-2649
E-mail: visit@whitworthinn.com
Web site: www.whitworthinn.com

This contemporary country inn on 5 wooded acres offers relaxing atmosphere, 10 uniquely decorated rooms with TV, air-conditioning, private bath, and guest living room. A full country breakfast is served. Thirty minutes northeast of Atlanta just off I-985 at Lake Lanier. Boating, golf, beaches, waterpark, Road Atlanta, Chateau Elan, and Mall of Georgia are all nearby. Northeast Georgia Mountains less than 1 hour away.

Hosts: Ken and Christine Jonick
Rooms: 9 (9PB) $69–79
Continental Breakfast
Credit Cards: A B C F
Notes: 2 5 7 8 9 10 12

HELEN

Chattahoochee Ridge Lodge

P. O. Box 175, Helen, GA 30545-0175
(706) 878-3144; (800) 476-8331
E-mail: rooms@alltel.net
Web site: www.alltel.net~rooms

Leave the world behind in nature's woodsy setting high above Main Street, 3 minutes away. Four rooms and suites (with kitchen). All have private entrances, full baths, TV, A/C, free phones, and Jacuzzis. Patio has grill, hammocks, and valley-viewing gazebo. You'll like the quiet seclusion, deep rock water, and solar energy for stewards of the earth. Our many

repeated guests enjoy the new "great room" and fireplace. We'll help you plan great vacation days!

Chattahoochee Ridge Lodge

Hosts: Bob and Mary Swift
Rooms: 4 (4PB) $45–70
Continental Breakfast
Credit Cards: A B C D
Notes: 2 5 7 8 9 10

HIAWASSEE

Henson Cove Place B & B

1137 Car Miles Road, Hiawassee, GA 30546
(706) 896-6195; (800) 714-5542
E-mail: relax@henson-cove-place.com
Web site: www.henson-cove-place.com

Henson Cove Place B & B, a circa 1940s farmhouse lovingly restored, is set in the country with a fabulous view of the surrounding mountains and meadows. The home has three guest rooms with private baths and offers comfort and security for those seeking the peace and quiet necessary for relaxation. B & B guests enjoy breakfast each morning. The cabin offers families a great gathering place. Small, well-behaved pets are welcome in the cabin also.

Hosts: Mike and Laurie Rhatican
Rooms: 3 (3PB) $60–80
Full Breakfast
Credit Cards: A B D
Notes: 2 5 7 9 10

6 Pets welcome; 7 Children welcome; 8 Tennis nearby; 9 Swimming nearby; 10 Golf nearby; 11 Skiing nearby; 12 May be booked through travel agent

MARIETTA

Sixty Polk Street, a B & B

60 Polk St., NW, Marietta, GA 30064-2349
(770) 419-1688; (800) 845-7266
E-mail: jmertes@aol.com
Web site: www.sixtypolkstreet.com

Fully restored to its original glory, this French Regency Victorian home built in 1872 features warm, inviting bedrooms. Delight in exquisite period antiques as you peruse the library, relax in the parlor, or savor afternoon sweets in the dining room. Wake to early coffee followed by a sumptuous Southern breakfast before walking to the antique shops, restaurants, museums, or the theater on Marietta Square.

Hosts: Joe and Glenda Mertes
Rooms: 4 (4PB) $95–150
Full Breakfast
Credit Cards: A B C
Notes: 2 5 8 10 12

SAUTEE NACOOCHEE

The Stovall House Country Inn and Restaurant

1526 Hwy. 255 N
    Sautee Nacoochee, GA 30571-2517
(706) 878-3355
E-mail: info@stovallhouse.com
Web site: www.stovallhouse.com

Our 1837 Victorian farmhouse, restored in 1983, is listed on the National Register of Historic Places. Located on 26 acres in the historic Sautee Valley, the inn has views of the mountains in all directions. The recipient of several awards for its attentive restorations, the inn is furnished with family antiques and decorated with hand-stenciling. The restaurant, open to the public, features regional cuisine prepared with a fresh difference and served in an intimate yet informal setting. It's a country experience!

The Stovall House Country Inn

Host: Hamilton (Ham) Schwartz
Rooms: 5 (5PB) $84–92
Continental Breakfast
Credit Cards: A B C
Notes: 2 4 5 7 8 9 10

SAVANNAH

Joan's on Jones B & B

17 W. Jones St., Savannah, GA 31401
(912) 234-3863; (888) 989-9806
    Fax (912) 234-1455
E-mail: joansonjones@aol.com
Web site: www.bbonline.com/ga/joans/

Joan's on Jones

Privacy is the outstanding feature of this charming, 1883, privately owned and run bed and breakfast. Each of the two garden-level, antique-filled suites features a private entrance, off-street parking, sitting room, queen bedroom, bath, and kitchen. Early reservations are a must!

Hosts: Joan Levy / Gary Levy
Rooms: 2 (2PB) $145–160
Continental Breakfast
Credit Cards: F
Notes: 2 5 6 7 8 9 10

Savannah's Bed and Breakfast Inn

117 W. Gordon St., Savannah, GA 31401-4908
(912) 238-0518; Fax (912) 233-2537
E-mail: bnbinn@msn.com
Web site: www.savannahbnb.com

An 1853 rowhouse in the residential section of the historic district of downtown Savannah. A peaceful, friendly home where guests can relax on the deck or in the gardens enjoying afternoon tea after a full day of sightseeing and shopping. A full breakfast will get you started in the morning. Come stay with us and enjoy all that Savannah has to offer.

Rooms: 15 (15PB) $89–169
Full Breakfast
Credit Cards: A B C D
Notes: 2 5 7 8 9 10

WARM SPRINGS

Hotel Warm Springs B & B Inn

P. O. Box 351, Warm Springs, GA 31830-0351

(706) 655-2114; (800) 366-7616
  Fax (706) 655-2406
E-mail: hotelwarmsprings@alltel.net

"Presidents, passion, and the past." Relive history and the Roosevelt era in our 1907 hotel, ice cream parlor, and gift shops. Authentically restored and beautifully decorated with Roosevelt furniture and family antiques. Featuring our cozy honeymoon suite with king bed, suspended canopy, Victorian antiques, red heart tub, gold fixtures, breakfast in bed, flowers, champagne, and chocolates. Our large living room and dining room with Queen Anne furniture, oriental rugs, and crystal teardrop chandelier are ideal for group meetings. Nestled in quaint Warm Springs Village—a shopper's paradise, home of FDR's Little White House, 14 miles from Callaway Gardens, and 1 hour from Atlanta. Award-winning cheese grits and homemade peach ice cream.

Rooms: 14 (14PB) $75–180
Full Breakfast
Credit Cards: A B C D
Notes: 2 5 7 8 9 10 12

Hotel Warm Springs

HAWAII

Hawaii

Kukuihaele
Honokaa Paauilo
Kamuela (Waimea) Papaikou Hilo
Kona Keaau
Mountain View Volcano
Kailua-Kona HoAualoa Pahoa
Kealakekua Honaunau Kehena Beach
Captain Cook
Waiohinu South Point
Ocean View

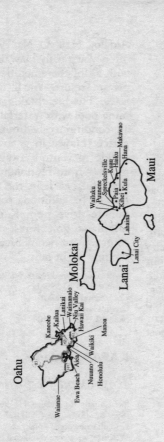

Maui

Makawao
Kula Haiku
Wailuku Kapu Hana
Puunene Spreckelsville
Paia
Kihei Kula
Lahaina

Lanai

Lanai City

Molokai

Oahu

Kaneohe
Kailua
Lanikai
Waimanalo
Nuu Valley
Hawaii Kai
Aiea Manoa
Ewa Beach Waikiki
Nuuanu
Waianae Honolulu

Kauai

Kilauea
Anahola
Kapaa
Wailua
Hanalei Koloa
Poipu
Kalaheo Lawai

Hawaii

KAMUELA, HAWAII

Kamuela Inn

P. O. Box 1994, Kamuela, HI 96743-1994
(808) 885-4243; (800) 555-8968
   Fax (808) 885-8857
E-mail: kaminn@aloha.net
Web site: www.kamuelainn.com

Kamuela Inn is a 30-room bed and breakfast accommodating our local visitors from different islands as well as visitors from afar. Comfortable, cozy rooms and suites with private baths, with or without kitchenettes, all with cable color televisions. Complimentary continental breakfast served in our lanai-art gallery every morning. Situated in a quiet, peaceful setting, just off Hwy. 19, conveniently located near shops, banks, theaters, parks, tennis courts, museums, restaurants, post office, and churches.

Host: Carolyn Cascavilla
Rooms: 30 (30PB) $59–185
Continental Breakfast
Credit Cards: A B C D E
Notes: 2 5 6 7 8 9 10 11

KAILUA, OAHU

Akialoa Hale O Na Wailele

1478 Akialoa Pl., Kailua, HI 96734
(808) 262-7466; (888) 489-9655
   Fax (808) 262-7466
E-mail: vickeryd001@hawaii.rr.com
Web site: www.kailuavacations.com

Akialoa Hale O Na Wailele B & B offers you a truly Hawaiian experience with all of the amenities of your own private resort. You'll never want to leave! The breathtaking views, swimming pool with waterfalls, and private air-conditioned bedrooms make it the perfect Hawaiian getaway. If you do decide to venture away, you are just minutes from Honolulu and the most beautiful beach in the world, Kailua Beach. In addition, you're just a 5-minute drive from Kailua town and Olomana golf links, a public golf course. Continental breakfast is served the first night only.

Hosts: Donald and Nastia Vickery
Rooms: 3 (3PB) $95–125
Continental Breakfast
Credit Cards: A B
Notes: 2 5 7 8 9 10

KAPAA, KAUAI

Rosewood Bed and Breakfast

872 Kamalu Rd., Kapaa, HI 96746-9701
(808) 822-5216; Fax (808) 822-5478
E-mail: rosewood@aloha.net
Web site: www.rosewoodkauai.com

Beautifully restored 100-year-old macadamia nut plantation located in the hills of Wailua at an altitude that enjoys perpetual springtime climate. Rosewood is located in the center of the island and only 3 miles to restaurants and beaches. The property features varied types of accommodations

---

NOTES: Credit cards accepted: A Master Card; B Visa; C American Express; D Discover; E Diners Club; F Other; 2 Personal checks accepted; 3 Lunch available; 4 Dinner available; 5 Open all year;

and prices for all needs. It has secluded thatched and Victorian cottages. Some of the amenities are: hardwood floors, all-white wicker furniture, king beds, screened and open dining with tropical birds that wake you in the morning, garden showers surrounded by orchids and rain forest. An abundance of extra touches are here to complete your holiday.

Hosts: Rosemary and Norbert Smith
Rooms: 6 (3PB;3SB) $40–125
Continental Breakfast
Credit Cards:
Notes: 2 5 7 8 9 10 11 12

KULA, MAUI

Gildersleeve's Country Vacation Rentals

1470 Naalae Rd., Kula, HI 96790-9446
(808) 878-6623; Fax (808) 878-2619

Located in a quiet country setting with splendid ocean and mountain views. All rooms have private baths, full kitchens, and sitting room privileges. Guests are welcome to cook breakfast or whatever meals they like. Next to our main house is a delightful cottage made to order for a family; it has a large kitchen, one bedroom with a queen bed, and twin beds in the loft. We ask that our guests do not smoke or drink. $70.00 three-night minimum.

Hosts: Elaine and Murray Gildersleeve
Rooms: 3 (3PB) $70
No Breakfast Served
Credit Cards:
Notes: 5 9 10

LAHAINA, MAUI

The Guesthouse

1620 Ainakea Rd., Lahaina, HI 96761
(808) 661-8085; (800) 621-8942
   Fax (808) 661-1896
E-mail: relax@mauiguesthouse.com
Web site: www.mauiguesthouse.com

Located between the historic whaling town of Lahaina and the beach resorts of Kaanapali, the Guesthouse is nestled in a quiet residential neighborhood, one block up from Wahikuli State Beach Park. All four rooms have private baths, air-conditioning, phones, TV/VCRs, refrigerators, and either an in-room Jacuzzi tub or a hot-tub out on the private patio! House amenities include kitchen, laundry, and pool. Receive discounts on rental cars and all island activities. Children over 12 are welcome.

Host: Tanna Swanson
Rooms: 4 (4PB) $129
Full Breakfast
Credit Cards: A B C D E
Notes: 2 5 7 8 9 10

---

6 Pets welcome; 7 Children welcome; 8 Tennis nearby; 9 Swimming nearby; 10 Golf nearby; 11 Skiing nearby; 12 May be booked through travel agent

IDAHO

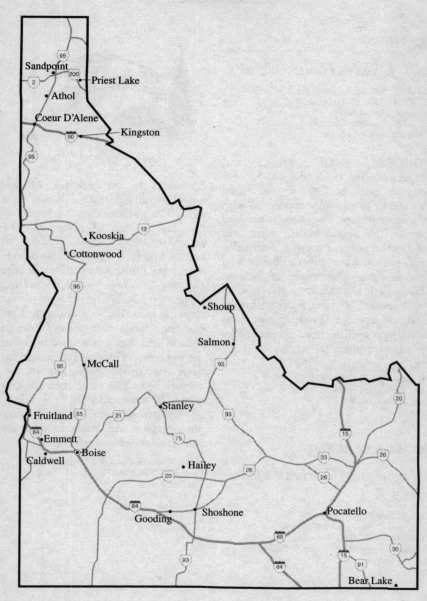

Idaho

BOISE

A J. J. Shaw House B & B

1411 W. Franklin St., Boise, ID 83702-5024
(208) 344-8899; (877) 344-8899
    Fax (208) 344-6677
E-mail: jjshaw@earthlink.net
Web site: www.jjshaw.com

Visit this beautiful historic inn and experience the grace and charm of a bygone era. The 1907 Queen Anne Victorian is tastefully appointed with vintage antiques. The mood is soft and serene, the neighborhood quiet, and the innkeepers are warm and friendly. All rooms have private baths and phone lines. Downtown or historic Hyde Park District are a lovely, short walk away. Delicious gourmet breakfasts are served, and sweet temptations are always available. Simply perfect for business or pleasure!

Host: Junia E. Stephens
Rooms: 5 (5PB) $79–119
Full Breakfast
Credit Cards: A B C D
Notes: 2 5 8 9 10 11 12

COEUR D' ALENE

Gregory's McFarland House B & B

601 E. Foster Ave.
    Coeur d' Alene, ID 83814-3048
(208) 667-1232; (800) 335-1232
Web site: www.bbhost.com/mcfarlandhouse

Gregory's McFarland House

Surrender to the elegance of this award-winning historical home, circa 1905. The full breakfast is gourmet to the last crumb. Guests will be delighted by an ideal blending of beauty, comfort, and clean surroundings. Jerry Hulse, travel editor for the *Los Angeles Times*, wrote, "Entering Gregory's McFarland House is like stepping back 100 years to an unhurried time when four-posters were in fashion and lace curtains fluttered at the windows." Our guest accommodations offer private baths and are air-conditioned. This is a nonsmoking house. If you're planning a wedding, our resident minister and professional photographer are available to make your special day beautiful.

Hosts: Winifred, Carol, and Stephen Gregory
Rooms: 5 (5PB) $90–175
Full Breakfast
Credit Cards: A B D
Notes: 2 8 9 10 11 12

NOTES: Credit cards accepted: A Master Card; B Visa; C American Express; D Discover; E Diners Club; F Other; 2 Personal checks accepted; 3 Lunch available; 4 Dinner available; 5 Open all year;

The Ponderosa

2579 E. Brunner Rd., Athol, ID 83801-0323
(208) 683-2251; (888) 683-2251
   Fax (208) 683-5112
E-mail: stay@theponderosa.net
Web site: www.theponderosa.net

Just minutes north of Coeur d'Alene, Idaho, you can experience the luxury and frontier setting of a 7,200-square-foot log home with spectacular mountain views and surrounded by beautiful lakes. The Ponderosa is nestled on a 10-acre wooded estate with nature trails that abound to observe local wildlife and seasonal wildflowers. Enjoy complimentary wine tasting in our 2,000-bottle wine cellar. For a romantic evening, relax in our enclosed whirlpool spa.

Hosts: Jack and Betty Bonzey
Rooms: 4 (4PB) $99–149
Full Breakfast
Credit Cards: A B
Notes: 2 5 8 9 10 11

GOODING

The Historic Gooding Hotel Bed and Breakfast

112 Main St., Gooding, ID 83330
(208) 934-4374; (888) 260-6656
Web site: http://goodingbb.hypermart.net

The rustic facade of The Historic Gooding Hotel B & B, circa 1900, belies the charm of its interior. The old-fashioned hospitality shown by innkeepers Dean and Judee Gooding has earned the hotel its reputation as "South Idaho's Home-away-from-home." There are ten individually decorated guest rooms: The main floor suite offers a private Victorian bathroom; the rooms upstairs share four bathrooms. A full breakfast features unique "house specials." The area provides year-round recreation and cultural and scenic attractions. This is a wonderful place from which to take a variety of day trips, then return "home" each night to kick back and relax. Families and groups are welcome.

Hosts: Dean and Judee Gooding
Rooms: 10 (1PB;9SB) $65–85
Full Breakfast
Credit Cards: A B C D
Notes: 5 7 9 10 11

SHOUP

Smith House B & B

3175 Salmon River Rd., Shoup, ID 83469
(208) 394-2121; (800) 238-5915
   Fax (208) 394-2121
E-mail: aesmith49@yahoo.com

Smith House

Since opening in 1987, Smith House has offered home-style atmosphere with top service at affordable rates. The well-appointed rooms offer breathtaking views of the famous Salmon River. Enjoy the hot tub, orchard, float trips, library, and covered decks. Kitchen, laundry, complimentary beverage and

6 Pets welcome; 7 Children welcome; 8 Tennis nearby; 9 Swimming nearby; 10 Golf nearby; 11 Skiing nearby; 12 May be booked through travel agent

snacks are available; the friendly hosts cater to your needs. Weekly rates. Ask about our Honeymoon/Anniversary Package. Open April 15–October 20.

Hosts: Aubrey and Marsha Smith
Rooms: 4 (2PB;2SB) $55–65
Full Breakfast
Credit Cards: A B
Notes: 2 6 7 9 11 12

ILLINOIS

Illinois

ALGONQUIN

Victorian Rose Garden

314 Washington St., Algonquin, IL 60102
(847) 854-9667; (888) 854-9667
E-mail: roses@mc.net
Web site: www.sleepandeat.com

Victorian Rose Garden

Built in 1886, the Victorian Rose
Garden invites guests to relax on its
wrap-around porch, read by the fireplace, play the baby grand piano, and
enjoy the old-fashioned barber corner.
Bedrooms are individually decorated
with antiques and collectibles. A delicious breakfast is served formally in
the dining room each morning.
Nearby you will find golf courses,
antiques, a bike trail, restaurants, and a
dinner boat. Chicago is only 1 hour
away. The Victorian Rose Garden is a
nonsmoking, nonalcoholic, animal-
free residence. Special guest packages
are available. Come and let us pamper
you! Children over 12 welcome.

Hosts: The Brewers
Rooms: 4 (4PB) $70–139
Full Breakfast
Credit Cards: A B C
Notes: 2 5 7 8 10

ARTHUR

Heart and Home

137 E. Illinois St., Arthur, IL 61911-1333
(217) 543-2910

Located in the heart of Illinois Amish
country and constructed in 1906,
Heart and Home is a Victorian bed
and breakfast filled with the warmth of
oak floors and stained-glass windows.
A large front porch and second-story
sunporch await guests for their relaxation. Choose from three nice guest
rooms, one with a pull-out Murphy
bed, ideal for an additional guest. All
guest rooms are upstairs (not handicapped accessible). Heart and Home is
a smoke- and alcohol-free lodging.
Situated only two blocks from downtown. We have central air-conditioning.
Open every day, April–October.

Hosts: Don and Amanda Miller
Rooms: 3 (3PB) $60–65
Full Breakfast
Credit Cards:
Notes: 2 7 10

BELLEVILLE

Swans Court B & B

421 Court St., Belleville, IL 62220-1201
(618) 233-0779; (800) 840-1058
    Fax (618) 277-3150
E-mail: mdixon@isbe.accessus.net
Web site: www.bbonline.com/il/swanscourt

Swans Court, built in 1883 and
restored in 1995, is in a federal historic

district. Furnished in period antiques, it reflects the gracious lifestyle of an earlier time without sacrificing modern amenities. Walk to shops, restaurants, and historic houses. Visit the many nearby attractions of southwestern Illinois; an easy 20-minute drive to downtown St. Louis.

Host: Monty Dixon
Rooms: 4 (2PB;2SB) $65–90
Full Breakfast
Credit Cards: A B C D
Notes: 2 5 8 9 10 12

CAHOKIA

Jerome Place B & B

827 Ester, Cahokia, IL 62206
(618) 337-1537
Web site: www.bbonline.com/il/jerome

Enjoy historic Cahokia, located only 10 minutes away from the attractions of downtown St. Louis. Treat yourself to a getaway. Come to relax; experience a warm, down home, comfortable feeling. Families as well as business travelers who want a change of pace are welcome. (Come as a Guest; Leave as a Friend.)

Host: Ruthanna Bryant
Rooms: 3 (3PB) $45–69
Full Breakfast
Credit Cards: A B C D
Notes: 2 5 7 8 9 10

Jerome Place

COLLINSVILLE

Maggie's B & B

2102 N. Keebler Ave., Collinsville, IL 62234-4713
(618) 344-8283
E-mail: maggies-b-n-b@charter-il.com
Web site: www.bnbfinder.com

Maggie's

A rustic 2-acre wooded area surrounds this friendly Victorian inn, once a boardinghouse. Rooms with 11-foot ceilings are furnished in exquisite antiques and art objects that Maggie has collected in her worldwide travels. Downtown St. Louis, the Gateway Arch, and the Mississippi Riverfront are just minutes away. The International Race Track and Cabrokia Mounds are just five minutes away. Maggie provides an all-natural breakfast with everything made from scratch—most fruits and vegetables are grown on the property. Children and pets are welcome by arrangement.

Host: Maggie Leyda
Rooms: 4 (3PB;1SB) $60–100
Full Breakfast
Credit Cards:
Notes: 2 5 6 7 10

6 Pets welcome; 7 Children welcome; 8 Tennis nearby; 9 Swimming nearby; 10 Golf nearby; 11 Skiing nearby; 12 May be booked through travel agent

ELSAH

Maple Leaf Cottages Bed and Breakfast

12 Selma; P. O. Box 156, Elsah, IL 62028
(618) 374-1684; (866) 323-5323
    Fax (618) 374-1684
E-mail: mapleleafcottage@aol.com
Web site: www.elsah.org

Maple Leaf Cottages

"I knew by the smoke that so gracefully curl'd above the green elms, that a cottage was near. And I said, If there's peace to be found in the world, a heart that was humble might hope for it here."—Thomas Moore

Over fifty years as a B & B. We offer the tradition of the past with today's quality hospitality. Fine food and lodging in a retreat garden setting. All accommodations have full private bath, bedroom, and sitting area. Your "somewhere INN time" is now. Children over 10 are welcome.

Host: Jerry Taetz
Rooms: 5 (5PB) $80–100
Full Breakfast
Credit Cards:
Notes: 2 5 7 9 10

EVANSTON

The Margarita European Inn

1566 Oak Ave., Evanston, IL 60201-4234
(847) 869-2273; Fax (847) 869-2353
E-mail: www.margaritainn.com

Housed in a stately vintage building, the inn provides comfortable lodging and pleasing service.

Rooms: 42 (22PB;20SB) $79–148
Continental Breakfast
Credit Cards: A B C E
Notes: 4 5 7 8 9 10 12

GALENA

Belle Aire Mansion Guest House

11410 Rte. 20 W., Galena, IL 61036
(815) 777-0893
E-mail: belleair@galenalink.com
Web site: www.galena-bnb.com/belleaire

Belle Aire Mansion Guest House is a pre–Civil War Federal home surrounded by 11 well-groomed acres that include extensive lawns, flowers, and a block-long, tree-lined driveway. Whirlpool and fireplace suites are available. We do our best to make guests feel like special friends.

Belle Aire Mansion Guest House

NOTES: Credit cards accepted: A Master Card; B Visa; C American Express; D Discover; E Diners Club; F Other; 2 Personal checks accepted; 3 Lunch available; 4 Dinner available; 5 Open all year;

Hosts: Jan and Lorraine Svec
Rooms: 5 (5PB) $90–170
Full Breakfast
Credit Cards: A B D
Notes: 2 7 8 10 12

Brierwreath Manor B & B

216 N. Bench St., Galena, IL 61036-2239
(815) 777-0608
E-mail: brierw@galenalink.com
Web site: www.brierwreath.com

Brierwreath Manor, circa 1884, is just one block from Galena's Main Street and has a dramatic, inviting wraparound porch that beckons after a hard day. The house is furnished in an eclectic blend of antique and Early American. You'll not only relax but feel right at home. Two suites offer gas log fireplaces; the third has an extra twin-size bed. Central air-conditioning, ceiling fans, and cable TV add to your enjoyment.

Hosts: Mike and Lyn Cook
Rooms: 3 (3PB) $90–120
Full Breakfast
Credit Cards: A B D
Notes: 2 5 8 9 10 11

Captain Harris Guest House

713 S. Bench St., Galena, IL 61036
(815) 777-4713; (800) 996-4799
   Fax (815) 777-4723
E-mail: inquiry@captainharris.com
Web site: www.captainharris.com

This circa 1836 home, built by a riverboat captain, was lovingly restored in 1920 with leaded-glass windows and doors by an associate of Frank Lloyd Wright. Each of the five guest rooms offers a private bath and cable TV. A double whirlpool/fireplace suite and detached honeymoon cottage with double whirlpool and fireplace are available. Full formal breakfast. One block from Main Street shops and restaurants.

Hosts: Judy Dixon and Ed Schmit
Rooms: 5 (5PB) $90–190
Full Breakfast
Credit Cards: A B D F
Notes: 2 5 10 11

Captain Harris Guest House

Hawk Valley Retreat, A Nature Lover's B & B and Cottages

2752 W. Cording Rd., Galena, IL 61036
(815) 777-4100; (888) 777-6016
   Fax (815) 777-1941
E-mail: hawkvaly@galenalink.com
Web site: www.hawkvalleyretreat.com

Hawk Valley Retreat

Luxurious home and cottages on 10

---

6 Pets welcome; 7 Children welcome; 8 Tennis nearby; 9 Swimming nearby; 10 Golf nearby; 11 Skiing nearby; 12 May be booked through travel agent

secluded acres with pond, walking trails, and gardens. Bird-watcher's paradise. Three guest rooms in main house (each with private entrance) and two cottages. Each unit has private bath, TV/VCR, king or queen bed. Each cottage also has a double whirlpool tub, fireplace, A/C, sitting area, phone, galley kitchen, covered porch. Main house has fireplace in living room, book/video library, central A/C, covered porch with swing, wrap-around deck. Sumptuous full breakfast included. Children under 12 by special arrangement. Limited one-night stays. Off-season, midweek, and multiple-night specials. Packages and gift certificates available. IBBA inspected (highest rating in 2000 and 2002). No smoking, no pets. Location of "Hawk Valley School of the Arts." Fully handicapped accessible. &

Hosts: Fritz and Jane Fuchs
Rooms: 5 (5PB) $75–200
Full Breakfast
Credit Cards: A B D
Notes: 2 5 7 8 9 10 11

Park Avenue Guest House

208 Park Ave., Galena, IL 61036-2306
(815) 777-1075; (800) 359-0743
 Fax (815) 777-1097
E-mail: parkave@galenalink.com
Web site: www.galena.com/parkave

This is an 1893 Queen Anne "painted lady." Wrap-around screened porch, gardens, and gazebo for summer. Fireplace and opulent Victorian Christmas in winter. One suite sleeps three, and there are three antique-filled guest rooms, all with queen beds and fireplaces. Located in a quiet resi-

dential area. Only a short walk to Grant Park or across a footbridge to Main Street shopping and restaurants.

Host: Sharon Fallbacher
Rooms: 4 (4PB) $95–135
Full Breakfast
Credit Cards: A B D
Notes: 2 5 8 9 10 11

Pine Hollow Inn

4700 N. Council Hill Rd., Galena, IL 61036
(815) 777-1071
E-mail: pinehollowinn@pinehollowinn.com
Web site: www.pinehollowinn.com

Pine Hollow Inn

Located on acres of unspoiled beauty, where blue heron fish in the stream and deer and wild turkeys are more common than not. You can enjoy sitting in front of the fireplace in one of our guest rooms or suites. In the spring, summer, or fall, you might want to sit on the wrap-around porch and bird-watch or just daydream. Amenities include large suites and guest rooms, individual wood-burning fireplaces, private baths and whirlpools, skylights, country kitchen, and gardens.

Host: Mary
Rooms: 5 (5PB) $95–135
Full Breakfast
Credit Cards: A B D F
Notes: 2 5 8 9 10 11

NOTES: Credit cards accepted: A Master Card; B Visa; C American Express; D Discover; E Diners Club; F Other; 2 Personal checks accepted; 3 Lunch available; 4 Dinner available; 5 Open all year;

JERSEYVILLE

The Homeridge Bed and Breakfast

1470 N. State St., Jerseyville, IL 62052-1127
(618) 498-3442; Fax (618) 498-5662
E-mail: innkeeper@homeridge.com
Web site: www.homeridge.com

The Homeridge

The Homeridge B & B is a beautiful, warm, brick, 1867 Italianate Victorian private home on 18 acres in an elegant country atmosphere. Drive through stately iron gates and a tree-lined driveway to the 14-room historic estate of Senator Theodore Chapman. Enter through an expansive, pillared front porch and up the hand-carved, curved stairway to the spacious guest rooms. Large swimming pool. Central air-conditioning. Located between St. Louis, Missouri, and Springfield, Illinois.

Hosts: Sue and Howard Landon
Rooms: 4 (4PB) $75–95
Full Breakfast
Credit Cards: A B C
Notes: 2 5 8 9 10

OAKLAND

Inn on the Square

3 Montgomery St., Oakland, IL 61943
(217) 346-2289; Fax (217) 346-2005
E-mail: innonsq@advant.net
Web site:
    www.bedandbreakfast.com/bbc/p210688.asp

Located 20 minutes from Eastern Illinois University, the inn specializes in fine food and friendly atmosphere. Best of all is the return of bed and breakfast tourism. Blending the old with the new, we offer warm hospitality and simple country pleasures, as well as historical sites, recreational activities, shopping, and plain old sittin' and rockin'. Three upstairs bedrooms are comfortably furnished for country living, each with a private bath. Dinner is available Fridays and Saturdays.

Hosts: Gary and Linda Miller
Rooms: 3 (3PB) $55–60
Full Breakfast
Credit Cards: A B   F
Notes: 2 3 5 7 8 9 10 12

ONARGA

Dairy on the Prairie

1437 N. State Rte. 49, Onarga, IL 60955-7514
(815) 683-2774

Situated among miles of corn and soybean fields on God's prairie is this recently remodeled homestead that has been "in the family" since 1892. Three tall silos and Holstein cows await you at the modern dairy/grain family farm. Enjoy the piano, organ, or keyboard along with hearty food, "down on the farm" hospitality, and a Christian atmosphere.

Hosts: Kenneth and Martha Redeker
Rooms: 3 (2PB;1SB) $50–60
Full Breakfast
Credit Cards:
Notes: 2 5 7 8 9 10

6 Pets welcome; 7 Children welcome; 8 Tennis nearby; 9 Swimming nearby; 10 Golf nearby; 11 Skiing nearby; 12 May be booked through travel agent

OTTAWA

Prairie Rivers B & B

121 E. Prospect Ave., Ottawa, IL 61350-3567
(815) 434-3226; (888) 2659 # 5
　Fax (815) 434-6433
E-mail: prairieriversbb@aol.com
Web site: www.prairieriversbandb.com

Prairie Rivers

High on a bluff where the Fox and Illinois Rivers converge, this 1890 New England cottage offers folks a taste of 19th-century charm. Rooms are spacious and sunny, and three fireplaces add romantic glow to the evening. Private baths and downy beds cater to creature comforts. Breakfast is served in the period dining room or in the sunroom overlooking the rivers. This is a friendly place where you can come and go just as you would in your own home.

Hosts: Carole and Ed Mayer
Rooms: 4 (3PB;1SB) $105–145
Full Breakfast
Credit Cards: A B
Notes: 2 5 7 8 10

PEORIA, IL

Old Church House Inn Bed and Breakfast

1416 E. Mossville, Mossville, IL 61552

(309) 579-2300
E-mail: churchhouse@prodigy.net
Web site:
　www.bedandbreakfast.com/bbc/p210657.asp

Come take sanctuary from the cares of life in our lovingly restored, 1869 "country church." Enjoy afternoon tea curled up by a wood-burning fire or on a bench among a riot of garden flowers. Experience 18-foot ceilings, a library loft, Victorian antiques, classical music, a crackling fire, pillow chocolates, featherbeds, flowers, and "made from scratch" breakfasts. Nearby are the Rock Island Bike Trail, tearooms, antiquing, fine dining, scenic drives, and sweet memories. Children welcome by arrangement.

Hosts: Dean and Holly Ramseyer and Family
Rooms: 2 (1PB;1SB) $75–115
Continental Breakfast
Credit Cards: A B D
Notes: 2 3 5 7 8 9 10 11 12

Old Church House

SPRINGFIELD

Country Dreams Bed and Breakfast

3410 Parks Ln., Rochester, IL 62563-8064
(217) 498-9210
E-mail: host@countrydreams.com
Web site: www.countrydreams.com

NOTES: Credit cards accepted: A Master Card; B Visa; C American Express; D Discover; E Diners Club; F Other; 2 Personal checks accepted; 3 Lunch available; 4 Dinner available; 5 Open all year;

Newly built (1997) on 16 acres of country serenity, but only 7 minutes from Springfield, IL and the Lincoln sites. Small, but immaculate! TV/VCR, air, fireplaces, whirlpool. Accommodations for families with children. Flowers, green grass, country sounds. Bring your fishing equipment.

Hosts: Ralph and Kay Muhs
Rooms: 6 (5PB;1SB) $75–160
Full Breakfast
Credit Cards: A B C D
Notes: 2 5 7

INDIANA

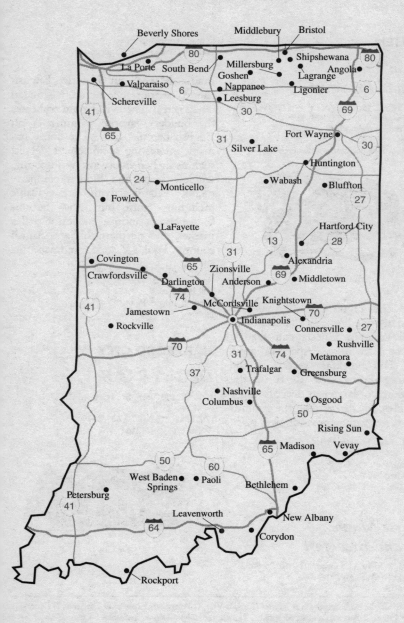

Indiana

GOSHEN

Indian Creek
Bed and Breakfast

20300 Cty. Rd. 18, Goshen, IN 46528-9513
(574) 875-6606; Fax (574) 875-8396
E-mail: indiancreekb&b@msn.com
Web site:
    www.bestinns.net/usa/in/indiancreek.html

Indian Creek

Come and enjoy our 10-year-old, Victorian-style home in the middle of Amish country. Guests can read a book or visit in our spacious great room. Full breakfast served in the adjoining dining area. Relax on the front porch or large rear deck. Located on 3 acres, you can wander the grounds to the water garden or wildflower path.

Hosts: Jim and Jeanette Vellenga
Rooms: 4 (4PB) $79
Full Breakfast
Credit Cards: A B C D
Notes: 2 5 7 10

Prairie Manor
Bed and Breakfast

66398 U. S. Hwy. 33, Goshen, IN 46526-9482
(574) 642-4761; (800) 791-3952
E-mail: jeston@npcc.net
Web site: www.prairiemanor.com

Prairie Manor, our historic, English country manor style-home, is situated on 12 acres. The living room replicates the builder's favorite painting of an English baronial hall. The house has many interesting architectural details, such as arched doorways, wainscoting, window seats, and hidden compartments. Many activities are available including antiquing, the famous Shipshewana antique auction and flea market, and northern Indiana Amish country. Pool, TV, and Grandma's attic.

Hosts: Jean and Hesston Lauver
Rooms: 4 (4PB) $72-95
Full Breakfast
Credit Cards: A B D
Notes: 2 5 7 8 9 10

HARTFORD CITY

De'Coy's B & B

1546 W. 100 North St., Hartford City, IN
    47348-8859
(765) 348-2164; (877) 692-3179
    Fax (765) 348-2164

De'Coy's

NOTES: Credit cards accepted: A Master Card; B Visa; C American Express; D Discover; E Diners Club; F Other; 2 Personal checks accepted; 3 Lunch available; 4 Dinner available; 5 Open all year;

Situated just west of Hartford City, De'Coy's Bed and Breakfast is conveniently located near Taylor University, Ball State University, and Indiana Wesleyan University. This charming country home offers its guests extraordinarily attractive accommodations with many extraspecial Hoosier touches. Visitors can relax in the quiet, rural atmosphere of this old, restored home, enriched with many amenities not customary to the typical motel or hotel setting. Each room demonstrates its own character with antique furnishings and comfortable arrangements.

Hosts: Chris and Tiann Coy
Rooms: 5 (3PB;2SB) $62–85
Full Breakfast
Credit Cards: F
Notes: 2 5 7 10 12

INDIANAPOLIS

The Old Northside B & B

1340 N. Alabama St.
   Indianapolis, IN 46202-2524
(317) 635-9123; (800) 635-9127
   Fax (317) 635-9243
E-mail: garyh@hofmeister.com
Web site: www.oldnorthsideinn.com

An 1885 mansion in the historic district (on National Register) with original wood in prime condition. Free movies, snack bar, cable TV/VCR, phone calls. Modern bathrooms with double Jacuzzis and working fireplaces. Antiques and artwork from around the world brought by owner. On parle français. Se habla Español.

Hosts: Gary and Jo Anne Hofmeister
Rooms: 7 (7PB) $85–165

Continental Breakfast
Credit Cards: A B C D
Notes: 2 5 12

LEESBURG

Prairie House B & B

495 E. 900 N., Leesburg, IN 46538-9025
(219) 658-9211
E-mail: marietom3@yahoo.com
Web site: www.prairiehouse.net

Come enjoy a peaceful farm atmosphere. Four tastefully decorated rooms with air-conditioning, TV, VCR, and fans are available. Close to Grace College, the Wagon Wheel Playhouse, Shipshewana Flea Market, Amish Acres, antique browsing, the Old Bag Factory at Goshen, swimming, skiing, boating, and golfing. Excellent dining in the area. Tours of the farm available. Prepare to be pampered!

Hosts: Everett and Marie Tom
Rooms: 4 (2PB;2SB) $45–65
Full Breakfast
Credit Cards: A B
Notes: 2 5 7 8 9 10

MADISON

Schussler House Bed and Breakfast

514 Jefferson St., Madison, IN 47250-3428
(812) 273-2068; (800) 392-1931
E-mail: schussler@voyager.net
Web site: www.schusslerhouse.com

Experience the quiet elegance of a circa 1849 Federal/Greek Revival home tastefully combined with today's modern amenities. Located in Madison's

---

6 Pets welcome; 7 Children welcome; 8 Tennis nearby; 9 Swimming nearby; 10 Golf nearby; 11 Skiing nearby; 12 May be booked through travel agent

historic district, where antique shops, historic sites, restaurants, and churches are within a pleasant walking distance. This gracious home offers spacious rooms decorated with antiques, reproductions, and carefully selected fabrics and wall coverings. A sumptuous breakfast in the sun-filled dining room begins your day.

Hosts: Ann and Larry Johnson
Rooms: 3 (3PB) $120
Full Breakfast
Credit Cards: A B D
Notes: 2 5 8 9 10 12

MIDDLEBURY

Bee Hive B & B

P. O. Box 1191, Middlebury, IN 46540-1191
(574) 825-5023

Be yourself at the Bee Hive Bed and Breakfast. Have a honey of a time relaxing with tea and honey. The Bee Hive has a two-story, open-floor plan with exposed, hand-sawn, red oak beams, and a loft. Enjoy Herb's steam engines and antique tractors. Snuggle under handmade quilts and wake to the smell of a full country breakfast being prepared. Located on a farm in the Amish community. Guest cottage available, also Amish Heartland Tours.

Hosts: Herb and Treva Swarm
Rooms: 3 (1PB;2SB) $60–80
Full Breakfast
Credit Cards: A B
Notes: 2 5 8 9 10 11

Bontreger Guest Rooms B & B

10766 Cty. Rd. 16, Middlebury, IN 46540-9550
(574) 825-2647

Bontreger Guest Rooms

This B & B is located between Middlebury and Shipshewana on a county road in an Amish neighborhood. Relax in the pleasant atmosphere of the sunroom where continental breakfast is served, or retreat to your cozy, air-conditioned room and common room, away from family space. Private baths and private entrance.

Hosts: Tom and Ruby Bontreger
Rooms: 2 (2PB) $59
Continental Breakfast
Credit Cards:
Notes: 2 5 7 8 9 10 11

Rust Hollar Bed and Breakfast

55238 C.R. 31, Bristol, IN 46507-9569
(574) 825-1111; (800) 313-7800
    Fax (574) 825-4614
E-mail: tim@rusthollar.com
Web site: www.rusthollar.com

Rust Hollar Bed and Breakfast is a rustic log home on a peaceful country road in a tranquil wooded "hollar." You may enjoy bird-watching, a country walk, or

---

NOTES: Credit cards accepted: A Master Card; B Visa; C American Express; D Discover; E Diners Club; F Other; 2 Personal checks accepted; 3 Lunch available; 4 Dinner available; 5 Open all year;

just relaxing on our oak-covered grounds. A full, hot breakfast is served each morning. The B & B is located in Amish country. Shipshewana, Middlebury (Das Essenhaus), Goshen, Elkhart, South Bend, and Nappanee are within a half-hour's drive. AAA-approved. Clergy discounts available.

Hosts: Tim and Janine Rust
Rooms: 4 (4PB) $60–79
Full Breakfast
Credit Cards: A B C D
Notes: 2 5 7 8 10 11

Rust Hollar

That Pretty Place

212 U. S. 20, Middlebury, IN 46540-9713
(574) 825-3021; (800) 418-9487
E-mail: inbasket@thatprettyplace.com
Web site: www.thatprettyplace.com

A long lane leads through the woods to our inn overlooking our private, stocked pond. You may feed the fish, take a quiet walk on the path through our woods, or sit on the deck that overlooks the pond. Choose from five rooms with private baths, including a honeymoon suite with a heart-shaped whirlpool tub. Hot breakfast is served. We are located in the heart of Amish country, close to the Shipshewana

Flea Market. Children over 12 or if whole facility rented by group.

Rooms: 5 (5PB) $80–115
Full Breakfast
Credit Cards: A B D
Notes: 2 5   10

Tiffany Powell's Bed and Breakfast

523 S. Main St., Middlebury, IN 46540
(219) 825-5951; Fax (219) 825-2992
E-mail: tiff@npcc.net
Web site: www.tiffanypowells.com

Tiffany's was built in 1914 and features oak woodwork and leaded glass in a warm Christian atmosphere. It is our goal to pass on the blessings God has given us. All rooms include full breakfast, TV, and air-conditioning. Children are welcome. This bed and breakfast was featured on Oprah's Angel Network. We do hope you will enjoy your stay with us. Let us pamper you.

Host: Judy Powell
Rooms: 3 (3PB) $85
Full Breakfast
Credit Cards:
Notes: 2 5 7 8 9 10

Tiffany Powell's

NAPPANEE

Christian S. Stahly— Olde Buffalo Inn

1061 Parkwood Dr., Nappanee, IN 46550
(219) 773-2223; (888) 773-2223
    Fax (219) 773-4275
E-mail: stay@olde-buffalo-b-b.com
Web site: www.olde-buffalo-b-b.com

Step back in time to an era that was peaceful and serene. The Olde Buffalo Inn has all of today's amenities and lots of 19th-century charm. The inn is surrounded by a white picket fence and a restored red barn, windmill, carriage house, brick sidewalk, and east patio. Situated on 2 1/2 acres with a beautiful view of the golf course.

Host: Larry Lakins
Rooms: 7 (7PB) $79–159
Full Breakfast
Credit Cards: A B D
Notes: 2 5 7 8 9 10

Homespun Country Inn

302 N. Main St., P. O. Box 369
    Nappanee, IN 46550-0369
(574) 773-2034; (800) 311-2996
    Fax (574) 773-3456
E-mail: home@hoosierlink.net
Web site: www.homespuninn.com

Our Queen Anne-style inn was built in 1902. Our home is filled with antiques and family pieces we have enjoyed collecting. We are located within walking distance of seven antique and craft shops. Enjoy homespun hospitality and friendly conversation in the heart of Amish country.

Hosts: Dennis and Dianne Debelak
Rooms: 5 (5PB) $59–79

Full Breakfast
Credit Cards: A B D
Notes: 2 5 7 8 9 10

Victorian Guest House

302 E. Market St., Nappanee, IN 46550-2102
(219) 773-4383
E-mail: vghouse@binn.net
Web site: www.victorianb-b.com

Antiques, stained-glass windows, and pocket doors highlight this 1887 Historical Register mansion nestled among the Amish countryside where antique shops abound. A warm welcome awaits as you return to gracious living with all the ambience of the 1800s. Everything has been designed to make your bed and breakfast stay a memorable one. Close to Notre Dame and Shipshewana. Two hours from Chicago. Complimentary evening tea and sweets. "Prepare for a memory."

Hosts: Bruce and Vickie Hunsberger
Rooms: 6 (6PB) $69–149
Full Breakfast
Credit Cards: A B D
Notes: 2 5 8 9 10

NASHVILLE

Day Star Inn

87 E. Main St.; Box 361, Nashville, IN 47448
(812) 988-0430

A friendly, homey atmosphere awaits as you retreat to the heart of Nashville's unique downtown shopping area. Short drive to Brown County State Park, golf courses, and other recreational areas. Five clean rooms can accommodate up to twenty-

NOTES: Credit cards accepted: A Master Card; B Visa; C American Express; D Discover; E Diners Club; F Other; 2 Personal checks accepted; 3 Lunch available; 4 Dinner available; 5 Open all year;

two guests (including children, if well supervised). Air-conditioning, cable television, private bath, and parking for guests. No smoking, alcohol, or pets, please.

Hosts: Edwin and Joanne Taggart
Rooms: 5 (5PB) $88–104.50
Continental Breakfast
Credit Cards: A B D
Notes: 2 5 9 10 11

PAOLI

Braxtan House Inn

210 N. Gospel St., Paoli, IN 47454-1410
(812) 723-4677; (800) 627-2982
    Fax (812) 723-2112
E-mail: braxtan@kiva.net
Web site: www.kiva.net/~braxtan

An 1830/1893 Victorian furnished with antiques. In a small historic town close to many attractions and outdoor activities, including antiquing, hiking, canoeing, skiing. Relaxed atmosphere—families are welcome. No smoking indoors.

Hosts: Duane and Kate Wilhelmi
Rooms: 6 (6PB) $60–65
Continental Breakfast
Credit Cards: A B C D
Notes: 2 5 7 8 9 10 11

PETERSBURG

Log Ends Farm B & B

2769 W. St. Dr. 56, P. O. Box 154
    Petersburg, IN 47567
(812) 354-2192; (877) LOG-ENDS

The Log Ends Farm B & B is nestled in the countryside on a working farm. This charming B & B incorporates two vintage 1853 log cabins, one at either end of a newly built, traditional two-story home. The four guest rooms are upstairs in the new section. Each carpeted bedroom includes a queen-size bed and private bath with clawfoot tub.

Hosts: Donna and Steve Mikels
Rooms: 4 (4PB) $60–65
Full Breakfast
Credit Cards:
Notes: 2 4 5 10

SOUTH BEND

Oliver Inn Bed and Breakfast

630 W. Washington St.
    South Bend, IN 46601-1444
(574) 232-4545; (888) 697-4466
    Fax (574) 288-9788
E-mail: oliver@michiana.org
Web site: www.oliverinn.com

Oliver Inn

Magnificent 1886 Victorian mansion on a 1-acre estate with carriage house and circa 1920 playhouse offers 9 rooms, private baths, A/C, TV, telephone, ceiling fans, double Jacuzzi, 7 fireplaces, and a computerized baby grand. Next to Tippecanoe Place Restaurant (the Studebaker Mansion). Lovely candlelight breakfast by the fire, complimentary snacks and refreshments from our Butler's Pantry.

6 Pets welcome; 7 Children welcome; 8 Tennis nearby; 9 Swimming nearby; 10 Golf nearby; 11 Skiing nearby; 12 May be booked through travel agent

Hosts: Dick and Vera Monahan
Rooms: 9 (7PB;2SB) $95–145
Full Breakfast
Credit Cards: A B C D
Notes: 2 5 6 7 8 9 10 11 12

VALPARAISO

Inn at Aberdeen, Ltd.

3158 S. State Rd. 2, Valparaiso, IN 46385-9676
(219) 465-3753; Fax (219) 465-9227
E-mail: inn@innataberdeen.com
Web site: www.innataberdeen.com

The Inn at Aberdeen, Ltd.

Inn at Aberdeen

Travel back in time to the late 1800s and relax in Queen Anne splendor. Private bath, Jacuzzi-for-two, cable TV/VCR, balcony, and a cozy fire—all for you. A library, solarium, and open kitchen provide quiet respite. An executive conference center is available for that important meeting, or you may lease the entire inn for that special occasion. Less than one hour from downtown Chicago. Championship golf, outdoor pool, day spa, microbrewery, boutique, walking paths, ponds, and streams on-site. Gift certificates.

Hosts: Bill Simon, Linda and John Johnson
Rooms: 11 (11PB) $99-172
Gourmet Breakfast
Credit Cards: A B C D E
Notes: 2 3 4 5 7 8 9 10 12

WEST BADEN SPRINGS

E. B. Rhodes House B & B

P. O. Box 7, West Baden Springs, IN 47469-0007
(812) 936-7378; (800) 786-5176
    Fax (800) 786-5176
E-mail: ebrhodes@bluemarble.net
Web site: www.bluemarble.net/~ebrhodes

Relax in the homey luxury of an 1890s Victorian home filled with beautiful carved wood and stained glass. Rock on one of the wrap-around porches and enjoy the peaceful view of the town park. Hoosier hospitality with a home-grown breakfast. Opportunity abounds for historians, sports buffs, and antique enthusiasts. Carriage house available with full bath and fireplace. Screened porch and garden view. Victorian Rose Suite with whirlpool, fireplace, queen-size bed— newly renovated.

Hosts: Marlene and Frank Sipes
Rooms: 4 (4PB) $45–75
Full Breakfast
Credit Cards: A B C D
Notes: 2 5 7 8 9 10 11

ZIONSVILLE

Country Gables Bed and Breakfast

9302 Indiana 334, Zionsville, IN 46077
(317) 873-5382; Fax (317) 873-5382
E-mail: countrygables@indy.rr.com
Web site: www.countrygables.com

This late 1800s Victorian farmhouse has been renovated to comfortably accommodate guests. The main suite offers a queen bedroom, private bath, and spacious room with fully equipped

---

kitchen. Two other rooms offer queen/double beds, private baths, and sitting areas. Quaint Zionsville is known for its antique/specialty shops as well as musical, historical, and festive events throughout the year. Twenty minutes from Indianapolis, this charming B & B offers a peaceful retreat, delicious full breakfast, and easy access.

Hosts: Garland and Jean Elmore
Rooms: 3 (3PB) $78–135
Full Breakfast
Credit Cards: A B
Notes: 2 5 7

Country Gables

IOWA

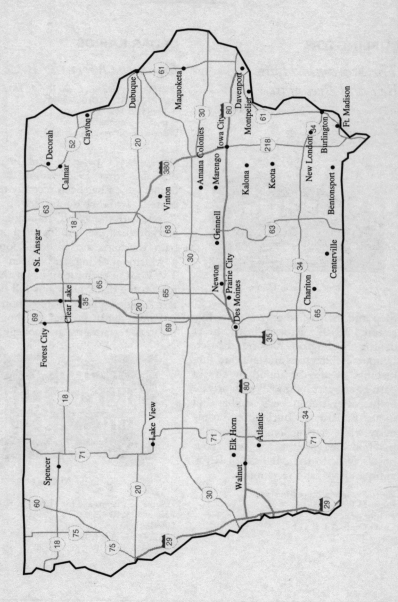

Iowa

BURLINGTON

The Schramm House Bed and Breakfast

616 Columbia St., Burlington, IA 52601-5118
(319) 754-0373
E-mail: visit@schramm.com
Web site: www.visit.schramm.com

The Schramm House

Step into the past when you enter this restored 1870s Victorian in the heart of the Burlington historic district. Unique architecture and antique furnishings create the mood of an era past. Four guest rooms, all with private baths, offer queen beds, quilts, and more. Experience Burlington hospitality while having lemonade on the porch or tea by the fire with your hosts. Walk to the Mississippi River, antique shops, and restaurants.

Hosts: Sandy and Bruce Morrison
Rooms: 5 (5PB) $85–150
Full Breakfast
Credit Cards: A B C D E
Notes: 2 5 7 8 9 10 12

CEDAR RAPIDS

Joy in the Morning B & B

1809 Second Ave., SE, Cedar Rapids, IA 52403
(319) 363-9731; (800) 363-5093
Fax (319) 363-7548
E-mail: joyinmorng@aol.com
Web site: www.joyinthemorning.cjb.net

"Elegant yet peaceful and inviting" describes this 1915 Colonial Villa home, which has been recently redecorated. It is characterized by the "Gone with the Wind" staircase in the entrance hall. Each room has a private bath; the romantic Garden Room has a whirlpool. King and queen beds, TV/VCR in each room. Enjoy the hot tub on the deck. Delicious full breakfast. Nestled among historic homes, it is conveniently located to shopping, theaters, restaurants, and colleges.

Joy in the Morning

Hosts: Ron Cuchna and Joy Miller-Cuchna
Rooms: 3 (3PB) $75-115
Full Breakfast
Credit Cards: A B C D
Notes: 2 5 8 9 10

NOTES: Credit cards accepted: A Master Card; B Visa; C American Express; D Discover; E Diners Club; F Other; 2 Personal checks accepted; 3 Lunch available; 4 Dinner available; 5 Open all year;

CENTERVILLE

One of a Kind

314 W. State St., Centerville, IA 52544-1713
(515) 437-4540

One of a Kind

One of a Kind is a stately, three-story brick home built in 1867. Situated in one of Iowa's delightful small communities, you'll be within walking distance of antique shops, the town square, city park with tennis courts, the swimming pool, and just 12 minutes from Lake Rathbun, Iowa's largest lake. Browse the gift shop filled with collectibles, original paintings, and more. Enjoy our special delicacies in the tearoom.

Hosts: Jack and Joyce Stufflebeem
Rooms: 5 (2PB;3SB) $35–65
Full Breakfast
Credit Cards: A B C D
Notes: 2 3 4 5 8 9 10 11 12

CLEAR LAKE

Blessing on Main B & B

1204 Main Ave., Clear Lake, IA 50428
(641) 357-0341; Fax (641) 357-5813
E-mail: blessing@netins.net
Web site:
    http://showcase.netins.net/web/blessingonmain/

Discover calm leisure in restored century-old Victorian home with antique furnishings/family heirlooms. Enjoy relaxation on front porch wicker furniture, back deck view of garden flowers and reflection pond waterfalls. Rest in the quiet parlor or cozy den. King, queen, twin beds, private baths. Main Avenue location 4 blocks from restored downtown—casual/fine dining, specialty stores, lake view/activities. Amenities include arrival refreshments, bountiful breakfast, blessing gift basket, and our commitment in making your stay memorable. "Our specialty is pampering you!"

Hosts: Jim and Janet Allard
Rooms: 2 (2PB) $85
Full Breakfast
Credit Cards: A B
Notes: 2 5 8 9 10

DUBUQUE

The Hancock House Bed and Breakfast Inn

1105 Grove Terrace, Dubuque, IA 52001
(563) 557-8989
Web site: www.thehandcockhouse.com

The Hancock House

Located in Dubuque's 11th Street historic district, this gracious Queen

Anne creates a timeless, romantic atmosphere. Fireplaces, antique-filled guest quarters, whirlpool baths, and an outstanding panoramic view combine to make your stay unforgettable. The home was featured in *Victorian Sampler* for its "warm hospitality, cloudlike feather beds, and a breakfast to ooh and aah over." Children over 12 welcome. Gift certificates available.

Hosts: Chuck and Susan Huntley
Rooms: 9 (9PB) $80–175
Full Breakfast
Credit Cards: A B C D
Notes: 2 5 8 9 10 11 12

The Mandolin Inn

199 Loras Blvd., Dubuque, IA 52001-4857
(563) 556-0069; (800) 524-7996
    Fax (563) 556-0587
E-mail: innkeeper@mandolininn.com
Web site: www.mandolininn.com

The Mandolin Inn

The Mandolin Inn is an Edwardian bed and breakfast dedicated to sharing the elegance and comfort of an earlier era with a few discerning guests. It's a perfect place to kindle romance with its gourmet breakfasts, queen beds, and beautifully furnished rooms. Handicapped accessible. Explore historic Dubuque, Galena, and other nearby lovely towns along the upper Mississippi River.

Host: Amy Boynton
Rooms: 8 (6PB;2SB) $85–175
Full Breakfast
Credit Cards: A B C D
Notes: 2 5 7 8 9 10 11

GRINNELL

Carriage House B & B

1133 Broad St., Grinnell, IA 50112-1626
(614) 236-7520; Fax (614) 236-5085
E-mail: irishbnb@iowatelecom.net
Web site:
    www.bedandbreakfast.com/bbc/p216752.asp

Carriage House

Queen Anne-style Victorian. Relax in the wicker on the front porch or enjoy several fireplaces in winter. Lovely rooms with queen beds and private baths. Central air, stained-glass windows, and a hand-painted ceiling. Elegant breakfasts with Irish soda bread. Excellent restaurants nearby. One block from Grinnell College; 1 hour from Des Moines and Iowa City. Member of the Iowa Bed and Breakfast Guild and Iowa Lodging Association. State licensed and inspected. Gift certificates available.

Hosts: Ray and Dorothy Spriggs
Rooms: 5 (5PB) $50–70

Full Breakfast
Credit Cards: A B C D
Notes: 2 5 8 9 10 11 12

IOWA CITY

A Bella Vista B & B

2 Bella Vista Pl., Iowa City, IA 52245-5840
(319) 338-4129
Web site: www.virtualcities.com/ia/bellavista.htm

Daissy Owen has furnished her lovely, air-conditioned, 1920s home with antiques and artifacts she has acquired on her travels in Europe and Latin America. The home is conveniently located on the city's historic north side with a beautiful view of the Iowa River. The Hoover Library, the Amana Colonies, and the Amish center of Kalona are all nearby. A full breakfast, with Daissy's famous coffee, is served in the dining room's unique setting each morning. Daissy is fluent in Spanish and speaks some French. From I-80, take Dubuque Street, Exit 244, turn left on Brown Street, then take the first left on Linn Street; it is 1 block to #2 Bella Vista Place Bed and Breakfast.

Host: Daissy P. Owen
Rooms: 5 (3PB;2SB) $70–135
Full Breakfast
Credit Cards:
Notes: 2 5 8 9 10

Haverkamps' Linn Street Homestay B & B

619 N. Linn St., Iowa City, IA 52245-1934
(319) 337-4363; Fax (319) 354-7057
E-mail: havb-b@soli.inav.net
Web site: www.bbhost.com/haverkampslinnstbb

Enjoy the warmth and hospitality of our 1908 Edwardian home filled with heirlooms and collectibles. Only a short walk to downtown Iowa City and the University of Iowa's main campus; just a short drive to the Hoover Library in West Branch, the Amish in Kalona, and seven Amana Colonies.

Haverkamps' Linn Street Homestay

Hosts: Clarence and Dorothy Haverkamp
Rooms: 3 (0PB;3SB) $45–50
Full Breakfast
Credit Cards:
Notes: 2 5 7 8 9 10 12

KALONA

The Carriage House

1140 Larch Ave., Kalona, IA 52247
(319) 656-3824
E-mail: chouse@kctc.net
Web site: www.carriagehousebb.net

Come and relax in the country. Watch the sunset and wake up to the sunrise. Stroll past neighboring Amish farms or sit on our porch swing. Visit Kalona's quilt, antique, craft, or Amish shops. Swim in local public pool or golf at Kalona's nearby course. Experience Kalona's charm.

6 Pets welcome; 7 Children welcome; 8 Tennis nearby; 9 Swimming nearby; 10 Golf nearby; 11 Skiing nearby; 12 May be booked through travel agent

Nearby is University of Iowa, 18 miles; Coral Ridge Mall, Tanger Outlet Mall, Herbert Hoover Museum.

Hosts: Dan and Edie Kemp
Rooms: 6 (4PB;2SB) $63–100
Full Breakfast
Credit Cards: A B
Notes: 2 3 4 5 7 9 10

MALCOM

Pleasant Country B & B

4386 110th St., Malcom, IA 50157-8011
(641) 528-4925
E-mail: pcbb@pcpartner.net
Web site: www.midiowa.com/pcbb

Welcome to our country farm home in central Iowa. Eugene and Mary Lou are third-generation farm family living in their home built in 1896. Eugene was born in the downstairs bedroom. We have lots to offer, being livestock and grain farmers. You are invited to enjoy and relax in quietness of the countryside. Wake up to a hearty country breakfast or a continental breakfast. It's your choice. "Let us be your home away from home." Looking forward to your visit.

Hosts: Mary Lou and Eugene Mann
Rooms: 2 (2SB) $50–55
Continental Breakfast
Notes: 2 5 7 8 9 10 11

MAQUOKETA

Squiers Manor Bed and Breakfast

418 W. Pleasant St., Maquoketa, IA 52060-2847
(563) 652-2359; Fax (563) 652-5995
E-mail: innkeeper@squiersmannor.com
Web site: www.squiersmanor.com

Squiers Manor B & B is located in the W. Pleasant Street historic district. This 1882 Queen Anne mansion features walnut, cherry, and butternut woods throughout. Enjoy period furnishings, queen beds, in-room phone and TV, and private baths, as well as single and double Jacuzzis. There are five rooms and three suites available. Come hungry and enjoy delicious, candlelight evening desserts and breakfasts (more like brunch) served in the elegant dining room. Virl's and Kathy's goal is to make your stay as pleasant and enjoyable as possible. Give us a call today!

Hosts: Virl and Kathy Banowetz
Rooms: 8 (8PB) $80–195
Full Breakfast
Credit Cards: A B C D
Notes: 2 5 8 9 10 11 12

SPENCER

Hannah Marie Country Inn

4070 Hwy. 71, Spencer, IA 51301
(712) 262-1286; Fax (712) 262-3294
Web site: hannahmarieinn.com

Hannah Marie Country Inn

There's a warm welcome here. The 1910 parlor and fireside room have welcomed guests through the years since 1986. Queen feathered beds, in-

---

room private whirlpools. Yummy breakfasts, butterfly gardens, a classical labyrinth, croquet, kites. Added value, central air, bath bubbles, softened water. Our Romance of Country theme inspired the trompe l'oeil flower and wall paintings. Our veranda is for: reading, sipping tea, playing marbles. Near: Iowa Great Lakes, antiquing, shopping. Come. . . grab a camera, pack lightly.

Host: Mary Nichols
Rooms: 6 (6PB) $79–120
Full Breakfast
Credit Cards: A B C D
Notes: 2 5 7 8 9 10 12

WALNUT

Clark's Country Inn Bed and Breakfast

701 Walnut St., P. O. Box 533
   Walnut, IA 51577-0533
(712) 784-3010
Web site: http://pionet.net/~inns/clarks.html

Established in June 1991. Over 7,000 guests from 13 countries and 42 states. Some guests have stayed over 24 nights during this time. Located at Exit 46, on I-80, between Omaha, NE, and Des Moines, IA. Walnut is Iowa's antique capital (with over 200 antique dealers). Our 1912, two-story home with oak interior, antiques, remodeled guest rooms, private baths, king and queen beds, and central air is open all year. No smoking, pets, or children under 12. Mastercard or Visa required to hold. Price includes tax.

Hosts: Mary Lou and Ron Clark
Rooms: 3 (3PB) $59–63 tax included

Full Breakfast
Credit Cards: A B
Notes: 2 5 8 9 10

Antique City Inn Bed and Breakfast

400 Antique City Dr., P. O. Box 584
   Walnut, IA 51577-0584
(712) 784-3722
E-mail: sylvias@netins.net
Web site: www.netins.netshowcase/walnutia

This 1911 Victorian home has been restored and furnished to its original state. All rooms are air-conditioned and have private baths; the carriage house has a double whirlpool. The inn is located one block north of eight malls and stores with 250 antique dealers. The home boasts beautiful woodwork, a dumbwaiter icebox, French doors, and a wrap-around porch.

Host: Sylvia Reddie
Rooms: 6 (5PB;1SB) $53–63.60
Full Breakfast
Credit Cards: A B C D
Notes: 2 10

---

6 Pets welcome; 7 Children welcome; 8 Tennis nearby; 9 Swimming nearby; 10 Golf nearby; 11 Skiing nearby; 12 May be booked through travel agent

KANSAS

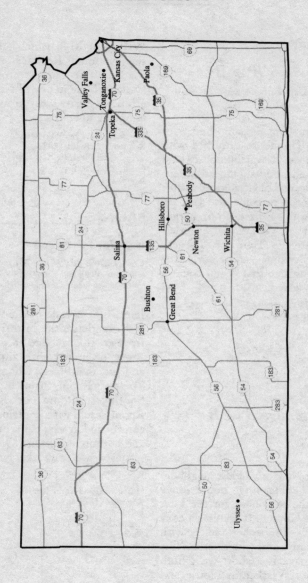

Kansas

GREAT BEND

Peaceful Acres B & B

R. R. 5, Box 153, Great Bend, KS 67530-9805
(620) 793-7527

Enjoy a mini-farm and sprawling, tree-shaded old farmhouse furnished with some antiques. If you like peace and quiet, chickens, calves, guineas, kittens in the spring, and old-fashioned hospitality, you need to come and visit us. Breakfast will be fixed from home-grown products. We are near historical areas—Sante Fe Trail, Ft. Larned, Cheyenne Bottoms—and close to the zoo and tennis courts. A full country breakfast is served.

Hosts: Dale and Doris Nitzel
Rooms: 3 (1PB;2SB) $35
Full Breakfast
Credit Cards:
Notes: 2 3 4 5 7 8 9 10 12

NEWTON

Old Parsonage B & B

330 E. 4th St., Newton, KS 67114-2245
(316) 283-6808

Located in Newton's oldest neighborhood, this charming home once served as the parsonage for the First Mennonite Church. It features a cozy yet spacious atmosphere filled with antiques and family heirlooms. The Old Parsonage is a short walk from the historical Warkentin House and Warkentin Mill, which are listed on the National Register of Historic Places. Two miles from Bethel College. Dine in one of Newton's fine ethnic eateries, or browse quaint antique and craft shops.

Hosts: Karl and Betty Friesen
Rooms: 3 (1PB;2SB) $48
Continental Breakfast
Credit Cards: A B
Notes: 2 5 7

SALINA

Trader's Lodge

1392 N. 210th Rd., Wells, KS 67467-5016
(785) 488-3930; (866) 360-1813
Web site: www.come.to/traderslodge

Join us for "a taste of the Wild West" and experience the history of the fur trade era in our lodge of fir and native stone, decorated with antiques, furs, and Indian artifacts. Choose from the Trapper's Room, Plains Indian Room, Southwest Room, or Renaissance Room, each with individual climate control and private bath. Fitness room and hot tub downstairs. Quiet country setting near a state lake. No alcohol or tobacco, please.

Hosts: Neal and Kathy Kindall
Rooms: 4 (4PB) $65–85
Full Breakfast
Credit Cards: C D
Notes: 2 3 4 5 7

NOTES: Credit cards accepted: A Master Card; B Visa; C American Express; D Discover; E Diners Club; F Other; 2 Personal checks accepted; 3 Lunch available; 4 Dinner available; 5 Open all year;

VALLEY FALLS

The Barn B & B Inn

14910 Blue Mound Rd.
 Valley Falls, KS 66088-4030
(785) 945-3225; (800) 869-7717
 Fax (785) 945-3432
E-mail: thebarn@thebarnbb.com
Web site: www.thebarnbb.com

Country living at its best in the rolling hills of northeast Kansas, this 108-year-old peg-barn has been converted into a bed and breakfast. Sitting high on a hill with a beautiful view, it has a large indoor heated pool, hot tub, fitness room, three large living rooms, and king-size beds in all rooms. A home-cooked dinner is included with your room as well as a full breakfast.

Hosts: Tom and Marcella Ryan
Rooms: 23 (23PB) $111.00–117.00
Full Breakfast
Credit Cards: A B C D
Notes: 2 3 4 5 7 8 9 10 12

WICHITA

The Castle Inn Riverside

1155 N. River Blvd., Wichita, KS 67203-3028
(316) 263-9300
E-mail: info@castleinnriverside.com
Web site: www.castleinnriverside.com

This luxurious inn is a stunning example of Richardsonian Romanesque architecture. The home includes 14 guest rooms, each individually appointed. Twelve of the guest rooms include a fireplace, and six have in-room two-person Jacuzzi tubs. Guests are pampered with a sampling of wine, cheeses, gourmet coffees and teas, after-dinner liqueurs, desserts, and a full gourmet breakfast in the morning. The inn offers many amenities for its business travelers, including rooms equipped with TVs, VCRs, telephones and data ports. The inn is just a few minutes from downtown Wichita, and near attractions like Old Town, Exploration Place, and the Wichita Art Museum.

The Castle Inn Riverside

Hosts: Dr. Terry and Paula Lowry
Rooms: 14 (14PB) $125–275
Full Breakfast
Credit Cards: A B D E
Notes: 2 5 7 8 9 10 12

KENTUCKY

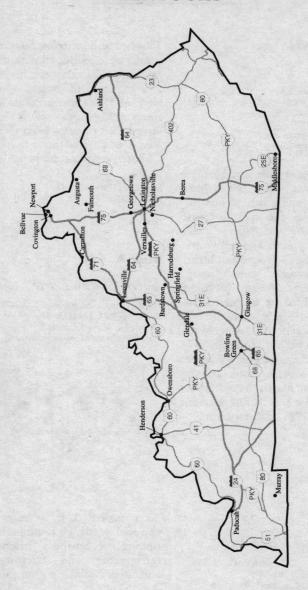

Kentucky

BARDSTOWN

Jailer's Inn

111 W. Stephen Foster Ave.
    Bardstown, KY 40004-1415
(502) 348-5551; (800) 948-5551
    Fax (502) 349-1837
E-mail: cpaul@jailersinn.com
Web site: www.jailersinn.com

Windows covered with iron bars, 30-inch-thick stone walls, and a heavy steel door slamming behind one may not sound like the typical tourist accommodation—and Jailer's Inn is anything but typical. The Jailer's Inn, circa 1819, offers a unique and luxurious way to "do time." Jailer's Inn is a place of wonderful, thought-provoking contrasts. Each of the six guest rooms is beautifully decorated with antiques and heirlooms, all in the renovated front jail. The back jail, built in 1874, is basically unchanged; guests will get a chilling and sobering look at what conditions were like in the old Nelson County jail that was in full operation as recently as 1987. Call for rates.

Host: Paul McCoy
Rooms: 6 (6PB) $70–135
Full Breakfast
Credit Cards: A B C D
Notes: 2 7 8 9 10 12

BELLEVUE

Mary's Belle View Inn

444 Van Voast Ave., Bellevue, KY 41073
(859) 581-8337; (888) 581-8875
Web site: www.bbonline.com/ky/belleview

This bed and breakfast features quiet, comfortable rooms, all with their own private bath. Each room has access to a large deck, offering a spectacular view of the Cincinnati skyline and surrounding areas. Full breakfast served. Ten minutes from Cincinnati. Visa and Mastercard accepted. Children welcome, no pets.

Host: Mary Bickers
Rooms: 3 (3PB) $55–110
Full Breakfast
Credit Cards: A B
Notes: 2 5 7

BEREA

Berea Shady Lane

123 Mt. Vernon Rd., Berea, KY 40403
(859) 986-9851; Fax (859) 986-9851
E-mail: lrwebber@aol.com
Web site: bbonline.com/ky/shadylane/

Berea Shady Lane

As a small B & B, we cater to your personal needs, be it shopping, vacationing, or business. Internet, fax, refrigerator, and microwave are amenities available to our guests. We

---

NOTES: Credit cards accepted: A Master Card; B Visa; C American Express; D Discover; E Diners Club; F Other; 2 Personal checks accepted; 3 Lunch available; 4 Dinner available; 5 Open all year;

have a verse displayed on the back of an old chair in the entryway that we enjoy sharing with our guests. "Life is happening—now sit here and listen." Our B & B is conveniently located near I-75, Berea College, Renfro Valley, local craft and antique shops. A day is twice blessed with ambience of a restful night.

Hosts: Les and Clarine Webber
Rooms: 2 (2PB) $55–70
Full Breakfast
Credit Cards:
Notes: 2 5 8 9 10

Cabin Fever Bed and Breakfast

112 Adams St., Berea, KY 40403-1531
(859) 986-9075; Fax (859) 986-6045
E-mail: alfredoescobar@hotmail.com
Web site: www.staycabinfever.com

Cabin Fever

See Kentucky's Folk Arts and Crafts Capital from the center of it all at Cabin Fever Bed and Breakfast! Choose from three lovely rooms, decorated artistically with family collections and the Escobars' own works of art, and enjoy all the modern conveniences while surrounded by all the old-world

ambience of a log home and traditional Southern hospitality.

Hosts: Alfredo and Jennifer Rose Escobar
Rooms: 3 (1PB;2SB) $75
Full Breakfast
Credit Cards: D
Notes: 2 5 6 7 8 9 10

BOWLING GREEN

Alpine Lodge

5310 Morgantown Rd.
    Bowling Green, KY 42101-8201
(270) 843-4846; (888) 444-3791
    Fax (270) 843-4833
E-mail: alplodge@aol.com
Web site:
    www.christianbb.com/ky/alpinelodge.htm

Alpine Lodge is a spacious, Swiss chalet-style home with 6,000 square feet, located on 12 acres. A full Southern breakfast is served. We have a swimming pool, hot tub, gazebo, and deck to enjoy. We are close to Mammouth Cave and Corvette City.

Hosts: Dr. and Mrs. David Livingston
Rooms: 5 (3PB;2SB) $65–90
Full Breakfast
Credit Cards:
Notes: 2 5 6 7 8 9 10 12

CARROLLTON

Ghent House Bed and Breakfast

411 Main St., U. S. 42, P. O. Box 478
    Ghent, KY 41045-0478
(502) 347-5807
Web site: www.bbonline.com/ky/ghent/

A historic river home, Ghent House is a gracious reminder of the antebellum

6 Pets welcome; 7 Children welcome; 8 Tennis nearby; 9 Swimming nearby; 10 Golf nearby; 11 Skiing nearby; 12 May be booked through travel agent

days of the old South. Walk back in time—visit this 1833 home. Relax in the whirlpool or by the fireplaces, walk in the English garden, view the Ohio River from your porch, or relax in the Rose Garden Cottage and gazebo. Stay in our Rose Garden Cottage. Come as a guest. Leave as a friend.

Ghent House

Hosts: Wayne and Diane Young
Rooms: 4 (4PB) $70–175
Full Breakfast
Credit Cards: A B C D F
Notes: 2 5 7 9 10

GEORGETOWN

Pineapple Inn B & B

645 S. Broadway St., Georgetown, KY 40324-1135
(502) 868-5453

Located in beautiful, historic Georgetown, our inn—built in 1876—is furnished with antiques and beautifully decorated. With three guest rooms on the second level. The Country and Victorian Rooms each have one full bed. Our Americana Room has two full beds and one twin bed. Our Derby Room is on the main floor with a queen canopy bed. In its private bath there is a hot tub as well as a shower. A full breakfast is served each morning in our French Country

dining room. You may also relax in our large living room.

Hosts: Les and Muriel
Rooms: 4 (4PB) $65–90
Full Breakfast
Credit Cards: A B
Notes: 2 5 7 8 9 10 12

HARRODSBURG

Bauer Haus
Bed and Breakfast

362 N. College St., Harrodsburg, KY 40330-1116
(859) 734-6289; (877) 734-6289
E-mail: bauerhaus@kycom.net
Web site: www.bbonline.com/ky/bauer

Bauer Haus

Savor the craftsmanship of the past in this 1880s Victorian home listed on the National Register and designated a Kentucky landmark. Nestle in the sitting room, sip tea or coffee in the dining room, repose in the parlor, or ascend the stairs to a private room for a relaxing visit. In Kentucky's oldest settlement, Bauer Haus is within walking distance of Old Fort Harrod State Park and historic Harrodsburg.

Hosts: Dick and Marian Bauer
Rooms: 4 (3PB;1SB) $70–135
Full Breakfast
Credit Cards: A B C
Notes: 2 5 8 10 12

NOTES: Credit cards accepted: A Master Card; B Visa; C American Express; D Discover; E Diners Club; F Other; 2 Personal checks accepted; 3 Lunch available; 4 Dinner available; 5 Open all year;

HENDERSON

L & N Bed and Breakfast Ltd.

327 N. Main St., Henderson, KY 42420-2952
(270) 831-1100; Fax (270) 826-0075
E-mail: info@lnbbky.com
Web site: www.lnbbky.com

L & N is a two-story Victorian home featuring oak woodwork and hardwood floors. The L & N has been completely restored including stained-glass transoms and central heat and air. The L & N is conveniently located in the heart of downtown Henderson next door to the railroad overpass and one block from the Ohio River. Restaurants and the Riverwalk are within walking distance. Four bedrooms are available, each with private bath, direct-dial telephone, and cable TV. Your innkeepers reside next door.

Hosts: Mary Elizabeth and Norris Priest
Rooms: 4 (4PB) $75
Continental Breakfast
Credit Cards:
Notes: 2 5 7 8 10 12

LEXINGTON

Sandusky House and O'Neal Log Cabin

1626 Delaney Ferry Rd.
   Nicholasville, KY 40356-8729
(859) 223-4370; Fax (859) 223-4730
E-mail: llchumphrey@cs.com
Web site: www.logcabinbandb.com

A tree-lined drive to the Sandusky House is just a prelude to a wonderful visit to the bluegrass. A quiet, 10-acre country setting amid horse farms, yet close to Lexington, Horse Park, and Shakertown. The Greek Revival Sandusky House was built circa 1850 from bricks fired on the farm. A 1,000-acre land grant from Patrick Henry, governor of Virginia, was given in 1780 to soldiers who had fought in the American Revolution. In addition to the Sandusky House, we have an 1820s reconstructed, two-story, two-bedroom log cabin with full kitchen and whirlpool bath. The cabin has a large stone fireplace and air-conditioning and is located in a wooded area close to the main house. An ideal getaway for the entire family! Please call for a brochure. Children over 12 are welcome in the house. All ages are welcome in the cabin.

O'Neal Cabin

Hosts: Jim and Linda Humphrey
Rooms: 5 (5PB) $85–135
Full Breakfast
Credit Cards: A B F
Notes: 2 5 6

LOUISVILLE

Pinecrest Cottage and Gardens B & B

2806 Newburg Rd., Louisville, KY 40205
(502) 454-3800; Fax (502) 452-9791
E-mail: pinecresbb@prodigy.net
Web site: www.pinecrestcottageandgardens.com

Situated on land deeded by forefather Patrick Henry, this century-old, fully renovated, 1,400-square-foot cottage near the Louisville Zoo and Kentucky Kingdom features a 6 1/2-acre wooded "yard," perennial beds, gazebo, tennis court, and pool. The guest house has a king bedroom, separate living room with two sofas (one folds out into a double bed), large bath, and sunporch. TV, VCR, phone, gas log fireplace, and kitchen stocked with breakfast and lunch goodies. Air-conditioned.

Hosts: Nancy and Allan Morris
Rooms: 1 (1PB) $110–165
Continental Breakfast
Credit Cards: A B C
Notes: 2 5 7 8 9

MIDDLESBORO

The RidgeRunner B & B

208 Arthur Heights, Middlesboro, KY 40965-1728
(606) 248-4299; Fax (606) 248-0011
Web site: www.bbonline.com/ky/ridgerunner/

Perched on top of the ridge, overlooking downtown Middlesboro. An 1890 Victorian home with furnishings from owners' ancestors. Front porch awaits guests for moments shared on the porch swings, a good book, and the rocking chairs, or guests may enjoy the parlor. Many historical opportunities and parks await your exploration.

The RidgeRunner

Rooms: 4 (2PB;2SB) $65–75
Full Breakfast
Credit Cards:
Notes: 2 5 9 10 12

NEWPORT

Cincinnati's Weller Haus B & B

319 Poplar St., Newport, KY 41073
(859) 431-6829; (800) 431-4287
   Fax (859) 431-4332
E-mail: innkeepers@wellerhaus.com
Web site: www.wellerhaus.com

Enjoy a stay in our historic home. The Weller Haus is within walking distance of the downtown stadiums, Riverboat Row restaurants, and the Newport Aquarium. Specializing in pampering our guests with all of the amenities they desire. Double Jacuzzi suited for the romantic at heart. Business travelers will find corporate rates, fax machine, in-room desk, meeting space, and other appointments with them in mind. A full, candlelit breakfast will start your day off right!

Hosts: Valerie and David Brown
Rooms: 5 (5PB) $89–168
Full Breakfast
Credit Cards: A B C D E
Notes: 2 5 7 10 11 12

NOTES: Credit cards accepted: A Master Card; B Visa; C American Express; D Discover; E Diners Club; F Other; 2 Personal checks accepted; 3 Lunch available; 4 Dinner available; 5 Open all year;

Gateway B & B

326 E. Sixth St., Newport, KY 41071
(859) 581-6447; (888) 891-7500
    Fax (859) 581-6447
Web site: www.gatewaybb.com

A warm welcome awaits you at the Gateway B & B in historic Newport, KY, just 5 minutes to Cincinnati. Your comfort is assured in one of our spacious rooms with queen-size beds and private bath. A full country breakfast is served, and you'll be on your way for antiquing, sightseeing, or your business trip. We invite you to our charming Victorian home and promise you a memorable stay.

Hosts: Ken and Sandy Clift
Rooms: 3 (3PB) $99.98
Full Breakfast
Credit Cards: A B C D
Notes: 2

OWENSBORO

Helton House Bed and Breakfast

103 E. 23rd St., Owensboro, KY 42303
(270) 926-7117; Fax (270) 926-6621
E-mail: graceeconley@aol.com
Web site:
    www.bbonline.com/ky/helton/index.html

Featured in the *Louisville Courier—Journal 2000*. Neighborhood songbirds issue the first welcome to visitors as they climb the steps to the open front porch of the circa 1910 arts and crafts home, which sits on a corner lot in the tree-lined Buena Vista neighborhood where streets are divided into boulevards by leafy medians. The sec-

ond-floor sun porch offers a panoramic view. Each room is individually decorated with antiques, Oriental carpet, and handmade cherry and walnut furniture. Almost as much attention has been given to planting the surrounding landscaping as to the decor and furnishing of the house. Guests from around the globe have enjoyed the comfort, peace, and love of the Helton House. Please inquire regarding private or shared baths.

Hosts: Don and Grace Conley
Rooms: 5 (3PB;2SB) $60–85
Full Breakfast
Credit Cards: A B C
Notes: 2 5 8 9 10 12

PADUCAH

Ehrhardt's Bed and Breakfast

285 Springwell Ln., Paducah, KY 42001
(270) 554-0644
E-mail: ziazio@vci.net

Our brick colonial home is located just 1 mile off I-24. We strive to make our guests feel at home with antique-filled bedrooms and a cozy den. Our home is all on one level and is easily accessible to most seniors. A 10% discount is available to seniors. A full breakfast is served. Come visit with us—we'd love to have you.

Hosts: Eileen and Phil Ehrhardt
Rooms: 2 (2SB) $60–65
Full Breakfast
Credit Cards:
Notes: 2 5   8 9 10

Trinity Hills Farm Inn / Spa Retreat

10455 Old Lovelaceville Rd.
  Paducah, KY 42001-9304
(270) 488-3999; (800) 488-3998
E-mail: info@trinityhills.com
Web site: www.trinityhills.com

Scott Station Inn

Trinity Hills Farm

Share the serenity of our 17-acre country retreat and guest house amidst beautiful gardens, hills, woods, and fishing lake. Enjoy a massage or a romantic "candlelight dinner for two." Features romantic whirlpools, stained glass, fireplaces, vaulted ceilings, and is wheelchair-accessible. Children or pets are welcome in our first-floor apartment suite with prior notice. Let Trinity Hills Farm be your haven for pleasure or business. We offer minister and missionary discounts.

Hosts: Mike and Ann Driver
Rooms: 7 (6PB;1SB) $90–200
Full Breakfast
Credit Cards: A B C D
Notes: 2 3 4 5 6 7 8 9 10 12

Beautifully refurbished in 1990, our inn has kept the charm and gracious air of an old Kentucky home. Each room has its own decorative theme reflecting the magic of small-town America. We are located in central KY. Just one block from Asbury College and Seminary and only 15 miles from Shakertown and other famous Kentucky attractions.

Hosts: Ruth and Ian Yorston
Rooms: 6 (4PB;2SB) $45–55
Full Breakfast
Credit Cards: A B C D
Notes: 2 5 7 8 9 10

WILMORE

Scott Station Inn

305 E. Main St., Wilmore, KY 40390-1323
(606) 858-0121

NOTES: Credit cards accepted: A Master Card; B Visa; C American Express; D Discover; E Diners Club; F Other; 2 Personal checks accepted; 3 Lunch available; 4 Dinner available; 5 Open all year;

LOUISIANA

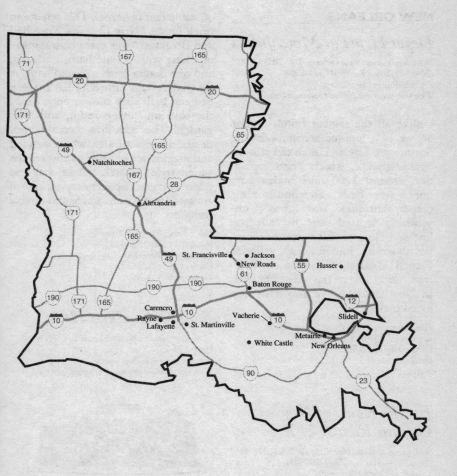

Louisiana

NEW ORLEANS

Depot House at Mme. Julia's

748 Okeefe Ave., New Orleans, LA 70113-1907
(504) 529-2952; Fax (504) 529-1908
E-mail: dhiltonlll@aol.com
Web site: www.mmejuliadepothouse.com

Unlike all the regular hotels around us, we have unique accommodations downtown. Located in an old railroad boardinghouse, which began operation around 1900, our rooms have queen-size beds, air-conditioning, carpet, antiques, and more. Conveniently located near the streetcar line and close to the convention center, aquarium, museums, art galleries, French Quarter, Superdome, Riverwalk, and some of the oldest churches in New Orleans! We also have free, gated parking.

Hosts: Joanne, Dennis, and Layne Hilton
Rooms: 15 (15PB) $65–125
Continental Breakfast
Credit Cards:
Notes: 2

Essem's House of New Orleans First B & B

3660 Gentilly Blvd., New Orleans, LA 70122-4910
(504) 947-3401; Fax (504) 838-2100
E-mail: nobba@bellsouth.net
Web site: www.neworleansbandb.com

Tree-shaded boulevards; direct transportation to the French Quarter (15–20 minutes); safe, convenient area

of stable family homes. This ten-room brick home, "New Orleans' First Bed and Breakfast," has three bedrooms—one king with private bath, one king, and one double with a shared bath. A separate cottage efficiency has a queen bed and bath with shower only. Enjoy the solarium, living room, and back garden! The area has recently been declared a historic area, where walking and jogging are enjoyed as you see the varied styles of architecture: arts and crafts cottages, Spanish styles, and of course New Orleans single and double shotguns.

Host: Sarah Margaret Brown
Rooms: 3 (2PB;1SB) $75–95
Continental Breakfast
Credit Cards: A B C D
Notes: 5 6 8 9 10

St. Charles Guest House

1748 Prytania St., New Orleans, LA 70130
(504) 523-6556
E-mail: dhiltonlll@aol.com
Web site: www.stcharlesguesthouse.com

St. Charles Guest House

Located in historic garden district, just minutes from the French Quarter,

---

Superdome, convention center, business district, museums, galleries, and shopping, either by trolley or on foot, the St. Charles Guest House has been welcoming guests for over fifty years. Rooms are simple and antique-cozy. Continental breakfast is served poolside. Hosts are helpful and full of suggestions for how to see the "real New Orleans." Restaurants, from Emeril's to Burger Kings, and much in between, are steps from the front door. Perfect location for travelers with no need for a car. Best value downtown.

Hosts: Joanne and Dennis Hilton
Rooms: 38 (28PB;10SB)
Continental Breakfast
Credit Cards: A B C
Notes: 2 5 9

ST. FRANCISVILLE

Lake Rosemound Inn

10473 Lindsey Ln.
   St. Francisville, LA 70775-5247
(225) 635-3176; Fax (225) 635-2224
Web site: www.lakerosemoundinn.com

Lake Rosemound is one of the most picturesque areas in the heart of plantation country, just minutes from historic St. Francisville. All four guest rooms have a view of the lake and king or queen beds, TV, AC, and paddle fans. The Rosemound and Feliciana suites have Jacuzzis-for-two. Start your day with a great country breakfast, then enjoy the hammocks, porch swings, canoe, paddleboat, and famous "help yourself" ice cream bar. The inn is handicapped accessible. Hiking and horseback riding are nearby.

Hosts: Jon and Jeane Peters
Rooms: 4 (4PB) $75–125
Full Breakfast
Credit Cards: A B C D
Notes: 2 5 6 7 9 10

---

6 Pets welcome; 7 Children welcome; 8 Tennis nearby; 9 Swimming nearby; 10 Golf nearby; 11 Skiing nearby; 12 May be booked through travel agent

MAINE

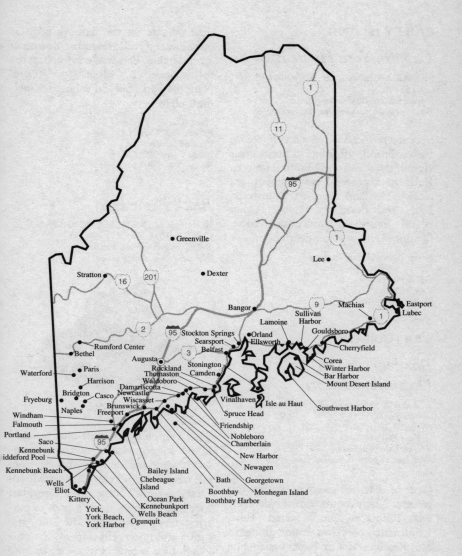

Maine

BAILEY ISLAND

Captain York House B & B

P. O. Box 298, Bailey Island, ME 04003-0298
(207) 833-6224
E-mail: athorn7286@aol.com
Web site: www.iwws.com/captainyork

Stay at a restored sea captain's house on Bailey Island, affording a spectacular view of the ocean and beautiful sunsets. Relax in a peaceful environment, yet close to Portland, Freeport, Brunswick, Bath, and Boothbay Harbor. Quiet island living in midcoast Maine. Quaint fishing villages nearby.

Hosts: Alan and Jean Thornton
Rooms: 5 (5PB) $90–130
Full Breakfast
Credit Cards: A B   F
Notes: 2 5 9 10

BAR HARBOR

Bar Harbor Inn Oceanfront Resort

P. O. Box 7, Newport Dr., Bar Harbor, ME
    04609-0007
(207) 288-3351; (800) 248-3351
    Fax (207) 288-8424
E-mail: bhinn@acadia.net
Web site: www.barharborinn.com

One of Maine's premier oceanfront resorts. Many rooms feature balconies, gas fireplaces, and jetted tubs. Continental breakfast. Enjoy dining in our Reading Room Restaurant—fine dining with a relaxed atmosphere, or dine outside on the harbor's edge at our Terrace Grille, featuring downeast lobster bakes. Personal service, best in-town location, close to Acadia National Park. Special value packages, meal plans.

Hosts: David J. Witham
Rooms: 153 (153PB) $75–335
Continental Breakfast
Credit Cards: A B C D E
Notes: 3 4   7 8 9 10 12

Black Friar Inn

10 Summer St., Bar Harbor, ME 04609-1424
(207) 288-5091; Fax (207) 288-4197
E-mail: blackfriar@blackfriar.com
Web site: www.blackfriar.com

Black Friar Inn

This completely rebuilt and restored home incorporates beautiful woodwork, windows, and bookcases from old mansions and churches on Mount Desert Island. Your gourmet breakfast may include homemade breads or pastries; fresh fruit; eggs du jour; and more; afternoon refreshments are provided. Our rooms have queen or king beds and AC; two have fireplaces.

NOTES: Credit cards accepted: A Master Card; B Visa; C American Express; D Discover; E Diners Club; F Other; 2 Personal checks accepted; 3 Lunch available; 4 Dinner available; 5 Open all year;

Walk to the waterfront, restaurants, and shops, with ample parking available. Less than 1 mile to Acadia National Park.

Hosts: Perry and Sharon Risley and Falke
Rooms: 7 (7PB) $105–150
Full Breakfast
Credit Cards: A B D
Notes: 2 7 8 9 10 11

Bluenose Inn

P. O. Box 7, Bar Harbor, ME 04609
(207) 288-3348; (800) 445-4077
    Fax (207) 288-2183
E-mail: reservations@bluenoseinn.com
Web site: www.bluenoseinn.com

Spectacular ocean views atop a granite-terraced hillside. Bar Harbor's only AAA 4-diamond and Mobil 4-star hotel offers elegant, immaculate, over-sized rooms with king and queen beds, many with fireplaces and private balconies. All have air-conditioning, HBO, and refrigerators. Enjoy our fabulous indoor/outdoor pools, Jacuzzi, and fitness center. Our Rose Garden Restaurant features 4-diamond cuisine—breakfast and dinner daily. The inn is 3/4 mile to downtown, $1/4$ mile to ferry to Nova Scotia, and 1 mile to Acadia National Park.

Hosts: David J. Witham
Rooms: 97 (97PB) $75–349
Continental Breakfast
Credit Cards: A B C D E
Notes: 4 7 8 9 10 11 12

Stratford House Inn

45 Mount Desert St.
    Bar Harbor, ME 04609-1748
(207) 288-5189; Fax (207) 288-4184
E-mail: info@stratfordinn.com

Web site: www.stratfordinn.com

Built in 1900 by the noted Boston publisher Lewis A. Roberts, the Stratford House Inn is styled with the romantic charm of an English Tudor manor. The inn boasts ten beautifully decorated bedrooms, each with its own individual charm and style. In the morning, guests are treated to a continental breakfast in the elegant dining room, replete with original period furnishings. After the day's events, find evening relaxation with a book in the library, interesting conversation on our large veranda, or try your hand at the grand piano in the music room.

Hosts: Norman and Barbara Moulton
Rooms: 10 (8PB;2SB) $85–175
Continental Breakfast
Credit Cards: A B D
Notes: 2 7 8 10

Stratford House Inn

Willows at Atlantic Oakes by the Sea

119 Eden St.; P. O. Box 3
    Bar Harbor, ME 04609
(800) 33MAINE; Fax (207) 288-8402
Web site: www.barharbor.com

This charming house was named "The Willows" after the willow trees on the

---

6 Pets welcome; 7 Children welcome; 8 Tennis nearby; 9 Swimming nearby; 10 Golf nearby; 11 Skiing nearby; 12 May be booked through travel agent

entrance drive. About 200 summer cottages were built in Bar Harbor from 1880 to 1890. "The Willows" was built in 1913—one of the last estates built. The large wooden hotels (now gone) were built from 1865 to 1885. No matter how large and ostentatious the summer homes were, they always were called "cottages." "The Willows" is located on the ground of the Atlantic Oakes by-the-Sea. There are four tennis courts and indoor and outdoor pools available for use by B & B guests. On the ocean close to Acadia National Park.

Hosts: Cough Family
Rooms: 9 (9PB) $78–270
Continental Breakfast
Credit Cards: A B C
Notes: 8 9 12

BELFAST

1 Church Street
The White House B & B

No. 1 Church St., Belfast, ME 04915
(207) 338-1901; (888) 290-1901
   Fax (207) 338-5161
E-mail: whitehouse@mainebb.com
Web site: www.mainebb.com

This 1840 Greek Revival mansion was designed to create the showcase of coastal Maine. You're invited to explore the elegant classical European-styled decor, signature breakfast, refreshing conversation, and warm hospitality embodied by our inn. Today, the White House is often called "the most photographed historic home in New England," evidencing that it still holds all the grandeur that was

intended 160 years ago. The White House is registered on the National Register of Historic Places. Sweeping views of its triangular-shaped parklike grounds, botanical gardens, and historic gazebo (ideal for weddings) instill a sense of peace and tranquility.

Hosts: Robert Hansen and Terry Prescott
Rooms: 6 (6PB) $95–165
Full Breakfast
Credit Cards: A B D
Notes: 2 4 5 8 9 10 11

Belhaven Inn B & B

14 John St., Belfast, ME 04915-6650
(207) 338-5435
E-mail: stay@belhaveninn.com
Web site: www.belhaveninn.com

Belhaven Inn is known for its warm, relaxed family attitude. We welcome you to bring your whole family, from infants to grandparents. There's something here for all. Built in 1851 by John Stanwood Caldwell, a direct descendant of one of the original Waldo Land Patent holders. The original cherry spiral staircase leads up to four bright and charmingly decorated guest rooms. Relax in one of four parlors, the shady veranda, or spacious grounds. Larger families, longer-stay guests, or pet owners will enjoy the fully equipped efficiency guest room with its kitchen, sun deck, and private entrance. Enjoy a three-course country breakfast that guests say "makes lunch unnecessary." Harbor, shops, restaurants, and attractions are just a short stroll away.

Hosts: Paul and Anne Bartels
Rooms: 5 (3PB;2SB) $75–115

NOTES: Credit cards accepted: A Master Card; B Visa; C American Express; D Discover; E Diners Club; F Other; 2 Personal checks accepted; 3 Lunch available; 4 Dinner available; 5 Open all year;

Full Breakfast
Credit Cards: A B
Notes: 4 5 6 7 8 9 10v11

BOOTHBAY HARBOR

Admiral's Quarters Inn

71 Commercial St.
　Boothbay Harbor, ME 04538-1828
(207) 633-2474; (800) 644-1878
　Fax (207) 633-5904
E-mail: loon@admiralsquartersinn.com
Web site: www.admiralsquartersinn.com

Admiral's Quarters Inn

Private baths, decks/patio, entrances.
Fireplaces, color-cable TVs, phones,
and central AC add to the amenities.
Linger over your full homemade
breakfast on the wrap-around deck or
by the woodstove in the glass solarium
gathering room. The inn overlooks the
entire harbor and meticulously manicured gardens. Afternoon refreshments greet you upon arrival. "We
don't claim to have the best views. . . .
Our guests make that claim!"

Hosts: Les and Deb Hallstrom
Rooms: 6 (6PB) $95–195
Full Breakfast
Credit Cards: A B D
Notes: 2　5　7 8 9 10 11 12

Anchor Watch B & B

9 Eames Rd., Boothbay Harbor, ME 04538-1882
(207) 633-7565
E-mail: diane@lincoln.midcoast.com
Web site: www.anchorwatch.com

On the beautiful shores of the Anchor
Watch, guests may watch boating
activities from our pier or lounge on
the shorefront patio. Walk to the village for dining and shopping, or stay
comfy under down comforters for an
afternoon nap. Our five charmingly
decorated rooms are light and airy;
most have windows facing the lovely
water views; all have private baths.
Guests rave about the delicious breakfast served in the sunny seaside room,
where local lobstermen can be seen
hauling traps right near our dock.
Your welcome begins on our front
porch with the cool sea breeze fresh
from the shore. Inside a warm ambience is created in the seaside room
with its gas-fired fireplace, pine floor,
and windows on the water.

Hosts: Diane Campbell and Kathy Reed
Rooms: 5 (5PB) $100–165
Full Breakfast
Credit Cards: A B
Notes: 2　8　9　10

Harbour Towne Inn on the Waterfront

71 Townsend Ave.
　Boothbay Harbor, ME 04538-1843
(207) 633-4300; (800) 722-4540
　Fax (207) 633-2442
E-mail: gtme@gwi.net

"The finest B & B on the waterfront."
Our refurbished Victorian inn retains

---

6 Pets welcome; 7 Children welcome; 8 Tennis nearby; 9 Swimming nearby; 10 Golf nearby; 11 Skiing
nearby; 12 May be booked through travel agent

turn-of-the-century ambience while providing all modern amenities. The colorful gardens and quiet, tree-shaded location slopes right to the edge of the beautiful New England harbor. Choose a room with outside deck for waterfront views. AC and new dock and float on the bay. Two-to five-minute scenic walk to harbor. Our luxurious penthouse is a modern, spacious home that sleeps up to six in luxury and privacy. Stay just once and you will know why our guests return year after year. No smoking or pets. Well-behaved children are welcome.

Harbour Towne Inn on the Waterfront

Hosts: George Thomas and Family
Rooms: 12 (12PB) $69–299
Continental Breakfast
Credit Cards: A B C D
Notes: 2 8 9 10 12

BOOTHBAY HARBOR REGION

Kenniston Hill Inn

P. O. Box 125, Boothbay, ME 04537-0125
(207) 633-2159; (800) 992-2915
    Fax (207) 633-2159
E-mail: innkeeper@maine.com
Web site: www.maine.com/innkeeper/

Oldest inn in the Boothbay region. Located on 4 acres of beautiful peren-

nial beds, wildflower gardens, oak and maple trees, and a picket-fenced patio, just a mile from the harbor. 1786 Georgian Colonial-style colonial; nine rooms; kings, queens, and doubles. Seven working fireplaces, five in guest rooms. Open year-round serving a full country breakfast each morning. Relax on the front porch and enjoy a cool drink and some delicious sweets.

Hosts: Gerry and Jim Botti
Rooms: 9 (9PB) $90–135
Full Breakfast
Credit Cards: A B C D
Notes: 2 5 7 8 9 10 12

BRIDGTON

Greenwood Manor Inn

52 Tolman Rd.; P. O. Box 551, Harrison, ME 04040
(207) 583-4445; (866) 583-4445
    Fax (207) 583-2480
E-mail: info@greenwoodmanorinn.com
Web site: www.greenwoodmanorinn.com

Greenwood Manor Inn is located at the tip of Long Lake on 108 secluded acres of lawns, gardens, and woodlands. Seven uniquely decorated guest rooms and two suites, all with private baths, some with fireplaces, are yours to choose. A full country breakfast is served on the covered deck overlooking the formal gardens. Canoes are available for use on nearby lakes. Greenwood Manor has facilities available for weddings and special occasions. Meeting room available for small (10–12 people) conferences.

Hosts: Patty Douthett and Mike Rosenbauer
Rooms: 9 (9PB) $99–189
Full Breakfast
Credit Cards: A B
Notes: 2 5 7 8 9 10 11 12

NOTES: Credit cards accepted: A Master Card; B Visa; C American Express; D Discover; E Diners Club; F Other; 2 Personal checks accepted; 3 Lunch available; 4 Dinner available; 5 Open all year;

DAMARISCOTTA

Brannon-Bunker Inn

349 State Rte. 129, Walpole, ME 04573
(207) 563-5941; (800) 563-5941
    Fax (207) 563-5941
E-mail: brbnkinn@lincoln.midcoast.com

Brannon-Bunker Inn is an intimate and relaxed country bed and breakfast situated only minutes from a sandy beach, lighthouse, and historic fort in Maine's midcoastal region. Located in a 1920s Cape, converted barn, and carriage house, the guest rooms are furnished in themes that combine the charm of yesterday with the comforts of today. You'll find antique shops nearby.

Hosts: Joe and Jeanne Hovance
Rooms: 7 (5PB;2SB) $75–85
Continental Breakfast
Credit Cards: A B C D E
Notes: 2 7 8 9 10

EASTPORT

Milliken House

29 Washington St., Eastport, ME 04631-1324
(207) 853-2955; (888) 507-9370
    Fax (207) 853-4830
E-mail: millikenhouse@eastport-inn.com

Step back into the 19th century in this large, gracious 1846 Victorian home, just two blocks up from Eastport's historic district waterfront. Victorian buffs will be delighted with the ornately carved, marble-topped furniture, knickknacks, and books with which the builder, Benjamin F. Milliken, furnished his home, and which he left intact. Mr. Milliken maintained a wharf on Eastport's busy waterfront from which he serviced the tall ships that used the harbor for a flourishing international trade throughout the 1800s.

Hosts: Bill and Mary Williams
Rooms: 6 (4PB;2SB) $65
Full Breakfast
Credit Cards: A B
Notes: 2 5 6 7

FREEPORT

White Cedar Inn

178 Main St., Freeport, ME 04032-1407
(207) 865-9099; (800) 853-1269
    Fax (207) 865-6636
E-mail: jgs@whitecedarinn.com
Web site: www.whitecedarinn.com

This historic Victorian home in the coastal village of Freeport has been restored with loving care for the comfort of our guests. Our 7 bedrooms, all with private baths, air-conditioning, and some with warming fireplaces, are spacious and furnished with antiques. Our location is perfect for an easy walk to most of Freeport's luxury outlets, a variety of restaurants, and of course, L. L. Bean. Summer and fall seasons offer you opportunities such as bicycling along the coast, hiking the ocean trails of Wolfe's Neck Woods State Park, or taking a local cruise trip for a lighthouse tour. During winter and spring seasons, you could enjoy cross-country skiing at local parks, peaceful walks through the village, and visiting shops during a quieter time.

Hosts: Gwen and Jim Sartoris
Rooms: 7 (7PB) $85–145
Full Breakfast
Credit Cards: A B C D
Notes: 2 5 7 9 10 12

6 Pets welcome; 7 Children welcome; 8 Tennis nearby; 9 Swimming nearby; 10 Golf nearby; 11 Skiing nearby; 12 May be booked through travel agent

KENNEBUNKPORT

The Captain Lord Mansion

P. O. Box 800, Kennebunkport, ME 04046-0800
(207) 967-3141; Fax (207) 967-3172
E-mail: innkeeper@captainlord.com
Web site: www.captainlord.com

An unforgettable romantic experience
is your reward when you reserve one of
the 16 large, beautifully appointed,
guest rooms at the Captain Lord
Mansion. Both your personal comfort
and intimacy are assured at this detail-
filled inn. Indulge yourself with luxurious amenities such as oversize four-
poster beds, cozy gas fireplaces, heated
marble/tile bathroom floors, or perhaps a double Jacuzzi, as well as fresh
flowers, full breakfasts, afternoon
sweets, and lots of personal attention.
The inn offers you a picturesque,
quiet, yet convenient location from
which to walk to enjoy the historic village of Kennebunkport. The inn is situated in a quiet residential neighborhood at the head of a sloping village
green, overlooking the Kennebunk
River. The Mansion also offers you
close proximity to exciting water-
based activities, as well as easy access
to bicycling, golf, tennis, antiquing,
and fine dining.

Hosts: Bev Davis and Rick Litchfield
Rooms: 16 (16PB) $99–399
Full Breakfast
Credit Cards: A B D E
Notes: 2 5 8 9 10 12

Maine Stay Inn and Cottages

P. O. Box 500 A, Kennebunkport, ME 04046-1800
(207) 967-2117; (800) 950-2117
   Fax (207) 967-8757

E-mail: innkeeper@mainestayinn.com
Web site: www.mainestayinn.com

Maine Stay Inn

A grand Victorian inn that exudes
charm, from its wrap-around porch to
its perennial flower garden and spacious lawn. The white clapboard
house, built in 1860 and listed on the
National Historic Register, and the
adjoining cottages sit grandly in
Kennebunkport's historic district. The
Maine Stay features a variety of
delightful accommodations, all with
private baths, color cable TV/VCR,
and air-conditioning. Many of the
rooms have fireplaces. A sumptuous
full breakfast and afternoon tea are
included. The inn is an easy walk from
the harbor, shops, galleries, and
restaurants. Mobil 3-star-rated.

Rooms: 17 (17PB) $105–250
Full Breakfast
Credit Cards: A B C
Notes: 2 5 7 8 9 10

KITTERY

Farmstead B & B

379 Goodwin Rd., Eliot, ME 03903-1221
(207) 748-3145; (888) 829-0332
   Fax (207) 748-3659
E-mail: farmsteadb@aol.com
Web site: www.farmstead.qpg.com

NOTES: Credit cards accepted: A Master Card; B Visa; C American Express; D Discover; E Diners
Club; F Other; 2 Personal checks accepted; 3 Lunch available; 4 Dinner available; 5 Open all year;

This lovely country inn is situated on 3 acres. Its warm, friendly atmosphere exemplifies farm life of the late 1800s. Each Victorian-style guest room has a mini-refrigerator and microwave for snacks or special diets. Breakfast may include blueberry pancakes or French toast, homemade syrup, fruit, and juice. Limited handicapped accessibility. Minutes from Kittery Factory Outlets, York beaches, Portsmouth, and historic sites. One hour from Boston.

Hosts: Meb and John Lippincott
Rooms: 6 (6PB) $62–72
Full Breakfast
Credit Cards: A B D
Notes: 2 5 6 7 8 10 12

Enchanted Nights B & B

Scenic Coastal Rte. 103; 29 Wentworth St.
  Kittery, ME 03904-1720
(207) 439-1489
Web site: www.enchantednights.org

The Enchanted Nights B & B is a Victorian fantasy for the romantic at heart. Step back in time to experience the romance and splendor in our 1890 Princess Anne Victorian with its French Country flare: whimsical and colorful, yet elegant French and Victorian decor, from sweetly tattered iron beds and hand-painted floral furnishings, to elegant hand-carved oak bed chamber sets. Stay in one of our three rooms that have whirlpool tubs for two (two rooms also have fireplaces), or a tiny but enchanting turret room, all with fanciful bedding. CATV and VCR.

Hosts: Nancy Bogerberger and Peter Lamandia
Rooms: 10 (8PB;2SB) $47–300

Full Breakfast
Credit Cards: A B C D E
Notes: 2 5 6 7 8 9 10 12

NAPLES

The Augustus Bove House

R. R. 1 Box 501, Naples, ME 04055-9801
(207) 693-6365; (888) 806-6249
E-mail: augbovehouse@pivot.net
Web site: www.naplesmaine.com

The Augustus Bove House

Guests are always welcome at the historic 1850 hotel. Originally known as Hotel Naples, it is restored for comfort and a relaxed atmosphere at affordable prices. Guest rooms have elegant yet homey furnishings, some with views of Long Lake. An easy walk to the water, shops, and recreation in a four-season area. Open all year, with off-season and midweek discounts. Telephones in each room. Air-conditioning, TV, VCR, and hot tub. Coffee or tea anytime.

Hosts: Dave and Arlene Stetson
Rooms: 10 (8PB;2SB) $89–175
Full Breakfast
Credit Cards: A B C D E
Notes: 2 5 9 10 11 12

---

6 Pets welcome; 7 Children welcome; 8 Tennis nearby; 9 Swimming nearby; 10 Golf nearby; 11 Skiing nearby; 12 May be booked through travel agent

ROCKLAND

Captain Lindsey House Inn

5 Lindsey St., Rockland, ME 04841-2913
(207) 596-7950; (800) 523-2145
    Fax (207) 596-2758
E-mail: lindsey@midcoast.com
Web site: www.lindseyhouse.com

Captain Lindsey House Inn

Built in 1832 and lovingly restored and filled with artifacts and furnishings from the world over, the inn is nestled among the seaport buildings of Rockland. Each room is appointed with modern amenities that never infringe upon the grace of the antique furnishings. Enjoy time in our parlor, well-stocked library, or on our flowered patio. Just blocks from museums, shops, galleries, antique emporiums, and more. No smoking. Lunch and dinner available next door at WaterWorks Restaurant.

Host: Ellen Barnes
Rooms: 9 (9PB) $65–175
Continental Breakfast
Credit Cards: A B C D
Notes: 5 7 9 10 11 12

SEARSPORT

1850 Brass Lantern Inn

81 W. Main St., Searsport, ME 04974
(207) 548-0150
E-mail: stay@brasslanternmaine.com
Web site: www.brasslanternmaine.com

Step back in time when you enter this beautiful circa 1850 sea captain's home. You will be treated to warm and casual hospitality in gracious surroundings. Ornate tin ceilings grace the dining room and one of the parlors. Glorious sunrises and glimpses of the bay can be seen from the windows, while the harbor, museum, shops, and restaurants are just a short walk away. Acadia National Park, Camden, Castine, and Stonington, all an easy drive away.

Hosts: Dick and Maggie Zieg
Rooms: 5 (5PB) $95–115
Full Breakfast
Credit Cards: A B D
Notes: 2 5 8 9 10 11 12

Inn Britannia

132 W. Main St., Searsport, ME 04974
(207) 548-2007; (866) INNBRIT
    Fax (207) 548-2006
E-mail: info@innbritannia.com
Web site: www.innbritannia.com

Open year-round, Inn Britannia offers all the amenities that promise a memorable stay. Each of the eight guest rooms has a private bath and is beautifully decorated with antiques and tasteful decor themed after some special place in England. Sleep beneath the stars in Nottingham Forest, spend the night in Warwick Castle, or relax in the royal splendor of Windsor! Enjoy a full, cooked, gourmet breakfast, beautiful English gardens, and the magnificent ocean air!

Hosts: Caren Lorelle / Susan Pluff
Rooms: 8 (8PB) $100–190
Full Breakfast
Credit Cards: A B
Notes: 2 5 6 7 9 11

NOTES: Credit cards accepted: A Master Card; B Visa; C American Express; D Discover; E Diners Club; F Other; 2 Personal checks accepted; 3 Lunch available; 4 Dinner available; 5 Open all year;

1794 Watchtide by the Sea!

190 W. Main St., Searsport, ME 04974
(207) 548-6575; (800) 698-6575
   Fax (207) 548-0938
E-mail: stay@watchtide.com
Web site: www.watchtide.com

Distinctive 18th-century seaside inn on National Register of Historic Places. Renowned for serving scrumptious breakfasts on the 60' sunporch overlooking Penobscot Bay and our bird and wildlife sanctuary. Five charming rooms w/en suite private baths and king/queen beds. Honeymoon suite with two-person Jacuzzi and first-floor suite with fireplace, whirlpool tub, and much more. Come, watch the tides, let us indulge you in life's little luxuries because we love to spoil our guests!

1794 Watchtide by the Sea

Hosts: Nancy-Linn Nellis and Jack Elliott
Rooms: 5 (5PB) $85–185
Full Breakfast
Credit Cards: A B D
Notes: 2 5 8 9 10 12

Old Glory Inn

89 W. Main St. / P. O. Box 461
   Searsport, ME 04974-0461
(207) 548-6232
E-mail: bhuddleston@webtv.net

Colonial brick sea captain's home, circa 1830, offering your choice of the captain's suite with full sitting room or either of two additional guest rooms, all with private baths. Allows you the peace, quiet, and hospitality only a small inn can provide. Antique shop on premises. Open May to December.

Old Glory Inn

Hosts: Bruce and Rita Huddleston
Rooms: 3 (3PB) $60–70
Continental Breakfast
Credit Cards:
Notes: 2 8 9 10

SOUTHWEST HARBOR

The Island House

P. O. Box 1006, 121 Clark Point Rd.
   Southwest Harbor, ME 04679-1006
(207) 244-5180
E-mail: islandab@downeast.net
Web site: www.islandhousebb.com

Begun as the first summer hotel on Mount Desert Island in the mid-1800s, The Island House still retains the old-fashioned charm of that period with its pumpkin board floors and spacious, restful rooms. Furnishings of Ann's childhood years in Southeast Asia blend comfortably with this Maine seacoast home. A flower-filled veranda and large tree-shaded garden add a homey and relaxed atmosphere.

6 Pets welcome; 7 Children welcome; 8 Tennis nearby; 9 Swimming nearby; 10 Golf nearby; 11 Skiing nearby; 12 May be booked through travel agent

Hosts: Ann and Charles Bradford
Rooms: 4 (4PB) $75–120
Full Breakfast
Credit Cards: A B
Notes: 2 5 7 8 9 10 11

The Island House

VINALHAVEN

Payne Homestead at the Moses Webster House

P. O. Box 216, Atlantic Ave.
  Vinalhaven, ME 04863
(207) 863-9963; (888) 863-9963
  Fax (207) 863-2295
E-mail: payne@foxislands.net
Web site: www.paynehomestead.com

The Moses Webster House is a French Victorian home built in 1873 by granite magnate Moses Webster. This elite house boasts the splendor of the era, yet preserves the casual comfort of island lifestyle. It is now on the National Register of Historic Places. The Payne Homestead has been in operation as a B & B since 1995. It's the ideal atmosphere in which to explore the history of this magical island. Our home is a unique island accommodation that caters to couples and families alike. After a day of exploring, parents can curl up in a quiet corner with a book while their children unwind in the game room with a selection from our children's video collection.

Hosts: Lee and Donna Payne
Rooms: 5 (1PB;4SB) $90–145
Full Breakfast
Credit Cards:
Notes: 2 5 7

WATERFORD

Kedarburn Inn

Rte. 35, Box 61, Waterford, ME 04088
(207) 583-6182; Fax (207) 583-6424
E-mail: kedarburn@cybertours.com
Web site: http://members.aol.com/kedar01

Located in historic Waterford Village, a place to step back in time while you enjoy the comforts of today. Charming bedrooms decorated with warm country touches, with handmade quilts by Margaret, will add pleasure to your visit. Each day will start with a hearty breakfast. A typical English high tea is available as requested. Whether you come for outdoor activities or simply to enjoy the countryside, let us pamper you in our relaxed and friendly atmosphere. Open year-round.

Kedarburn Inn

NOTES: Credit cards accepted: A Master Card; B Visa; C American Express; D Discover; E Diners Club; F Other; 2 Personal checks accepted; 3 Lunch available; 4 Dinner available; 5 Open all year;

Hosts: Margaret and Derek Gibson
Rooms: 7 (5PB;2SB) $85–130
Full Breakfast
Credit Cards: A B C D
Notes: 2 5 6 7 9 10 11 12

WEST PARIS

Bradford House
Bed and Breakfast

98 Tuelltown Rd., West Paris, ME 04289
(207) 674-5696
E-mail: innkeeper@bradford-house.com
Web site: www.bradford-house.com

Bradford House is a completely restored circa 1840 country home. Guests enjoy bedrooms with private baths, swimming pool, and views that any artist would love to paint—right from their own private balcony. Relax with a panoramic view of the White Mountains and spectacular sunsets, all from a quiet country setting. Start your day by enjoying a full breakfast of juice, coffee, tea, homemade muffins, and other specialties of the cook. Then set out on your own to explore the local mountains, old quarry rock piles, antique shops, Shaker Village, and a large network of country roads. Bradford House is centrally located between Norway/South Paris and Bethel.

Hosts: Bob and Judy Sellers
Rooms: 4 (4PB) $60–110
Full Breakfast
Credit Cards:
Notes: 2 5 9 10 11

---

6 Pets welcome; 7 Children welcome; 8 Tennis nearby; 9 Swimming nearby; 10 Golf nearby; 11 Skiing nearby; 12 May be booked through travel agent

MARYLAND

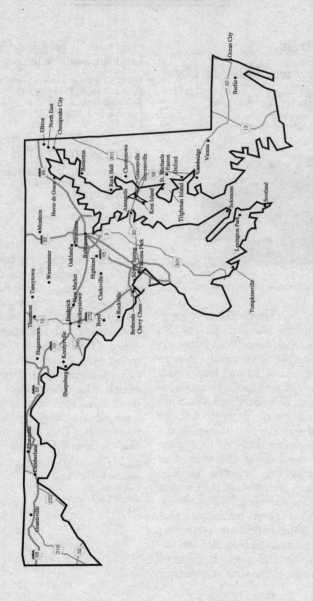

Maryland

ANNAPOLIS

The Barn on Howard's Cove

500 Wilson Rd., Annapolis, MD 21401-1052
(410) 266-6840; Fax (410) 266-7293
E-mail: gdgutsche5@aol.com
Web site: bnbweb.com/howards-cove.html

The Barn on Howard's Cove

The Barn on Howard's Cove welcomes you with warm hospitality to a converted 1850s horse barn overlooking a beautiful cove of the Severn River. You will be located just outside the hubbub of Annapolis and convenient to both Baltimore and Washington, D.C. Begin the day with a choice of full breakfast served in the dining area, on a sunny deck, or in a solarium—all overlooking the river. Our guests enjoy the beautiful gardens, rural setting, antiques, quilts, Oriental rugs, and the charming Noah's ark collection. Two guest bedrooms, each with a private bathroom, await you. One room has a sleeping loft and private deck on the river. Both guest rooms overlook the river. Docking in deep water is provided. Canoes and a kayak are available for guests to use.

Hosts: Graham and Libbie Gutsche
Rooms: 2 (2PB) $125 plus tax
Full Breakfast
Notes: 2 5 7 8 9 10

Chez Amis B & B

85 East St., Annapolis, MD 21401-1729
(410) 263-6631; (888) 224-6455
    Fax (410) 295-7889
E-mail: stay@chezamis.com
Web site: www.chezamis.com

Around 1900, Chez Amis, "House of Friends," was a grocery store. Still evident are the original oak display cabinet, tin ceiling, and pine floors. One-half block from the capitol, 1 block from the harbor, and minutes by foot from the naval academy. "European country" decor with antiques and quilts. Four guest rooms with private baths. King and queen brass beds, TVs, central AC, robes, coffee service, and down comforters in every room. Don is a retired army lawyer, Mickie a former tour guide. They welcome you with true "Southern" Christian hospitality!

Hosts: Don and Mickie Deline
Rooms: 4 (4PB) $135–165
Full Breakfast
Credit Cards: A B
Notes: 2 5

BERLIN

Merry Sherwood Plantation

8909 Worcester Hwy., Berlin, MD 21811-3016
(410) 641-2112; (800) 660-0358
  Fax (410) 641-9528
E-mail: info@merrysherwood.com
Web site: www.merrysherwood.com

Guests at this elegant Victorian (circa 1859) can truly relax amid the beautiful formal and parklike gardens, a setting conducive to weddings and special events, located near Ocean City and Assateague. It's in the heart of a growing golf community; recreational activities are available.

Host: W. Kirk Burbage
Rooms: 8 (6PB;2SB) $125–175
Full Breakfast
Credit Cards: A B
Notes: 2 5 7 8 9 10 12

BETTERTON

Lantern Inn

115 Ericsson Ave., P. O. Box 29
  Betterton, MD 21610-0029
(410) 348-5809; (800) 499-7265
  Fax (410) 348-2323
E-mail: lntrninn@crosslink.net
Web site:
  www.virtualcities.com/ons/md/s/mds5601.htm

Lantern Inn

Circa 1904, four-story Victorian inn with a two-story front porch, located one block from the nettle-free beach on the Chesapeake Bay. Comfortable rooms are furnished with individual themes and handmade quilts. The surrounding area offers wildlife preserves, excellent bicycling, antiquing, historical sites, boating, hunting, fishing, sporting clays, and tennis. Cycling maps are available for trips of 10–90 miles around Kent County. Holiday specials available.

Hosts: Ray and Sandi Sparks
Rooms: 14 (4PB;10SB) $75–95
Continental Breakfast
Credit Cards: A B F
Notes: 2 5 8 9

CUMBERLAND

The Inn at Walnut Bottom

120 Greene St., Cumberland, MD 21502-2934
(301) 777-0003; (800) 286-9718
  Fax (301) 777-8288
E-mail: iwb@iwbinfo.com
Web site: www.iwbinfo.com

If visiting the terminus of the C & O Canal in Cumberland, be sure to try The Inn at Walnut Bottom for its historic charm, proximity to the canal, and friendly staff, who go out of their way to make you feel at home. Complimentary bicycles are available for those wishing to explore the canal. Wake up to a delightful breakfast served with joyful courtesy in the inn's bright dining room, following which you may want to stroll the historic district, ride the scenic train, or venture out to tour Frank Lloyd Wright's

Fallingwater. "Outrageous French Toast," *Baltimore Magazine*. Mobil—3 Stars. Only 2½ hours from Washington, D.C., Baltimore, and Pittsburgh.

Hosts: Grant M. Irvin and Kirsten O. Hansen
Rooms: 12 (8PB;4SB) $89–147
Full Breakfast
Credit Cards: A B C D
Notes: 2 5 7 9 10 11 12

ELKTON

Garden Cottage at Sinking Springs

234 Blair Shore Rd., Elkton, MD 21921-8025
(410) 398-5566; Fax (410) 392-2889
Web site: www.cecilcounty.com/sinkspring/

With an early plantation house, including a 400-year-old sycamore, the cottage nestles at the edge of a meadow flanked by herb gardens and a historic barn with a gift shop. Sitting room with fireplace, bedroom, bath, air-conditioning, electric heat. Freshly ground coffee and herbal teas are offered with breakfast. Longwood Gardens and Winterthur Museum are 50 minutes away. Chesapeake City is nearby (excellent restaurants!). Twenty-five-dollar charge for a third person in the separate room. Enter at Elk Forest Road.

Hosts: Bill and Ann Stubbs
Rooms: 1 (1PB) $97
Full Breakfast
Credit Cards: A B
Notes: 2 5 6 7 8 10 12

FLINTSTONE

Mt. Valley Farm

20500 Root Rd., P. O. Box 87
 Flintstone, MD 21530
(301) 478-2497
E-mail: mvfarm28@hereintown.net
Web site: www.interstate68.com/mvfarmb&b

Beautiful farm in western Maryland near the town of Flintstone. We offer two lovely rooms with a balcony view and a third-floor efficiency apartment with a skylight. Well-stocked pond. Hiking and bike riding. Ice skating, swimming, and tree house for the children. Full country breakfast with homemade bread. Nearby are Rocky Gap State Park and Rocky Gap Golf Course. Historic Cumberland with Western Maryland Railroad, antiques, and craft stores.

Hosts: Ann and Donnie Swope
Rooms: 3 (1PB;2SB) $60–85
Full Breakfast
Credit Cards:
Notes: 2 5 7 9 10

FREDERICK

Hazelwood Heights

12101 Glissans Mill Rd.
 Union Bridge, MD 21791
(301) 831-9220; (866) 444-4048
 Fax (301) 631-0220
Web site: www.hazelwoodheights.com

You will make lasting memories with a taste of simplicity at "Grandma's Treasured Haven." The gentle, relaxing atmosphere is ideal for a leisure retreat, the business traveler, a family vacation, or a couples romantic getaway. A lovely

NOTES: Credit cards accepted: A Master Card; B Visa; C American Express; D Discover; E Diners Club; F Other; 2 Personal checks accepted; 3 Lunch available; 4 Dinner available; 5 Open all year;

three-bedroom single dwelling has privacy, comfort, and country charm. It's the perfect place to begin and end the day. Fully equipped kitchen. AC, cable, TV/VCR, washer and dryer. Complimentary continental breakfast, no smoking inside. We are centrally located with easy access to Washington, D.C., Baltimore's Inner Harbor, the Civil War battlefields at Antietam, Gettysburg, Harpers Ferry, and the Monocacy. Historic Frederick, the C & O Canal, and New Market, Maryland's antique capital, are also nearby.

Hosts: Marion and Glenna Hazelwood
Rooms: 3 (3SB) $65–95
Continental Breakfast
Credit Cards: A B C D
Notes: 5 7 8 9 10 11

Middle Plantation Inn

9549 Liberty Rd., Frederick, MD 21701-3246
(301) 898-7128
E-mail: bandb@mpinn.com
Web site: www.mpinn.com

Middle Plantation Inn

From this charming inn built of stone and log, you can drive through horse country to the village of Mt. Pleasant. The inn is located several miles east of Frederick on 26 acres. Each guest room is furnished with antiques and has a private bath, television, and air-conditioning. The keeping room, a

common room, features stained glass and a stone fireplace. Nearby you can find antique shops, museums, and a number of historic attractions. Middle Plantation Inn is located within 40 minutes of such Civil War-era sites as Gettysburg, Antietam Battlefield, and Harpers Ferry.

Hosts: Shirley and Dwight Mullican
Rooms: 4 (4PB) $99–125
Continental Breakfast
Credit Cards: A B C
Notes: 2 5 8 9 10 12

NORTH EAST

Sandy Cove Ministries Hotel and Conf. Center

60 Sandy Cove Rd., North East, MD 21901-5436
(410) 287-5433; (800) 234-COVE
    Fax (410) 287-3196
E-mail: info@sandycove.org
Web site: www.sandycove.org

Enjoy the cozy warmth of our beautiful rooms and suites on the headwaters of the Chesapeake Bay. Savor a full breakfast in our main dining room overlooking the bay. Get away—take time after a conference or come for a midweek break and escape to peace and comfort.

Rooms: 153 (153PB) $75–110 plus tax
Full Breakfast
Credit Cards: A B D
Notes: 2 4 5 7 8 9 10

ST. MICHAELS

Wades Point Inn on the Bay

P. O. Box 7, Wades Point Rd.
    St. Michaels, MD 21663-0007

---

6 Pets welcome; 7 Children welcome; 8 Tennis nearby; 9 Swimming nearby; 10 Golf nearby; 11 Skiing nearby; 12 May be booked through travel agent

(410) 745-2500; (888) 923-3466
Fax (410) 745-3443
E-mail: wadesinn@wadespoint.com
Web site: www.wadespoint.com

On the eastern shore of Chesapeake Bay, this historic country inn is ideal for those seeking country serenity and bay splendor. The main house, circa 1819, was built by a noted shipwright. From 1890 to present time, the inn has provided a peaceful setting for relaxation and recreation such as fishing and crabbing and a 1-mile nature trail on 120 acres.

Hosts: The Feiler Family
Rooms: 24 (17PB;7SB) $115–230
Continental Breakfast
Credit Cards: A B
Notes: 2 7 8 9 10

TILGHMAN ISLAND

Sinclair House

5718 Black Walnut Point Rd.
   Tilghman Island, MD 21671
(410) 886-2147; (888) 859-2147
   Fax (410) 886-2171
E-mail: miraflores2@msn.com
Web site: www.tilghmanisland.com/sinclair

The Sinclair House invites you to enjoy bed and breakfast at its best. Relax in the quiet and picturesque surroundings of Tilghman Island, on Maryland's Eastern Shore at the Island's original bed and breakfast. Centrally located on the Chesapeake Bay, this quaint watermen's village is reminiscent of a bygone era and lifestyle. Each guest room has its own special country decor and private bath. Enjoy a full country breakfast with homemade goodies, catch the breeze from the front porch. Play tennis, ride bikes, fish, crab, or walk around the island. Then enjoy fresh seafood at our local restaurants.

Hosts: Monica and Jake Jacobsen
Rooms: 4 (4PB) $109–119
Full Breakfast
Credit Cards: A B C D
Notes: 2 5 8 9 10

NOTES: Credit cards accepted: A Master Card; B Visa; C American Express; D Discover; E Diners Club; F Other; 2 Personal checks accepted; 3 Lunch available; 4 Dinner available; 5 Open all year;

MASSACHUSETTS

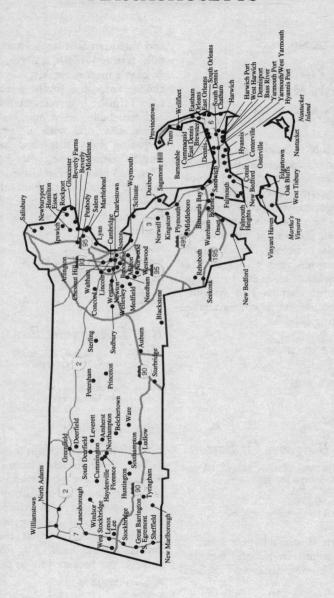

Massachusetts

BLACKSTONE

Morin's Victorian Hideaway B & B

48 Mendon St., Blackstone, MA 01504
(508) 883-7045

A unique B & B, nestled on 3½ acres, overlooking the scenic Blackstone River. Hosts Chip and Lynn Morin provide a warm and cozy atmosphere for their guests, with a fully stocked kitchen, where you can help yourself to snacks or libations at any time. All the comforts of home... In season, the Morins provide yard games such as horseshoes and croquet. In-ground pool accommodations also available. Discounted long-term rates available. Nonsmoking B & B.

Hosts: Chip and Lynn Morin
Rooms: 4 (1PB;3SB) $75–95
Continental Breakfast
Credit Cards:
Notes: 2 5 7 8 9 10

BOSTON

A B & B Agency Of Boston

47 Commercial Wharf, Boston, MA 02110-3804
(617) 720-3540; (800) 248-9262
    Fax (617) 523-5761
E-mail: bosbnb@aol.com
Web site: www.boston-bnbagency.com

Downtown Boston's largest selection of guest rooms in historic bed and breakfast homes, including Federal and Victorian townhouses and beautifully restored 1840s waterfront lofts. Available nightly, weekly, monthly. Or choose from the lovely selection of fully furnished, private studios, one- and two-bedroom condos, corporate suites, and lofts with all amenities, including fully furnished kitchens, private baths (some with Jacuzzis), TVs, and phones. Exclusive locations include waterfront, Faneuil Hall/ Quincy Market, North End, Back Bay, Beacon Hill, Copley Square, and Cambridge.

Host: Ferne Mintz
Rooms: 150 (140PB;10SB) $90–180
Continental Breakfast
Credit Cards: A B C
Notes: 5 12

B & B Associates Bay Colony

P. O. Box 57166, Boston, MA 02457
(781) 647-4949; (888) 429-7596
    Fax (781) 647-7437
E-mail: info@bnbboston.com
Web site: www.bnbboston.com

Appleton Studios #1

In a 19th-century South End townhouse, three blocks from Copley Square, enjoy the privacy and convenience of this small, pleasantly decorated studio apartment with Murphy bed, futon couch, and cooking nook. On one of Boston's prettiest residential streets. Private bath, TV, telephone, and AC. No breakfast foods provided.

Rooms: 1 (1PB) $99–135.

NOTES: Credit cards accepted: A Master Card; B Visa; C American Express; D Discover; E Diners Club; F Other; 2 Personal checks accepted; 3 Lunch available; 4 Dinner available; 5 Open all year;

B & B Associates Bay Colony

P. O. Box 57166, Boston, MA 02457
(781) 647-4949; (888) 429-7596
    Fax (781) 647-7437
E-mail: info@bnbboston.com
Web site: www.bnbboston.com

Appleton Studios #2

This newly redone studio apartment is a spacious front unit with a queen bed and a double futon couch, a well-equipped kitchenette, bay window, decorative fireplace, and Victorian details. Located on the second floor of the same Appleton Street townhouse where the host resides. Private bath, cable TV, phone, AC, smoke-free. No breakfast food provided.

Rooms: 1 (1PB) $125–165

B & B Associates Bay Colony

P. O. Box 57166, Boston, MA 02457
(781) 647-4949; (888) 429-7596
    Fax (781) 647-7437
E-mail: info@bnbboston.com
Web site: www.bnbboston.com

The Back Bay Lookout

A large, unhosted 4th-floor studio apartment overlooking Beacon Street. Recent renovation includes hardwood floors, new furnishings, and kitchen with dishwasher and microwave. Fresh and welcoming atmosphere. This unit offers sleeping for up to four guests on a queen Murphy bed plus a double sleep sofa. Private bath, TV/VCR, phone, AC, smoke-free, fireplace, no breakfast foods provided.

Rooms: 1 (1PB) $140–180

B & B Associates Bay Colony

P. O. Box 57166, Boston, MA 02457
(781) 647-4949; (888) 429-7596
    Fax (781) 647-7437
E-mail: info@bnbboston.com
Web site: www.bnbboston.com

Back Bay Studio

A garden-level suite for those who want the very finest. This grand Victorian townhouse in Boston's desirable Back Bay has been impeccably restored, and a separate entry suite was created to provide deluxe, private accommodations. Features include: a new kitchenette and bath, designer built-ins, TV, telephone, and French doors to a brick patio. Private bath, fireplace, and AC. Smoke-free. No breakfast foods provided. Off-street parking $15.

Rooms: 1 (1PB) $125–150

B & B Associates Bay Colony

P. O. Box 57166, Boston, MA 02457
(781) 647-4949; (888) 429-7596
    Fax (781) 647-7437
E-mail: info@bnbboston.com
Web site: www.bnbboston.com

Beacon Hill Studios

This sweet little studio is a cozy first-floor apartment with a comfortable queen bed, traditional furnishings, and a small kitchen nook. Private bath, TV/VCR, AC, smoke-free, private phone line, fireplace. No breakfast provided. (Coffee shop at corner.)

Rooms: 1 (1PB) $100–150

---

6 Pets welcome; 7 Children welcome; 8 Tennis nearby; 9 Swimming nearby; 10 Golf nearby; 11 Skiing nearby; 12 May be booked through travel agent

B & B Associates Bay Colony

P. O. Box 57166, Boston, MA 02457
(781) 647-4949; (888) 429-7596
    Fax (781) 647-7437
E-mail: info@bnbboston.com
Web site: www.bnbboston.com

Berkeley B & B

Close to Copley Square, on a quiet
street, this professional couple has a
large, sunny third-floor guest room
with double bed and private bath in
their restored Victorian townhouse.
Since breakfast is not provided, the
guest room has a small refrigerator
and a setup for coffee/tea. Private
bath, TV, A/C, smoking permitted.

Rooms: 1 (1PB) $75–85

B & B Associates Bay Colony

P. O. Box 57166, Boston, MA 02457
(781) 647-4949; (888) 429-7596
    Fax (781) 647-7437
E-mail: info@bnbboston.com
Web site: www.bnbboston.com

Braddock Suites

This host couple offers one apartment
unit on the ground level of their
Victorian townhouse in the South
End area near Copley Square.
Pleasant decor with a double bed, plus
a single sleep sofa in the parlor.
Immaculate, quiet, and convenient for
walking around Boston. One studio
apartment and a one-bedroom apartment are both available at discounted
weekly and monthly rates. Private
bath, private phone line, TV/VCR,
AC, smoke-free, full kitchen with
breakfast foods provided.

Rooms: 1 (1PB) $130–165

B & B Associates Bay Colony

P. O. Box 57166, Boston, MA 02457
(781) 647-4949; (888) 429-7596
    Fax (781) 647-7437
E-mail: info@bnbboston.com
Web site: www.bnbboston.com

Courtyard Apartment

This totally delightful one-bedroom
apartment offers romance, charm, and
style in a historic Beacon Hill townhouse. Enter through your own private courtyard garden. Queen bed, full
kitchen, living room with new queen
sleep sofa, beamed ceiling, pine floors,
and huge fireplace. Private bath,
TV/VCR, private phone line, smoke-
free, fireplace, no breakfast provided.

Rooms: 1 (1PB) $150–200

B & B Associates Bay Colony

P. O. Box 57166, Boston, MA 02457
(781) 647-4949; (888) 429-7596
    Fax (781) 647-7437
E-mail: info@bnbboston.com
Web site: www.bnbboston.com

Emma's Garden

The perfect Beacon Hill oasis. This
darling one-bedroom garden-level
apartment has just been completed.
The unit offers a lovely guest room
with double bed and gorgeous linens
plus a decorative fireplace. Guests
have their own large living room with
full kitchenette, a new bath, and private brick patio! Private bath, TV,
phone, smoke-free, self-serve continental breakfast.

Rooms: 1 (1PB) $145–185

NOTES: Credit cards accepted: A Master Card; B Visa; C American Express; D Discover; E Diners
Club; F Other; 2 Personal checks accepted; 3 Lunch available; 4 Dinner available; 5 Open all year;

B & B Associates Bay Colony

P. O. Box 57166, Boston, MA 02457
(781) 647-4949; (888) 429-7596
   Fax (781) 647-7437
E-mail: info@bnbboston.com
Web site: www.bnbboston.com

First Landing

On the waterfront at Boston Harbor, this romantic retreat has the best views in Boston! Your private-entry, penthouse-corner guest room overlooks the city, the harbor, and the charming North End. The room is sunny and cheerful. It features a king bed, an antique desk, and a small refrigerator. You will be delighted to view the famous Customs House Clock Tower outside your wraparound windows! Private entry, private bath, cable TV, air-conditioning, smoke-free. Continental breakfast foods are provided.

Rooms: 1 (1PB) $160–$200
Continental Breakfast

B & B Associates Bay Colony

P. O. Box 57166, Boston, MA 02457
(781) 647-4949; (888) 429-7596
   Fax (781) 647-7437
E-mail: info@bnbboston.com
Web site: www.bnbboston.com

Monument House Apartment

Located in Charlestown, in a quiet neighborhood at the end of the famous Freedom Trail, it is a quick trip (5–10 minutes by bus or 30 minutes on foot) into the center of Boston. This delightful, ground-level apartment offers privacy and space in an 1870s Victorian townhouse near the base of the famed Bunker Hill Monument. This fully furnished apartment offers private entry, an antique double bed, a Pullman kitchen, and a cozy living room with sleep sofa and TV. Private bath, private phone line, smoke-free, continental breakfast delivered daily, cat (not in apartment). Weekly and monthly rates offered.

Rooms: 1 (1PB) $100–135

B & B Associates Bay Colony

P. O. Box 57166, Boston, MA 02457
(781) 647-4949; (888) 429-7596
   Fax (781) 647-7437
E-mail: info@bnbboston.com
Web site: www.bnbboston.com

On the Park

This B & B host couple offers a wealth of knowledge about Boston along with their kind attention to guest needs. They have two pleasant 4th-floor guest rooms (two twins and king bed available), which share a bath in the hall. Located near Copley Square, their brownstone townhouse is convenient to Boston's tourist attractions and convention locations. Shared bath, TV in guest parlor, AC, smoke-free, served continental breakfast, 2 Scottie dogs.

Rooms: 2 (1SB) $90–100

---

6 Pets welcome; 7 Children welcome; 8 Tennis nearby; 9 Swimming nearby; 10 Golf nearby; 11 Skiing nearby; 12 May be booked through travel agent

B & B Associates Bay Colony

P. O. Box 57166, Boston, MA 02457
(781) 647-4949; (888) 429-7596
    Fax (781) 647-7437
E-mail: info@bnbboston.com
Web site: www.bnbboston.com

The Victorian

This historic 1869 brick townhouse is
near the Hynes Convention Center
and Copley Square. Two pretty second-
floor guest rooms, each with a queen
bed, decorative fireplace, delightful
antiques, and a sitting area where
breakfast will be served. Shared bath in
hall. TV and AC. Smoke-free. Off-
street parking $12.

Rooms: 2 (2PB) $95–120

1810 House
Bed and Breakfast

147 Old Oaken Bucket Rd.
    Norwell, MA 02061-1320
(781) 659-1810; (888) 833-1810
    Fax (781) 659-1810
E-mail: tuttle1810@earthlink.net
Web site: www.1810house.com

1810 House

A comfortable bed and breakfast lovingly restored and enlarged. The
antique half-Cape features original
beamed ceilings, wide-pine floors, and
stenciled walls. Three bright, cheery
rooms share two full baths. Breakfast
is served next to the fireplace in the
country kitchen or, weather permitting, on the screened porch. The large,
fireplaced family room with piano,
TV, and VCR welcomes you to relax
after a busy day. Oceanfront dining,
interesting antique shops, and major
highways are just minutes away.

Hosts: Susanne and Harold Tuttle
Rooms: 3 (2PB;1SB) $95
Full Breakfast
Notes: 2 5 8 9 10

Greater Boston Hospitality

P. O. Box 1142, Brookline, MA 02146-0009
(617) 277-5430
E-mail: kelly@bostonbedandbreakfast.com
Web site: www.bostonbedandbreakfast.com

Hundreds of B & B rooms in inns and
private homes throughout the greater
Boston area. All include breakfast.
Some include parking, and others are
on our excellent public transport system. Visit Boston like a native rather
than a tourist.

Rooms: 200 (150PB;50SB) $75–200
Continental Breakfast
Credit Cards: A B
Notes: 2 5 7 8 9 12

Joan's B & B

210 R Lynn St., Peabody, MA 01960
(978) 532-0191; Fax (978) 536-2726
E-mail: joansbandb@rcn.com

Joan's Bed and Breakfast is in a prime
New England location, only 10 minutes
from historic Salem, 25 minutes from

NOTES: Credit cards accepted: A Master Card; B Visa; C American Express; D Discover; E Diners
Club; F Other; 2 Personal checks accepted; 3 Lunch available; 4 Dinner available; 5 Open all year;

Boston, and 1 hour from the many shopping outlets. Numerous great restaurants, theaters, and shopping malls are in the area. The 16-by-32-foot, in-ground pool is available for use by the guests. Make my home your home! Children 5 years and older are welcome.

Host: Joan Hetherington
Rooms: 4 (0PB;2SB) $60–80
Full Breakfast
Credit Cards: F
Notes: 2 5 7 9

BROOKLINE

Beacon Plaza

1459 Beacon St., Brookline, MA 02446-4734
(617) 232-6550; Fax (617) 738-5140
E-mail: beaconplaza@aol.com
Web site: www.beaconplaza.net

A circa 1900 brownstone located minutes from downtown Boston. Easily accessible from Logan Airport by public transportation. Close to Boston's historical and cultural sites. Overnight parking available at additional cost. Family owned and operated for over 40 years.

Hosts: The Pappas Family
Rooms: 36 (24PB;12SB) $65–85 + tax
No Breakfast Served
Credit Cards: A B D
Notes: 5 7

CAPE COD

Augustus Snow House

528 Main St., Harwich Port, MA 02646-1897
(508) 430-0528; (800) 320-0528
    Fax (508) 432-6638
E-mail: info@augustussnow.com
Web site: www.augustussnow.com

Augustus Snow House

Chosen as "One of the Most Romantic Inns on Cape Cod." For the ultimate splurge. . . "The Augustus Snow House has few rivals in all of New England." This romantic 1901 Victorian inn offers luxurious accommodations: exquisitely decorated bedrooms, queen or king beds, fireplaces, TVs, air-conditioning, telephones, elegant private baths (some with Jacuzzis). A wonderful gourmet breakfast is served each day. The private beach is just a 3-minute stroll away. Walk to restaurants and shops. Every guest is promised a memorable and pampered visit.

Hosts: Joyce and Steve Roth
Rooms: 7 (7PB) $125–250
Full Breakfast
Credit Cards: A B C D
Notes: 2 5 8 9 10 12

CONCORD

Hawthorne Inn

462 Lexington Rd., Concord, MA 01742
(978) 369-5610; Fax (978) 287-4949
E-mail: inn@concordmass.com
Web site: www.concordmass.com

Fast by the ancient way, that the minutemen trod to first face the British

---

6 Pets welcome; 7 Children welcome; 8 Tennis nearby; 9 Swimming nearby; 10 Golf nearby; 11 Skiing nearby; 12 May be booked through travel agent

Regulars, rests this most colorful inn where history and literature gracefully entwine. On earth once claimed by Emerson, Hawthorne, and the Alcotts, the Hawthorne Inn beckons the traveler to refresh the spirit in a winsome atmosphere abounding with antique furnishings and delight the eye exploring rooms festooned with handmade quilts, original artworks, and archaic artifacts.

Host: G. Burch
Rooms: 7 (7PB) $165–305
Continental Breakfast
Credit Cards: A B C D
Notes: 2 5 7 8 9 11 12

Hawthorne Inn

DEERFIELD SOUTH

Deerfield's Yellow Gabled House

111 N. Main St., Deerfield-South, MA 01373
(413) 665-4922

Located on the site of the historic battle Bloody Brook Massacre of 1675, and 1½ miles from the crossroads of I-91, Route 116, and Routes 5 and 10, is a picturesque house with gardens

and three decorated bedchambers. Close to five-college area. Guests have access to a sitting room and library for reading and meeting fellow travelers. Enjoy early morning coffee in the summer room. Located 1 mile from Yankee Candle and Historic Deerfield. Featured on the cover page of the *Springfield Republican*.

Deerfield's Yellow Gabled House

Host: Edna Julia Stanelek
Rooms: 3 (1PB;2SB) $75–140
Full Breakfast
Notes: 2 5 8 9 10 11 12

DENNISPORT

The Rose Petal B & B

152 Sea St., Dennisport, MA 02639
(508) 398-8470
E-mail: info@rosepetalofdennis.com
Web site: www.rosepetalofdennis.com

Surrounded by a white picket fence and picturesque gardens, the Rose Petal is situated in the heart of Cape Cod, a short walk past century-old homes to the sandy beaches of Nantucket Sound. Home-baked pastries highlight a superb full breakfast.

NOTES: Credit cards accepted: A Master Card; B Visa; C American Express; D Discover; E Diners Club; F Other; 2 Personal checks accepted; 3 Lunch available; 4 Dinner available; 5 Open all year;

Three rooms all have spacious, bright, private baths, queen beds, and A/C. Heirlooms and lace appoint a beautiful antique home built in 1872 for Almond Wixon, a seafaring Mayflower descendant. AAA 3-diamond Award.

Hosts: Dan and Gayle Kelly
Rooms: 3 (3PB) $79–119
Full Breakfast
Credit Cards: A B C
Notes: 4 7 8 9 10 12

DUXBURY

The Winsor House Inn

390 Washington St., Duxbury, MA 02332
(781) 934-0991; Fax (781) 934-5955
E-mail: winsorhouse@dreamcom.net

Built in 1803 by sea captain Nathaniel Winsor, this charming, antique-filled country inn is located 35 miles south of Boston in the quaint seaside village of Duxbury. The four cozy, sunlit bedrooms are complete with canopy beds. Enjoy casual dining in the English-style pub, a gourmet dinner in the flower-filled carriage house, or a romantic evening in the candlelit dining room. Rates are subject to change.

Hosts: David and Patricia O'Connell
Rooms: 4 (4PB) $140–210
Full Breakfast
Credit Cards: A B C D
Notes: 2 4 5 7 8 9 10 12

EAST ORLEANS

Nauset House Inn

P. O. Box 774; 143 Beach Rd.
East Orleans, MA 02643
(508) 255-2195; (800) 771-5508
Fax (508) 240-6276
E-mail: info@nausethouseinn.com
Web site: www.nausethouseinn.com

A real, old-fashioned country inn farmhouse, circa 1810, is located on 3 acres with an apple orchard, 1/2 mile from Nauset Beach. A quiet, romantic getaway. Large commons room with fireplace, brick-floored breakfast room, and a beautiful 1907 glass conservatory filled with wicker furniture and blooming plants. Cozily furnished with antiques, eclectic—a true fantasy.

Hosts: Diane Johnson and Cindy and John Vessella
Rooms: 14 (8PB;6SB) $75–160
Full Breakfast
Credit Cards: A B D
Notes: 2 7 8 9 10

Ship's Knees Inn

186 Beach Rd., P. O. Box 756
East Orleans, MA 02643-0756
(508) 255-1312; Fax (508) 240-1351
E-mail: skinauset@aol.com
Web site: www.capecodtravel.com/shipskneesinn

This 170-year-old restored sea captain's home is a 3-minute walk to beautiful sand-duned Nauset Beach. Inside the warm, lantern-lit doorways are nineteen rooms individually appointed with special, colonial color schemes and authentic antiques. Some rooms feature authentic ship's knees, hand-painted trunks, old clipper ship models, braided rugs, and four-poster beds. Tennis and swimming are available on the premises. Three miles away, overlooking Orleans Cove, the Cove House offers three rooms, a one-bedroom efficiency, and two cottages. Children welcome at the Cove House and cottages.

Host: Donna Anderson
Rooms: 19 (8PB;11SB) $45–140
Continental Breakfast
Credit Cards: A B
Notes: 2 5 8 9 10 12

FALMOUTH

Captain Tom Lawrence House Inn

75 Locust St., Falmouth, MA 02540
(508) 548-9178; (800) 266-8139
E-mail: capttomhouse@aol.com
Web site: www.captaintomlawrence.com

Captain Tom Lawrence House Inn

Elegant and historic, beautifully restored 1861 whaling captain's residence. Five-minute walk to the main street and the village green of the historic village of Falmouth. Close to sea beaches, numerous golf courses, myriad restaurants, and ferries to Martha's Vineyard and Nantucket. Central air-

conditioning. Cable TV and refrigerator in each room. Bicycles available. Family apartment: Fully furnished apartment w/AC—sleeps 3 to 4. Cable TV. Ideal for family of 4.

Hosts: Anne Grebert and Jim Cotter
Rooms: 7 (7PB) $90–220
Full Breakfast
Credit Cards: A B C
Notes: 2 5 8 9 10

Village Green Inn

40 Main St., Falmouth, MA 02540
(508) 548-5621; (800) 237-1119
    Fax (508) 547-5051
E-mail: vgi40@aol.com
Web site: www.villagegreeninn.com

Village Green Inn

This gracious, 1804, colonial-Victorian is ideally located on Falmouth's historic village green. Walk to fine shops and restaurants, or bike to beaches and picturesque Woods Hole along the Shining Sea Bike Path. Enjoy 19th-century charm and warm hospitality amidst elegant surroundings. Four lovely guest rooms and one romantic suite all have private baths and unique fireplaces (two are working). A full gourmet breakfast features delicious house specialties. Many thoughtful amenities are included. Air-conditioned, CCTV. Phones, robes, hairdryers, and guest refrigerator with complimentary beverages.

Hosts: Diane and Don Crosby
Rooms: 5 (5PB) $90–225
Full Breakfast
Credit Cards: A B C
Notes: 5 8 9 10 12

FALMOUTH CAPE COD

Grafton Inn

261 Grand Ave., S.
   Falmouth Cape Cod, MA 02540
(508) 540-8688; (800) 642-4069
   Fax (508) 540-1861
Web site: www.graftoninn.com

Grafton Inn

This oceanfront Victorian is 30 steps to a sandy beach and offers breathtaking views of Martha's Vineyard. Rooms feature comfortable queen and king beds and period antiques. A sumptuous, full breakfast is served at individual tables overlooking Nantucket Sound. Air-conditioning, heat, and CCTV. Thoughtful amenities including fresh flowers, homemade chocolates, evening wine and cheese, and beach chairs and

towels. Eight-minute walk to island ferry. Dining 1 block away. AAA- and Mobil-rated 3 stars.

Rooms: 10 (10PB) $169–265
Full Breakfast
Credit Cards: A B C
Notes: 8 9 10

HYANNIS

Cape Cod Ocean Manor

543 Ocean St., Hyannis, MA 02601
(508) 771-2186
E-mail: rentals@capecodoceanmanor.com
Web site: www.capecodoceanmanor.com

The inn is located across from Veterans Beach. Rooms overlook a saltwater marsh and have views of Nantucket Sound. Rooms are very comfortably furnished, and all have king-size beds. Walking distance to ferries for the islands, shopping, and restaurants. Relax and enjoy the wildlife on our oversized deck, which overlooks a saltwater marsh.

Host: Patricia Gibney
Rooms: 6 (6PB) $85–130
Continental Breakfast
Credit Cards: A B C D
Notes: 2 5 8 9 10 12

LENOX

Seven Hills Country Inn and Restaurant

40 Plunkett St., Lenox, MA 01240-2795
(413) 637-0060; (800) 869-6518
   Fax (413) 637-3651
E-mail: 7hills@berkshire.net
Web site: www.sevenhillsinn.com

---

6 Pets welcome; 7 Children welcome; 8 Tennis nearby; 9 Swimming nearby; 10 Golf nearby; 11 Skiing nearby; 12 May be booked through travel agent

Seven Hills is located on 27 acres with beautiful terraced lawns, stunning gardens. Showcase antiques throughout. There are 15 Manor House, 37 Terrace House, and 6 Carriage House guest rooms (4 are ADA handicapped accessible). All rooms w/private bathroom, A/C, phone, cable TV, hairdryer, iron/board, etc. Some rooms w/fireplace/jet tub/kitchenette. The Seven Hills Inn has long been noted as a site for banquets, weddings, business retreats, and conferences. Come enjoy.

Hosts: Patricia and Jim Eder
Rooms: 58 (58PB) $85–350
Continental Breakfast
Credit Cards: A B C D E
Notes: 2 4 5 6 7 8 9 10 11 12

MARBLEHEAD

Harborside House

23 Gregory St., Marblehead, MA 01945-3241
(781) 631-1032
E-mail: stay@harborsidehouse.com
Web site: www.harborsidehouse.com

This handsome 1850 home in the historic district overlooks Marblehead Harbor. Enjoy water views from the fireplaced parlor, the period dining room, the third-story deck, and from the summer breakfast porch, where guests may sample home-baked breads and muffins. Walk to historic sights, excellent restaurants, unique shops, and public transportation. Your hostess is a retired bridal dressmaker and a nationally ranked Master swimmer. Thirty minutes north of Boston and Logan Airport. Enjoy quiet comfort and convenience. Children over 8 welcome.

Harborside House

Host: Susan Livingston
Rooms: 2 (2SB) $85–95
Continental Breakfast
Notes: 2 5 9

NANTUCKET

Forty West Chester St. Nantucket

40 W. Chester St., Nantucket, MA 02554
(508) 228-2740; (800) FORTYWC
   Fax (508) 228-2740

Forty West Chester St. Nantucket

Nantucket has something for almost everybody. Our B & B and cottage are located in the heart of historic Nantucket, yet in walking distance to beaches, town, restaurants, museums, shops as well as deserted moors.

Rooms have AC, TV/VCR, table-top refrigerator. A continental breakfast is served on our covered porch each A.M. Rooms have a two-night minimum @ $125.00 per night (2 persons); cottage is rented by week @ $875.00 per week (1 or 2 only).

Host: Florence Fraser
Rooms: 4 (1PB;3SB) $120–130
Continental Breakfast
Notes: 2 7 8 9 10 12

The Woodbox Inn

9 Fair St., Nantucket, MA 02554
(508) 228-0587; Fax (508) 228-7527
E-mail: woodbox@nantucket.net
Web site: www.woodboxinn.com

The Woodbox is Nantucket's oldest Inn, built in 1709. Located 1½ blocks from the center of Nantucket, the inn serves "the best breakfast on the Island" and offers gourmet dinners by candlelight. Queen-size beds, private baths. One- and two-bedroom suites have working fireplaces.

Host: Dexter Tutein
Rooms: 9 (9PB) $185–215
Continental Breakfast
Notes: 2 4 7 8 9 10

NORTHAMPTON

The Autumn Inn

59 Elm St., Northampton, MA 01060
(413) 584-7660; Fax (413) 586-4808
E-mail: info@hhgmail.com
Web site: www.hampshirehospitality.com

The Autumn Inn is conveniently located in downtown Northampton and in close proximity to the five-college area. The Autumn Inn is colonial in style and furnishing, a fine place for rest, relaxation, and renewal. Amenities include: 28 beautifully furnished guest rooms, 2 suites, outdoor pool, barbeque area, and complimentary continental breakfast.

Host: Rick Heroux, General Mgr.
Rooms: 30 (30PB) $89–150
Continental Breakfast
Credit Cards: A B C D E
Notes: 5 7 9

PLYMOUTH

Foxglove Cottage

101 Sandwich Rd., Plymouth, MA 02360-2503
(508) 747-6576; (800) 479-4746
    Fax (508) 747-7622
E-mail: tranquility@foxglove-cottage.com
Web site: www.foxglove-cottage.com

Elegant and romantic lodging for the discerning traveler. Lovingly restored 1820 Cape in a pastoral setting, away from the bustle of tourist traffic, yet close to Plantation and beaches. All our antique-furnished rooms have en suite private baths, AC/heat, a sitting area, and working fireplaces. Enjoy a full breakfast on our deck off the large common room. Foxglove Cottage is the perfect "hub" for day trips to Boston, the islands, Newport, and Cape Cod. Listed in Fodor's *Best Bed and Breakfasts in America*.

Hosts: Mr. and Mrs. Charles K. Cowan
Rooms: 3 (3PB) $90–115
Full Breakfast
Notes: 2 5 8 9 10

Pets welcome; 7 Children welcome; 8 Tennis nearby; 9 Swimming nearby; 10 Golf nearby; 11 Skiing nearby; 12 May be booked through travel agent

REHOBOTH

Five Bridge Inn

154 Pine St., Rehoboth, MA 02769
(508) 252-3190; Fax (508) 252-3190
E-mail: info@fivebridgeinn.com
Web site: www.fivebridgeinn.com

Five Bridge Inn is located near Providence and less than an hour's drive of Newport, RI; Boston; Plymouth; New London, CT; and more. We are on 90 acres of forest and fields. Rooms are colonial appointed. Some have fireplaces, canopy beds, and Jacuzzis. Relax and enjoy home-cooked New England breakfasts.

Hosts: Harold and Ann Messenger
Rooms: 5 (3PB;2SB) $88–135
Full Breakfast
Credit Cards: A B D
Notes: 2 5 6 7 8 9 10 11 12

Gilbert's Tree Farm B & B

30 Spring St., Rehoboth, MA 02769
(508) 252-6416
E-mail: glbrtsbb@aol.com
Web site: http://members.aol.com/glbrtsbb

Gilbert's Tree Farm

Our 17-acre tree farm provides a quiet place to enjoy the beauty of nature and God's bountiful gifts. The body is nour-

ished with hearty breakfasts and refreshed with hikes through the wood and exercise in the in-ground swimming pool. Two rooms have fireplaces. Also available for retreats and theme weekends. House was built in mid 1830s. Within an hour's drive of Boston, Newport, Mystic, and Plymouth. 15 minutes from Providence, RI.

Host: Jeanne Gilbert
Rooms: 5 (2PB;3SB) $70–85
Full Breakfast
Notes: 2 5 7 8 9 10 12

ROCKPORT

Tuck Inn B & B

17 High St., Rockport, MA 01966-1644
(978) 546-7260; (800) 789-7260
E-mail: tuckinn@shore.net
Web site: www.thetuckinn.com

This welcoming, 1790 colonial home is located on a quiet secondary street just 1 block from the village center. The nearby train station offers convenient access to Boston as well. Featuring antiques, colorful quilts, and local artwork throughout, the inn offers all private baths, CCTVs, air conditioning, and an in-ground pool. Nonsmoking, pet-free environment. Breakfast each morning is a hearty home-baked buffet. The Woods graciously invite you to "come and stay with us!"

Hosts: Liz and Scott Wood
Rooms: 11 (11PB) $69–109
Continental Breakfast
Credit Cards: A B
Notes: 2 5 7 8 9 10

NOTES: Credit cards accepted: A Master Card; B Visa; C American Express; D Discover; E Diners Club; F Other; 2 Personal checks accepted; 3 Lunch available; 4 Dinner available; 5 Open all year;

SALEM

Amelia Payson House

16 Winter St., Salem, MA 01970
(978) 744-8304
E-mail: stay@ameliapaysonhouse.com
Web site: www.ameliapaysonhouse.com

Welcome to our home! Built in 1845 for Amelia and Edward Payson, 16 Winter Street is one of Salem's finest examples of Greek Revival architecture. Elegantly restored and beautifully decorated, each room is furnished with period antiques and warmed by a personal touch. Comfort amenities include: private bath, AC, cable TV, radio, and hair dryer. Guests will not only enjoy the grace and charm that is tradition at a B & B host home but will also appreciate our convenient historic district location just steps from all of Salem's limitless activities.

Hosts: Ada and Donald Roberts
Rooms: 4 (4PB) $95–150
Continental Breakfast
Credit Cards: A B C D
Notes: 8 9 10

The Salem Inn

7 Summer St., Salem, MA 01970-3315
(978) 741-0680; (800) 446-2995
    Fax (978) 744-8924
E-mail: salem.inn@verizon.net
Web site: www.saleminnma.com

The Salem Inn, which is comprised of the West House (c. 1834), the Curwen House (c. 1854), and the Peabody House (c. 1874), testifies to the glory that was 19th-century Salem. These impressive and historical buildings are centrally located a short walk from Salem's museums, antique shops, and the waterfront. The inn's individually decorated rooms and suites provide an array of modern amenities. Many feature kitchenettes, canopy beds, fireplaces, and oversized Jacuzzis. Antiques and tasteful furnishings grace all of the buildings.

Rooms: 42 (42PB) $119–230
Continental Breakfast
Credit Cards: A B C D E
Notes: 5 6 7 9 12

WARE

Antique 1880 Bed and Breakfast

14 Pleasant St., Ware, MA 01082
(413) 967-7847
E-mail:
Web site:

Built in 1876, this Colonial-style inn has pumpkin and maple hardwood floors, beamed ceilings, six fireplaces, and antique furnishings. Afternoon tea is served by the fireplace, breakfast in the dining room or on the porch, weather permitting. It is a short, pretty country ride to historic Old Sturbridge Village and Old Deerfield Village. Hiking, fishing nearby. Midway between Boston and the Berkshires.

Host: Margaret Skutnik
Rooms: 5 (2PB;3SB) $40–65
Full Breakfast
Notes: 2 5 8 9 10 11 12

---

6 Pets welcome; 7 Children welcome; 8 Tennis nearby; 9 Swimming nearby; 10 Golf nearby; 11 Skiing nearby; 12 May be booked through travel agent

WAREHAM

Mulberry B & B

257 High St., Wareham, MA 02571-1407
(508) 295-0684; (866) 295-0684
E-mail: mulberry257@aol.com

Mulberrry

Mulberry Bed and Breakfast sits on a
half-acre lot shaded by a majestic,
seven-trunk mulberry tree. This Cape
Cod-style home, built in 1847 by a
blacksmith, offers three cozy guest
rooms with three shared baths and
a hearty, homemade breakfast.
Mulberry is 1 mile from I-195 and
I-495. The historic, picturesque cities
of Boston, Newport, New Bedford, and
Plymouth are within an hour's drive.

Host: Frances Murphy
Rooms: 3 (3SB) $60–75
Full Breakfast
Credit Cards: A B C D
Notes: 2 5 7 8 9 10

WEST STOCKBRIDGE

Card Lake Inn

P. O. Box 38, 29 Main St.
   West Stockbridge, MA 01266-0038
(413) 232-0272
E-mail: cardlake@bcn.net
Web site: www.cardlakeinn.com

A 14-room inn located 2 miles from
Tangleweed, Butternut Ski, and
Norman Rockwell Museum. Rooms
charmingly furnished, restaurant open
in season.

Hosts: Ed and Lisa Robbins
Rooms: 14 (8PB;6SB) $85–165
Continental Breakfast
Credit Cards: A B D
Notes: 2 3 4 5 7 8 9 10 11 12

YARMOUTH PORT

Colonial House Inn
and Restaurant

Rte. 6A (277 Main St.)
   Yarmouth Port, MA 02675
(508) 362-4348; (800) 999-3416
E-mail: info@colonialhousecapecod.com
Web site: www.colonialhousecapecod.com

A romantic old sea captain's mansion, located in the heart of Cape
Cod. All of our 21 rooms are
appointed with antiques. Full or half
canopy beds, private baths, AC, cable
color television, and phones. Your
room rate includes a light breakfast
and dinner entree for two, for the
length of your stay. We also have an
indoor heated pool and Jacuzzi.

Host: Malcolm J. Perna
Rooms: 21 (21PB) $90-130
Continental Breakfast
Credit Cards: A B
Notes: 2 3 4 5 6 7 8 9 10 12

NOTES: Credit cards accepted: A Master Card; B Visa; C American Express; D Discover; E Diners
Club; F Other; 2 Personal checks accepted; 3 Lunch available; 4 Dinner available; 5 Open all year;

MICHIGAN

Michigan

BATTLE CREEK

Greencrest Manor

6174 Halbert Rd. E
  Battle Creek, MI 49017-9449
(616) 962-8633; Fax (616) 962-7254
E-mail: greencrestmanor@aol.com
Web site: www.greencrestmanor.com

To experience Greencrest Manor is to step back in time to a way of life that is rare today. From the moment you enter the iron gates, you will be mesmerized. This French Normandy mansion, situated on the highest elevation of St. Mary's Lake, is constructed of sandstone, slate, and copper. The three levels of formal gardens include fountains, stone walls, iron rails, and cut sandstone urns. The home offers AC. Greencrest Manor was the featured "Inn of the Month" in *Country Inns* magazine, August 1992, and was chosen as one of the magazine's top twelve inns in the nation for that year.

Hosts: Kathy and Tom Van Daff
Rooms: 8 (6PB;2SB) $95–235
Continental Breakfast
Credit Cards: A B C E
Notes: 2 5 7 8 10 11

BAY CITY

Clements Inn

1712 Center Ave., Bay City, MI 48708-6122
(989) 894-4600; (800) 442-4605
  Fax (989) 891-9442
E-mail: clementsinn@chartermi.net
Web site: www.clementsinn.com

Once the home of a wealthy industrialist, the Clements Inn has provided comfortable accommodations and has been a welcome respite to guests for 16 years. Incredible woodwork, original light fixtures, antiques, and fine reproductions grace the interior of this 1886 Queen Anne. Six comfortably decorated guest rooms, including two whirlpool suites, include private baths, telephones, modems, TVs and VCRs. A continental breakfast is served by candlelight in the inn's dining room.

Hosts: Shirley and David Roberts
Rooms: 6 (6PB) $75–190
Continental Breakfast
Credit Cards: A B C D F
Notes: 2 5 8 9 10 12

Keswick Manor (a Luxury City Inn)

1800 Center Ave., Bay City, MI 48708
(989) 893-6598
E-mail: keswickmanor@aol.com
Web site: www.keswickmanor.com

Keswick Manor

Welcome to Keswick Manor (a luxury city inn), extraordinary in every way. Unsurpassed service. Exquisite food. Elegant suites. Convenient to downtown Bay City's riverfront, shopping, and restaurants. A beautiful, historic 1896 English-inspired inn designed with antiques and works of art. A grand staircase leads to three glorious suites. Gorgeous gardens and fountains. Endless amenities and luxuries. Keswick Manor takes elegance to its highest level. Keswick Manor is easy to find but very hard to leave.

Hosts: Thomas and Deborah Pietrzak
Rooms: 3 (3PB) $89–189
Full Breakfast
Credit Cards: A B C
Notes: 5 8 9 10 11

BITELY

Cottage of Content B & B

10511 Lake St. N., Bitely, MI 49309
(231) 745-3634
E-mail: cofcbnb@carrinter.net

Cottage of Content

This 4th-generation family cottage, in the Manistee National Forest, offers an atmosphere of peace and content-ment. Cozy gathering room with fireplace; beautifully decorated luxurious bed/sitting rooms; library loft; covered porches; and views of quiet lake, gardens, and woods invite you to enjoy a romantic getaway. Afternoon tea and evening refreshments on request. Swimming, sunbathing, canoeing, and fishing, paddleboat rides, bird and wildlife watching, hiking, Nordic skiing, biking, snowmobiling, and campfires, friendly collie. Smoke free.

Hosts: Gordon and Connie Taylor
Rooms: 3 (1PB;2SB) $75–100
Full Breakfast
Notes: 2 3 4 9 10 11

DIMONDALE

Bannicks Bed and Breakfast

4608 Michigan Rd., Dimondale, MI 48821-9663
(517) 646-0224

This large, ranch-style home features a stained-glass entry, nautical-style basement, and a Mona Lisa bathroom. Accommodations include a large comfortable bedroom with TV, queen bed, and fresh hot coffee. Almost 3 rural acres offer a quiet escape from the fast pace of a working world. Located on a main highway (M99), Bannicks is 5 miles from Lansing, and Michigan State University is just 8 miles away. Breakfast specialties are frittatas or Polish apple pancakes.

Hosts: Pat and Jim Bannick
Rooms: 1 (1SB) $45
Full Breakfast
Notes: 5 9 10

---

6 Pets welcome; 7 Children welcome; 8 Tennis nearby; 9 Swimming nearby; 10 Golf nearby; 11 Skiing nearby; 12 May be booked through travel agent

FLUSHING

Main Street Manor Bed and Breakfast

516 E. Main St., Flushing, MI 48433
(810) 487-1888; (877) 487-1888
E-mail: mainstreetmanor@att.net
Web site: www.bbonline.com/mi/mainstreet

Main St. Manor is an 1888 Victorian Painted Lady located in Flushing, 4 miles west of Flint off I-75. We feature two comfortable rooms with queen beds, luxury linens, fresh flowers, antiques, lace, and Jacuzzi, along with small-town ambience. We serve evening refreshments as well as a full breakfast. Whether you are visiting the area, are here for business or a romantic retreat, you will be pampered and refreshed by your stay.

Hosts: Tim and Sue Sodeman
Rooms: 2 (2PB) $95–110
Full Breakfast
Credit Cards: A B C D E
Notes: 2 5 8 10

FRANKENMUTH

Bavarian Town B & B

206 Beyerlein St., Frankenmuth, MI 48734-1502
(989) 652-8057
E-mail: btbedb@juno.com
Web site: www.laketolake.com/bavarian

Beautifully decorated Cape Cod dwelling with central air-conditioning in a peaceful, residential district of Michigan's most popular tourist town, just 3 blocks from Main Street. Bilingual hosts are descendants of original German settlers of Frankenmuth

who will serve as guides of the area, including historic St. Lorenz Lutheran Church. TVs in each room. Shared recipes and superb hospitality. Hot tub on deck and sauna in basement.

Bavarian Town

Hosts: Louie and Kathy Weiss
Rooms: 3 (2PB;1SB) $80–100
Full Breakfast
Credit Cards: A B D
Notes: 2 5 7 8 10

GRAND HAVEN

Seascape B & B

20009 Breton, Spring Lake, MI 49456
(616) 842-8409; Fax (616) 842-8409
Web site: www.bbonline.com/mi/seascape

Seascape

Seascape B & B, located on private, sandy Lake Michigan beach, offers scenic, relaxing, lakefront rooms. Enjoy the warm hospitality and "coun-

NOTES: Credit cards accepted: A Master Card; B Visa; C American Express; D Discover; E Diners Club; F Other; 2 Personal checks accepted; 3 Lunch available; 4 Dinner available; 5 Open all year;

try living" ambience of our nautical lakeshore home. A full homemade breakfast is served in the gathering room with fieldstone fireplace or on the large sundeck. Either provides a panoramic view of Grand Haven Harbor. Stroll or cross-country ski on duneland nature trails. Open all year, with a kaleidoscope of scenes reflecting the changing seasons. A separate Victorian cottage sleeps eight.

Host: Susan Meyer
Rooms: 4 (4PB) $125–195
Full Breakfast
Credit Cards: A B
Notes: 2 5 8 9 10 11

HILLSDALE

Munro House

202 Maumee, Jonesville, MI 49250
(517) 849-9292; (800) 320-3792
  Fax (517) 849-7685
E-mail: stay@munrohouse.net
Web site: www.munrohouse.com

This spectacular Greek Revival mansion was once a station on the Underground Railroad (1834). Seven guest rooms all have private bath, queen bed, cable TV, and VCR. Some have gas fireplace or two-person Jacuzzi tub. 100% air-conditioned and smoke free. Country style breakfast (famous on 6 continents) served every day. Resident Scottish terriers. Ideal for group retreats. Specialize in chef night and therapy weekends.

Hosts: Mike and Lori Venturini
Rooms: 7 (7PB) $99–199
Full Breakfast
Credit Cards: A B C D
Notes: 5 7 10 12

HOLLAND

Dutch Colonial Inn

560 Central Ave., Holland, MI 49423-4846
(616) 396-3664; Fax (616) 396-0461
E-mail: dutchcolonialinn@juno.com
Web site: www.dutchcolonialinn.com

Dutch Colonial Inn

Relax and enjoy a gracious, 1928 Dutch Colonial. Your hosts have elegantly decorated their home with family heirloom antiques and furnishings from the 1930s. Guests enjoy the cheery sunporch, honeymoon suites with fireplaces, and rooms with TVs and double whirlpool tubs. Nearby are Dutch attractions, charming downtown shops, Hope College, Michigan's finest beaches, bike paths, and cross-country ski trails, plus the Tulip Festival. Corporate rates are available for business travelers.

Hosts: Bob and Pat Elenbaas
Rooms: 4 (4PB) $100–160
Full Breakfast
Credit Cards: A B C D
Notes: 2 5 8 9 10 11

---

6 Pets welcome; 7 Children welcome; 8 Tennis nearby; 9 Swimming nearby; 10 Golf nearby; 11 Skiing nearby; 12 May be booked through travel agent

HOUGHTON

Charleston House Historic Inn

918 College Ave., Houghton, MI 49931-1821
(906) 482-7790; (800) 482-7404
    Fax (906) 482-8608
E-mail: inquiries@charlestonhouseinn.com
Web site: www.charlestonhouseinn.com

Charleston House Historic Inn

Turn-of-the-century Georgian house with double veranda, ceiling fans, and wicker furniture. The inn features ornate woodwork, leaded- and beveled-glass windows, a library with fireplace, and grand interior staircase. Comfortable period reproduction and antique furnishings with king canopy and twin beds. All private baths, air-conditioning, cable color TV, and telephones. Full breakfast. Walk to university and downtown. Smoking limited to the garden. Children 12 and older welcome. AAA 3-diamond award.

Hosts: John and Helen Sullivan
Rooms: 4 (4PB) $118–168
Full Breakfast
Credit Cards: A B
Notes: 2 5 8 9 10 11 12

HUDSON

Quigley's Log Home B & B

8450 Acker Hwy., Hudson, MI 49247
(517) 448-1057
E-mail: quigleybnb@tc3net.com

Entering the front door of this lovely log home located on 40 acres, you will feel the warm welcome of wood. Freshly baked cinnamon bread hints of the gourmet breakfasts. Choose bedrooms in the loft or family suite on walkout lower level. Air-conditioned rooms are beautifully decorated. Enjoy fabulous sunsets or walks around the wildlife pond. Visit many kinds of recreation. Leave refreshed and planning a return visit. Packages available. No tobacco or alcohol.

Hosts: Jack and Choyce Quigley
Rooms: 4 (2PB;2SB) $65–130
Full Breakfast
Credit Cards:
Notes: 2 3 4 5 9 10 12

IONIA

Union Hill Inn

306 Union St., Ionia, MI 48846-1647
(616) 527-0955
E-mail: uonhilbb@1serv.net
Web site: www.unionhillbb.com

Union Hill Inn

This elegant, 1868 Italianate-style home served as a station for the Underground Railroad. The inn is beautifully furnished with antiques. Enjoy the living area with its fireplace, piano, porcelain village, and dolls. The home is air-conditioned. Flower beds surround the home, which is noted for its expansive veranda and panoramic view overlooking the historic city. With all the beauty at Union Hill Inn, the greatest thing you will experience is God's love and peace that abide here.

Hosts: Tom and Mary Kay Moular
Rooms: 6 (1PB;5SB) $50–125
Full Breakfast
Credit Cards:
Notes: 2 5 7 8 9 10 12

JONESVILLE

Horse and Carriage Bed and Breakfast

7020 Brown Rd., Jonesville, MI 49250
(517) 849-2732; Fax (517) 849-2732
E-mail: horsecarriagebb@yahoo.com
Web site: www.hcbnb.com

Horse and Carriage

Coming from near or far, here's an oasis for the traveler looking for a relaxing, quiet country setting. Enjoy fireside hospitality and starry-night sleeping. After a delicious breakfast served on the sunporch, step back in time with an old-fashioned carriage ride. There are stories of days gone by told behind the rhythmic *clip-clop* of Rosa, our Amish mare. No smoking or alcohol. Lots of nearby antiquing.

Hosts: Keith L. Brown and Family
Rooms: 3 (1PB;2SB) $50–100
Full Breakfast
Credit Cards:
Notes: 2 5 7 9 10

LAKE CITY

Bed and Breakfast in the Pines

1940 Schneider Park Rd., Lake City, MI 49651
(231) 839-4876

Pick your own raspberries and apples from our orchard when in season. Located 13 miles east of Cadillac. Enjoy downhill/cross-country skiing, fishing, swimming, hiking, biking, and boating. No alcohol, smoking, or pets. Handicapped ramp. Two-week advance reservation with $50 deposit required. Check-in time 4:00–8:00 P.M. Check-out time 10:00 A.M. May be booked with AAA of Livonia.

Host: Reggie Ray
Rooms: 2 (1PB;1SB) $100
Full Breakfast
Credit Cards:
Notes: 2 5 8 9 10 11

LELAND

Manitou Manor

P. O. Box 864, Leland, MI 49654-0864
(231) 256-7712; Fax (231) 256-7941
Web site: www.bbhost.com/manitoumanorbb

6 Pets welcome; 7 Children welcome; 8 Tennis nearby; 9 Swimming nearby; 10 Golf nearby; 11 Skiing nearby; 12 May be booked through travel agent

A spacious country estate that makes staying in Leelanau County a peaceful experience. Open year-round, the home features private baths and family-style breakfasts. Unique guest rooms all have inviting themes. A perfect place to celebrate the seasons.

Hosts: Mike and Sandy Lambdin
Rooms: 5 (5PB) $140
Full Breakfast
Credit Cards: A B D
Notes: 2 5 7 8 9 10 11

LUDINGTON

Bed and Breakfast at Ludington

2458 S. Beaune Rd., Ludington, MI 49431
(231) 843-9768
E-mail: bedbkfst@carrinter.net
Web site: www.carrinter.net/bedbkfst

Bed and Breakfast at Ludington

Tall shade trees, a babbling brook, and 16 acres of lawn and trails. AC in summer; hot tub/Jacuzzi for winter skiers and sledders. Try out our sliding hill or our snowshoes. Our popular "Barnloft" is cozy and very private and includes a sofa bed for the kids. A tree swing encourages young-at-heart, or make s'mores and tell tales around the camp-

fire. Twenty percent discount for successive nights.

Hosts: Grace and Robert Schneider
Rooms: 3 (2PB;1SB) $45–75
Full Breakfast
Credit Cards: F
Notes: 2 5 6 7 9 10 11

The Inn at Ludington

701 E. Ludington Ave.
  Ludington, MI 49431-2032
(231) 845-7055; (800) 845-9170
E-mail: diane@inn-ludington.com
Web site: www.inn-ludington.com

The Inn at Ludington

Enjoy the charm of the past with the comfort of today. No stuffy, hands-off museum atmosphere here—our vintage furnishings invite you to relax and feel at home. The bountiful breakfast will sustain you for a day of beach-combing, biking, or antiquing. In winter, cross-country skiing awaits at Ludington State Park. Looking for something different? Murder mysteries are a specialty. Make this your headquarters for a Ludington/Lake Michigan adventure. Just look for the "Painted Lady" with the three-story turret. The Inn at Ludington is a non-smoking home.

Hosts: Diane and David Nemitz
Rooms: 6 (6PB) $90–110
Full Breakfast
Credit Cards: A B C D
Notes: 2 5 7 8 9 10 11 12

Snyder's Shoreline Inn

903 W. Ludington Ave., P. O. Box 667
    Ludington, MI 49431-0667
(231) 845-1261; Fax (231) 843-4441
E-mail: sharon@snydersshoreinn.com
Web site: www.snydersshoreinn.com

Snyder's Shoreline Inn offers a beautiful location on the edge of town, nestled at the harborfront. View the Ludington Lighthouse, sailboats, freighters, and sunsets from room patios or private balconies. Sleep comfortably in pleasant guest rooms individually decorated with stenciled walls, pieced quilts, antiques, and reproductions. Honeymoon suites feature in-room whirlpools. A great, quiet retreat or romantic getaway. Luxury, barrier-free, handicapped-accessible rooms. Heated outdoor pool and spa. Smoke-free. No pets. AAA.

Rooms: 44 (44PB) $65–289
Continental Breakfast
Credit Cards: A B C
Notes: 8 9 10

MACKINAC ISLAND

Haan's 1830 Inn

P. O. Box 123, Mackinac Island, MI 49757-0123
(906) 847-6244
Web site: www.mackinac.com

The earliest Greek Revival home in the Northwest Territory, this completely restored inn is on the Michigan Historic Registry. It is located in a quiet neighborhood 3 blocks around Haldiman Bay from the bustling 1800s downtown and Old Fort Mackinac. Adjacent to St. Anne's Church and gardens. Rooms are furnished with antiques. Experience the 19th-century ambience of horse-drawn buggies and wagons. Closed late October to mid-May.

Hosts: Nick and Nancy Haan
Rooms: 9 (7PB;2SB) $95–175
Continental Breakfast
Credit Cards:
Notes: 2 7 8 9 10

MANISTIQUE

Royal Rose B & B

230 Arbutus Ave., Manistique, MI 49854
(906) 341-4886; (877) 443-0016
    Fax (906) 341-4886
E-mail: rrbnb@chartermi.net
Web site: www.royalrose-bnb.com

Royal Rose

Experience luxurious accommodations in this newly restored 1903 historic home. This B & B features 2 fireplaces, a relaxing sun-filled morning room, a wrap-around deck, and a formal dining room with Bohemian crystal lighting. Four guest rooms are

---

6 Pets welcome; 7 Children welcome; 8 Tennis nearby; 9 Swimming nearby; 10 Golf nearby; 11 Skiing nearby; 12 May be booked through travel agent

elegantly decorated with private baths. In addition, 2 of the guest rooms have their own pedestal sinks. Other features include queen beds and TV. Jacuzzi bath is also available. Enjoy a scrumptious full breakfast, elegantly served, that includes fresh-baked breads and muffins. Cookies and beverages are available during the day in the morning room.

Hosts: Gilbert and Rosemary Sablack
Rooms: 4 (4PB) $75–110
Full Breakfast
Credit Cards: A B D
Notes: 2 8 9 10 11

MUSKEGON

Port City Victorian Inn

1259 Lakeshore Dr., Muskegon, MI 48117
(231) 759-0205; (800) 274-3574
 Fax (231) 759-0205
E-mail: pcvicinn@gte.net
Web site: www.portcityinn.com

Port City Victorian Inn

An 1877 romantic Victorian located on the bluffs of Muskegon Lake, Michigan's largest natural harbor with Lake Michigan's white sandy beaches only minutes away. Business and leisure travelers feel a real sense of

home. Five bedrooms with private baths and views of the lake, two with double-whirlpool tubs. Enjoy the rooftop pergola and TV/VCR room with views of the lake. Two parlors filled with antiques and Victorian decor. Remote control AC, CATV, AAA-approved. Open year-round.

Hosts: Fred and Barbara Schossau
Rooms: 5 (5PB) $80–150
Full Breakfast
Credit Cards: A B C D E F
Notes: 2 5 7 8 9 10 11 12

NEW BUFFALO

Sans Souci Euro Inn and Cottages

19265 S. Lakeside Rd.
 New Buffalo, MI 49117-9276
(616) 756-3141
E-mail: sans-souci@worldnet.att.net
Web site: www.sans-souci.com

Sans Souci Euro Inn

Sans Souci is a nature retreat offering 50 acres of towering trees, groomed landscapes, and a myriad of wildlife, including beautiful waterfowl right at home on our shimmering, secluded lake. Inside our gated sanctuary are family vacation homes, romantic getaway suites, and lakeside cottages for the fisherman. The interiors, of European character and design with wood-burning fireplaces and whirlpool baths, guarantee a niche for the solitude-seeking couple, the wedding party, small business group, or family reunion.

Host: Angie Siewert
Rooms: 9 (9PB) $160–230
Full Breakfast
Credit Cards: A B C D
Notes: 2 5 7 8 9 10 11 12

ONEKAMA

Lake Breeze House

5089 Main St., Onekama, MI 49675-0301
(231) 889-4969
Web site: www.manistee.com/lakebreeze.html

Our two-story frame house on Portage Lake is yours with a shared bath, living room, and breakfast room. Each room has its own special charm with family antiques. Come, relax, and enjoy our back porch and the sounds of the babbling creek. By reservation only. Boating and charter service available.

Hosts: Bill and Donna Erickson
Rooms: 3 (1PB;2SB) $55–65
Full Breakfast
Credit Cards:
Notes: 2 7 8 9 10 11

OWOSSO

Rossman's R and R Ranch

308 E. Hibbard Rd., Owosso, MI 48867-8931
(517) 723-2553; Fax (517) 729-9064

A newly remodeled farmhouse from the 1900s, the ranch sits on 130 acres overlooking the Maple River Valley. A large, concrete circular drive with white board fences leads to stables of horses and cattle. Area wildlife includes deer, fox, rabbits, pheasant, quail, and songbirds. Observe and explore from the farm lane, river walk, or outside deck. Countrylike accents adorn the farmhouse interior, and guests are welcome to use the family parlor, garden, game room, and fireplace. Central air-conditioning.

Hosts: Carl and Jeanne Rossman
Rooms: 3 (3SB) $55–60
Full Breakfast
Credit Cards:
Notes: 2 5 6 7 10

PENTWATER

Historic Nickerson Inn

P. O. Box 986; 262 Lowell St.
Pentwater, MI 49449-0986
(231) 869-6731; (800) 742-1288
Fax (231) 869-6151
E-mail: nickerson@voyager.net
Web site: www.nickersoninn.com

Pentwater is nestled between the white sand beach of Lake Michigan and the calm waters of Pentwater Lake. The Nickerson Inn sits high on a hill just 2 short blocks from the beach with views of both lakes. Our village will remind you of a small New England town. The Nickerson Inn, with its distinctive veranda, has been a Pentwater landmark since 1913. Extensively renovated from 1990 to the present, the traditional sense of grace and casual charm has been maintained. Featuring casual, fine dining in our candlelit din-

---

6 Pets welcome; 7 Children welcome; 8 Tennis nearby; 9 Swimming nearby; 10 Golf nearby; 11 Skiing nearby; 12 May be booked through travel agent

ing room. Refresh your spirit; recapture fond memories!

Hosts: Gretchen and Harry Shiparski
Rooms: 13 (13PB) $85–235
Full Breakfast
Credit Cards: A B D
Notes: 2 4 8 9 10 11 12

PETOSKEY

Terrace Inn

1549 Glendale, P. O. Box 266,
  Petoskey, MI 49770-0266
(231) 347-2410; (800) 530-9898
  Fax (231) 347-2407
E-mail: info@theterraceinn.com
Web site: www.theterraceinn.com

Located in the Victorian community of Bay View among 400-plus, turn-of-the-century cottages. Bay View originated in 1875 as a summer retreat for the United Methodist Church. The Chautauqua programs continue to offer spectacular religious, cultural, and family activities. The Terrace Inn was built in 1910 and is furnished with original furniture and Victorian floral and lace. Each guest room is different in décor, and each has a private bath. The dining room is open Saturday for dinner in the off-season (October–May), but offers dining Tuesday–Saturday during the summer. You may choose to enjoy our famous planked whitefish while viewing Lake Michigan sunsets from the spacious veranda. Guests have use of private beach, tennis courts, bicycles, and Bay View programs, including world-class concerts. The absence of TVs and telephones creates a quiet, relaxing atmosphere.

Hosts: Tom and Denise Erhart
Rooms: 43 (43PB) $49–108
Continental Breakfast
Credit Cards: A B C F
Notes: 2 4 5 7 8 9 10 11 12

PITTSFORD

Rocking Horse Inn

8652 North St., Pittsford, MI 49271
(517) 523-3826
E-mail: rockingh@frontiernet.net
Web site: bbonline.com/mi/rockinghorse

Rocking Horse Inn

Our guests love sitting on the wrap-around porch of this Italianate-style farmhouse while sipping lemonade and eating the "dessert of the evening." The morning brings wonderful aromas of a full breakfast. Close to Hillsdale College, shopping, and golf. Twenty-five minutes to MIS Speedway for NASCAR and Indy races. Packages and corporate rates are available. Four rooms are air-conditioned with TV/VCR, private bath, and full and queen beds.

Hosts: Mary Ann and Phil Meredith
Rooms: 4 (4PB) $60–80
Full Breakfast
Credit Cards: A B F
Notes: 2 3 4 5 7 8 9 10

NOTES: Credit cards accepted: A Master Card; B Visa; C American Express; D Discover; E Diners Club; F Other; 2 Personal checks accepted; 3 Lunch available; 4 Dinner available; 5 Open all year;

PORT HOPE

Stafford House

489 Main St. (m-25), P. O. Box 204,
  Port Hope, MI 48468
(89) 428-4554
-mail: staffordhouse@centurytel.net
Web site: www.staffordhousepthope.com

Enjoy your stay in our 1886 Country Victorian home featuring original woodwork, marble fireplace, full and queen beds. We are on the National Historic Register. Full breakfast served. Bicycles, snowshoes, historic walking tours, lighthouses, plus many summer and winter activities. Located 1/3 mile from Lake Huron. AC, CATV. Business or pleasure travelers welcome.

Hosts: Greg and Kathy Gephart
Rooms: 4 (4PB) $65–90
Full Breakfast
Credit Cards: A B
Notes: 2 5 7 9 10 11 12

Pets welcome; 7 Children welcome; 8 Tennis nearby; 9 Swimming nearby; 10 Golf nearby; 11 Skiing nearby; 12 May be booked through travel agent

MINNESOTA

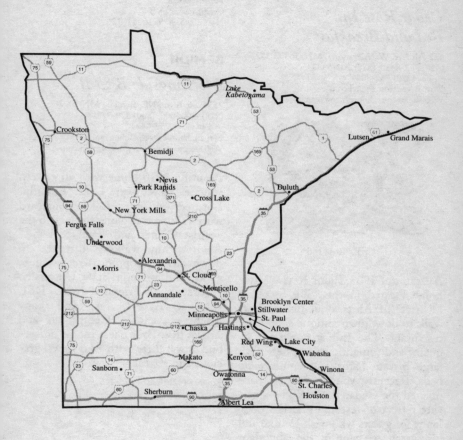

Minnesota

ALEXANDRIA

Cedar Rose Inn
Bed and Breakfast

422 7th Ave. W., Alexandria, MN 56308-1722
(320) 762-8430; (888) 203-5333
    Fax (320) 762-8044
E-mail: cedarose@gctel.com
Web site: www.echopress.com/cedarose

Cedar Rose Inn

A beautiful 1903 Tudor Revival-style home located in the "Silk Stocking District" of Alexandria. Just a short walk to downtown antique shops and restaurant. The Inn is noted for its quaint and romantic atmosphere with large private baths and comfortable beds. Recently, your innkeepers have opened the Cedar Rose Wild—a private retreat of restored prairie woodlands for guests who wish to hike and birdwatch or capture the abundant wildlife on film by traversing the 32 miles of clover-carpeted trails. The preserve is located in the picturesque rolling Minnesota lake country within 12 miles of the inn.

Hosts: Aggie and Florian Ledermann

Rooms: 4 (4PB) $85–145
Full Breakfast
Credit Cards: A B
Notes: 2 5 8 9 10 11 12

BEMIDJI

Morningside B & B

915 Lake Blvd., NE, Bemidji, MN 56601
(218) 444-5000; (800) 320-7728;
    Fax (218) 759-0424
E-mail: hamneggs@paulbunyan.net
Web site: www.morningsidebemidji.com

Beautiful 1910 home with an eastern sunrise view over Lake Bemidji. Located on quiet Lake Boulevard with walking trail along the lake to the Tourist Center and "Paul & Babe." Also within walking distance to downtown, shopping, restaurants, parks, and Bemidji State University. "Professional Friendly" with DSL Internet Access, fax, and copy machine available. Central air and smoke free. Four guest rooms on second story; three with lake views; gracious and restful.

Rooms: 4 (2PB;2SB) $75–115
Full Breakfast
Credit Cards: F
Notes: 2 7 8 9 10 11

CHATFIELD

Lund's Guest House

218 SE Winona St., Chatfield, MN 55923
(507) 867-4003

NOTES: Credit cards accepted: A Master Card; B Visa; C American Express; D Discover; E Diners Club; F Other; 2 Personal checks accepted; 3 Lunch available; 4 Dinner available; 5 Open all year;

Two houses from early 1900s furnished in '20s and '30s style. Each house has four bedrooms, four bathrooms, kitchen, dining room, living room, screened-in front and back porches, soft water. Air-conditioned. We are 100 miles SE of Twin Cities, 20 miles from Rochester, 9 miles to bike and ski trail, 17 miles to historic Lanesboro. Prices: $70 includes breakfast. $65 without breakfast.

Host: Marion Lund
Rooms: 8 (8PB) $65–70
Continental Breakfast
Notes: 2 5 8 9 10

DULUTH

Pj's Bed and Breakfast

5757 Bergquist Rd., Duluth, MN 55804-9666
(218) 525-2508; Fax (218) 525-0249
E-mail: pjsbb@duluth.com
Web site: www.pjsbb.com

"The Inn with the Superior View," Pj's is perched on a ridge with a 160-degree panoramic view of Lake Superior. Located between Duluth and Two Harbors, we are minutes away from fine dining and city life. The large corner fireplace in the lounging area adds a relaxing atmosphere. Pj's is a great place to retreat and relax! Special rates for retreats when all rooms are rented.

Hosts: Phil and Jan Hanson
Rooms: 5 (5PB) $75–155
Full Breakfast
Notes: 2 5 9 10 11

FERGUS FALLS

Bakketopp Hus B & B

20571 Hillcrest Rd.
  Fergus Falls, MN 56537-9649
(218) 739-2915; (800) 739-2915
E-mail: ddn@prtel.com
Web site: www.bbonline.com/mn/bakketopp

Bakketopp Hus

Quiet, spacious, lake home with vaulted ceilings, fireplaces, private spa, flower garden patio, and lakeside decks. Antique furnishings from family homestead; four-poster, draped, French canopy bed; and private baths. Here you can listen as loons call to each other across the lake in the still of dusk, witness the falling foliage splendor, relax by the crackling fire, or sink into the warmth of the spa after a day of hiking or skiing. Near antique shops and Maplewood State Park. Ten minutes off I-94. Gift certificates available. Reservation with deposit.

Hosts: Dennis and Judy Nims
Rooms: 3 (3PB) $70–105
Full Breakfast
Credit Cards: A B D
Notes: 2 5 8 9 10 11

6 Pets welcome; 7 Children welcome; 8 Tennis nearby; 9 Swimming nearby; 10 Golf nearby; 11 Skiing nearby; 12 May be booked through travel agent

HOUSTON

Addie's Attic Bed and Breakfast

117 S. Jackson, P. O. Box 677, Houston, MN 55943
(507) 896-3010; Fax (507) 896-4010
Web site: www.bbonline.com

Addie's Attic

Beautiful, turn-of-the-century home, circa 1903. Cozy front parlor with curved-glass window. Games, TV, player piano. Rooms are decorated and furnished with "attic finds." Hearty breakfast served in dining room. Near hiking, biking, cross-country ski trails, canoeing, and antique shops. Weekday rates.

Hosts: Fred and Marilyn Huhn
Rooms: 3 (0PB;3SB) $40–50
Full Breakfast
Notes: 2 5 10

LUTSEN

Lindgren's Bed and Breakfast on Lake Superior

5552 Cty. Rd. 35, P. O. Box 56
Lutsen, MN 55612-0056
(218) 663-7450; Fax (218) 663-7450
E-mail: info@lindgrensbb.com
Web site: www.lindgrenbb.com

A 1920s Northwoods, rustic lodge log home in Superior National Forest on Lake Superior's walkable shoreline. This romantic, secluded hideaway on spacious, manicured grounds is like being on the ocean, surrounded by forest. Truly away from it all! Wildlife decor with Finnish sauna, fireplaces, whirlpool, baby grand piano, and TVs/VCRs/CD. In the center of area known for skiing, fall colors, Superior Hiking Trail, golf, state parks, rock collecting, fishing, mountain biking, horseback riding, Alpine slide, Boundry Waters Canoe Area Wilderness, and art. One-half mile off scenic Highway 61 on the Lake Superior Circle Tour. Gift certificates. 3-diamond AAA-rated. Children over 12 welcome.

Host: Shirley Lindgren
Rooms: 4 (4PB) $105–150
Continental Breakfast
Credit Cards: A B
Notes: 2 3 5 8 9 10 11 12

Lindgren's

MANKATO

Butler House B & B

704 S. Broad St., Mankato, MN 56001-3820
(507) 387-5055; Fax (507) 388-5462
E-mail: butlerhouse@bresnanlink.net
Web site: www.butlerhouse.com

Butler House

This English-style (1905) mansion is elegantly furnished and includes a palatial porch, beautiful suites, canopy beds, whirlpool, fireplace, and private baths. Features include hand-painted murals, a Steinway grand piano, window seats, and a large dining room. No smoking. Near the state trail, civic center, biking, skiing, golf, and antiquing. Come join us for an escape into a world of comfort and relaxation.

Hosts: Ron and Sharry Tschida
Rooms: 5 (5PB) $55–115
Full Breakfast
Credit Cards: A B C
Notes: 2 5 8 9 10 11 12

OWATONNA

The Northrop-Oftedahl House B & B

358 E. Main St., Owatonna, MN 55060
(507) 451-4040; Fax (507) 451-2755
E-mail: northoft@thebestbnb.com
Web site: www.northrop-oftedahl.com

One of 12 historical homes—1898; stained glass, original family furnishings, oak woodwork; 6-ft. footed bathtub. Home of the late Dr. Harson A. Northrop, candidate for governor/U.S.

Senate, and Tessie Oftedahl Northrop, humanitarian. Three blocks downtown; 6 miles Cabela's/Medford Outlet; 38 miles Mayo Clinic; 50 miles Mall of America. Antiques/collectibles from estate on sale. Lunch/dinner w/prior arrangement. See the Art Linkletter Room, Dr. Joyce Brothers Room (celebrity guests). Explore history with John Howard Northrop (Nobel Prize)/Jack Northrop (Flying wing/Stealth bomber), and more.

Hosts: Jean and Darrell Stewart and Gregory Northrop
Rooms: 7 (2PB;5SB) $70–125
Full Breakfast
Notes: 2 3 4 5 6 7 8 9 10 11 12

The Northrop-Oftedahl House

SAINT CHARLES

Thoreson's Carriage House B & B

606 Wabasha Ave., Saint Charles, MN 55972-1119
(507) 932-3479

Located near beautiful Whitewater State Park with its swimming, trails, and demonstrations by the park naturalist. Horseback riding available nearby. We are in Amish territory and just minutes from the world-famous

Mayo Clinic. Piano and videos available. Write for brochure.

Host: Moneta Thoreson
Rooms: 2 (0PB;2SB) $45–50
Full Breakfast
Notes: 2 5 7 8 9 10

SHERBURN

Four Columns Inn

668 140th St., Sherburn, MN 56171-9732
(507) 764-8861
E-mail: oenor@frontiernet.net

Four Columns Inn

Enjoy Scandinavian hospitality in an antique-filled, lovingly remodeled, Greek Revival inn. Four antique-filled bedrooms, clawfoot tubs, and working fireplaces welcome guests. A library, circular stairway, living room with grand piano, and a solarium with Jacuzzi make a stay here memorable. A hideaway bridal suite, perfect for honeymooners or anniversary couples, has access to a roof deck with a super view of the countryside. A hearty breakfast is served in the formal dining room, on the balcony, in the gazebo, or in the kitchen by the fireplace. Air-conditioning. Near Iowa's Lake Okobogi, antiques, amusement park, and live summer theater. Two miles north of I-90 between Chicago and the Black

Hills. Call for brochure. No smoking. Children welcome by arrangement.

Hosts: Norman and Pennie Kittleson
Rooms: 5 (5PB) $70–80
Full Breakfast
Notes: 2 5 7 8 9 10 11 12

STILLWATER

James Mulvey Residence Inn

622 W. Churchill St.
  Stillwater, MN 55082-5733
(651) 430-8008; (800) 820-8008
  Fax (651) 430-2801
E-mail: truettldem@aol.com
Web site: www.jamesmulveyinn.com

This is an enchanting place. Built in 1878 by lumberman James A. Mulvey, the Italianate residence and stone carriage house grace the most visited historic river town in the upper Midwest. Exclusively for you are the grand parlour, formal dining room, Victorian sunporch, and seven fabulously decorated guest rooms filled with exquisite art and antiques. The inn offers a four-course breakfast, double whirlpools, fireplaces, mountain bikes, and air-conditioning. You'll receive grace-filled service from innkeepers who care.

Hosts: Truett and Jill Lawson
Rooms: 7 (7PB) $99–219
Full Breakfast
Credit Cards: A B C D F
Notes: 2 5 8 9 10 11 12

NOTES: Credit cards accepted: A Master Card; B Visa; C American Express; D Discover; E Diners Club; F Other; 2 Personal checks accepted; 3 Lunch available; 4 Dinner available; 5 Open all year;

MISSISSIPPI

Mississippi

BILOXI

The Old Santini House B & B

964 Beach Blvd., Biloxi, MS 39530
(228) 436-4078; (800) 686-1146
    Fax (228) 432-9193
E-mail: jad39530@cs.com
Web site: www.santinibnb.com

The Old Santini House

American Cottage style, circa 1837, listed on National Register of Historic Places, National Trust and Historic Inns Network of Civil War Preservation Trust. Last home of Confederate General Alexander P. Stewart, "Old Straight," also known as the Soldier of Tennessee. Children over 12 welcome.

Hosts: James and Patricia Dunay
Rooms: 5 (5PB) $75–150
Full Breakfast
Credit Cards: A B C D F
Notes: 5 9 10 12

CORINTH

Generals' Quarters

924 Fillmore St., Corinth, MS 38834-4125
(662) 286-3325; (800) 664-1866
    Fax (662) 287-8188
E-mail: genqtrs@tsixroads.com
Web site: www.tsixroads.com/~gengtrs

Two Victorian homes (circa 1872 and 1909), connected by lovely gardens, are located in the historic district of an old Civil War town. Both homes have recently been remodeled and provide a taste of history combined with modern conveniences. All rooms have TV/VCR, fireplaces, telephones, data ports, antique furnishings, lovely views, and private baths. A wonderful breakfast is prepared each day by our chef. Early morning coffee and muffins are also available. Our inn is rated among the top 10 B & Bs in the state and has been featured on PBS and in *Mississippi* magazine.

Hosts: Luke and Charlotte Doehner
Rooms: 10 (10PB) $75–120
Full Breakfast
Credit Cards: A B D F
Notes: 5 7 8 9 10 12

JACKSON

Fairview Inn

734 Fairview St., Jackson, MS 39202-1624
(601) 948-3429; (888) 948-1908
    Fax (601) 948-1203
E-mail: fairview@fairviewinn.com
Web site: www.fairviewinn.com

NOTES: Credit cards accepted: A Master Card; B Visa; C American Express; D Discover; E Diners Club; F Other; 2 Personal checks accepted; 3 Lunch available; 4 Dinner available; 5 Open all year;

Fairview Inn

The Fairview Inn is a Colonial Revival mansion listed on the National Historic Register. Its elegant and comfortable ambience is accented by fine fabrics and antiques in a historic neighborhood. Near churches, shopping, two colleges, and major medical complexes. AAA award, 4 diamonds; "Top Inn of 1994" award by *Country Inns* magazine. "The Fairview Inn is southern hospitality at its best." —*Travel & Leisure*.

Hosts: Carol and Bill Simmons
Rooms: 18 (18PB) $115–290
Full Breakfast
Credit Cards: A B C D
Notes: 2 4 5 8 9 10 12

LONG BEACH

Red Creek Inn, Vineyard, and Racing Stable

7416 Red Creek Rd.
    Long Beach, MS 39560-8804
(228) 452-3080; (800) 729-9670
    Fax (228) 452-4450
E-mail: info@redcreekinn.com
Web site: www.redcreekinn.com

This raised French cottage was built in 1899 by a retired Italian sea captain to entice his young bride away from her parents' home in New Orleans. Red Creek Inn, Vineyard, and Racing Stable is situated on 11 acres with ancient live oaks and fragrant magnolias and is a delight with its peaceful comforts. A 64-foot-long porch, complete with porch swings, provides relaxation for guests, and the inn is furnished in antiques for guests' enjoyment. A new marble Jacuzzi awaits in the Victorian Room. A 10% ministerial discount is offered.

Hosts: Karl and Toni Mertz
Rooms: 7 (5PB;2SB) $49–124
Continental Breakfast
Notes: 2 3 4 5 7 9 10 12

Red Creek Inn

6 Pets welcome; 7 Children welcome; 8 Tennis nearby; 9 Swimming nearby; 10 Golf nearby; 11 Skiing nearby; 12 May be booked through travel agent

MISSOURI

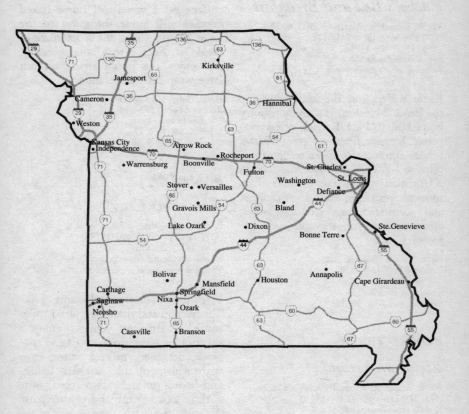

Missouri

ANNAPOLIS

Rachel's Bed and Breakfast

202 W. Second St., Annapolis, MO 63620
(573) 598-4656; (888) 245-7771
   Fax (573) 598-3439
E-mail: info@rachelsbb.com
Web site: www.rachelsbb.com

Rachel's Bed and Breakfast (formerly the Bolch Mansion) is a lovely country home built in 1921. Rachel's offers two-person Jacuzzis, fireplaces, private baths, private entrances, in-room refrigerators, satellite TV/VCR, and fabulous food in a Christian atmosphere. Rachel's offers romantic packages, candlelight dinners, and specializes in small weddings, officiated by retired minister and innkeeper Joseph Cluck.

Hosts: Joe and Sharon Cluck
Rooms: 6 (6PB) $65–130
Full Breakfast
Credit Cards: A B C D
Notes: 2 4 5 7 9 10 12

BONNE TERRE

Victorian Veranda

207 E. School St., Bonne Terre, MO 63628
(573) 358-1134; (800) 343-1134
E-mail: victoriaveranda@ldd.net
Web site: www.bbim.org/vicveranda

This elegant, 1880 Victorian mansion overlooks the town's Bicentennial Park. Choose from four romantic guest rooms, all with a private bath. Guests may relax in the parlor or cozy up to the fireplace in the gathering room. The aroma of freshly ground coffee and a variety of home-baked goodies will guide the guest to the large dining room for a candlelight breakfast. Escape to a quiet getaway, and enjoy the porch swing on our large wrap-around veranda.

Hosts: Galen and Karen Forney
Rooms: 4 (4PB) $70–110
Full Breakfast
Credit Cards: A B D
Notes: 2 5 7 8 9 10 12

BRANSON

Cameron's Crag

P. O. Box 295, Branson, MO 65726
(417) 335-8134; (800) 933-8529
   Fax (417) 335-8134
E-mail: kay@camerons-crag.com
Web site: www.camerons-crag.com

High on a bluff overlooking Lake Taneycomo and the valley, just 3 miles south of Branson. Guests enjoy a spectacular view from two new, spacious, detached, private suites, each with whirlpool tub, kitchen, living-and-bedroom area. Two-room suite with indoor hot tub and private bath. A fourth room has a great view of the lake and a private hot tub on the deck. All rooms have king-size beds, private secluded hot tubs, private entrances, TV/VCRs, and a video library.

Hosts: Glen and Kay Cameron
Rooms: 4 (4PB) $85–135

NOTES: Credit cards accepted: A Master Card; B Visa; C American Express; D Discover; E Diners Club; F Other; 2 Personal checks accepted; 3 Lunch available; 4 Dinner available; 5 Open all year;

Full Breakfast
Credit Cards: A B D
Notes: 2 5 12

Grandpa's Farm B & B / This N' That Shoppe

4738 W. State Hwy. 86, Lampe, MO 65681-9801
(417) 779-5106
E-mail: keithpat@interlinc.net
Web site: www.grandpasfarmbandb.com

A real, old-time, 116-acre Ozark Mountain farm with plenty of friendly animal life. Choose from the luxurious Honeymoon Suite with spa, Red Bud Suite with large whirlpool tub, Dogwood Suite with kitchenette, and Mother Hen Room. Near Branson, Missouri, and Eureka Springs, Arkansas. A big country breakfast is served on a screened-in porch. There are secret hideout lofts for children.

Hosts: Keith and Pat Lamb
Rooms: 4 (4PB) $65–95
Full Breakfast
Credit Cards: A B D
Notes: 2 5 7 9 12

Josie's Peaceful Getaway

508 Tablerock Circle, Branson, MO 65616-9613
(417) 338-2978; (800) 289-4125
Web site: www.josiesbandb.com

Pristine, gorgeous lakefront scenery on Table Rock Lake, where sunsets and moonlit nights lace the sky. The contemporary-designed suite features cathedral ceilings and stone fireplaces mingled with a Victorian flair. Cozy, wood-burning fireplaces, lavish Jacuzzi spas, candlelight, and fresh flowers abound. Dine in luxury as you enjoy breakfast served on china and crystal. Celebrate your honeymoon or anniversary in style. Eight miles from Branson and music shows; 5 minutes from Silver Dollar City/Marina. Smoke-free environment.

Hosts: Bill and Jo Anne Coats
Rooms: 1 (1PB) $125
Continental Breakfast
Credit Cards: A B C D
Notes: 2 5 7 9 10 12

Lakeshore Bed and Breakfast

47 Elm Ln., Branson, MO 65616-9607
(417) 338-2698; (800) 285-9739
    Fax (417) 338-2698
Web site: www.lakeshorebandb.com

Lakeshore

A peaceful place on beautiful Table Rock Lake, 2 miles from Silver Dollar City, this contemporary home offers boat docks, a paddleboat, and glide swing-for-four. All three units have queen beds, TV/VCR, coffee bar, refrigerator and microwave, and private bath. A family unit for six has a private entrance, a covered patio overlooking the lake, kitchen, and sitting area with sofa and chairs. The Honeymoon unit has a private deck, sofa and chair, and whirlpool tub. A

6 Pets welcome; 7 Children welcome; 8 Tennis nearby; 9 Swimming nearby; 10 Golf nearby; 11 Skiing nearby; 12 May be booked through travel agent

nutritious, hearty breakfast is served. A smoke-free environment.

Host: Gladys Lemley
Rooms: 3 (3PB) $55–90
Full Breakfast
Notes: 2 5 7 9 10 11 12

Ozark Mountain Country Bed and Breakfast Service

P. O. Box 295, Branson, MO 65616
(417) 334-4720; (800) 695-1546
    Fax (417) 335-8134
E-mail: mgcameron@aol.com
Web site: www.ozarkbedandbreakfast.com

Ozark Mountain Country has been arranging accommodations for guests in southwestern Missouri and north-western Arkansas since 1982. Our services are free. In the current list of more than 100 homes and small inns, some locations offer private entrances, fantastic views, guest sitting areas, swimming pools, Jacuzzis, and/or fire-places. Most locations are available all year. Personal checks accepted. Some homes welcome children; a few wel-come pets (even horses). Coordinator: Kay Cameron. $45–195. Visa, Mastercard, and Discover welcomed.

CAMERON

Cook's Country Cottage B & B

7880 N. E. Bacon Rd., Cameron, MO 64429-8022
(816) 632-1776

A perfect country hideaway to escape the fast pace of today's society. Relax in luxury and have your every whim

catered to. Water gardens, lakes to fish, trails to walk, birds and wildlife to watch, and porches where you may rock are a few options to enjoy. Candlelight dinners and day tours to historical sites and Missouri's largest Amish community. "Coming home" was never better!

Hosts: Don and Loura Cook
Rooms: 2 (2PB) $65–85
Full Breakfast
Notes: 2 3 4 5   8 9 10 11

DEFIANCE

Parsons House B & B

211 Lee St., Defiance, MO 63341-0038
(636) 987-2929; (800) 355-6878
    Fax (636) 798-2220
E-mail: mkeyes1@win.org
Web site: www.theparsonshouse.com

Parsons House

This stately 1842 Federalist home overlooks the Missouri River Valley. Listed in the Historic Survey, it pro-vides antique-furnished guest rooms and a large gathering room. On 8 acres, the gardens feature fountains, a hammock, and spa. This antebellum home has fireplaces, a large library, and an enclosed porch where after-

---

NOTES: Credit cards accepted: A Master Card; B Visa; C American Express; D Discover; E Diners Club; F Other; 2 Personal checks accepted; 3 Lunch available; 4 Dinner available; 5 Open all year;

noon tea is served. Nearby are the Daniel Boone Home, wineries, and Katy Bicycle Trail, yet St. Louis is only 35 miles away. Amenities include central air-conditioning and private baths. Our huge, country breakfast is an "Event!"

Hosts: Al and Carol Keyes
Rooms: 3 (3PB) $95–110
Full Breakfast
Credit Cards: A B D
Notes: 2 7 10

FAYETTE

Bedford House B & B

308 S. Main St., Fayette, MO 65248
(660) 248-2204
E-mail: gkoelker@coin.org
Web site: www.bedfordhousebandb.com

This circa 1860 Federal-style home offers one suite and one spacious bedroom, both with queen-size beds, central heat and air, and private baths. Hardwood floors with inlays and ornately carved doors and mantels have earned it a spot on the National Registry. Antiques and traditional furnishings enhance the public areas. We are located a few blocks from the Courthouse Square and Central Methodist College. Relax on the porch overlooking the brick street and enjoy a slice of rural America.

Hosts: Georgette and Rod Koelker
Rooms: 2 (2PB) $50–65
Full Breakfast
Notes: 2 5 7 8 9 12

FULTON

Loganberry Inn

310 W. 7th St., Fulton, MO 65251-2608
(573) 642-9229; (888) 866-6661
E-mail: loganberry@socket.net
Web site: www.loganberryinn.com

Loganberry Inn

Located between Kansas City and St. Louis, 5 minutes from I-70, the Loganberry Inn has welcomed guests such as Margaret Thatcher and her Scotland Yard detectives. This grand 1899 Victorian home in historic Fulton features pampered elegance and is in strolling distance to the quaint downtown area of Fulton with its brick streets, unique antique and specialty shops, the Winston Churchill Memorial and Museum, and the Berlin Wall Breakthrough sculpture. Cathy's gourmet breakfasts are a great way to start the day. Children over 8 are welcome.

Hosts: Carl and Cathy McGeorge
Rooms: 5 (5PB) $75–160
Full Breakfast
Credit Cards: A B C D F
Notes: 5 6 7 8 10

---

6 Pets welcome; 7 Children welcome; 8 Tennis nearby; 9 Swimming nearby; 10 Golf nearby; 11 Skiing nearby; 12 May be booked through travel agent

Romancing the Past Victorian Inn

830 Court St., Fulton, MO 65251-1970
(573) 592-1996
E-mail: innkeeper@socket.net
Web site: www.romancingthepast.com

A spacious lawn and serene gardens enfold this 1860s home in mid-Missouri. A most elegant Victorian inn in a beautiful, historic neighborhood. The inn boasts a grand hall with magnificent arch and staircase and elegantly appointed rooms with period adornments. Lavish antiques, bed drapings, and florals can be found throughout, as well as six fireplaces, luxurious baths, indoor and outdoor spas, and aromatherapies. Enjoy excellent food; many amenities to pamper you. Walk to many fascinating amusements. Children over 8 welcome.

Hosts: Jim and Renee Yeager
Rooms: 3 (3PB) $100–170
Full Breakfast
Credit Cards: A B C D
Notes: 2 3 4 7 8 9 10

GRAVOIS MILLS

Buck Creek B & B

32907 Buck Creek Acres Rd.
   Gravois Mills, MO 65073
(573) 372-1212; Fax (573) 372-3737
Web site: www.buckcreekbb.com

Four guest rooms on the second floor; have your choice of a king- or queen-size bed. Full breakfast served daily at 8 A.M. Overlooking the beautiful Lake of the Ozarks. "A beautiful place to relax in a family atmosphere."

Hosts: Richard and June Hackathorn
Rooms: 4 (2PB;2SB) $65–115
Full Breakfast
Credit Cards: A B C D
Notes: 2 5 9 10

HOUSTON

Windstone House B & B

539 Cleveland Rd., Houston, MO 65483-2102
(417) 967-2008
E-mail: windstone@pcis.net

Windstone House

A large, two-story home with a wrap-around balcony overlooking 90 acres of Missouri fields and woodlands. Furnished with antiques, the perfect place to unwind and relax. Whether in the formal dining room or on the balcony, you are in for a treat when the old school bells rings to call you to breakfast. There is a special sitting room for your enjoyment with games, books, TV, and VCR.

Host: Barbara Kimes
Rooms: 3 (1PB;2SB) $50–60
Full Breakfast
Credit Cards:
Notes: 2 5 10

NOTES: Credit cards accepted: A Master Card; B Visa; C American Express; D Discover; E Diners Club; F Other; 2 Personal checks accepted; 3 Lunch available; 4 Dinner available; 5 Open all year;

INDEPENDENCE

Woodstock Inn B & B

1212 W. Lexington Ave., Independence, MO 64050
(816) 833-2233; (800) 276-5202
Web site: www.independence-missouri.com

Nestled within Independence's famous historical district, the Woodstock Inn B & B, a turn-of-the-century doll and quilt factory, has an ideal location. The inn is just a short stroll from all the major sites of Independence, and any Kansas City destination is less than 30 minutes from the inn. Today, the Woodstock Inn is a luxury B & B featuring a fenced-in courtyard and garden area, thermo-massage spa tubs, fireplaces, TVs and VCRs, CD players, and a wealth of fine collectibles, rare antiques, and priceless artwork from around the world. All eleven of the inn's uniquely and beautifully appointed guest rooms include a minibar refrigerator, hair dryer, extension makeup mirror, alarm clock/radio, individual climate control, Sprint PCS phone, private bath, and of course our full breakfast featuring our famous malted Belgian waffles. Be sure to ask about our special romance packages and, remember, gift certificates make great presents!

Hosts: Todd and Patricia Justice
Rooms: 11 (11PB) $75–207
Full Breakfast
Credit Cards: A B C D F
Notes: 2 5 12

KANSAS CITY, MO

Mulberry Hill B & B

226 N. Armstrong, Pleasant Hill, MO 64080
(816) 540-3457
E-mail: mulberryhill@kcweb.net
Web site: www.mulberryhillbandb.com

Come relax and let us pamper you in our 1904 Colonial-style home located in a quiet country town only 30–45 minutes from most Kansas City attractions. Locally, enjoy antiques, golf, swimming, country music show, and relaxing. A delicious full breakfast is served daily featuring our melt-in-your-mouth Belgian waffles. Our spacious honeymoon suite has a Jacuzzi-for-two and is perfect for your wedding night, anniversary, or other special occasion. Please call ahead of stay for children.

Mulberry Hill

Hosts: Roy and Patricia Keck
Rooms: 5 (5PB) $60–100
Full Breakfast
Credit Cards: A B D
Notes: 2 5 9 10 12

6 Pets welcome; 7 Children welcome; 8 Tennis nearby; 9 Swimming nearby; 10 Golf nearby; 11 Skiing nearby; 12 May be booked through travel agent

KIRKSVILLE

Travelers Inn Christian Bed and Breakfast

301 W. Washington St., Kirksville, MO 63501
(660) 665-5191; (800) 320-5191
   Fax (660) 665-0825
Web site: www.travelers-inn-bnb.com

Built in 1923. Twenty-two theme rooms with elegant decor. The inn still reflects a rich history from the days when Harry S. Truman walked its hallways. Located just a short drive from Thousand Hills State Park and Lake, it provides the perfect setting for a getaway or overnight stay. You'll find a peaceful atmosphere with Christian hospitality and a hot breakfast every morning of your stay. The Inn has a restaurant, bookstore, chocolate and gift shop, and conference room on-site. Historical sites and shopping within walking distance. Every room air-conditioned with extra amenities. Single, double, and suites available.

Travelers Inn

Host: Janice Smith
Rooms: 22 (22PB) $74.95–125
Full Breakfast
Credit Cards: A B C D
Notes: 3 5 7 8 9 10 12

NIXA

Wooden Horse B & B

1007 W. Sterling Ct., Nixa, MO 65714
(417) 724-8756; (800) 724-8756
   Fax (417) 725-3853
E-mail: bigoaktree@msn.com
Web site: www.bbonline.com/mo/woodenhorse/

Come "create a memory" in this quiet country setting as our only special guest. You'll experience the warm, homey atmosphere, sprinkled with antiques and collections for your pleasure. A wood-burning stove, TV/VCR, and twin rockers await you in the living room. Take time to ponder in the tranquil gazebo garden, or relax in the hot tub while star gazing—before retiring. With dawn comes "too much" breakfast to enjoy! We are located 7 miles from Springfield's #1 attraction, BASS Pro and the Wonders of Wildlife.

Host: Valeta Hammar
Rooms: 2 (2PB) $90
Full Breakfast
Credit Cards:
Notes: 2 5 6 7 8 9 10 12

OZARK

Dear's Rest Bed and Breakfast

1408 Capp Hill Ranch Rd.
   Ozark, MO 65721-6149
(417) 581-3839; (800) 588-2262
   Fax (417) 581-3839
E-mail: stay@dearsrest.com
Web site: www.dearsrest.com

Luxury accommodations, Amish-built cabin surrounded by nature—enjoy hot tub "under the stars" or cozy up to

---

NOTES: Credit cards accepted: A Master Card; B Visa; C American Express; D Discover; E Diners Club; F Other; 2 Personal checks accepted; 3 Lunch available; 4 Dinner available; 5 Open all year;

stone (wood-burning) fireplace. Start your day with plentiful breakfast, enjoy hiking or exploring Bull Creek, then maybe a shopping trip for antiques or many outlet malls; entertainment abounds in Branson. We accommodate only 1 party at a time, providing our guests complete privacy. Isaiah 40:31.

Dear's Rest

Hosts: Linda and Allan Schilter
Rooms: 1 (1PB) $125
Full Breakfast
Credit Cards: A B D
Notes: 2 5 6 7 9 10 12

SPRINGFIELD

Virginia Rose Bed and Breakfast

317 E. Glenwood St., Springfield, MO 65807-3543
(417) 883-0693; (800) 345-1412
Web site: www.bbonline.com/mo/virginiarose

This two-story farmhouse, built in 1906, offers country hospitality right in town. Situated on a tree-covered acre, our home is furnished with early-1900s antiques, quilts on queen beds, and rockers on the porch. Relax in the parlor with a book, puzzle, or game, or watch a movie on the TV/VCR. We are located only minutes from BASS Pro Outdoor World, restaurants, shopping, antique shops, and miniature golf, and only 40 miles from Branson. Inspected and approved by the Bed and Breakfast Inns of Missouri.

Hosts: Jackie and Virginia Buck
Rooms: 5 (5PB) $60–120
Full Breakfast
Credit Cards: A B C D
Notes: 2 5 7 9 10 12

STE. GENEVIEVE

The Inn St. Gemme Beauvais

78 N. Main St., Ste. Genevieve, MO 63670-1336
(573) 883-5744; (800) 818-5744
Fax (573) 883-3899
E-mail: buffin@msn.com
Web site: www.bbhost.com/innstgemme

A 3-diamond rating by AAA with 4-diamond hospitality! All rooms have private baths, fresh flowers, and queen or king beds. Fireplaces and double whirlpool tubs are available in some suites. Outside guests will find a beautiful garden with fountain and gazebo. Other amenities include: homemade cake and tea (teatime), beverages, hors d'oeuvres, and a full, three-course, gourmet breakfast served at individual candlelit tables. Breakfast in bed can be arranged for some rooms.

Hosts: Janet Joggerst, Mark and Connie Smith
Rooms: 14 (14PB) $89–189
Full Breakfast
Credit Cards: A B C D F
Notes: 2 5 7 8 9 10

---

6 Pets welcome; 7 Children welcome; 8 Tennis nearby; 9 Swimming nearby; 10 Golf nearby; 11 Skiing nearby; 12 May be booked through travel agent

VERSAILLES

The Hilty Inn B & B

206 E. Jasper St., Versailles, MO 65084-1248
(573) 378-2020; (800) 667-8093
E-mail: hiltyinn@plantetsos.com
Web site: www.bbim.org/hiltyinn

Come enjoy a relaxing atmosphere away from the rush. This is off the beaten path on your way to Branson, midway through Missouri. There is a Mennonite community to visit, as well as the Lake of the Ozarks. We also have a community theater group that gives wonderful performances. Please check the schedule with me. Children 7 and over welcome.

The Hilty Inn

Host: Doris Hilty
Rooms: 4 (4PB) $65–125
Full Breakfast
Credit Cards: A B C D
Notes: 2 5 7 10 12

WARRENSBURG

The Camel Crossing B & B

210 E. Gay St., Warrensburg, MO 64093-1841
(660) 429-2973; Fax (660) 429-2722
E-mail: camelx@iland.net
Web site: www.bbim.org/camelx/index.html

Ride a magic carpet to this bed and breakfast that is homey in atmosphere, but museum-like in its decor. Brass, copper, hand-tied carpets, and furnishings from the Far East will captivate your imagination. An oasis for mind and body. Philippians 4:8. If you come a stranger, you'll leave as a friend. Smoking permitted outside only.

Hosts: Ed and Joyce Barnes
Rooms: 4 (2PB;2SB) $70–90
Full Breakfast
Credit Cards: A B   F
Notes: 2 5 8 9 10

Good House Bed and Breakfast

707 N. Holden, Warrensburg, MO 64093
(660) 747-9563
E-mail: goodhous@iland.net

Mutiple sitting areas create a pastoral setting at this 1903 Victorian mansion, inside and out. The original stained, leaded, and cut-glass windows, golden oak staircase, fireplace, and entry mirror let visitors revisit the past without loss of modern amenities. There is ample off-street parking. Come, relax, and enjoy our combined eras under majestic oaks.

Host: Nita Good
Rooms: 3 (3PB) $75
Full Breakfast
Credit Cards: A B C D
Notes: 2 5 7 8 9 10

MONTANA

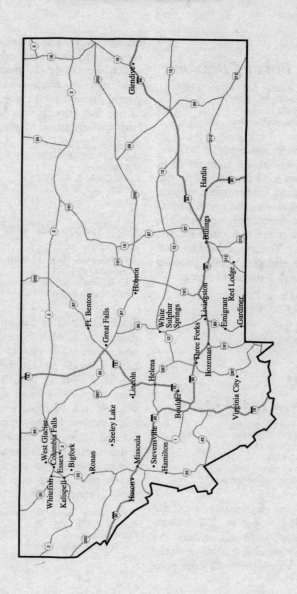

Montana

Josephine Bed and Breakfast

514 N. 29th St., Billings, MT 59101-1128
(406) 248-5898; (800) 552-5898
E-mail: josephine@imt.net
Web site: www.thejosephine.com

A lovely, historic home within walking distance of downtown, minutes from airport, 1 hour to skiing and Little Big Horn Battlefield. Comfortable, elegant, antique-filled rooms, each with private bath, modem-friendly phone, cable TV, and AC. Two suites, one with romantic whirlpool tub. Yesteryear dining room, study, parlor, and porch. Full gourmet breakfast. AAA 2-diamond rating.

Hosts: Doug and Becky Taylor
Rooms: 5 (5PB) $75–160
Full Breakfast
Credit Cards: A B C D
Notes: 2 5 8 9 10 11 12

BOZEMAN

Cottonwood Inn B & B

13515 Cottonwood Canyon Rd.
  Bozeman, MT 59718-8990
(406) 763-5452; (888) 879-4667
  Fax (406) 763-5639
E-mail: info@cottonwood-inn.com
Web site: www.cottonwood-inn.com

Our small inn looks out over the Galatin Mountains. A hand-hewn home of pine, redwood, cedar, and stained-glass windows, with a firelit hearth and views that will take your breath away! The area is home to moose, elk, deer, and other wildlife, which can be viewed from your window or the wrap-around covered porch. Named for nearby rivers, each of our five guest rooms has a private bath and incredible views.

Hosts: Joe and Debbie Velli
Rooms: 5 (5PB) $85–129
Full Breakfast
Credit Cards: A B C D
Notes: 2 5 7 9 10 11 12

Fox Hollow Bed and Breakfast

545 Mary Rd., Bozeman, MT 59718-7927
(406) 582-8440; (800) 431-5010
  Fax (406) 582-9752
E-mail: foxhollow@bozeman-mt.com
Web site: www.bozeman-mt.com

Settle into one of five spacious guest rooms, each with beautiful furnishings, mountain views, and private bath. View the sunset, the stars, or the shocking blue of the Montana sky from the wrap-around deck. Indulge yourself in a soothing soak in the hot tub. Awaken to the aroma of freshly brewed coffee and the anticipation of a delicious gourmet breakfast. This is the perfect way to start your day of sightseeing, hiking, or touring Yellowstone National Park.

Hosts: Nancy and Michael Dawson
Rooms: 5 (5PB) $75–135
Full Breakfast
Credit Cards: A B C D
Notes: 2 5 8 9 10 11 12

NOTES: Credit cards accepted: A Master Card; B Visa; C American Express; D Discover; E Diners Club; F Other; 2 Personal checks accepted; 3 Lunch available; 4 Dinner available; 5 Open all year;

The Lehrkind Mansion B & B

719 N. Wallace Ave., Bozeman, MT 59715-3063
(406) 585-6932; (800) 992-6932
E-mail: lehrkindmansion@imt.net
Web site: www.bozemanbedandbreakfast.com

Featured on the cover of *Victorian Homes* and in *Montana Living*, the Lehrkind Mansion offers one of Montana's most elegant lodging opportunities and finest examples of Queen Anne architecture. Built in 1897, the mansion is listed in the National Register and is still surrounded by a spacious yard, gardens, and porches. A three-story corner tower is among its most spectacular features. Period antiques abound, including a rare 7-foot-tall music box. Queen beds, down comforters, overstuffed chairs, an outdoor hot tub, and a peaceful atmosphere provide relaxation. Only seven blocks from Bozeman's historic Main Street.

Hosts: Jon Gerster and Christopher Nixon
Rooms: 5 (3PB;2SB) $79–159
Full Breakfast
Credit Cards: A B C D
Notes: 2 5 7 8 9 10 11

EMIGRANT

Johnstad's B & B and Log Cabin

03 Paradise Lane; P.O. Box 981
   Emigrant, MT 59027
(406) 333-9003; (800) 340-4993
   Fax (406) 333-9003
E-mail: rjohnstad@aol.com
Web site: www.johnstadsbb.com

Johnstad's Bed and Breakfast and Log Cabin are strategically located in Paradise Valley, just 36 miles north of Yellowstone National Park. The newly built B & B was designed for the comfort of our guests and features spacious, beautifully decorated rooms, all with private baths and spectacular views of the valley. Each morning our guests enjoy a hearty breakfast served either in the dining room or on the deck. And just a few feet away you can enjoy fly-fishing at its best in the Yellowstone River. Also available is our log cabin which features 3 bedrooms, 2 baths, a fully equipped kitchen, laundry facilities, and panoramic views of the Absaroka Mountain range. Come and enjoy classic Montana hospitality in the heart of Paradise Valley. Member of the Montana B & B Association.

Hosts: Ron and Mary Ellen Johnstad
Rooms: 3 (3PB) $85–150
Full Breakfast
Notes: 2 5 9 10 11 12

EUREKA

Tucker's Inn and Guest Ranch

P. O. Box 128; 227 Magnesia Creek Rd.
   Trego, MT 59934-0220
(406) 882-4200; (800) 500-3541
   Fax (406) 882-4201
E-mail: tuckrinn@libby.org
Web site: www.tuckersinn.com

Tucker's Inn and Guest Ranch: A beautiful family ranch nestled in Montana's Glacier Outback and featuring an outdoor hot tub, log-style cabins, Jacuzzi suite, and lodge. Truly a place where hospitality abounds. Experience the people of Montana as well as the beauty of the land. Enjoy horseback riding, white-water rafting, chuckwagon dinners, Glacier Park, canoeing, and evening bonfires. Winter offers snowmobiling, snowshoes, and sledding. Where you come as a guest but leave as family!

Hosts: Charles and Jan Tucker
Rooms: 5 (5PB) $125–175
Continental Breakfast
Credit Cards: A B C D
Notes: 2 5 7 9 10 11 12

GARDINER

Headwaters of the Yellowstone Bed and Breakfast

P. O. Box 25; 9 Olson Ln., Gardiner, MT 59030
(406) 848-7073; (888) 848-7220
　Fax (406) 848-7420
E-mail: mervo@headwatersbandb.com
Web site: www.headwatersbandb.com

Our home on the pristine Yellowstone River, 5 minutes from the north entrance of Yellowstone Park, is a quiet place where you can enjoy the spectacular views of Yellowstone's high country and native wildlife, cast a line in the river, have a picnic in the shade, or just appreciate a respite after viewing the wonders of Yellowstone. Each guest room has a great view, a private bath, and a comfortable bed to provide a refreshing night's sleep. In the morning we will send you on your way after a hearty Montana breakfast. Also available are 2 one-bedroom cabins for families. Rated by and member

of Montana Bed and Breakfast Association.

Hosts: Joyce and Merv Olson
Rooms: 5 (5PB) $85–150
Full Breakfast
Credit Cards: A B C
Notes: 2 5 7 9 11 12

Paradise Gateway B & B Log Cabins

P. O. Box 84, Emigrant, MT 59027-0084
(406) 333-4063; (800) 541-4113
　Fax (406) 333-4626
E-mail: paradise@montanadsl.net
Web site: www.wtp.net/go/paradise

Paradise Gateway

Paradise Gateway Bed and Breakfast, on 20 acres just minutes from Yellowstone National Park, offers quiet, charming, comfortable guest rooms in the shadow of the majestic Rocky Mountains. As day breaks, enjoy a country, gourmet breakfast by the banks of the Yellowstone River, a noted blue-ribbon trout stream. A "cowboy treat tray" is served in the afternoon. The Emigrant Peak Log Cabin is located on 28 acres of Yellowstone River frontage next to the bed and breakfast. Yellowstone Meadow Cabin, 35 feet from the river, will set your mood to

---

NOTES: Credit cards accepted: A Master Card; B Visa; C American Express; D Discover; E Diners Club; F Other; 2 Personal checks accepted; 3 Lunch available; 4 Dinner available; 5 Open all year;

enjoy a very peaceful bit of "Paradise." Decorated in country charm with every convenience of home. Extremely private. Member of the Montana Bed and Breakfast Association. Pets welcome in kennels only. Full breakfast served in B & B, continental in cabin.

Hosts: Pete and Carol Reed
Rooms: 4 (4PB) $85–200
Full Breakfast
Credit Cards: A B
Notes: 2 5 7 8 9 10 11 12

GLENDIVE

The Hostetler House B & B

113 N. Douglas St., Glendive, MT 59330-1619
(406) 377-4505; (800) 965-8456
   Fax (406) 377-8456
E-mail: hostetler@midrivers.com

The Hostetler House

Two blocks from downtown shopping and restaurants, the Hostetler House Bed and Breakfast is a charming, 1912 historic home with three comfortable guest rooms, a sitting room, sunporch, tandem bicycle, and hot tub. A full gourmet breakfast is served on Grandma's china. Located on I-94 and the Yellowstone River, close to parks, swimming pool, tennis courts, golf course, antique shops, and churches.

Enjoy relaxing in our hot tub. Craig and Dea invite you to "arrive as a guest and leave as a friend."

Hosts: Craig and Dea Hostetler
Rooms: 3 (1PB;2SB) $50–65
Full Breakfast
Notes: 2 5 8 9 10 11

LIVINGSTON

Greystone Inn Bed and Breakfast and Cabins

122 S. Yellowstone St., Livingston, MT 59047-2634
(406) 222-8319; Fax (406) 222-8319
Web site: www.montanagreystoneinn.com

"Step back in time" at the Greystone Inn, with its turn-of-the-century charm. The inn is located 2 blocks from historic downtown Livingston and 4 blocks from the Yellowstone River. Enjoy a made-from-scratch breakfast. We also have 2 cabins to choose from. One is a stone's throw to the Yellowstone River, great for fishermen and families. The other is in the mountains, located just this side of heaven.

Hosts: Lin and Gary Lee
Rooms: 3 (1PB;2SB) $65–90
Full Breakfast
Notes: 2 5 7 8 9 10 11 12

VIRGINIA CITY

Stonehouse Inn B & B

306 E. Idaho, P. O. Box 205
   Virginia City, MT 59755-0205
(406) 843-5504
E-mail: roojake@3rivers.net
Web site: www.stonehouseinnbb.com

Stonehouse Inn

Located on a quiet street only blocks
from the historic section of Virginia
City, this Victorian stone home is listed
on the National Register of Historic
Places. Brass beds and antiques in every
room give the inn a romantic touch.
Five bedrooms share two baths. Full
breakfasts are served each morning,
and smoking is allowed on our porches.
Skiing, snowmobiling, golfing, hunting, and fly-fishing nearby.

Hosts: John and Linda Hamilton
Rooms: 5 (5SB) $65–80
Full Breakfast
Credit Cards: A B
Notes: 2 7 8 10 12

NEBRASKA

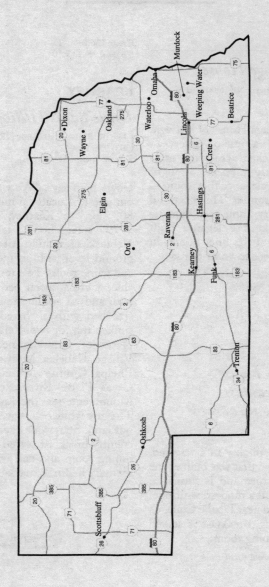

Nebraska

BERWYN

1909 Heritage House

101 Curran Ave., Berwyn, NE 68819-0196
(308) 935-1136

The 1909 Heritage House of Berwyn, Nebraska, recalls a time of yesteryear, when trains tracked across the open prairie and early pioneers brought with them what elegance they could to tame the new frontier. This beautiful Victorian country home is a dramatic example of that kind of elegance. Built in 1909 as one of the finer homes in the railroad service town of Berwyn.

Hosts: Dale and Meriam Thomas
Rooms: 6 (2PB;4SB) $60–125
Continental Breakfast
Notes: 2 5 9 10

CRETE

The Parson's House Bed and Breakfast

638 Forest Ave., Crete, NE 68333-2935
(402) 826-2634

Enjoy warm hospitality in a restored, four-square home that was built at the turn of the century and is furnished with antiques and a modern whirlpool bathtub. Located near Doane College's beautiful campus. Breakfast is served in the formal dining room.

Hosts: Sandy and Harold Richardson
Rooms: 2 (2SB) $45
Full Breakfast

Credit Cards: F
Notes: 2 5 8 9 10

KEARNEY

Uncle Sam's Hilltop Lodge

74451 R. R., Box 110, Funk, NE 68940-9772
(308) 995-5568
E-mail: ssschrock@aol.com

Uncle Sam says, "We want you to be our guest." Located 5 minutes from I-80, close to Kearney, our spacious 1979 solar home is built into Nebraska's sandhills. All four levels are ground level with an indoor sandpile and game room. Two rooms are available, a brass queen bed with private bath and an antique four-poster full-size bed with a shared bath and a sunken tub for two. Relax by the fireplaces or tour the nearby Pioneer Village, Cabela's, Morris Cookbooks, Phelps County Museum, and the Great Platte River Road Archway Monument; see the sandhill cranes. The rare white ones have been seen on our land. Start your day with a hearty country breakfast served in the formal dining room and end with a complimentary bedtime snack.

Hosts: Sam and Sharon
Rooms: 2 (1PB;1SB) $50–60
Full Breakfast
Credit Cards: D F
Notes: 2 5 6 7 8 9 10

LINCOLN

Atwood House

740 S. 17th St., Lincoln, NE 68508
(402) 438-4567; (800) 884-6554
Fax (402) 477-8314
E-mail: larry@atwoodhouse.com
Web site: www.atwoodhouse.com

Atwood House

"Experience the Elegance" of a suite in this 7,500-plus-square-foot 1894 Neoclassical Georgian Revival mansion. Suites have queen/king beds, private sitting areas with TV/VCR, and private bath (three with two-person whirlpools). The Atwood Suite is Lincoln's most elegant bridal suite. It provides more than 800 square feet of ambience. Breakfast is served as late as 11 A.M. on bone china with sterling flatware, Waterford crystal, and linens. Great for the business traveler as well as for that special occasion.

Hosts: Ruth and Larry Stoll
Rooms: 4 (4PB) $85–179
Full Breakfast
Credit Cards: A B C D F
Notes: 2 5 8 9 10

OAKLAND

Benson Bed and Breakfast

402 N. Oakland Ave., Oakland, NE 68045-1135
(402) 685-6051
E-mail: sanderson@genesisnet.net
Web site:
     www.virtualcities.com/ons/ne/e/nee3701.htm

Located in the center of a small town, Benson Bed and Breakfast is beautifully decorated and offers a breakfast you won't soon forget, served in the dining room with all its finery. Now in its ninth year of operation. Features include a large collection of soft-drink collectibles, a library full of books, a beautiful garden room to relax in, and a large whirlpool tub with color TV on the wall. All rooms are on the second level. Visit our new addition, our own gift shop. Three blocks west of Highway 77. No smoking.

Benson Bed and Breakfast

Hosts: Stan and Norma Anderson
Rooms: 3 (3SB) $55–60
Full Breakfast
Credit Cards: D
Notes: 2 5 8 9 10 12

---

6 Pets welcome; 7 Children welcome; 8 Tennis nearby; 9 Swimming nearby; 10 Golf nearby; 11 Skiing nearby; 12 May be booked through travel agent

OMAHA

The Farm House Bed and Breakfast

32617 Church Rd., Murdock, NE 68407-2117
(402) 867-2062
E-mail: farmhouse@web-unwired.net

A 100-year-old home in the country on paved road. Handmade quilts, antiques, and angel collection. Near aircraft museum, zoo safari, antique shops and malls, summer theater, variety of restaurants, 2 state parks, 2 auto racetracks. Quiet, relaxed, affordable. Thirty minutes from Lincoln or Omaha. Air-conditioned. Hiking and biking trails, porch swing, horseshoe pits, croquet set, games, videos, private parlor.

Hosts: Mike and Pat Meierhenry
Rooms: 4 (2PB;2SB) $40–55
Full Breakfast
Credit Cards:
Notes: 2 5 7 8 9 10

The Jones'

1617 S. 90th St., Omaha, NE 68124-1207
(402) 397-0721

Large, private residence with large deck and gazebo in the back. Fresh cinnamon rolls are served for breakfast. Your hosts' interests include golf, travel, needlework, and meeting other people. Located 5 minutes from I-80.

Hosts: Theo and Don Jones
Rooms: 3 (2PB;2SB) $35
Continental Breakfast
Notes: 2 6 7 8

ORD

The Shepherds Inn

Rte. 3, Box 108 A, Ord, NE 68862
(308) 728-3306; (800) 901-8649
   Fax (308) 728-7030
E-mail: ddvshep@cornhusker.net
Web site: www.bbonline.com/ne/shepherd

Treat yourself to a quiet escape in the heart of the country. Watch the sunrise, walk along a country road, or spend a lazy afternoon on our lawn swing. Spend an evening reading in the parlor or gaze at the star-studded skies while relaxing in the outdoor hot tub. This charming, early 1900's farmhouse is furnished with exquisite antiques in Victorian decor. A full country breakfast is served. Innkeepers live a shout away.

Hosts: Doris and Don Vancura
Rooms: 3 (3PB) $65
Full Breakfast
Credit Cards: A B F
Notes: 2 5 7 8 9 10

The Shepherds Inn

OSHKOSH

The Locust Tree B & B

400 W. 5th St., Oshkosh, NE 69154-5001
(308) 772-3530
E-mail: pregier@lakemac.net
Web site: www.rimstarintl.com/loc00001.htm

Enjoy small-town hospitality in a contemporary family home. The large brick home is graced with majestic spruce and locust trees. Gracious guest rooms with baths. Continental breakfast. Access to free summer swimming, spa, Pony Express route, Ash Hollow State Park, and museum.

Hosts: Pete and Ardena Regier
Rooms: 2 (1PB;1SB) $55–75
Continental Breakfast
Notes: 2 5 7 9 10

RAVENNA

Aunt Betty's B & B

804 Grand Ave., Ravenna, NE 68869-1012
(308) 452-3739; (800) 632-9114
    Fax (308) 452-3739
E-mail: auntbetty@auntbettysbb.com
Web site: www.auntbettysbb.com

Aunt Betty's

Enjoy the peace of a small town while staying at Aunt Betty's three-story Victorian bed and breakfast. Four bedrooms are furnished in antiques at the main house. Two guest rooms are furnished in antiques with a "Grandma's House" theme at "Grandma's Cottage." All guests are treated to a full "Nebraska" breakfast that includes Aunt Betty's sticky buns. Both houses offer a hot tub for your relaxation. Antique shop is located at the B & B.

Hosts: Harvey and Betty Shrader

Rooms: 6 (1PB;5SB) $60–90
Full Breakfast
Credit Cards: A B C D
Notes: 2 3 4 5 7 8 9 10

SCOTTSBLUFF

Barn Anew B & B

170549 Cty. Rd. L, Mitchell, NE 69357
(308) 632-8647
E-mail: barnanew@alltel.net
Web site: www.prairieweb.com/barnanew

Enjoy a country formal setting in this "reborn" 100-year-old barn located just minutes west of Scottsbluff in the shadow of Scotts Bluff National Monument and Museum. Very close to the historic Oregon Trail. Guest rooms furnished in Victorian antique furniture and appointments. Leisure room and sunroom. The formal dining room is surrounded by a mural of the farm in 1910. Breakfast by candlelight. Mini-museum and antique shop. Peace and quiet guaranteed. Double occupancy—husband/wife.

Hosts: Dick and Jane Snell
Rooms: 4 (4PB) $85–90
Full Breakfast
Credit Cards: A B C D E
Notes: 2 5 10

SYRACUSE

Alte Haus B & B

579 Thorne St., Syracuse, NE 68446
(402) 269-3559
E-mail: information@altehaus.com
Web site: www.altehaus.com

"Stepping Back in Time" is the feeling when you enter the Alte Haus B & B.

---

6 Pets welcome; 7 Children welcome; 8 Tennis nearby; 9 Swimming nearby; 10 Golf nearby; 11 Skiing nearby; 12 May be booked through travel agent

Relax and enjoy the ambience of this Arts and Crafts home that greets you with an open staircase, antiques, and oak wood floors. Warm yourself by the wood-burning fireplace or enjoy a day of reading on the front porch. A full breakfast is prepared on a 100-year-old stove. Only 16 miles from historic Nebraska City.

Hosts: Dave and Mary Coleman
Rooms: 2 (2PB) $60
Full Breakfast
Notes: 2 5 9 10

NEVADA

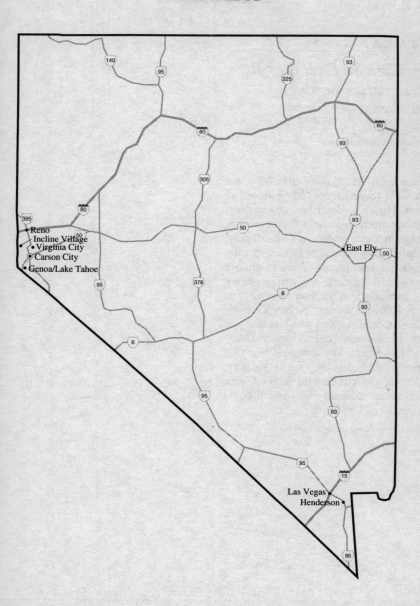

NEVADA

Mi Casa Su Casa B & B Reservation Service

P. O. Box 950, Tempe, AZ 85280
(480) 990-0682; (800) 456-0682
  Fax (480) 990-3390
E-mail: micasa@azres.com
Web site: www.azres.com

Founded in 1981, our name, Mi Casa Su Casa (Spanish for "My House [is] Your House"), describes our service, for our intent is to help visitors feel at home in the Southwest. Our friendly, helpful hosts have host homes in safe, quiet neighborhoods. You can choose from 250 historic-to-contemporary accommodations in four states. (See our listings under Arizona, New Mexico, and Utah.) In Nevada, we list: Henderson (near Hoover Dam) and Las Vegas. We also represent two luxury villas, one in Puerto Vallarta, Mexico, and the second in the Costa Brava area of Spain and a few B & Bs in southern California.

Hosts: Ruth Young (coordinator)

NEW HAMPSHIRE

New Hampshire

BETHLEHEM

The Mulburn Inn
At Bethlehem

2370 Main St., Bethlehem, NH 03574-4915
(603) 869-3389; (800) 457-9440
E-mail: info@mulburninn.com
Web site: www.mulburninn.com

The Mulburn Inn at Bethlehem

Step into a gracious age of elegance when you visit this historic inn originally built in 1908 as a Woolworth family summer estate. This beautiful inn boasts of its wrap-around porches, hardwood floors, stained glass, and three fireplaces. Relax in the cozy atmosphere where legends such as Cary Grant and Barbara Hutton once stayed. The Mulburn Inn is located in the heart of New Hampshire's White Mountains, where hiking, golfing, skiing, and all of nature's splendor abound.

Hosts: Christina Ferraro and Alicia Loveless
Rooms: 7 (7PB) $80–145
Full Breakfast
Credit Cards: A B
Notes: 2 5 7 8 9 10 11 12

BRADFORD

Candlelite Inn

5 Greenhouse Ln., Bradford, NH 03221-3505
(603) 938-5571; (888) 812-5571
Fax (603) 938-2564
E-mail: candlelite@conknet.com
Web site: www.candleliteinn.com

Voted as the 2001 Inn of the Year, this 1897 Country Victorian inn has all the grace and charm for that perfect getaway. We serve a full breakfast—down to dessert—in the Sun Room, which overlooks the pond. Relax on the gazebo porch sipping lemonade on a lazy summer day, or curl up in the parlor in front of a crackling fire with a cup of warm cranberry cider. Come and experience the relaxed atmosphere and the quiet elegance of this all-seasons inn.

Hosts: Marilyn and Les Gordon
Rooms: 6 (6PB) $90–125
Full Breakfast
Credit Cards: A B C D E
Notes: 2 5 8 9 10 11 12

Candlelite Inn

NOTES: Credit cards accepted: A Master Card; B Visa; C American Express; D Discover; E Diners Club; F Other; 2 Personal checks accepted; 3 Lunch available; 4 Dinner available; 5 Open all year;

GLEN

Covered Bridge House

Rte. 302 Box 989, Glen, NH 03838
(603) 383-9109; (800) 232-9109
E-mail: info@coveredbridgehouse.com
Web site: www.coveredbridgehouse.com

Feel at home in our cozy bed and breakfast on the Saco River located next to a restored 1850s covered bridge. With just six guest rooms and a cozy living room, our inn offers a comfortable, informal atmosphere. Awaken to a hearty country breakfast. In warm weather, enjoy the beauty of the Saco River in our backyard—swim, tube, fish, or sunbathe on the rocks. Just minutes from Attitash. Relax in our outdoor hot tub, which is open all year.

Hosts: Dan and Nancy Wanek
Rooms: 6 (4PB;2SB) $59–109
Full Breakfast
Credit Cards: A B C D
Notes: 2 5 7 9 10 11 12

HANOVER

Shaker Farm Bed and Breakfast

597 N H Rte. 4-A, Enfield, NH 03748-9317
(603) 632-7664; (800) 613-7664
    Fax (603) 632-9290
E-mail: charlotte.toms@valley.net
Web site: www.shakerfarm.com

Historical country inn. Circa 1794. Beautifully restored with large rooms, king beds, AC, TV, and private baths. Antiques and period decor throughout, legendary breakfast, quiet country setting. Mascoma Lake, water sports.

Hiking trails. We pamper our guests. Dartmouth College 10 miles.

Hosts: Hal and Charlotte Toms
Rooms: 6 (4PB;2SB) $75–135
Full Breakfast
Credit Cards: A B
Notes: 2 5 9 10 11

HOLDERNESS

The Inn on Golden Pond

Rte. 3, P. O. Box 680, Holderness, NH 03245
(603) 968-7269; Fax (603) 968-9226
E-mail: innongp@lr.net
Web site: www.innongoldenpond.com

The Inn on Golden Pond

This 1879 Colonial home is nestled on 50 wooded acres, offering guests a traditional New England setting. A short distance away is Squam Lake, setting for the classic film *On Golden Pond*. Guest rooms are individually decorated in traditional country style. A hearty, home-cooked breakfast each morning features farm-fresh eggs, homemade muffins and breads, and delicious house specialties.

Hosts: Bill and Bonnie Webb
Rooms: 8 (8PB) $115–165
Full Breakfast
Credit Cards: A B C D
Notes: 2 5 8 9 10 11 12

6 Pets welcome; 7 Children welcome; 8 Tennis nearby; 9 Swimming nearby; 10 Golf nearby; 11 Skiing nearby; 12 May be booked through travel agent

JACKSON

Ellis River House

R. R. 16, Box 656, Jackson, NH 03846
(603) 383-9339; (800) 233-8309
　Fax (603) 383-4142
E-mail: innkeeper@erhinn.com
Web site: www.ellisriverhouse.com

Ellis River House

Sample true New England hospitality at this enchanting, small hotel/country inn within a short stroll of the village. The house has comfortable king and queen guest rooms decorated with Laura Ashley prints, some with fireplaces and two-person Jacuzzis, cable TV, scenic balconies, and period antiques; all with individually controlled heat and AC. Also available are two-room and family suites, a riverfront cottage, hot tub, sauna, heated pool, sitting and game rooms, and a sundeck overlooking the pristine Ellis River. Enjoy a breakfast with homemade breads or a delicious trout dinner. Relax with libations and billiards in the pub.

Hosts: Monica and Jim Lee
Rooms: 21 (21PB) $95–255
Full Breakfast
Credit Cards: A B C D
Notes: 2 5 8 9 10 11 12

JEFFERSON

Jefferson Inn

Rte. 2, Jefferson, NH 03583-9306
(603) 586-7998; (800) 729-7908
　Fax (603) 586-7808
E-mail: jeffinn@ncia.net
Web site: www.jeffersoninn.com

A warm, romantic 1896 renovated Victorian home nestled in the northern White Mountains. There are mountain views in all directions. Each of the nine unique rooms and two family suites has a private bath and distinctive decor. Wake up each morning to a full breakfast. Spend the day hiking, cycling, or swimming in the summer and skiing, ice skating, or snowmobiling in the winter. The outdoor opportunities and attractions abound. Afternoon tea and homemade baked goods are served at the end of the day before you return to the comfort of your well-appointed room for another restful night.

Hosts: Mark and Cindy Robert and Bette Bovio
Rooms: 11 (11PB) $85–175
Full Breakfast
Credit Cards: A B C D　F
Notes: 2 5 7 8 9 10 11 12

NORTH CONWAY

Nereledge Inn

River Rd. off Main St., North Conway, NH 03860
(603) 356-2831; (888) 355-2831
　Fax (603) 356-7085
E-mail: info@nereledgeinn.com
Web site: www.nereledgeinn.com

Season after season guests return to Nereledge Inn for warm hospitality

---

NOTES: Credit cards accepted: A Master Card; B Visa; C American Express; D Discover; E Diners Club; F Other; 2 Personal checks accepted; 3 Lunch available; 4 Dinner available; 5 Open all year;

and hearty breakfasts. Nereledge has an informal atmosphere with eleven air-conditioned guest rooms and two large comfortable living rooms. Help yourself to a cup of tea or refrigerate perishables in the guest pantry. Walk to village for shopping, dining, and theater or to the river for swimming, canoeing, and fishing. Hike, bike, and climb nearby. Close to all major ski areas. Families welcome.

Nereledge Inn

Hosts: Dave and Betsy Halpin
Rooms: 11 (6PB;5SB) $64–159
Full Breakfast
Credit Cards: A B C D
Notes: 2 5 7 8 9 10 11 12

NORTH WOODSTOCK

Wilderness Inn Bed and Breakfast

Rtes. 3 and 112, North Woodstock, NH 03262
(603) 745-3890; (800) 200-9453
E-mail: info@thewildernessinn.com
Web site: www.thewildernessinn.com

This 1912 "Craftsman Style" country inn offers seven guest bedrooms, family suites with Jacuzzi tubs, and a honeymoon cottage with Jacuzzi tub and fireplace. A full gourmet breakfast and

afternoon tea served on the front porch are included. No smoking please. Families welcome; central to the White Mountains; downhill skiing is within 3 miles.

Hosts: Rosanna and Michael Yarnell
Rooms: 8 (8PB) $65–150
Full Breakfast
Credit Cards: A B C
Notes: 2 5 7 8 9 10 11 12

PLYMOUTH

Colonel Spencer Inn

3 Colonel Spencer Rd., Campton, NH 03223
(603) 536-3438
Web site: www.colonelspencerinn.com

A 1764 center-chimney Colonial with antique furnishings, wide pine floorboards, hand-hewn beams, and Indian shutters. Seven antique-appointed bedrooms with private baths welcome guests. A full country breakfast is served in a fireplaced dining room. The inn is convenient to both lake and mountain attractions, at Exit 27 off I-93, 1/2 mile south on Route 3.

Hosts: Carolyn and Alan Hill
Rooms: 7 (7PB) $45–75
Full Breakfast
Notes: 2 5 7 8 9 10 11 12

Highland Farm B & B

148 County Farm Rd., Dover, NH 03820-6022
(603) 743-3399
E-mail: highlandfarm@attbi.com

A large, brick Victorian country home offering spacious guest rooms, easy access to seacoast and mountains via

---

6 Pets welcome; 7 Children welcome; 8 Tennis nearby; 9 Swimming nearby; 10 Golf nearby; 11 Skiing nearby; 12 May be booked through travel agent

the nearby Spaulding Turnpike. All on quiet, rolling fields with nature trails along the Cocheco River. A full gourmet breakfast with fresh fruits, pastry, and a touch of Scottish hospitality.

Hosts: Noreen and Michael
Rooms: 4 (2PB;2SB) $90–120
Full Breakfast
Credit Cards: A B
Notes: 2 5 10 11

WATERVILLE VALLEY

The Valley Inn and Red Fox Tavern

P. O. Box 1, Tecumseh Rd.
    Waterville Valley, NH 03215
(603) 236-8336; (800) 343-0969
    Fax (603) 236-4294
E-mail: info@valleyinn.com
Web site: www.valleyinn.com

Waterville Valley's only full-service resort. Red Fox Tavern offers family dining and room service. Forty-nine well-appointed rooms. Heated indoor/outdoor pool open year-round. Whirlpool jet tubs and in-room coffeemakers. Seasonal recreation packages included and continental breakfast. Check out Web site for hot deals and packages. AAA and senior discounts. Fully air-conditioned. Great conference and banquet space. Group rates available.

Host: Lynn T. McArdle
Rooms: 49 (49PB) $78–169
Continental Breakfast
Credit Cards: A B C D E
Notes: 4 5 7 8 9 10 11 12

NOTES: Credit cards accepted: A Master Card; B Visa; C American Express; D Discover; E Diners Club; F Other; 2 Personal checks accepted; 3 Lunch available; 4 Dinner available; 5 Open all year;

NEW JERSEY

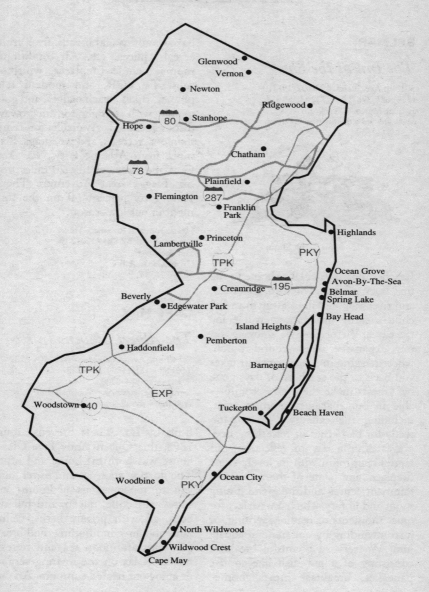

New Jersey

BELMAR

The Inn at the Shore

301 4th Ave., Belmar, NJ 07719-2104
(732) 681-3762; Fax (732) 280-1914
E-mail: tomvolker@aol.com
Web site: www.theinnattheshore.com

The Inn at the Shore

Beaches, boardwalk, lake (home to the first flock of swans bred in America), and riverwalk just steps away from our child-friendly inn. Guests will enjoy the casual Victorian-style ambience on our expansive wrap-around porch, where relaxing in a rocking chair takes you back to the seashore of days gone by. Guests make themselves comfortable in our spacious common areas, including the cafe-style brick patio ready for barbecues or refreshing beverages after a day of reflection, our large living room with its lovely stone fireplace and state-of-the-art entertainment center, and the grand dining room and library, which are perfect for quiet moments of reading, writing, or just unwinding by our tranquil aquarium. We serve a bountiful breakfast consisting of a hot dish like sunrise pancakes, breakfast meats, home-baked muffins and breads, fresh fruits, cereals, juices, etc. Air-conditioned rooms include fireplaces, whirlpool tubs, TV/VCR, and modem telephones. Bikes, beach badges, and guest pantry with refrigerator, microwave, dishes included. Available for family reunions, retreats, and weddings. Sixty miles from Atlantic City, New York City, and Philadelphia; 20 miles from Six Flags Great Adventure Theme Park. Fifty percent off on the third night in our low season.

Hosts: Tom and Rosemary Volker
Rooms: 10 (4PB;6SB) $120–205
Full Breakfast
Credit Cards: A B C
Notes: 2 5 7 8 9 10 12

CAPE MAY

The Albert Stevens Inn

127 Myrtle Ave., Cape May, NJ 08204-1237
(609) 884-4717; (800) 890-2287
    Fax (609) 884-8320
E-mail: albertstevensinn@hotmail.com
Web site: www.albertstevensinn.com

Built by Dr. Albert Stevens around 1898, this Queen Anne Free Classic house was both his home and office. The floating staircase and tower guide you to ten spacious bedrooms and suites with king, queen, and full-size beds, all with private baths, ceiling fans, and air-conditioning. Full breakfast with afternoon tea and refreshments. Relax on the inviting veranda or enjoy our heated sunroom. An out-

---

NOTES: Credit cards accepted: A Master Card; B Visa; C American Express; D Discover; E Diners Club; F Other; 2 Personal checks accepted; 3 Lunch available; 4 Dinner available; 5 Open all year;

side hot tub and free on-site parking with the beach and shopping only three blocks away. Epicurean and family restaurants are only 1/2 block away. Beach towels and beach chairs available to our guests. Children over 12 are welcome.

The Albert Stevens Inn

Hosts: Jim and Lenanne Labusciano
Rooms: 10 (10PB) $90–230
Full Breakfast
Credit Cards: A B
Notes: 2 5 7 8 9 10

Bedford Inn

805 Stockton Ave., Cape May, NJ 08204-2446
(609) 884-4158; Fax (609) 884-6320
E-mail: info@bedfordinn.com
Web site: www.bedfordinn.com

Bedford Inn

This fully restored Victorian B & B is romantic and elegant. All rooms and "honeymoon" suites are furnished with authentic antiques and have private bath, television, VCR, hair dryer, and air-conditioning; most with queen beds. We also have two suites with king beds available. Rates include gourmet breakfast and afternoon tea and treats, beach towels, beach chairs, and limited on-site parking. Great location—very close to the beach and town center. Parlor fireplace and two-story porch.

Hosts: James and Cindy Schmucker
Rooms: 10 (10PB) $95–235
Full Breakfast
Credit Cards: A B C D
Notes: 2 8 9 10 12

Buttonwood Manor B & B

115 N. Broadway, Cape May, NJ 08204
(609) 884-4070
E-mail: ring@dandy.net
Web site: www.buttonwoodmanorbb.com

Buttonwood Manor is an elegant Colonial Revival house built in 1908. It is just four short blocks from the beach. Cape May is known for its lovely beaches, outstanding restaurants, quaint shops, antique stores, birding activities, lighthouse, and fishing. The home showcases many antique furnishings including American Brilliant Cut Glass. All rooms have queen- or king-sized beds, private baths, ceiling fans, and air-conditioning. A full breakfast is served, with refreshments each afternoon. There is off-street parking for all guests, children 12 and over are welcome. Your hosts, Diane and Roger, invite you to join them in front of the cozy parlor fireplace or on the shady terrace to relax and "find rest for your

---

6 Pets welcome; 7 Children welcome; 8 Tennis nearby; 9 Swimming nearby; 10 Golf nearby; 11 Skiing nearby; 12 May be booked through travel agent

soul." Open all year. Swimming at beach nearby.

Buttonwood Manor

Hosts: Diane and Roger Ring
Rooms: 7 (7PB) $95–200
Full Breakfast
Credit Cards: A B
Notes: 2 5 7 8 9 10

Captain Mey's Inn

202 Ocean St., Cape May, NJ 08204-2322
(609) 884-7793; (800) 981-3702
    Fax (609) 884-7793
E-mail: innkeeper@snip.net
Web site: www.captainmeys.com

The inn is an 1890 Colonial Revival Victorian named after the Dutch explorer Captain Cornelius Mey. The Dutch heritage is evident from the Persian rugs on the tabletops to the Delft Blue china collection. The wraparound veranda is furnished with wicker furniture, hanging ferns, and Victorian wind curtains. A full breakfast is served by candlelight with classical music in the formal dining room; in the summer, breakfast is served on the veranda. Children over 8 welcome.

Hosts: George and Kathleen Blinn
Rooms: 7 (7PB) $85–235
Full Breakfast
Credit Cards: A B C
Notes: 2 7 9 10

Duke of Windsor Inn

817 Washington St., Cape May, NJ 08204-1651
(609) 884-1355; (800) 826-8973
    Fax (609) 884-1887
E-mail: innkeeper@dukeofwindsorinn.com
Web site: www.dukeofwindsorinn.com

Sense the romance of a classic Victorian, Queen Anne B & B inn. The Duke of Windsor Inn, built in 1896 with a 45-foot tower, has a large, central foyer with a three-story, carved oak staircase and Tiffany stained-glass windows. The parlor with a corner fireplace, two formal dining rooms, and ten guest rooms decorated with lovely antique furnishings extend a feeling of warmth and elegance. Gourmet breakfasts, afternoon tea and treats, on-site parking, and air-conditioned rooms await our guests. Open year-round.

Host: Patricia Joyce
Rooms: 10 (10PB) $95–235
Full Breakfast
Credit Cards: A B
Notes: 2 5 8 9 10

The Henry Sawyer Inn

722 Columbia Ave., Cape May, NJ 08204-2332
(609) 884-5667; (800) 449-5667
    Fax (609) 884-9406
Web site: www.henrysawyerinn.com

An elegant 1877 Victorian bed and breakfast inn. All our spacious, airy rooms and suites have private baths, refrigerators, air-conditioners, TVs, and hair dryers. Some accommodations have other amenities, including a private veranda, fireplaces, a whirlpool tub, and VCRs. All accommodations include a full breakfast and afternoon refreshments; the use of beach tags, towels, and chairs; private hot and cold beach showers; and off-street parking. It's just a short walk to the Washington Street Mall, Washington Square stores, major antique shops, tennis courts, ocean promenade and beach, and fine restaurants. Children over 10 are welcome.

Hosts: Mary and Barbara Morris
Rooms: 5 (5PB) $85–225
Full Breakfast
Credit Cards: A B C D E F
Notes: 2 5 7 8 9 10 12

Jeremiah Hand House

814 Washington St., Cape May, NJ 08204
(609) 884-1135; (800) 532-6559
E-mail: innkeeper@jeremiahhandhouse.com
Web site: www.jeremiahhandhouse.com

The Jeremiah Hand House was built as a parsonage for the Presbyterian church. The inn has four beautifully decorated bedrooms, a relaxing parlor, front and side porches, and a patio to enjoy. The walking mall is 2 blocks away, while the beach is about 4 blocks away. Breakfast is served in the beautiful toile-papered dining room at individual tables. Afternoon sweets are served at 4 P.M. Come and enjoy beautiful Victorian Cape May. Children over 7 are welcome.

Hosts: Barbara Downs and Bill Fisher
Rooms: 4 (4PB) $100–175
Full Breakfast
Credit Cards: A B
Notes: 2 5 7 8 9 10

Primrose Inn

1102 Lafayette St., Cape May, NJ 08204-1722
(609) 884-8288; (800) 606-8288
   Fax (609) 884-2358
E-mail: primrose98@juno.com
Web site: www.theprimroseinn.com

Primrose Inn

Any season of the year is lovely in Cape May. The Primrose Inn, located conveniently to harbor, museums, shopping, and beach, is a quaint 1850 farmhouse furnished in an eclectic style. All rooms have private baths (some tubs have jets), air-conditioning, ceiling fans, clock/radios, and color television. Several have fireplaces to add warmth in the winter. Our package includes full breakfast, afternoon refreshment, on-site parking, bicycles, and beach chairs and towels. AAA-approved. Come! Enjoy!

Hosts: Bart and Sally Denithorne
Rooms: 6 (6PB) $90–260
Full Breakfast
Credit Cards: A B D
Notes: 2 5 7 8 9 10

The Queen Victoria®
Bed and Breakfast

102 Ocean St., Cape May, NJ 08204-2320
(609) 884-8702
Web site: www.queenvictoria.com

---

6 Pets welcome; 7 Children welcome; 8 Tennis nearby; 9 Swimming nearby; 10 Golf nearby; 11 Skiing nearby; 12 May be booked through travel agent

The Queen Victoria offers twenty-one antique-furnished rooms and suites in two faithfully restored homes located in the center of the historic district, just one block to the Atlantic Ocean and shops. All rooms have a private bath, mini-refrigerator, and air-conditioning. Luxury suites have a whirlpool tub and television. A hearty buffet breakfast is served each morning, and a proper tea is enjoyed each afternoon. Complimentary bicycles, beach chairs, beach towels, and beverages are available. Open all year.

The Queen Victoria

Hosts: Joan and Dane Wells
Rooms: 21 (21PB) $100–300
Full Breakfast
Credit Cards: A B
Notes: 2 5 8 9 10

Windward House

24 Jackson St., Cape May, NJ 08204-1465
(609) 884-3368; Fax (609) 884-1575
Web site: www.windwardhouseinn.com

This elegant Edwardian seaside inn has an entryway and staircase that are perhaps the prettiest in town.

Spacious guest rooms filled with fine antiques have king and queen beds, mini-refrigerators, AC, and TV/VCR. Three sun and shade porches, cozy parlor fireplace, Christmas finery. In an unbeatable location in the historic district, one-half block from the beach, shopping mall, and wonderful restaurants. Beach towels are available. Homemade breakfast and afternoon refreshments. Midweek discounts during the off-season. Children 8 and over are welcome.

Hosts: Sandy, Owen and Vicki Miller
Rooms: 8 (8PB) $100–230
Full Breakfast
Credit Cards: A B
Notes: 2 7 8 9 10 12

EDGEWATER PARK

Historic Whitebriar B & B

1029 Cooper St., Beverly, NJ 08010-1757
(609) 871-3859

Historic bed and breakfast inn 10 blocks from Delaware River. Fifteen period buildings to choose: include Underground Railroad, Revolutionary Dunks Ferry Inn, Riverhouse B & B Inn, Woodrow Wilson's Sanctuary B & B Inn, etc. Visit the family farm (ponies, pigs, poultry, and goats). House tours/tea parties/meals.

Hosts: Carole and Bill Moore
Rooms: 45 (3PB;42SB) $50–165
Full Breakfast
Credit Cards:
Notes: 2 3 4 5 6 7 8 9

NOTES: Credit cards accepted: A Master Card; B Visa; C American Express; D Discover; E Diners Club; F Other; 2 Personal checks accepted; 3 Lunch available; 4 Dinner available; 5 Open all year;

GLENWOOD

Apple Valley Inn

P. O. Box 302; 967 Rte. 517
    Glenwood, NJ 07418-0302
(973) 764-3735; Fax (973) 764-1050
E-mail: appleinn@warwick.net
Web site: www.applevalleyinn.com

Apple Valley Inn

Elegant bed and breakfast in the Early American tradition. An 1831 Colonial mansion. Pool, trout stream, apple orchard, antique shop, Old Grist Mill, skiing, water park, Appalachian Trail, West Point, Botanical Gardens, two state parks, and Hudson Valley attractions are within a short drive. Holidays two-night minimum. Reduced rates for 6+ days. Special events weekends.

Host: Elizabeth
Rooms: 8 (3PB;5SB) $115–150
Full Breakfast
Credit Cards: A B   F
Notes: 4 5 7 8 9 10 11

HADDONFIELD

Haddonfield Inn

44 W. End Ave., Haddonfield, NJ 08033-2616
(856) 428-2195; (800) 269-0014
    Fax (856) 354-1273

E-mail: innkeeper@haddonfieldinn.com
Web site: www.haddonfieldinn.com

Recently remodeled Victorian featuring elegant rooms and suites. All with fireplaces and many with whirlpools. All rooms include private baths, cable television, telephone with voice mail and internet access. Gourmet breakfast included, as well as complimentary snacks and beverages. Within walking distance to over 200 shops and restaurants in a lovely picturesque village. Short walk to the train for fast transportation to Rutgers University, the NJ Aquarium, Delaware Waterfront, and Downtown Philadelphia. Catered affairs and business conferences welcome. Offering Sunday afternoon tea service by reservation.

Hosts: Fred and Nancy Chorpita
Rooms: 9 (9PB) $120–215
Full Breakfast
Credit Cards: A B C D
Notes: 2 3 4 5 6 7 8 9 10 12

Haddonfield Inn

OCEAN CITY

Delancey Manor

869 Delancey Pl., Ocean City, NJ 08226-4137
(609) 398-6147

---

6 Pets welcome; 7 Children welcome; 8 Tennis nearby; 9 Swimming nearby; 10 Golf nearby; 11 Skiing nearby; 12 May be booked through travel agent

Delancey Manor is a turn-of-the-century summer house situated just 100 yards from a great beach and our 2½-mile boardwalk. Summer fun is available for families and friends at "America's greatest family resort." We have two breezy porches with ocean views. Guests can walk to nearby restaurants, boardwalk fun, and the Tabernacle with its renowned speakers. The inn is located in a residential neighborhood in a dry town. Larger family rooms are available. Advance reservations are recommended. Two-night minimum applies.

Hosts: Stewart and Pam Heisler
Rooms: 6 (3PB;3SB) $65–95
Notes: 2 7 8 9 10

The Ebbie

820 E. 6th St., Ocean City, NJ 08226-3837
(609) 399-4744
E-mail: ebbienj@hotmail.com
Web site: www.ebbie.com

The Ebbie

Circa 1920, this family-owned and -operated seashore house includes seven rooms, one two-bedroom apartment, and two studio apartments. The two-bedroom apartment has a living area and kitchen, as well as the two studio apartments. Guest quarters and common areas are decorated in a comfortable, relaxed Country style. The home is only 1/2 block from the beach and boardwalk and 11 miles south of Atlantic City.

Hosts: The Warringtons
Rooms: 7 (5PB;2SB) $50–100
Continental Breakfast
Credit Cards: A B
Notes: 7 8 9 10

Inn the Gardens B & B

48 Wesley Rd., Ocean City, NJ 08226-4462
(609) 399-0800
E-mail: innthegardens@aol.com
Web site: www.innthegardens.com

This picturesque seashore haven enchants visitors with beautiful beaches, fresh ocean breezes, and a 2 1/2-mile boardwalk. Families and couples find hospitality with affordability at Inn the Gardens. We have seven spacious guest rooms and one apartment. Enjoy your stay while celebrating a family reunion, an anniversary, or any special occasion. Ocean City provides fine dining and entertainment and numerous attractions. Ideally located only 8 miles from Atlantic City and just 30 minutes from Historic Cape May. Come and enjoy our hospitality at Inn the Gardens! Both Spanish and English are spoken here.

Host: Jennifer Torres
Rooms: 7 (7PB) $71
Continental Breakfast
Credit Cards: A B
Notes: 2 5 7 8 9 10

NOTES: Credit cards accepted: A Master Card; B Visa; C American Express; D Discover; E Diners Club; F Other; 2 Personal checks accepted; 3 Lunch available; 4 Dinner available; 5 Open all year;

Inn the Gardens

Scarborough Inn

720 Ocean Ave., Ocean City, NJ 08226
(609) 399-1558; (800) 258-1558
    Fax (609) 399-4472
E-mail: cgbruno@earthlink.net
Web site: www.scarboroughinn.com

An area landmark since 1895, this award-winning inn affords visitors a vacation residence reminiscent of an old-fashioned European-style inn small enough to be intimate, yet large enough to offer privacy. The Scarborough Inn's convenient center-of-town location places you within easy walking distance of beaches, boardwalk, shopping, and recreational facilities. Individually decorated rooms accented with antiques, private baths, and air-conditioning.

Rooms: 24 (24PB) $80–220
Full Breakfast
Credit Cards: A B C D
Notes: 7 8 9 10 12

Serendipity Bed and Breakfast

712 Ninth St., Ocean City, NJ 08226
(609) 399-1554; (800) 842-8544
E-mail: info@serendipitynj.com
Web site: www.serendipitynj.com

Serendipity is a Mobil-approved, fully air-conditioned, and beautifully renovated 1912 inn. Rooms of wicker and pastels feature private baths with hair dryers and cable TV w/VCRs. A full breakfast of your choice is served in the spacious dining room or on the garden veranda. Vegetarian, heart healthy, and macrobiotic diets are accommodated. Serendipity is just 1/2 block to the Ocean City Beach and boardwalk and minutes to Atlantic City's shows/casinos and Victorian Cape May.

Serendipity

Hosts: Clara and Bill Plowfield
Rooms: 6 (4PB;2SB) $69–169
Full Breakfast
Credit Cards: A B C D
Notes: 2 4 5 8 9 10 12

OCEAN GROVE

The Carriage House Bed and Breakfast

18 Heck Ave., Ocean Grove, NJ 07756
(732) 988-3232; Fax (732) 988-9441
E-mail: carriagehouseog@aol.com
Web site: www.carriagehousenj.com

Ocean Grove's newest! Innkeepers Kathi and Phil will greet the 21st century with a 19th-century Ocean

---

6 Pets welcome; 7 Children welcome; 8 Tennis nearby; 9 Swimming nearby; 10 Golf nearby; 11 Skiing nearby; 12 May be booked through travel agent

Grove treasure. The Carriage House is a gem of elegance, a block from the ocean and a block from town, in the heart of Ocean Grove's charming historic section. Enjoy newly renovated, spacious, AC suites with TVs, queen-size beds, private baths, fireplaces, and ocean-view porches. We are open all seasons to pamper you.

The Carriage House

Hosts: Kathi and Phil Franco
Rooms: 8 (8PB) $120–160
Full Breakfast
Credit Cards: A B C D
Notes: 2 5 9 10

House by the Sea

14 Ocean Ave., Ocean Grove, NJ 07756-1664
(732) 775-4771; Fax (732) 502-0403
E-mail: housebysea@monmouth.com
Web site:
    www.travelguides.com/bb/house_by_the_sea

House by the Sea

Ocean Grove is a Victorian seaside community founded in 1869, featuring a large auditorium for Christian worship. The House by the Sea is an oceanfront bed and breakfast with eighteen rooms and three large porches facing the Atlantic Ocean. Centrally located within walking distance of all activities, shops, and restaurants. Your innkeepers live here year-round and share their home from Memorial Day weekend to Labor Day.

Hosts: Sally and Alyn Heim
Rooms: 18 (10PB;8SB) $70–120
Continental Breakfast
Credit Cards: A B F
Notes: 8 9 10

Love Letter Inn

19 Broadway, Ocean Grove, NJ 07756-1338
(732) 897-0700
E-mail: loveletterinnog@aol.com
Web site: www.loveletterinn.com

An intimate French Victorian inn with the most incredible panoramic views of the Atlantic Ocean and Fletcher Lake. Each room has been uniquely decorated to charm and romance you. Our Bridal Suite features a balcony with views to make you feel like you are in heaven. All rooms have large private baths to accommodate claw-foot tubs and oversized soaking tubs. Friendly service and attention to detail will make every traveler's haven a dream come true in Ocean Grove. Open year-round, 2-night stay on weekends, 3 nights on holiday weekends. All rooms have AC and some fireplaces. No

smoking. Gourmet breakfast and afternoon tea and desserts are served daily.

Hosts: Lynne and Phil Bruno
Rooms: 5 (5PB) $100–225
Full Breakfast
Notes: 2 5   8 9 10

PLAINFIELD

The Pillars of Plainfield Bed and Breakfast

922 Central Ave., Plainfield, NJ 07060-2311
(908) 753-0922; (888) PILLARS
　　Fax (603) 719-2177
E-mail: info@pillars2.com
Web site: www.pillars2.com

The Pillars of Plainfield

Close to New York, Newark airport—
I-95, I-78, I-287. An 1870 Victorian
mansion lovingly restored for your
comfort. In the Van Wyck Brooks historic district, where homes are quietly
secluded on acre lots. Private baths,
digital cable TV, VCRs, modem, voice
mail. Full Swedish breakfast, fireplaces, evening sherry, cookies, chocolates, soda, turn-down service. Nonsmoking. We have a Cairn terrier,
"Mac." The Pillars is special—for your
business week or getaway weekend.

Hosts: Tom and Chuck Hale

Rooms: 7 (7PB) $114–250
Full Breakfast
Credit Cards: A B C
Notes: 2 5 6 7 8 9 10 12

SPRING LAKE

The Hewitt–Wellington Hotel

200 Monmouth Ave.
　　Spring Lake, NJ 07762-1127
(732) 974-1212; Fax (732) 974-2338
E-mail: reservations@hewittwellington.com
Web site: www.hewittwellington.com

Three-diamond award winner. Twelve
beautifully appointed single rooms and
17 two-room suites on the lake overlooking the ocean have private balconies,
wrap-around porches, air-conditioning,
ceiling fans, private marble baths, remote
cable TV/VCRs, clock/radio, small
refrigerators, coffeemakers, and phones.
Heated pool and free beach passes.
Children 12 and over welcome. Call for
brochure. Continental breakfast offered
summer only.

Rooms: 29 (29PB) $95–290
Continental Breakfast
Credit Cards: A B C D E
Notes: 2 5 8 10 12

Sea Crest by the Sea

19 Tuttle Ave., Spring Lake, NJ 07762-1533
(732) 449-9031; (800) 803-9031
　　Fax (732) 974-0403
E-mail: capt@seacrestbythesea.com
Web site: www.seacrestbythesea.com

Your romantic fantasy escape. A
Spring Lake bed and breakfast inn just
for the two of you. Lovingly restored
1885 Queen Anne Victorian for
adults on holiday. Only 1 1/4 hours

6 Pets welcome; 7 Children welcome; 8 Tennis nearby; 9 Swimming nearby; 10 Golf nearby; 11 Skiing
nearby; 12 May be booked through travel agent

from NYC and Philadelphia. Ocean views, open fireplaces, luxurious linens, feather beds, Jacuzzis for two, antique-filled rooms, sumptuous breakfast and afternoon tea, bicycles, beach badges, and chairs. *Victoria Magazine* called it "a perfect ocean refuge." Your innkeepers welcome you with old-fashioned hospitality to an atmosphere that will soothe your weary body and soul.

Sea Crest by the Sea

Hosts: Barbara and Fred Vogel
Rooms: 11 (11PB) $200–500
Full Breakfast
Credit Cards: A B C
Notes: 2 5 8 9 10 12

NEW MEXICO

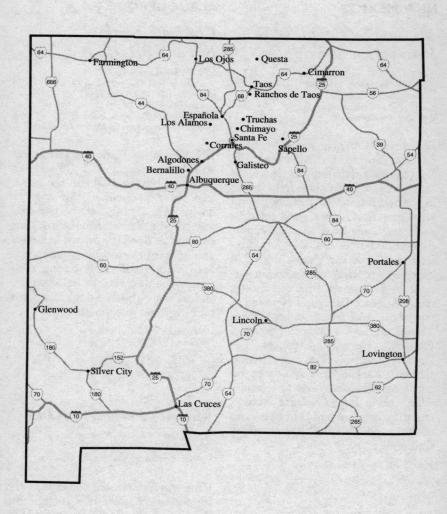

New Mexico

Mi Casa Su Casa B & B Reservation Service

P. O. Box 950, Tempe, AZ 85280
(480) 990-0682; (800) 456-0682
   Fax (480) 990-3390
E-mail: micasa@azres.com
Web site: www.azres.com

Founded in 1981, our name, Mi Casa Su Casa (Spanish for "My House [is] Your House"), describes our service, for our intent is to help visitors feel at home in the Southwest. Our friendly, helpful hosts have host homes, guest cottages, and inns. Some hosts have accommodations and rates available for long-term stays. You can choose from 250 historic-to-contemporary accommodations in four states. (See our listings under Arizona, Utah, and Nevada.) A few of the cities where we list in New Mexico are: Albuquerque, Bernalillo, Chimayo, Corrales, Espanola, Las Cruces, Lincoln, Los Ojos (near Chama), Rancho de Taos, Santa Fe, and Taos. We also represent two luxury villas, one in Puerto Vallarta, Mexico, and the second in the Costa Brava area of Spain and a few B & Bs in southern California.

Host: Ruth Young (coordinator)

ALBUQUERQUE

Chocolate Turtle Bed and Breakfast

1098 W. Meadowlark Ln.
   Corrales, NM 87048-9673
(505) 898-1800; (800) 898-1842
   Fax (505) 899-8734
E-mail: turtlebb@aol.com
Web site: www.collectorsguide.com/chocturtle

The Chocolate Turtle is a territorial-style home located on 1 1/2 acres in historic Corrales, NM, on the north edge of Albuquerque. We enjoy a quiet, rural setting with a beautiful view of the Sandia Mountains. Our desire is to provide a warm, homelike atmosphere to welcome our guests and keep them comfortable during their stay. We're delighted to be of service and to share this blessing. Discounts for clergy and missionaries.

Hosts: Hank and Deb Humiston
Rooms: 4 (4PB) $65–125
Full Breakfast
Credit Cards: A B
Notes: 2 5 7 10 11

Maggie's Raspberry Ranch

9817 Eldridge Rd., NW, Albuquerque, NM 87114
(505) 897-1523; (800) 897-1523
Web site: www.maggiesraspberryranch.com

Ranch-style house embodies country comfort and hospitality, a paradise for children to explore, swim, sing, feed the

---

chickens, turtles, rabbits, doves, and gather eggs. Garden-grown breakfasts.

Host: Maggie Lilley
Rooms: 6 (2PB;3SB) $85–125
Full Breakfast
Credit Cards:
Notes: 2 5 6 7 8 9 10 11

CHIMAYO

Casa Escondida B & B

P. O. Box 142, 64 C. R. 0100
  Chimayo, NM 87522-0142
(505) 351-4805; (800) 643-7201
  Fax (505) 351-2575
E-mail: casaes@newmexico.com
Web site: www.casaescondida.com

Ideally located for many of the most splendid daytrips and ski outings throughout all of northern New Mexico. Just 35 minutes north of Santa Fe. Secluded and serene. Nestled on 6 acres in the awe-inspiring mountains, in the historic village of Chimayo, just off of the "high road to Taos." Some rooms offer fireplaces, private decks, patios, wood-burning stoves, kitchenette, etc. End your day of sightseeing with a soak in our outdoor hot tub.

Rooms: 8 (8PB) $80–140
Full Breakfast
Credit Cards: A B
Notes: 2 5 6 7 10 11

Hacienda Rancho de Chimayo

P. O. Box 11, Chimayo, NM 87522-0011
(505) 351-2222; (888) 270-2320
  Fax (505) 351-2222
E-mail: rdc@espanola-nm.com
Web site: www.ranchodechimayo.com

Built in the adobe tradition, the home has been renovated into seven lovely guest rooms. Each guest room opens onto an enclosed courtyard, and within each room one can find turn-of-the-century antiques, a private bath, a quiet sitting area, and fireplace. In the old world tradition, a continental breakfast with pastry, fruit, freshly squeezed orange juice, and coffee or tea awaits each guest in the morning.

Host: Viola Martinez
Rooms: 7 (7PB) $69–105
Continental Breakfast
Credit Cards: A B C D
Notes: 5

CORRALES

La Posada de Corrales B & B

909 Loma Larga, Corrales, NM 87048
(505) 899-0483; Fax (505) 899-0483
E-mail: laposadanm@hotmail.com
Web site: www.collectorsguide.com/laposadanm

Old World hospitality and comfort await each of our guests in this modern hacienda-style hideaway. Its interiors, with brick floors, viga ceilings, and kiva fireplaces, reflect the Hispanic-influenced Southwestern culture and offer privacy, elegance, and sanctuary in a quintessential romantic New Mexico location. Where the wind wafts gently through the cottonwoods, the spirit clouds float in a clear blue sky, and the desert and mountain vistas stretch for glorious golden miles, guests will enjoy La Posada's impeccable service and charm. Easy access abounds to restaurants, shop-

---

6 Pets welcome; 7 Children welcome; 8 Tennis nearby; 9 Swimming nearby; 10 Golf nearby; 11 Skiing nearby; 12 May be booked through travel agent

ping, day trips to Santa Fe or to one of the many Indian Pueblos. Wake up to the scent of country fresh air and the aroma of a scrumptious full breakfast. *"Mi Casa es Su Casa."*

Hosts: Grace and Mel
Rooms: 3 (3PB) $99–169
Full Breakfast
Credit Cards: A B C D
Notes: 2 5 8 9 10 11

LAS CRUCES

T. R. H. Smith Mansion Bed and Breakfast

909 N. Alameda Blvd.
   Las Cruces, NM 88005-2124
(505) 525-2525; (800) 526-1914
   Fax (505) 524-8227
E-mail: smithmansion@zianet.com
Web site: www.smithmansion.com

This beautifully preserved Prairie-style mansion, surrounded by parklike grounds and tall pecan and sycamore trees, has a somewhat notorious past. The home was designed by Henry Trost and was built by banker/embezzler T. R. H. Smith. The mansion was rumored to have served as a bordello and to have buried treasure somewhere within its walls. Its 5,700 square feet of living area make it the largest residence in the city. The inn offers four well-appointed guest rooms in a variety of styles including Latin American, European, Southwest, and Pacific Rim. Guests will enjoy a hearty German-style breakfast of fresh fruits, home-baked breads, imported meats and cheeses, along with fresh ground

coffee and teas made from herbs grown on the grounds.

T. R. H. Smith Mansion

Hosts: Marlene and Jay Tebo
Rooms: 4 (4PB) $68–150
Full Breakfast
Credit Cards: A B C D
Notes: 2 5 6 7 8 9 10 12

SANTA FE

El Paradero B & B Inn

220 W. Manhattan Ave.
   Santa Fe, NM 87501-2622
(505) 988-1177; Fax (505) 988-3577
E-mail: info@elparadero.com
Web site: www.elparadero.com

"El Paradero," The Stopping Place, is a 200-year-old, 14-room historic adobe located downtown just minutes walking from the plaza. All rooms are individually decorated, and many have fireplaces. Guests tell us they love our full breakfasts, open courtyard, and sense of home. The inn is nonsmoking.

Hosts: Matt and Jennifer Laessig
Rooms: 14 (12PB;2SB) $70–160
Full Breakfast
Credit Cards: A B C
Notes: 5 6 7 8 9 10 11

NOTES: Credit cards accepted: A Master Card; B Visa; C American Express; D Discover; E Diners Club; F Other; 2 Personal checks accepted; 3 Lunch available; 4 Dinner available; 5 Open all year;

NEW YORK

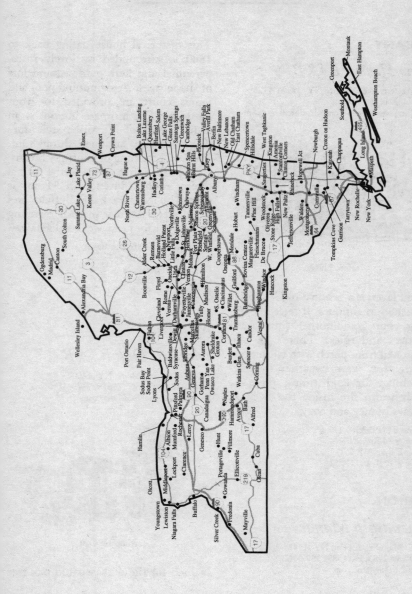

New York

ALBANY

Pine Haven B & B

531 Western Ave., Albany, NY 12203-1721
(518) 482-1574
Web site: www.pinehavenbedandbreakfast.com

Pine Haven

Pine Haven is a century-old Victorian furnished in antiques. It feels like visiting your grandmother (minus the relatives and rules). There's an old-fashioned front porch with wicker furniture for warm-weather people-watching. In cold times, there's a lovely warm fire inside the B & B. Always homey and cozy.

Rooms: 8 (5PB;3SB) $59–89
Continental Breakfast
Credit Cards: A B C D
Notes: 2 8 9 10 11 12

ALBION

Friendship Manor

349 S. Main St., Albion, NY 14411-1602
(585) 589-2983; Fax (585) 589-1162
E-mail: baker@iinc.com

This historical house dating back to 1880 is surrounded by lovely roses, perennial and herb gardens, and lots of shade trees. A swimming pool and tennis court are provided for your pleasure. The intimate interior is an artful blend of Victorian-style furnishings with antiques throughout. Enjoy a breakfast of muffins, breads, fruit, juice, coffee or tea in the formal dining room. Friendship Manor is central to Niagara Falls, Buffalo, and Rochester. A great place if traveling through or for just a weekend getaway.

Hosts: John and Marylin Baker
Rooms: 4 (2PB;2SB) $65
Continental Breakfast
Credit Cards: A B D
Notes: 2 7 8 9 10 12

ALDEN

Majestic Oak B & B

12925 Main St., Alden, NY 14004
(716) 937-6447; Fax (716) 937-7361
E-mail: majestic_oak@juno.com

Majestic Oak

Named for the 400-year-old oak tree

---

in the front yard. Century-old house built in 1876, surrounded by maple trees and many flowers. Many antiques including an 1830 parlor grand piano. Picnic area to the rear of the house. 30 minutes from Buffalo Int'l. Airport. 45 minutes from Niagara Falls. 15 Minutes from Darien SIX FLAGS amusement park. Guests will be serenaded by singing canaries while they enjoy a full country breakfast. No smoking in house.

Host: Sarah Tooley
Rooms: 3 (1PB;2SB) $45–55 plus tax
Full Breakfast
Notes: 2 5 7 10

ALEXANDRIA BAY

Hart House Inn

21979 Club Rd., Wellesley Island, NY 13640
(315) 482-5683; (888) 481-5683
    Fax (315) 482-5683
E-mail: info@harthouseinn.com
Web site: www.harthouseinn.com

In the heart of the Thousand Islands, our grand gentleman's cottage is a true destination for your special occasion. Adjacent to a golf course, with a fine St. Lawrence River view, we're just minutes from major boat cruises. Wellesley Island is accessible by car, located just 5 minutes from I-81 and 10 minutes from the Canadian border. Thousand Islands is an all-season getaway—with a difference! We offer luxury accommodations: canopied beds with decorator sheeting, cozy fireplaces, and private whirlpool baths featuring Italian ceramic tile. All of this

plus a stunning wedding chapel that seats 50.

Hosts: Rev. Dudley and Kathy Danielson
Rooms: 8 (6PB;2SB) $115–295
Full Breakfast
Credit Cards: A B C D F
Notes: 2 4 5 7 8 9 10 12

BINGHAMTON

Angels in the Bell Tower Retreat

242 Ward Loomis Rd., Bainbridge, NY 13733
(607) 967-8745; (800) 497-8745
    Fax (607) 967-2227
E-mail: angelsretreat@berryhillgardens.com
Web site: www.angelsinthebelltower.com

Angels in the Bell Tower Retreat

This charming, 1898 country church is now available for short retreats. It is situated in a small hamlet along the Tioughnioga River, 12 miles north of Binghamton, NY. Full kitchen, 2 bedrooms, large open living room with original cathedral ceiling, fireplace, and stained-glass windows. Country craft and antique shops are nearby. Great location when visiting Binghamton University. Short drive to wineries, Ithaca College, and Cornell University. Sleeps 4 to 6 people. Children over 10 years old welcome.

Rooms: 2 (1PB) $500–800 weekly
No Breakfast Served
Credit Cards: A B C F
Notes: 2 8 9 10 11

Berry Hill Gardens B & B

242 Ward Loomis Rd., Bainbridge, NY 13733
(607) 967-8745; (800) 497-8745
    Fax (607) 967-2227
E-mail: info@berryhillgardens.com
Web site: www.berryhillgardens.com

Berry Hill Gardens

This restored 1820s farmhouse on a hilltop is surrounded by extensive flower and herb gardens and 200 acres where you can hike, swim, fish, birdwatch, cross-country ski, or sit on the wrap-around porch and watch the nature parade. Our rooms are furnished with comfortable antiques. A 10-minute drive takes you to restaurants, golf, auctions, and antique centers. You can buy plants, dried flowers, and wreaths grown and handcrafted on the farm. Cooperstown and most local colleges are only 45 minutes away. Three hours from New York City. Weekly rental of a private, two-bedroom riverside cottage is also available.

Rooms: 5 (2PB;3SB) $75–125
Full Breakfast
Credit Cards: A B C F
Notes: 2 5 7 8 9 10 11 12

CANDOR

The Edge of Thyme, a Bed and Breakfast Inn

6 Main St. , P. O. Box 48, Candor, NY 13743
(607) 659-5155
Web site: www.edgeofthyme.com

Featured in *Historic Inns of the Northeast.* Located in this quiet rural village is a large, gracious Georgian home. Leaded glass, windowed porch, marble fireplaces, period sitting rooms, gardens, and pergola. Epicurean breakfast served in a genteel manner. The location is central to Cornell, Ithaca College, Corning, Elmira, Watkins Glen, and wineries. Gift shoppe. High tea is served by appointment. Cross-country skiing is available. Well-behaved children welcome.

Hosts: Eva Mae and Frank Musgrave
Rooms: 5 (3PB;2SB) $75–135
Full Breakfast
Credit Cards: A B C
Notes: 2 5 7 8 9 10 11 12

The Edge of Thyme

CATSKILL MOUNTAINS

Albergo Allegria B & B

#43 Rte. 296, P. O. Box 267, Windham, NY 12496

NOTES: Credit cards accepted: A Master Card; B Visa; C American Express; D Discover; E Diners Club; F Other; 2 Personal checks accepted; 3 Lunch available; 4 Dinner available; 5 Open all year;

(518) 734-5560; Fax (518) 734-5570
E-mail: mail@albergousa.com
Web site: www.albergousa.com

An 1892 Victorian mansion nestled in the Catskill Mountain Forest Preserve. 4-diamond "Exceptional" Award winner AAA. Condé Nast Johansens Award and members of Select Registry, Distinguished Inns of America. Registered Historic Site. All 21 rooms modern amenities. Suites with Jacuzzi and gas fireplace. Full gourmet breakfast included. 24-hour guest pantry, over 300 complimentary videos. Italian for the "Inn of Happiness," Albergo Allegria offers a uniquely different bed and breakfast experience. Voted "Inn of the Year 2000" out of 21,000 inns worldwide.

Hosts: Leslie and Marianna Leman
Rooms: 21 (21PB) $73–299
Full Breakfast
Credit Cards: A B
Notes: 5 8 9 10 11 12

CORNING

1865 White Birch B & B

69 E. 1st St., Corning, NY 14830-2715
(607) 962-6355
Web site: www.corningny.com/whitebirch

The White Birch, Victorian in structure but decorated in Country, has been refurbished to show off its winding staircase, hardwood floors, and wall window in the dining room overlooking the backyard. We are located in a residential area, 2 blocks from restored historic Market Street, and 6 blocks from the Corning Museum.

Our large common room welcomes guests where TV is available. A full home-baked gourmet breakfast is served each morning, and we are on the National Historic Register.

Hosts: Kathy and Joe Donahue
Rooms: 4 (2PB;2SB) $75–90
Full Breakfast
Credit Cards: A B C
Notes: 2 5 7 8 9 10 11

CROWN POINT

Crown Point B & B

P. O. Box 490, 2695 Main St., Rte. 9 N
   Crown Point, NY 12928
(518) 597-3651; Fax (518) 597-4451
E-mail: mail@crownpointbandb.com
Web site: www.crownpointbandb.com

A charming Victorian "Painted Lady" dressed in ten shades of beige, pink, burgundy, and blue set on parklike grounds in the heart of the "Adirondack Reserve." One-quarter mile from Lake Champlain on the Vermont border. Six distinctively decorated bedchambers feature a variety of floral wallpapers, antique furnishings, and Victorian finery, which complement the Inn's beautifully crafted wood paneling. Within the manor are four working carved stone fireplaces, three porches, and three parlors. The inn is situated on 5 1/2 acres, complete with two fountains and beautiful gardens. A gourmet breakfast is served.

Hosts: Hugh and Sandy Johnson
Rooms: 6 (6PB) $70–140
Full Breakfast
Credit Cards: A B C
Notes: 2 5 7 8 9 10 11 12

---

6 Pets welcome; 7 Children welcome; 8 Tennis nearby; 9 Swimming nearby; 10 Golf nearby; 11 Skiing nearby; 12 May be booked through travel agent

CUBA

Helen's Tourist Home

7 Maple St., Cuba, NY 14727-1124
(585) 968-2200

Your hostess has been welcoming tourists to her comfortable, turn-of-the-century home for 47 years. Located on a quiet residential street. Guests have the run of the house, including the large living room with TV. Coffee, a toaster, and a refrigerator are always available. Visit Cuba Lake, Cuba Cheese Shop, and Seneca Oil Springs—first oil discovered in America. A restaurant is just around the corner; a small shopping center is nearby.

Host: Dora W. Wittmann
Rooms: 5 (1PB;4SB) $35–45
Notes:　5　7

DELHI

The Old Stage Line Stop

P. O. Box 125; 2617 Catskill Turnpike Rd.
　Meridale, NY　13806-0125
(607) 746-6856
E-mail: stagebb@catskill.net
Web site: www.catskill.net/stagebb

The Old Stage Line Stop

This early 1900s farmhouse, once part of a dairy farm, is high on a hill overlooking the peaceful countryside. Comfortable rooms are decorated tastefully with country furnishings. Guests enjoy a variety of attractions, relaxing on the porch, and taking walks to absorb the beautiful views. A full breakfast and afternoon treats are served with pleasure. Delhi, Oneonta, and Hartwick Colleges are nearby. We are within a short drive of Cooperstown and many other attractions—antiques, fairs, auctions, and historical sites such as Hanford Mills. Well-behaved children welcome.

Host: Rose Rosino
Rooms: 4 (1PB;3SB) $60–75
Full Breakfast
Credit Cards: A B
Notes: 2　5　7　8　10

EAST HAMPTON

Hedges Inn

74 James Ln., East Hampton, NY　11937-2722
(631) 324-7100; Fax (631) 324-5816
E-mail: jameslanecafe@aol.com
Web site: www.thepalm.com

Charming, historical inn situated at the entry of East Hampton Village. The main floor has public rooms and a restaurant overlooking tree-surrounded flagstone patios. Upper two floors have eleven charming guest rooms, each with private bath and air-conditioning. Situated between main beach and village business district, within walking distance of both.

Host: Linda Calder
Rooms: 11 (11PB) $275–375

NOTES: Credit cards accepted: A Master Card; B Visa; C American Express; D Discover; E Diners Club; F Other; 2 Personal checks accepted; 3 Lunch available; 4 Dinner available; 5 Open all year;

Continental Breakfast
Credit Cards: A B C
Notes: 4 5 7 8 9 10

FILLMORE

Just a (Plane) B & B

11152 Rte. 19 A, Fillmore, NY 14735-8671
(585) 567-8338

Just a (Plane) B & B

Enjoy a relaxing, peaceful stay at Just a "Plane." Situated on the banks of the historic Genesee Valley Canal, the three-story Dutch Colonial home was constructed in 1926. Renovated in 1995, it has four guest rooms, each with a private bath. The "Plane" in the name refers to the scenic airplane rides, offered for an additional fee. Your host, Craig, a licensed commercial pilot, flies a Piper PA-22, which is hangared on the farm. In the morning, enjoy a full country breakfast in the dining room or sunroom.

Hosts: Audrey and Craig Smith
Rooms: 4 (4PB) $65
Full Breakfast
Credit Cards: A B C
Notes: 2 5 7 8 10 11

GLENS FALLS

Crislip's B & B

693 Ridge Rd., Queensbury, NY 12804-6901
(518) 793-6869

Located in the Adirondack area just minutes from Saratoga Springs and Lake George, this landmark Federal home provides spacious accommodations with period antiques, four-poster beds, and down comforters. The country breakfast menu features such items as buttermilk pancakes, scrambled eggs, and sausages. Your hosts invite you to relax on their porches and enjoy the beautiful mountains of Vermont.

Hosts: Ned and Joyce Crislip
Rooms: 3 (3PB) $65–85
Full Breakfast
Credit Cards: A B D
Notes: 2 5 6 7 8 9 10 11

Crislip's

GOWANDA

The Teepee

14396 4 Mile Level Rd., Rte. 438
  Gowanda, NY 14070
(716) 532-2168
E-mail: play7635@aol.com

This bed and breakfast is operated by Seneca Indians on the Cattaraugus

---

6 Pets welcome; 7 Children welcome; 8 Tennis nearby; 9 Swimming nearby; 10 Golf nearby; 11 Skiing nearby; 12 May be booked through travel agent

Indian Reservation near Gowanda. Tours of the reservation and the Amish community nearby are available.

Hosts: Phyllis and Max Lay
Rooms: 4 (1PB;3SB) $50
Full Breakfast
Notes: 2 5 7 8 9 10 11

The Teepee

HAMBURG

Sharon's Lake House B & B

4862 Lake Shore Rd., Hamburg, NY 14075-5542
(716) 627-7561; Fax (716) 627-7561
E-mail: sharonsbb@freewwweb.com

Located on Lake Erie 10 miles from Buffalo. Fine restaurants and shopping area within walking distance. Large bedroom with attached porch overlooking the lake. Large private bath with step-up bathtub that will accommodate two people. Children welcome by reservation.

Hosts: Vincent and Sharon Di Maria
Rooms: 2 (1PB;1SB) $75–110
Gourmet Breakfast
Credit Cards: A B
Notes: 2 5 8 9 10 11 12

HAMMONDSPORT

Amity Rose Bed and Breakfast

8264 Main St., Hammondsport, NY 14840
(607) 569-3402; (800) 982-8818
    Fax (607) 569-3483
E-mail: bbam@infoblud.net
Web site: www.amityroseinn.com

"Country Inn the Village," a quaint Finger Lakes historic village, where guests can find antiques, shops, restaurants, or just relax. Eight wineries surround the area. Swim or boat on the lake nearby. The Corning Glass Museum and Watkins Glen Raceway are just 30 minutes away. Niagara Falls just a couple of hours away. All rooms have queen beds and AC. Two have whirlpool soaking tubs and fireplaces. Enjoy the spacious guest parlor with fireplace and soft music. A scrumptious breakfast is served. Join us for a delightful stay!

Rooms: 4 (4PB) $95–125
Full Breakfast
Credit Cards:
Notes: 2 8 9 10

Gone with the Wind B & B

453 W. Lake Rd., Branchport, NY 14418-9643
(607) 868-4600; Fax (607) 868-0388
Web site: www.yatesny.com

The name paints the picture—an 1887 stone Victorian on 14 acres overlooking our quiet lake cove (adorned by an inviting picnic gazebo). Feel the magic of total relaxation and peace of mind soaking in the solarium hot tub or walking on our pleasant nature trails. Fireplaces, delectable breakfasts, private beach, and dock. Reserve our log lodge for small retreats and friendly gatherings. Located just 1 1/2 hours south of Rochester, NY, and 45 minutes from Corning; on Keuka Lake in the Finger Lakes wine country. Come see us soon.

Hosts: Linda and Robert Lewis
Rooms: 10 (4PB;6SB) $80–130
Full Breakfast
Notes: 2 5 8 9 10 11

LEROY

Oatka Creek B & B

71 E. Main St. , Rte. 5, Leroy, NY 14482
(585) 768-6990; (877) 768-6990
E-mail: ocbb@eznet.net

Oatka Creek

Oatka Creek B & B, a turn-of-the-century, Colonial Revival home located in the beautiful historic village of LeRoy, NY—birthplace of Jell-O. Air-conditioned guest rooms with private baths. Full homemade breakfast and afternoon refreshments. Just 5 minutes off I-90 NYS Thruway Exit 47. Walk to Jell-O museum, choice restaurants, shopping. Public golf 1 mile. Located on the 5 and 20 antique

trail between Buffalo and Rochester. Ninety minutes to Niagara Falls. AAA approved. We look forward to hosting your visit to the heart of western New York.

Hosts: Craig and Lynn Bateman
Rooms: 4 (4PB) $79–100
Full Breakfast
Credit Cards: A B C
Notes: 2 5 7 8 9 10 12

MADRID

Brandy-View Bed and Breakfast

24 Walker Rd., Madrid, NY 13660
(315) 322-4429; Fax (315) 322-4678
E-mail: hargrove@northnet.org
Web site: www.brandy-view.com

Enjoy true country hospitality in a country brick home built in 1849 by Jim's great-grandfather. Located in St. Lawrence County, on the U.S.–Canadian border. The home is furnished with family heirlooms. Relax in the claw-foot tub and snuggle under homemade quilts. See a modern dairy farm in action; guests are encouraged to tour the milking facility, meander through the meadows, woods, or along the babbling Brandy Brook. Nearby are the Adirondack Mountains, the St. Lawrence Seaway, the 1,000 Islands, many Canadian landmarks and attractions, including Ottawa, the capital. Have central air-conditioning.

---

6 Pets welcome; 7 Children welcome; 8 Tennis nearby; 9 Swimming nearby; 10 Golf nearby; 11 Skiing nearby; 12 May be booked through travel agent

Brandy-View

Hosts: Grace and James Hargrave
Rooms: 4 (0PB;4SB) $60
Full Breakfast
Credit Cards: D
Notes: 2 5 7 8 9 10 11

MAYVILLE

The Village Inn B & B

111 S. Erie St., Mayville, NY 14757-1120
(716) 753-3583
Web site: www.bbonline.com/ny/villageinn

The Village Inn is a turn-of-the-century Victorian home located near the shores of Lakes Chautauqua and Erie, 3 miles from Chautauqua Institution and less than a 30-minute drive from Peek 'n' Peak and Cockaigne ski centers. We offer comfort in both single and double rooms in a home furnished with many antiques and trimmed in woodwork crafted by European artisans. In the morning, enjoy a breakfast of homemade waffles, nut kuchen, in-season fruit, coffee, and juice in our sunny breakfast room. Please inquire about pets.

Host: Dean Hanby
Rooms: 3 (1PB;2SB) $65–90
Full Breakfast
Credit Cards: C
Notes: 2 5 7 8 9 10 11

MUMFORD

The Genesee Country Inn, Circa 1833

948 George St., Mumford, NY 14511
(585) 538-2500; (800) 697-8297
   Fax (585) 538-4565
E-mail: room2escapeinn@aol.com
Web site: www.geneseecountryinn.com

Don't visit us unless you bring someone you want to like You very much! This historic, romantic old mill, minutes from downtown Rochester, is just 3 hours from Toronto. Relax, fly-fish, walk our unique 8 acres, visit the Genesse Country Museum Nature Center (third largest USA), or take daytrips to Niagara Falls, Letchworth State Park, Rochester, New York, wineries. All private baths, TV, AC. Tea, gourmet breakfast. Gift shop. Select Registry, AAA, Mobil.

Hosts: Glenda Barcklow and Kim Rasmussen
Rooms: 9 (9PB) $105–170
Full Breakfast
Credit Cards: A B D E
Notes: 2 5 8 10 12

NEW YORK CITY

Holy Family Bed and Breakfast

10-11 49th Ave., L.I.C.
   New York City, NY 11101
(718) 392-7597; Fax (718) 786-3640
E-mail: holyfamilybnb@aol.com
Web site: www.holyfamilybedandbreakfast.com

Close to the core of the Big Apple, the B & B is just a 3-minute subway train ride to Midtown Manhattan, from where guests can walk to Manhattan's interesting spots: the Empire State Building, Fifth Avenue, Rockefeller Center, Times Square, and a host of favorite tourist places. Full breakfast, fully equipped guests' kitchen, library, organ/piano, telephones, TVs/VCRs. Guests are given free tips on how to get around Manhattan. Nearby are restaurants, diners, stores, and the Gantry Plaza State Park, offering a panoramic view of the Manhattan skyline. The B & B is 2 blocks away from the East River, across from the United Nations. On a starry night, the B & B guests can bask in the glorious sight of the Empire State Building. Saint Mary's Catholic Church, across the street, looms tall over the B & B.

Holy Family

Hosts: Tom and Sonia Salerni
Rooms: 4 (2PB;3SB) $75–120
Full Breakfast
Credit Cards: A B C D E
Notes: 5 7 8

NIAGARA FALLS

Cameo Manor

3881 Lower River Rd., Rte. 18 F
   Youngstown, NY 14174-9702
(716) 745-3034

E-mail: cameoinn@adelphia.net
Web site: www.cameoinn.com

Located just 7 miles north of Niagara Falls, our English manor house is the perfect spot for that quiet getaway you have been dreaming about. Situated on 3 secluded acres, Cameo Manor North offers a great room with fireplaces, solarium, library, and an outdoor terrace for your enjoyment. Our beautifully appointed guest rooms include suites with private sunrooms and cable television. A breakfast buffet is served daily.

Hosts: Greg and Carolyn Fisher
Rooms: 5 (3PB;2SB) $75–130
Full Breakfast
Credit Cards: A B D
Notes: 5 7 8 9 10 11 12

The Country Club Inn

5170 Lewiston Rd., Lewiston, NY 14092-1931
(716) 285-4869; Fax (716) 285-5614
E-mail: ctyclubinn@pcom.net
Web site: www.countryclubinn.com

Located just minutes from Niagara Falls, the Country Club Inn is a non-smoking bed and breakfast. Three large and beautifully decorated guest rooms each have a private bath, queen-size bed, and cable TV. A great room with a wood-burning fireplace and pool table leads to a covered patio overlooking the golf course. A full breakfast is served at guests' convenience in our elegant dining room. Convenient to the NYS thruway and bridges to Canada.

6 Pets welcome; 7 Children welcome; 8 Tennis nearby; 9 Swimming nearby; 10 Golf nearby; 11 Skiing nearby; 12 May be booked through travel agent

The Country Club Inn

Hosts: Barbara Ann and Norman Oliver
Rooms: 3 (3PB) $90–115
Full Breakfast
Notes: 2 5 7 9 10

Manchester House

653 Main St., Niagara Falls, NY 14301-1701
(716) 285-5717; (800) 489-3009
    Fax (716) 282-2144
E-mail: carl@manchesterhouse.com
Web site: www.manchesterhouse.com

This brick-and-shingle residence was built in 1903 and used as a doctor's residence and office for many years. After extensive renovation, Manchester House opened as a bed and breakfast in 1991. Carl and Lis received a Niagara Falls beautification award for their work. Manchester House is within easy walking distance of the falls, aquarium, and geological museum. Off-street parking.

Hosts: Lis and Carl Slenk
Rooms: 3 (3PB) $60–100
Full Breakfast
Credit Cards: A B D
Notes: 2 5 10 12

OLIVEREA

Slide Mountain Forest House

805 Oliverea Rd., Oliverea, NY 12410-5317
(845) 254-5365; Fax (845) 254-6107
E-mail: slide_mtn@yahoo.com
Web site: www.slidemountain-inn.com

Nestled in the Catskill Mountains State Park, our inn offers the flavor and charm of the old country. A 1900s farmstead with views of apple orchard lawns, towering evergreens, and gentle mountains. Come enjoy our beautiful country setting, superb lodging, fine dining, and chalet rentals. Family run for 65 years, we strive to give you a pleasant and enjoyable stay. Hiking, fishing, tennis, pool, and lawn sports available on site. Open all year—chalets only.

Hosts: Ralph and Ursula Combe
Rooms: 19 (15PB;4SB) $50–120
Full Breakfast
Credit Cards: A B D
Notes: 2 3 4 5 7 8 9 10 11

ONEONTA

The Murphy House

33 Walnut St., Oneonta, NY 13820-1839
(607) 432-1367; Fax (607) 432-1367
E-mail: mmurphy@dmcom.net
Web site: www.community-mine.com/murphy

Gracious accommodations in the historic district of Oneonta, a small rural city nestled among the hills of upstate New York. This 1920 bed and breakfast home features delightful breakfasts and is within walking distance of Main

---

NOTES: Credit cards accepted: A Master Card; B Visa; C American Express; D Discover; E Diners Club; F Other; 2 Personal checks accepted; 3 Lunch available; 4 Dinner available; 5 Open all year;

Street. Nearby attractions include The National Soccer and Baseball Halls of Fame, the beauty of God's four seasons, and cultural events ranging from opera to dancing under the stars. Thirty minutes from Cooperstown, 3½ hours from New York City.

Hosts: Nancy and Mike Murphy
Rooms: 2 (2PB) $85–95
Full Breakfast
Notes: 2 5 7

SILVER CREEK

Pinewoods Cottage Bed and Breakfast

11634 York Rd., Silver Creek, NY 14136
(716) 934-4173; Fax (716) 934-2415
E-mail: estelle@crinopinewoodscottage.com
Web site: www.crinopinewoodscottage.com

Pinewoods Cottage

Pinewoods Cottage B & B offers an eclectic atmosphere and decor with three guest rooms and private baths, AC, TV. The Loft has a kitchen, bath, private entrance, housing four persons, weekly. A gourmet breakfast is offered to those in the main house. Enjoy afternoon tea and snacks in the family room or sunroom. Relax on the covered front porch, sunroom, or back deck. Take a walk through the 20 acres of woodlands or play board games in the sunroom. Nonsmoking facility. Children over 12 years welcome.

Host: Estelle M. Crino, Ed.D.
Rooms: 3 (3PB) $65–85
Full Breakfast
Credit Cards: A B
Notes: 2 5 7 9 10 11

SOUTH COLTON

Braeside Bed and Breakfast

20 A Cold Brook Dr., South Colton, NY 13687
(315) 262-2553; Fax (208) 247-2077
E-mail: braesidebb@webtv.net
Web site: www.braesidebb.com

Braeside, a modified Cape Cod riverfront home with a wrap-around deck and two docks, is situated on a hill on the Raquet River, nestled in the northern foothills of the Adirondacks. Featuring antique furnishings and collections, the B & B offers four cozy, comfortable country guest rooms. Nature beckons you to hike, bike, canoe, bird-watch, fish, kayak, crosscountry ski, or just relax. Rowboat and canoe available. Golf, museums, antiquing, and colleges are nearby. Freshly prepared, full breakfast at riverside, in dinette, or gazebo. Package deals. Air-conditioning.

Host: Joann E. Ferris
Rooms: 4 (4SB) $60–85
Full Breakfast
Notes: 2 5 7 8 9 10 11 12

6 Pets welcome; 7 Children welcome; 8 Tennis nearby; 9 Swimming nearby; 10 Golf nearby; 11 Skiing nearby; 12 May be booked through travel agent

SYRACUSE

High Meadows B & B

3740 Eager Rd., Jamesville, NY 13078-9779
(315) 492-3517; (800) 854-0918
    Fax (315) 492-0343
E-mail: nancy@himeadows.com
Web site: www.himeadows.com

Nancy Mentz invites you to share country hospitality with them high in the hills just 10 miles south of Syracuse between Jamesville and LaFayette, New York. Owner-designed and -built California contemporary with lots of light. Furnished with traditional and comfortable pieces. You will experience quiet serenity in one of the custom-designed areas. Relax in front of a fire in the living room, among the plants in the solarium, or on the wrap-around deck looking at the 60-mile view. A full breakfast is included, and you won't go away hungry.

Hosts: Nancy Mentz
Rooms: 4 (2PB;2SB) $55–95
Full Breakfast
Credit Cards: A B C D
Notes: 2 5 7 8 9 10 11 12

UTICA

The Iris Stonehouse B & B

16 Derbyshire Pl., Utica, NY 13501-4706
(315) 732-6720; (800) 446-1456
    Fax (315) 797-5134
E-mail: irisbnb@borg.com
Web site:
    www.innsmart.com/newyork/central/smartlistings/

The Iris Stonehouse B & B offers hospitality and charm within. A 1930 English Tudor historic register house with leaded-glass windows and iris motifs throughout has been outfitted with central air-conditioning to quietly cool your sleep on those hot nights of summer and a sitting room fireplace to warm conversations on those snowy days of winter. The hospitality starts with a warm "Welcome" from hosts Jim and Nellie Chanatry. It is sustained with an appetizing full breakfast offered daily with special attention given to those with dietary requests. Four electrically furnished bedrooms, two of them with private baths, offer rest and relaxation for up to eight guests. One of the most popular rooms is the queen bedroom with a private bath. This room features a unique shower with 6 side sprays and the overhead shower. Guests often call and request "the Room with the Great Shower."

The Iris Stonehouse

Hosts: Jim and Nellie Chanatry
Rooms: 4 (2PB;2SB) $59–89
Full Breakfast
Credit Cards: A B D
Notes: 2 5 7 8 10 11

VALLEY FALLS

Maggie Towne's B & B

P. O. Box 82, Valley Falls, NY 12185
(518) 663-8369

NOTES: Credit cards accepted: A Master Card; B Visa; C American Express; D Discover; E Diners Club; F Other; 2 Personal checks accepted; 3 Lunch available; 4 Dinner available; 5 Open all year;

This lovely old Colonial home is located amid beautiful lawns and trees. Guests may enjoy a cup of tea or glass of wine before the huge fireplace in the family room. Use the music room or curl up with a book on the screened porch. Mornings, your host serves home-baked goodies. She will gladly prepare a lunch for you to take on tour or enjoy at the house. It's 20 miles to historic Bennington and 30 to Saratoga.

Host: Maggie Towne
Rooms: 3 (0PB;3SB) $45
Full Breakfast
Notes: 2 3 5 6 7 8 9 10 11

WARRENSBURG

White House Lodge

3760 Main St., Warrensburg, NY 12885
(518) 623-3640

An 1847 Victorian home in the heart of the queen village of the Adirondacks, an antiquer's paradise. The home is furnished with many Victorian antiques, which send you back in time. Five minutes to Lake George, Fort William Henry, and Great Escape. Walk to restaurants. Enjoy air-conditioned TV lounge for guests only, window, and Casablanca fans. Children over 7 welcome.

Hosts: Jim and Ruth Gibson
Rooms: 3 (0PB;3SB) $85
Continental Breakfast
Credit Cards: A B
Notes: 5 7 8 9 10 11

WATKINS GLEN

South Glenora Tree Farm B & B

546 S. Glenora Rd., Dundee, NY 14837-8848
(607) 243-7414
Web site: www.fingerlakes.net/treefarm

South Glenora Tree Farm

Nationally Rated!!! See our Web site!!! Two converted barns with 5 bedrooms (2 suites), private baths, AC, fireplaces, and all on 110-acre tree farm. Come enjoy something very special!!!

Hosts: Steve and Judy Ebert, D.Min.
Rooms: 5 (5PB) $88–139
Full Breakfast
Credit Cards: A B D
Notes: 2 5 7 8 9 10 11

WINDHAM

Country Suite B & B

P. O. Box 700, Windham, NY 12496-0700
(518) 734-4079; (888) 883-0444
    Fax (518) 734-6091
E-mail: ctrysuite@aol.com

"First you notice the level of taste, the fit and finish. Then you see the gracious rooms, the sprawling grounds, the perfectly placed gazebo. Here, you'll discover exquisite country elegance with a distinctly urban flair." — *Inn Review*. This beautifully restored 1865 farmhouse is located just 2 miles from Ski Windham. Nestled deep in

---

6 Pets welcome; 7 Children welcome; 8 Tennis nearby; 9 Swimming nearby; 10 Golf nearby; 11 Skiing nearby; 12 May be booked through travel agent

the heart of Greene County's Catskill Mountains, this retreat invites you to take a deep breath, relax, and indulge yourself. It offers five guest rooms, each with its own private bath, and king or queen beds. Country Suite is a favorite for those interested in quiet romantic stays. All visits include a full gourmet breakfast. Nearby, you'll find excellent dining, quaint shops, historic sites, golfing, biking, swimming, boating, tennis, hiking, skiing, horseback riding, and a wealth of antiques. Experience the magic of the Catskills and the beauty of the New York countryside at Country Suite, "a noteworthy bed and breakfast." You will certainly find your stay enjoyable.

Hosts: Sondra Clark and Lorraine Seidel
Rooms: 5 (5PB) $99–189
Full Breakfast
Credit Cards: A B C
Notes: 2 5 9 10 11 12

WINDSOR

Country Haven

66 Garrett Rd., Windsor, NY 13865-1601
(607) 655-1204
E-mail: cntryhaven@aol.com

Country Haven is a "haven" for today's weary travelers, as well as a weekend hideaway where warm hospitality awaits you. We offer guest rooms in a restored 1800s family farmhouse and a new log home, all in a quiet country setting on 350 acres. A new conference room is now open and small retreats are welcome. Browse through our gift shop. We are located 1 mile from I-17, exit 78; 12 miles east of Binghamton; and 7 miles from I-81.

Country Haven

Host: Rita Saunders
Rooms: 6 (6PB) $45–65
Full Breakfast
Credit Cards: A B D
Notes: 2 5 7 9 10

WOLCOTT

The Inn at Lake Bluff

6964 Lake Bluff Rd., Wolcott, NY 14590
(315) 587-2160; (877) 882-6551
    Fax (315) 587-9048
E-mail: cdorman1@yahoo.com
Web site: www.theinnatlakebluff.com

Overlooking Sodus Bay and apple orchards, this charming farmhouse offers four comfortable rooms. Air-conditioned, private baths, hearty breakfasts. Convenient waterfront dining within walking distance from the inn. Wineries nearby. Your one-stop fishing headquarters. Charters available; fishing licenses sold on premises. Open year-round. Hunters and snowmobilers welcome.

Hosts: Carol and Charlie Dorman
Rooms: 4 (2PB;2SB) $70
Full Breakfast
Credit Cards: A B C D

NOTES: Credit cards accepted: A Master Card; B Visa; C American Express; D Discover; E Diners Club; F Other; 2 Personal checks accepted; 3 Lunch available; 4 Dinner available; 5 Open all year;

NORTH CAROLINA

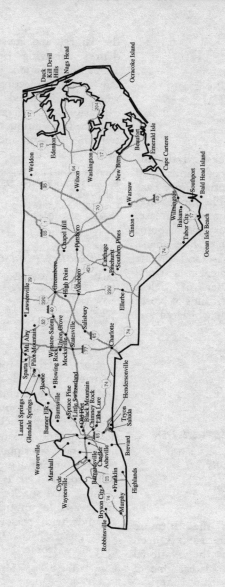

North Carolina

ASHEVILLE

Albemarle Inn

86 Edgemont Rd., Asheville, NC 28801
(828) 255-0027; (800) 621-7435
 Fax (828) 236-3397
E-mail: info@albemarleinn.com
Web site: www.albemarleinn.com

An elegant 1909 Greek Revival mansion on 3/4 acre of landscaped grounds in the residential Grove Park section of Asheville. The inn features an exquisite carved oak staircase, exceptionally spacious guest rooms with period furnishings, fine linens, televisions, telephones, and private baths. Full gourmet breakfasts at private tables. Member of Select Registry, Distinguished Inns of North America. Rooms with whirlpool and fireplace available.

Hosts: Cathy and Larry Sklar
Rooms: 11 (11PB) $145–295
Full Breakfast
Credit Cards: A B C D
Notes: 2 5 8 10 12

Cedar Crest Victorian Inn

674 Biltmore Ave., Asheville, NC 28803
(828) 252-1389; (800) 252-0310
 Fax (828) 253-7667
E-mail: stay@cedarcrestinn.com
Web site: www.cedarcrestinn.com

Three blocks from the Biltmore Estate entrance, this 1890 Queen Anne is listed on the National Register of Historic Places. One of the largest and most opulent residences surviving from Asheville's 1890s boom period. It boasts a captain's walk, projecting turrets, lavish woodwork, stained glass, and an expansive double veranda. Rooms are furnished in antiques and Victorian trappings of satin and lace. Children over 10 welcome.

Hosts: Bruce and Rita Wightman
Rooms: 12 (12PB) $160–295
Full Breakfast
Credit Cards: A B C D
Notes: 2 5 7 10 12

The Colby House

230 Pearson Dr., Asheville, NC 28801
(828) 253-5644; (800) 982-2118
 Fax (828) 259-9479
E-mail: colbyhouse@cs.com
Web site: www.colbyhouse.com

Colonial elegance with contemporary comfort in the Montford Historic District. Beautiful gardens, sitting porch, inviting fireplaces. The home has four guest rooms and a fully equipped cottage, each with individual decor, queen or king beds, private baths, and a whirlpool tub in the cottage. A bountiful breakfast is varied daily, social hour is offered in the evening, and snacks and soft drinks are available anytime. Hospitality abounds with personal attention to every guest's needs. Children 12 and over are welcome.

Hosts: Peter and Bonnie Marsh

NOTES: Credit cards accepted: A Master Card; B Visa; C American Express; D Discover; E Diners Club; F Other; 2 Personal checks accepted; 3 Lunch available; 4 Dinner available; 5 Open all year;

Rooms: 5 (5PB) $140–240
Full Breakfast
Credit Cards: A B C D
Notes: 2 5 7 8 10 12

Dry Ridge Inn

26 Brown St., Weaverville, NC 28787
(828) 658-3899; (800) 839-3899
   Fax (828) 658-9533
E-mail: innkeeper@dryridgeinn.com
Web site: www.dryridgeinn.com

Our charming three-story home has
eight rooms with private baths, some
with fireplaces; and some can be combined to make suites for large families.
You will find our home comfortable,
food delicious, and our spacious
grounds inviting and relaxing. Enjoy a
book on the porch swing or gaze into
our water garden and let the waterfall
soothe you.

Hosts: Howard and Kristen Dusenberg
Rooms: 8 (8PB) $95–155
Full Breakfast
Credit Cards: A B C D
Notes: 2 5 7 10 11

The Old Reynolds Mansion

100 Reynolds Hts., Asheville, NC 28804-1302
(828) 254-0496; (800) 709-0496
E-mail: innkeeper@oldreynoldsmansion.com
Web site: www.oldreynoldsmansion.com

The Old Reynolds Mansion

An antebellum mansion in a country
setting, this elegant, restored inn has
mountain views from all rooms, huge
verandas, wood-burning fireplaces,
swimming pool, and AC. A continental breakfast and evening beverage are
served. Located just minutes from
area attractions, but far enough away
from the inner city to experience what
coming to the mountains is all about.

Hosts: Fred and Helen Faber
Rooms: 14 (14PB) $90–165
Full Breakfast
Credit Cards: A B C D
Notes: 2 5 8 9 10 11

BANNER ELK

1902 Turnpike House

317 Old Turnpike Rd., Banner Elk, NC 28604
(828) 898-5611; (888) 802-4487
   Fax (828) 898-5611
E-mail: info@1902turnpikehouse.com
Web site: www.1902turnpikehouse.com

This delightful, restored farmhouse
offers guests a refreshing retreat and is
reminiscent of a bygone era. The turn-
of-the-century farmhouse is located at
the foot of Beech Mountain in the
picturesque town of Banner Elk, just
20 minutes from the Blue Ridge
Parkway (exit state route 221) and
Grandfather Mountain. After a
hearty breakfast, enjoy a day in the
mountains: downhill skiing at Sugar
and Beech Mountains, white-water
rafting, fishing, hiking, horseback riding, or just browsing through the
many shops in Banner Elk and nearby
Blowing Rock. Families welcome.

Hosts: Ernest and Rebecca Du Ross

6 Pets welcome; 7 Children welcome; 8 Tennis nearby; 9 Swimming nearby; 10 Golf nearby; 11 Skiing
nearby; 12 May be booked through travel agent

Rooms: 5 (5PB) $85–119
Full Breakfast
Credit Cards: A B C F
Notes: 2 5 8 9 10 11 12

BLACK MOUNTAIN

Friendship Lodge B & B

P. O. Box 877, Black Mountain, NC 28711
(828) 669-9294; (888) 669-6066

A cozy haven on Old 70 East in Ridgecrest, 2 miles east of Black Mountain. We have ten nicely decorated bedrooms, most with two double beds and private baths and two with king-size beds, each decorated in country decor. A delicious breakfast is served in our dining room. Groups and reunions are welcome. We can accommodate twenty-four people. It's like going to Grandma's house. We are ¼ mile from Ridgecrest Conference Center entrance and minutes away from Montreat and Blue Ridge Assembly and Christmont.

Mid-May–November: (828) 669-9294
December–Mid-May: (727) 895-4964
Toll-free summer: (888) 669-6066
Hosts: Bob and Sarah Labrant
Rooms: 10 (8PB;2SB) $50–55
Full Breakfast
Credit Cards: F
Notes: 2 7 8 9 10

BOONE

The Gragg House

Kalmia Acres, 210 Ridge Point Dr.
  Boone, NC 28607-7628
(828) 264-7289; (800) 242-1636
E-mail: gragghouse@boone.net
Web site: www.gragghousebandb.com

Nestled on a densely wooded ridge, the Gragg House is 10 minutes from the Blue Ridge Parkway and only 1 mile from downtown Boone and Appalachian State University. Every portal opens to a lush landscape of native wildflowers and perennial gardens. This secluded, restful haven is best described as an atmosphere of interior design elegance offered with true Southern hospitality. Immaculate, spacious, private rooms and a silver-service, full breakfast ensure a truly wonderful B & B stay. Children over 12 welcome.

The Gragg House

Hosts: Judy and Robert Gragg
Rooms: 3 (3PB) $99
Full Breakfast
Credit Cards:
Notes: 2 5 7 8 9 10 11

BRYSON CITY

Randolph House Country Inn

223 Fryemont St., P. O. Box 618
  Bryson City, NC 28713-0618
(828) 488-3472; (800) 480-3472
Web site: www.randolphhouse.com

This 1895 mansion with its twelve gables overhead and as many rocking

---

NOTES: Credit cards accepted: A Master Card; B Visa; C American Express; D Discover; E Diners Club; F Other; 2 Personal checks accepted; 3 Lunch available; 4 Dinner available; 5 Open all year;

chairs on the granite-pillared front porch is listed in the National Register of Historic Places—an honor to the inn's builder, Captain Amos Frye, an attorney and land baron, and his wife, Lillian Frye, the first woman licensed to practice law in North Carolina. About 25 years ago, Ruth Randolph Adams and her husband, Bill, began operating the Randolph House, naming it in honor of her uncle John Randolph.

Hosts: Bill and Ruth Randolph Adams
Rooms: 7 (3PB;4SB) $60–80 per person
Full Breakfast
Credit Cards: A B C D
Notes: 2 4 7 8 9 10 12

BURNSVILLE

A Little Bit of Heaven Bed and Breakfast

345 Prospect Dr., Burnsville, NC 28714-6539
(828) 675-5379
Web site: www.bbonline.com/nc/heaven

North Carolina's best-kept secret! Very private, yet very convenient to town. Large home on top of mountain with breathtaking views. Unique stone structure with circular stone wall and fireplace in great room. All guest rooms have private baths. Traditionally decorated. We specialize in hospitality and great food!

Hosts: Shelley and John Johnson
Rooms: 4 (4PB) $75–90
Full Breakfast
Credit Cards: A B
Notes: 2 5 7 8 9 10 11

CAPE CARTERET

Harborlight Guest House B & B

332 Live Oak Dr., Cape Carteret, NC 28584-9268
(252) 393-6868; (800) 624-VIEW
   Fax (252) 393-6868
E-mail: inn@clis.com
Web site: www.harborlightguesthousenc.com

The Harborlight is a romantic, secluded inn situated on a peninsula with a water view on three sides! All suites feature two-person Jacuzzis, and/or fireplaces, and stunning water views. A gourmet breakfast is served en suite or deckside. Favorite guest activities include barrier island excursions for shelling and pristine beaches, visiting the outdoor drama "Worthy Is the Lamb"—a story of the life of Christ, or shopping in the waterfront villages of Beaufort and Swansboro. Visit our website for photos/descriptions of all suites.

Hosts: Bobby and Anita Gill
Rooms: 7 (7PB) $140–250
Full Breakfast
Credit Cards: A B C
Notes: 5 8 9 10

EMERALD ISLE

Emerald Isle Inn and Bed and Breakfast by the Sea

502 Ocean Dr., Emerald Isle, NC 28594-6949
(252) 354-3222
E-mail: jimnormile@coastalnet.com
Web site: www.emeraldisleinn.com

At one of the most beautiful beaches in the Carolinas. Located on the

---

6 Pets welcome; 7 Children welcome; 8 Tennis nearby; 9 Swimming nearby; 10 Golf nearby; 11 Skiing nearby; 12 May be booked through travel agent

Crystal Coast, this Jewel of the Island is peacefully awaiting your discovery. A tranquil haven surrounded by many activities close by. Full private baths, entrances, shaded porches, and swings and rockers. AC, TV/VCR, beach umbrellas and chairs provided. Drive to a relaxing stay "Island Style!"

Hosts: Elaine and Jim Normile
Rooms: 4 (4PB) $85–160
Continental Breakfast
Credit Cards: A B D F
Notes: 5 7 8 9 10 12

HIGHLANDS

Long House Bed and Breakfast

P. O. Box 2078, Highlands, NC 28741-2078
(828) 526-4394; (877) 841-9222
    Fax (828) 526-4394
E-mail: lylong@aol.com

Long House B & B is a rustic mountain retreat located at the 4000-foot level in the Blue Ridge Mountains of western North Carolina. Our four rooms are decorated in a country motif and all have private baths. Our full, filling breakfasts are usually a highlight of your stay. There are also lots of hiking trails, waterfalls, and scenic areas within easy reach.

Long House

Hosts: Lynn and Valerie Long
Rooms: 4 (4PB) $75–150
Full Breakfast
Credit Cards: A B
Notes: 2 5 7 8 9 10

HIGH POINT

The Bouldin House Bed and Breakfast

4332 Archdale Rd., High Point, NC 27263-3070
(336) 431-4909; (800) 739-1816
    Fax (336) 431-4914
E-mail: relax@bouldinhouse.com
Web site: www.bouldinhouse.com

The Bouldin House

Fine lodging and hospitality amid America's finest home furnishings showrooms! A 1915 historic home with large wrap-around front porch, on 3 acres of country gardens. Casual elegance, large guest rooms with king-sized beds, early morning coffee and tea, gourmet breakfasts pamper you as you explore the furniture showrooms and antique shops nearby.

Hosts: Chuck and Rebecca George
Rooms: 5 (5PB) $100–120
Full Breakfast
Credit Cards: A B C D
Notes: 2 5 8 10 12

NOTES: Credit cards accepted: A Master Card; B Visa; C American Express; D Discover; E Diners Club; F Other; 2 Personal checks accepted; 3 Lunch available; 4 Dinner available; 5 Open all year;

KILL DEVIL HILLS

Cypress House Bed and Breakfast

500 N. Virginia Dare Trail
Kill Devil Hills, NC 27948
(252) 441-6127; (800) 554-2764
Fax (252) 441-2009
E-mail: cypresshse@aol.com
Web site: www.cypresshouseinn.com

Cypress House B & B, a romantic seaside inn, is ideally located only 150 yards from the Atlantic Ocean in Kill Devil Hills. Originally built in the 1940s as a private, Outer Banks hunting and fishing lodge, the interior is noted for its soft cypress tongue-and-groove paneled walls and ceilings. The six guest rooms offer private shower baths, ceiling fans, central air-conditioning, and color cable television. A hearty, full breakfast is served each morning, as well as afternoon tea.

Hosts: Karen and Leon Faso
Rooms: 6 (6PB) $75–150
Full Breakfast
Credit Cards: A B C D
Notes: 2 5 8 9 10 12

The White Egret Bed and Breakfast

1057 Colington Rd., Ocean Bay Blvd.
Kill Devil Hills, NC 27948
(252) 441-7719; (888) 387-7719
Fax (252) 480-1931
E-mail: jparsons@pinn.net
Web site: www.whiteegret.com

A central location on North Carolina's Outer Banks gives access to historical areas such as the Wright Brothers Memorial, The Lost Colony, Elizabeth I sailing ship, and much more. Our spacious rooms are furnished with king-size beds, private baths with Jacuzzis, central air, ceiling fans, TV/VCR, room phones, antiques, and fireplaces. Beautifully decorated, each room has a relaxing view of the bay. Amenities include: full breakfast, bicycles (bike trails), kayak and canoe, beach chairs, and a common lounge with kitchenette. Children 14 and over welcome.

Hosts: Jo Ann Parsons and daughter in-law Judy
Rooms: 3 (3PB) $75–150
Full Breakfast
Credit Cards: A B C D
Notes: 2 5 8 9 10

LAWSONVILLE

Southwyck Farm Bed and Breakfast

R. R. 1 Box 456, Lawsonville, NC 27022-9768
(336) 593-8006; (866) 593-8006
Fax (336) 593-9180
E-mail: southwyckfarm@mindspring.com
Web site: www.southwyckfarm.com

Southwyck Farm

Southwyck Farm is in the foothills of the Blue Ridge Mountains in Lawsonville, NC, near Hanging Rock State Park and the Dan River. The

---

6 Pets welcome; 7 Children welcome; 8 Tennis nearby; 9 Swimming nearby; 10 Golf nearby; 11 Skiing nearby; 12 May be booked through travel agent

hosts have created the ambience of a New England gentleman's farm with two houses. We have whirlpool baths and king-size beds and fireplaces. There are walking trails, both easy and difficult, with views of the mountains and the meadows. We have a bass pond and dock for fishing. We offer three-course gourmet meals at an extra charge. Please let us know if you want dinner at the time of reservations. Southwyck Farm was built by Captain Robert Carl, a Sandy Hook pilot, to be a haven for friends and family. His wife and son have continued this tradition. There is canoeing available on the Dan River and Kibler Valley.

Hosts: Diana Carl and David Hoskins
Rooms: 6 (4PB;2SB) $90–125
Full Breakfast
Credit Cards: A B D
Notes: 2 3 4 5 7 9 12

MARSHALL

Marshall House B & B

100 Hill St., Marshall, NC 28753
(828) 649-9205; Fax (828) 649-2784
E-mail: ruth.marshallhouse@prodigy.net
Web site: www.marshallhouse.org

Built in 1903, the inn overlooks the peaceful town of Marshall and the French Broad River. This country inn, listed on the National Historic Register, is decorated with fancy chandeliers, antiques, and pictures, and boasts four fireplaces, a formal dining room, parlor, and upstairs TV/reading room. Enjoy storytelling about the house, the town, the people, and the history. Our loving housepets

will gladly welcome your pets, also. The toot of a train and good service make your visit a unique experience. Smoking permitted.

Hosts: Ruth and Jim Boylan
Rooms: 5 (2PB;3SB) $40–85
Full Breakfast
Credit Cards: A B C D E
Notes: 5 6 7 10 11 12

MT. AIRY

Briar Patch B & B

150 Wild Rose Trail, Dobson, NC 27017
(336) 352-4177; Fax (336) 352-3381
E-mail: philneel@surry.net
Web site: www.briarpatchbedandbreakfast.com

Briar Patch

Beautiful log home surrounded by 48 acres of wooded land in the foothills of northwestern North Carolina. Within a short driving distance of the Blue Ridge Parkway, western Virginia, and several historic sites. A great place to spend a quiet week, weekend, or day. Come and spend time with God in the quiet of nature, away from the sights and sounds of the city.

Hosts: Chaplain Phil and Sharon Neel
Rooms: 3 (1PB;2SB) $70–75
Full Breakfast
Credit Cards: A B F
Notes: 2 5 7 10

NOTES: Credit cards accepted: A Master Card; B Visa; C American Express; D Discover; E Diners Club; F Other; 2 Personal checks accepted; 3 Lunch available; 4 Dinner available; 5 Open all year;

MURPHY

A Gathering of Angels Inn

P. O. Box 404, Murphy, NC 28906
(828) 837-3202; (888) 837-2463
 Fax (828) 837-3202
Web site: www.a-gathering-of-angels.com

A Gathering of Angels

Twelve guest rooms with private baths. Come and enjoy a restful get-away for couples, weddings, family gatherings, workshops/seminars, clubs or groups. Enjoy 50 wooded acres with hiking trails, mountain stream with a 45-foot waterfall, several tranquil flower gardens, one with a 25-foot waterfall, and a big exotic fish-pond. Country-style breakfast is included. Located near lots of fun things to do in the area.

Host: Steven Williams
Rooms: 12 (12PB) $40–65
Full Breakfast
Credit Cards: A B
Notes: 2 5 6 7 8 9 10 11

Huntington Hall B & B Inn

272 Valley River Ave., Murphy, NC 28906-2829
(828) 837-9567; (800) 824-6189
 Fax (828) 837-2527

E-mail: huntington@grove.net
Web site: www.bed-breakfast-inn.com

Each of the five spacious guest rooms, one of which is a separate cottage, has a personality of its own with period furnishings. Individual heating/air-conditioning unit, color TV, and private bath are part of each room. A full breakfast, afternoon refreshments, and nightly turn-down services are part of a guest's stay. Huntington Hall is charming, relaxing, and inviting: an escape from hurry and worry. A place to be pampered.

Hosts: Nancy and Curt Harris
Rooms: 5 (5PB) $70–125
Full Breakfast
Credit Cards: A B C D F
Notes: 2 5 7 8 9 10

Park Place B & B

54 Hill St., Murphy, NC 28906
(828) 837-8842
Web site: www.bbonline.com/nc/parkplace

Park Place

Welcome to your home away from home! For your comfort, Park Place—a two-story clapboard/brick house, circa 1900—offers three, well-appointed, climate-controlled guest rooms, each with private bath. A full gourmet breakfast is served each

---

6 Pets welcome; 7 Children welcome; 8 Tennis nearby; 9 Swimming nearby; 10 Golf nearby; 11 Skiing nearby; 12 May be booked through travel agent

morning. The hosts greatly enjoy sharing with guests the home's congenial atmosphere and its eclectic decor of family treasures, antiques, collectibles, and hand-knotted Oriental rugs. While relaxing on the screened, tree-top-level porch, guests love shooting the breeze or just rocking the time away. Willkommen—Wir sprechen Deutsch!

Hosts: Rikki and Neil Wocell
Rooms: 3 (3PB) $80–100
Full Breakfast
Notes: 2 5 8 10 12

NEW BERN

Aerie Inn Bed and Breakfast

509 Pollock St., New Bern, NC 28562
(252) 636-5553; (800) 849-5553
   Fax (252) 514-2157
E-mail: aeriebb@coastalnet.com
Web site: www.aerieinn.com

Aerie Inn

Experience the warmth and charm of historic New Bern by day and relax in comfort at night in the AERIE, an 1880s Victorian inn located in the heart of the historic district. Choose from seven air-conditioned bedrooms with private baths, TV, and telephone.

A full breakfast with choice of three hot entrees starts your day. Stroll through the herbal gardens, discuss Civil War battles, or relax in the parlor. Southern hospitality at its best.

Hosts: Donna and Doug Bennetts
Rooms: 7 (7PB) $89–109
Full Breakfast
Credit Cards: A B D
Notes: 2 5 7 8 9 10

Harmony House Inn

215 Pollock St., New Bern, NC 28560
(252) 636-3810; (800) 636-3113
E-mail: harmony@cconnect.net
Web site: www.harmonyhouseinn.com

Comfortable, yet elegant historic inn in the heart of New Bern, a quaint, relaxing town located at the confluence of the Neuse and Trent Rivers. Seven rooms and three suites (two with heart-shaped Jacuzzis). Walk to Tryon Palace, antique and specialty shops, Fireman's Museum, Trolley Tours, restaurants, riverfront, and Union Point Park. Full homemade breakfast. Private bathrooms. Relaxing front porch with swings and rocking chairs. Each room personally decorated by the innkeepers. Many "extras."

Hosts: Ed and Sooki Kirkpatrick
Rooms: 10 (10PB) $99–150
Full Breakfast
Credit Cards: A B D
Notes: 2 5 7 8 9 10 12

Howard House Victorian B & B

207 Pollock St., New Bern, NC 28560-4942
(252) 514-6709; (800) 705-5261

NOTES: Credit cards accepted: A Master Card; B Visa; C American Express; D Discover; E Diners Club; F Other; 2 Personal checks accepted; 3 Lunch available; 4 Dinner available; 5 Open all year;

Fax (252) 514-6710
E-mail: info@howardhousebnb.com
Web site: www.howardhousebnb.com

Step back in time to a gracious, elegant era by staying in this 1890 Victorian-style bed and breakfast. Located in the downtown historic district of New Bern, the Howard House is within walking distance of the riverfront, a variety of restaurants, historic homes, and sites like Tryon Place and specialty shops. The Wynns offer desserts, refreshments, and good conversation on the front porch or in the parlor as you return from a busy day around town. A bountiful breakfast is served each morning in the formal dining room. We await your arrival. . . .

Howard House

Hosts: Steven and Kimberly Wynn
Rooms: 5 (5PB) $99–119
Full Breakfast
Credit Cards: A B C D F
Notes: 2 5 8 9 10

SALISBURY

Rowan Oak House

208 S. Fulton St., Salisbury, NC 28144-4845
(704) 633-2086; (800) 786-0437
    Fax (704) 633-2084
E-mail: info@rowanoakbb.com
Web site: www.rowanoakbb.com

An elegant, high Victorian located in the historic district. Stained and leaded glass, seven fireplaces, wrap-around porch, and gardens adorn this 100-year-old mansion. Each of the four guest rooms is lavishly furnished with antiques, a sitting area, desk, phone, duvet with down comforter, reading lights, fruit, and flowers. Private baths (one room has a double Jacuzzi). Central air-conditioning and heat. Color TV, books, magazines, and board games are in the upstairs parlor. Smoking limited. Full gourmet breakfast is served. Close to furniture shopping and Lowe's Motor Speedway near Charlotte. Within walking distance of downtown churches, antique shopping, historic buildings, and fine restaurants. Children over 10 welcome.

Hosts: Barbara and Les Coombs
Rooms: 4 (4PB) $120–165
Full Breakfast
Credit Cards: A B D
Notes: 2 5 8 9 10 12

Rowan Oak House

STATESVILLE

The Kerr House
Bed and Breakfast

519 Davie Ave., Statesville, NC 28677

6 Pets welcome; 7 Children welcome; 8 Tennis nearby; 9 Swimming nearby; 10 Golf nearby; 11 Skiing nearby; 12 May be booked through travel agent

(704) 881-0957; (877) 308-0353
  Fax (704) 878-6380
E-mail: thekerrhouse@abts.net
Web site: www.statesville-nc-lodging.com

Come and experience Southern hospitality at the Kerr House, a lovely Queen Anne Victorian located within walking distance of downtown Statesville. The Kerr House features four impeccably maintained guest rooms, all with private baths. A gourmet breakfast is served in the family dining room. Much attention has been paid to detail for your comfort and pleasure. Please come and experience our motto: "There is no place like home. . .except the Kerr House!"

Hosts: Edmond and Margaret Pendrich
Rooms: 4 (4PB) $80–95
Full Breakfast
Credit Cards: A B E
Notes: 10

Madelyn's in the Grove

1836 W. Memorial Hwy.; P. O. Box 249
  Union Grove, NC 28689-0249
(704) 539-4151; (800) 948-4473
  Fax (704) 539-4080
E-mail: innkeeper@madelyns.com
Web site: www.madelyns.com

Listen to the birds and unwind. Touch the stars and relax! Only minutes from I-40 and 2 miles from I-77. A great stop for snowbirders. We have five beautiful rooms with private baths. Madelyn, an award-winning cook and cookbook author, serves a delightful three-course breakfast and snacks. This is a great place for adult church retreats and marriage seminars.

Host: Madelyn Hill
Rooms: 5 (5PB) $75–175

Full Breakfast
Credit Cards: F
Notes: 2 5 10 11 12

WAYNESVILLE

Windsong: a Mountain Inn

459 Rockcliffe Ln., Clyde, NC 28721-9293
(828) 627-6111; Fax (828) 627-8080
E-mail: russ@windsongbb.com
Web site: www.windsongbb.com

Windsong has earned its nickname, "hidden treasure of the Smokies," with its romantic setting, seclusion, gourmet breakfasts, and luxurious rooms. Rooms feature unique decorating motifs, wood-burning fireplaces, tubs for two, and deck. Luxuriate in our hot tub under the stars. From $120. Also, 2 BR cottages from $165. Feature stories have appeared in *National Geographic Traveler, Southern Living*, and many others. Near I-40 and Waynesville.

Hosts: Russ and Barbara Mancini
Rooms: 7 (7PB) $115–180
Full Breakfast
Credit Cards: A B C D E
Notes: 2 3 4 5 7 8 9 10 11 12

WILMINGTON

C. W. Worth House Bed and Breakfast

412 S. 3rd St., Wilmington, NC 28401-5102
(910) 762-8562; (800) 340-8559
  Fax (910) 763-2173
E-mail: relax@worthhouse.com
Web site: www.worthhouse.com

Let us pamper you in our circa 1893 Queen Anne Victorian home. After a

---

NOTES: Credit cards accepted: A Master Card; B Visa; C American Express; D Discover; E Diners Club; F Other; 2 Personal checks accepted; 3 Lunch available; 4 Dinner available; 5 Open all year;

restful night, enjoy a sumptuous breakfast in the formal dining room. Walk to unique shops, fine dining, and attractions. Beaches are 20 minutes away.

Hosts: Margi and Doug Erickson
Rooms: 7 (7PB) $115–150
Full Breakfast
Credit Cards: A B C D
Notes: 2 5 7 8 9 10 12

Taylor House Inn

Hosts: Karen and Scott Clark
Rooms: 5 (5PB) $95–150
Full Breakfast
Credit Cards: A B C
Notes: 2 5 7 8 9 10 11 12

C. W. Worth House

WILSON

Miss Betty's B & B Inn

600 W. Nash St., Wilson, NC 27893
(252) 243-4447; (800) 258-2058
    Fax (252) 243-4447
E-mail: info@missbettysbnb.com
Web site: www.missbettysbnb.com

Taylor House Inn

14 N. Seventh St., Wilmington, NC 28401
(910) 763-7581; (800) 382-9982
E-mail: taylorhousebb@aol.com
Web site: www.taylorhousebb.com

You'll find this haven of warm Southern hospitality and thoughtfulness in the downtown historic district, just blocks from the Cape Fear River. The five bedrooms are filled with period antiques, fresh flowers, and beautiful linens. A full gourmet breakfast is served in the formal dining room by candlelight. A slice of heaven—allow yourself to be pampered and enjoy all that the Cape Fear area has to offer.

Miss Betty's

Selected as one of the "best places to stay in the South," Miss Betty's is ideally located midway between Maine and Florida along the main north-south route, I-95. Comprised of four beautifully restored structures in the downtown historic section,

---

6 Pets welcome; 7 Children welcome; 8 Tennis nearby; 9 Swimming nearby; 10 Golf nearby; 11 Skiing nearby; 12 May be booked through travel agent

the National Registered Davis-Whitehead-Harriss House (circa 1858), the Riley House (circa 1900), Rosebud (circa 1942), and the Queen Anne (circa 1911) have recaptured the elegance and style of quiet Victorian charm, but with modern conveniences. Guests can browse for antiques in the numerous shops that give Wilson the title "Antique Capital of North Carolina." A quiet town famous for its barbecue, Wilson has four beautiful golf courses and many tennis courts. Rooms include three king honeymoon/anniversary suites.

Hosts: Betty and Fred Spitz
Rooms: 14 (14PB) $60–85
Full Breakfast
Credit Cards: A B C D E
Notes: 2 5 8 9 10

WINSTON SALEM

Lady Anne's Victorian B & B

612 Summit St., Winston Salem, NC 27101-1117
(336) 724-1074
E-mail: ladyabb@bellsouth.net
Web site: www.bbonline.com/nc/ladyannes/

Warm, Southern hospitality surrounds you in this 1890 Victorian home, listed on the National Register of Historic Places. An aura of romance touches each suite or room. All are individually decorated with period antiques, treasures, HBO/cable TV, robes, hair dryer, and telephones. Some rooms have two-person whirlpools, stereo, music tapes, microwave, coffee, refrigerators, private entrances, and balconies. An evening sweet tea and full breakfast are served. Lady Anne's is ideally located near downtown attractions, performances, restaurants, shops, and Old Salem Historic Village. Smoking permitted on the porch only please. Children over 12 welcome.

Rooms: 4 (4PB) $60–185
Full Breakfast
Credit Cards: A B C D F
Notes: 5 7 8 9 10 12

NOTES: Credit cards accepted: A Master Card; B Visa; C American Express; D Discover; E Diners Club; F Other; 2 Personal checks accepted; 3 Lunch available; 4 Dinner available; 5 Open all year;

NORTH DAKOTA

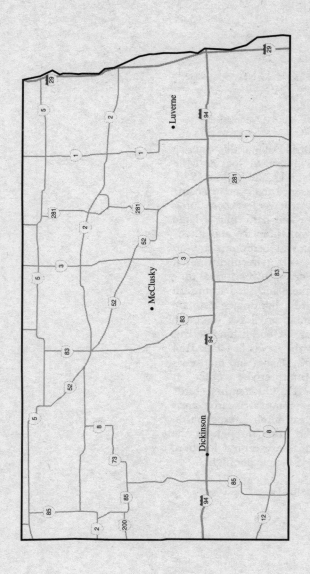

North Dakota

MCCLUSKY

Midstate B & B

980 Hwy. 200 NE, Mcclusky, ND 58463-9232
(701) 363-2520; (888) 434-2520
    Fax (701) 363-2520
E-mail: midstatebb@webtv.net
Web site: www.bbonline.com/nd/midstate/

In central North Dakota, this country home is very easy to locate: Mile Marker 232 on ND 200. Built in 1980. The guest entrance takes you to a complete and private lower level containing your bedroom and bath, plus a large TV lounge with fireplace and kitchenette. Additional bedrooms are on the upper level. Air-conditioning. Breakfast is served in the formal dining room or the plant-filled atrium. In an area of great hunting; guests are allowed hunting privileges on more than 4,000 acres. Good fishing nearby. Very close to the Lewis & Clark Trail through North Dakota and the Lewis & Clark Interpretive Center at Washburn, ND. Outstanding birdwatching on premises. Nearby areas noted for great birding experiences. Plan your day trips throughout the state from this very central location. $40 single–$45 couple per night.

Host: Grace Faul
Rooms: 4 (1PB;3SB) $45
Full Breakfast
Notes: 2 3 4 5 6 7 8 9

OHIO

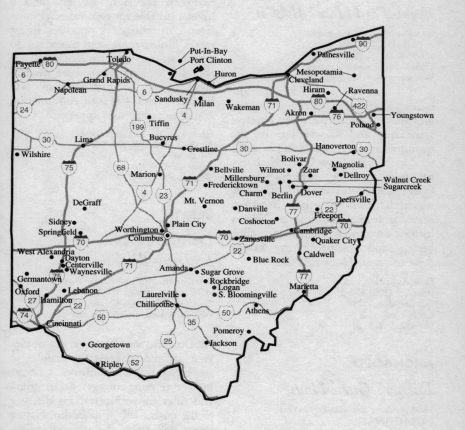

Ohio

AMANDA

Dum-Ford House B & B

P. O. Box 496; 123 W. Main St.
  Amanda, OH 43102
(740) 969-3010; (877) 271-9598
E-mail: dum-fordbb@buckeyenet.net
Web site: www.dum-fordbb.com

Circa 1845 brick Federal house, located midway between the cities of Lancaster and Circleville, in the quaint village of Amanda and adjacent to Zane's Trace (now U.S. 22). Large rooms offer ample room for sitting. Gardens and courtyard with miniature waterfall. Full gourmet breakfast served in formal dining room. Nearby historic attractions, antiquing, hiking, biking, and golfing. Thirty-minute drive to scenic Hocking Hills.

Host: Anna Ford
Rooms: 2 (2PB) $70–85
Full Breakfast
Credit Cards: A B
Notes: 2 5 8 9 10

ARCHBOLD

Diener's Guest House

18 Miller Ave., Archbold, OH 43502
(419) 445-5796

Enjoy the relaxing, friendly atmosphere of Diener's Guest House, located in Archbold, home of the famous Sauder Furniture Museum and Village. This smoke-free facility has four unique bedrooms, with private bath, phone, and TV, one large bedroom for eight or less, and a lounge suitable for committee or conference meetings. A spacious living room, dining room, and music studio with piano are ideal for family fellowship and singing. Rooms are moderately priced. A hearty, homestyle breakfast, served at your convenience, is sure to satisfy your appetite.

Hosts: Edward and Esther Diener
Rooms: 5 (4PB;1SB) $39–69
Full Breakfast
Credit Cards: A B
Notes: 2 5 7 8 9

BERLIN

Donna's Premier Lodging B & B

P. O. Box 307; 307 East St., Berlin, OH 44610
(330) 893-3068; (800) 320-3338
E-mail: info@donnasb-b.com
Web site: www.donnasofberlin.com

At Donna's, we offer a variety of elegant accommodations for couples to share their hopes and dreams. Charming and relaxing cottages, bridal suites, and villas are within walking distance to the quaint village of Berlin. Nature lovers will enjoy the steep, winding, paved driveway that leads to our original log cabin, chalets, and cedar log cabins, one of which is our luxurious "Romancing the Stone" Cabin, where you can unwind in the light rose, heart-shaped Jacuzzi in a log alcove that faces

---

NOTES: Credit cards accepted: A Master Card; B Visa; C American Express; D Discover; E Diners Club; F Other; 2 Personal checks accepted; 3 Lunch available; 4 Dinner available; 5 Open all year;

a magnificent rock with water cascading over it. Please ask about breakfast.

Hosts: Johannes and Donna Marie Schlabach
Rooms: 19 (19PB) $55–369
Continental Breakfast
Credit Cards: A B D
Notes: 2 5 8 9 10 12

The Oaks Inn

P. O. Box 421; 4752 State Rte. 62
  Berlin, OH 44610-0421
(330) 893-3061; (800) 246-2504
  Fax (330) 893-0417
E-mail: theoaks@valkyrie.net
Web site: www.theoaksinn.com

Hometown lodging within walking distance to all Berlin shops and eateries. Featuring four attractively decorated Country/Victorian rooms, including two master suites. The master lofted suite is unique with skylights, whirlpool/shower, and a private sitting room, very romantic. All rooms have private baths, entrances, AC, cable TV, are smoke-free and exceptionally clean. An in-room continental breakfast is provided. Located in Berlin, 500 ft. N. or SR 39 on US 62.

Hosts: Steve and Ruth Schlabach
Rooms: 4 (4PB) $65–139
Continental Breakfast
Credit Cards: A B D F
Notes: 2 5 7 8 10

BLUE ROCK

McNutt Farm II / Outdoorsman Lodge

6120 Cutler Lake Rd.
  Blue Rock, OH 43720-9740
(740) 674-4555

Country bed and continental breakfast in rustic quarters on a working farm in the quiet of the Blue Rock hill country. Only 11 miles from I-70, 35 miles from I-77, and 60 miles from I-71. Guests enjoy their own private kitchen, living room with fireplace or wood-burner, private bath, porch with swing, and beautiful view with forests and pastured livestock. Choose the log cabin or the carriage house. For those who want more than an overnight stay, please ask about our log cabin by the week or weekend. A cellar house cabin (somewhat primitive) is also available. Sleep to the sounds of whippoorwills and tree frogs. Awaken to the crowing rooster and the wild turkey calling; sometimes the bleating of a newborn fawn can be heard. We welcome you by reservation and deposit.

McNutt Farm II

Hosts: Don R. and Patty L. McNutt
Rooms: 3 (3PB) $40 per person
Continental Breakfast
Credit Cards:
Notes: 2 5 6 7 9 10

BOLIVAR

Enchanted Pines B & B and Tea Room

1862 Old Trail Rd., NE, Bolivar, OH 44612

---

6 Pets welcome; 7 Children welcome; 8 Tennis nearby; 9 Swimming nearby; 10 Golf nearby; 11 Skiing nearby; 12 May be booked through travel agent

(330) 874-3197; (877) 536-7508
  Fax (330) 874-2405
E-mail: linda@wilkshire.net
Web site: www.enchantedpines.com

Enchanted Pines

Enchanted Pines B & B is nestled on 6 wooded acres in central Ohio. Being just 2 miles from I-77, 15 miles from Canton Football Hall of Fame, and 20 miles from the largest Amish settlement in the world makes our B & B very accessible. Our English Ivy suite includes two large rooms, which sleep four with bath. Other uniquely decorated rooms available. Amenities include a pool, hot tub, and spacious decks.

Hosts: Linda and Earl Menges
Rooms: 4 (4PB) $75–145
Full Breakfast
Credit Cards: A B D
Notes: 3 5 9 10

CALDWELL

The Harkins House Inn

715 West St., Caldwell, OH 43724-1230
(740) 732-7347
E-mail: harkinsinn@cs.com
Web site: www.bbonline.com/oh/harkins/

Come spend an enchanted evening in this immaculately restored home.

Built in 1905 by an influential family of the Caldwell area (ancestors of the proprietors), the inn features bountiful original woodwork with oak and heart pine flooring and a stately library with fireplace and French doors. Enjoy your stay in one of our rooms with air-conditioning and cable television. Then savor breakfast in the formal dining room. Caldwell is only 25 minutes between Cambridge and Marietta.

Hosts: Jeff and Stacey Lucas
Rooms: 2 (2PB) $53–75
Full Breakfast
Credit Cards: A B C
Notes: 2 5 7 8 9 10

CAMBRIDGE

The Colonel Taylor Inn B & B

633 Upland Rd., Cambridge, OH 43725
(740) 432-7802; Fax (740) 432-3152
E-mail: coltaylr@coltaylorinnbb.com
Web site: www.coltaylorinnbb.com

The historic Victorian Taylor mansion, built in 1878, is now a romantically elegant inn. There are four guest rooms with private baths, queen four-poster beds, gas fireplaces, and ceiling fans. White robes and slippers and other nice amenities are furnished. Central air-conditioning. Afternoon snack and gourmet breakfasts are served. For business or pleasure, you will find the inn to be exceptional year-round lodging.

Hosts: Jim and Patricia Irvin
Rooms: 4 (4PB) $105–175
Full Breakfast
Credit Cards: A B D
Notes: 5 7 9 10 12

NOTES: Credit cards accepted: A Master Card; B Visa; C American Express; D Discover; E Diners Club; F Other; 2 Personal checks accepted; 3 Lunch available; 4 Dinner available; 5 Open all year;

CENTERVILLE

Yesterday Bed and Breakfast

39 S. Main St., Centerville, OH 45458
(937) 433-0785; (800) 225-0485
E-mail: yesterdaybandb@webtv.net

Yesterday

Yesterday is located in the Centerville historic district, 10 miles south of downtown Dayton, adjoining a group of fine antique shops. The house was built in 1882 and furnished with antiques and uniques. Walking distance to restaurants and two museums. Easy drive to U.S. Air Force Museum, King Island theme park, historic Waynesville and Lebanon, both major antique centers. The University of Dayton and Wright State University are 15 minutes away. Children over 12 are welcome.

Hosts: Judy and Chuck Haun
Rooms: 3 (3PB) $75–95
Full Breakfast
Credit Cards:
Notes: 2 5 7 8 9 10

CHARM

Guggisberg Swiss Inn / Amish Country Riding Stable

5025 State Rte. #557, P. O. Box 1
   Charm, OH 44617
(330) 893-3600; (877) 467-9477
E-mail: iamswiss@valkyrie.net
Web site: www.bbonline.com/oh/guggisberg

Nestled in the rolling hills of Holmes County, Ohio, the world's largest Amish settlement, is the Guggisberg Swiss Inn and Amish Country Riding Stables. In-room coffee, TV and VCRs, evening snacks, and Swiss breakfasts overlooking large duck pond. Guided horseback trail rides, horse-drawn sleigh rides (seasonal). Large enough to accommodate couples' retreats. "Come to stay after a busy day. . .leave relaxed spiritually and physically." Gift certificates available.

Hosts: Eric and Julia Guggisberg and Family
Rooms: 24 (24PB) $49–159
Continental Breakfast
Credit Cards: A B D
Notes: 2 5 7 9 10 11

COLUMBUS

Shamrock B & B

5657 Sunbury Rd., Columbus, OH 43230-1147
(614) 337-9849; Fax (614) 337-9439
E-mail: shamrockbb@juno.com

Half a mile from I-270, close to the airport, 15 minutes from downtown and major attractions. All guest rooms are on the first floor. More than an acre of landscaped gardens, patio, arbor, and pond. Bedrooms with queen-size beds, quiet ambience of antiques and art. Very restful. Guests have complete use of the first floor (living room, TV and music room, large solarium). Close to Polaris, New Easton Shoppes, gardens, movies, galleries. Air-conditioned.

Host: Tom Mc Laughlin
Rooms: 2 (2PB) $60–75
Full Breakfast
Credit Cards: A B D
Notes: 2 3 5 8 9 10

Westerville Inn Bed and Breakfast

5 S. West St., Westerville, OH 43081
(614) 882-3910; (877) 816-5247
E-mail: westervilleinn@columbus.rr.com
Web site: www.westervilleinn.com

Westerville Inn

The inn was originally built in 1854 to house a widow and her 11 children. This one-time log cabin sits on 1/2 acre fringed by a white picket fence. It is adjacent to Otterbein College, surrounded by Alum Creek Park, and conveniently close to historic uptown Westerville.

Hosts: Brenda, Terry and Caleb Winebrenner
Rooms: 3 (3PB) $65–85
Full Breakfast
Credit Cards: A B D
Notes: 2 5 7 8 9 10

COSHOCTON

Apple Butter Inn Bed and Breakfast

455 Hill St., Roscoe Village
   Coshocton, OH 43812-1029
(740) 622-1329; (888) 279-0247
Web site: www.spiker.net/applebutter/

Make yourself at home in this charming 1840 Victorian home in historical Roscoe Village. Curt Crouso, with Molly and Schnitzel, his Yorkies, welcome you to a relaxing stay in their antique-decorated Main House or the luxurious Carriage House Suites. In addition to all the amenities, a full breakfast is served in the morning.

Host: William Curt Crouso
Rooms: 9 (9PB) $69–125
Full Breakfast
Credit Cards: A B C D F
Notes: 2 5 6 7 9 10 12

DOVER

The Olde World B & B

2982 State Rte. 516, NW, Dover, OH 44622-7247
(330) 343-1333; (800) 447-1273
   Fax (330) 364-8022
E-mail: owbb@tusco.net
Web site: www.oldeworldbb.com

The Olde World

NOTES: Credit cards accepted: A Master Card; B Visa; C American Express; D Discover; E Diners Club; F Other; 2 Personal checks accepted; 3 Lunch available; 4 Dinner available; 5 Open all year;

In the spirit of Queen Victoria, experience royalty at our home with a serene respite or a delightful "Queen's Tea." Our home and guest rooms are filled with antiques and family heirloom photos. The veranda offers a view of the countryside, our bountiful gardens and pond. Homemade cuisine creates a royal treat at our family-style breakfasts and properly served teas. Enjoy a soak in our private two-person hot tub in a log cabin beside the house. Inquire about our romantic escapes!

Host: Jonna Cronebaugh
Rooms: 4 (4PB) $80–120
Full Breakfast
Credit Cards: A B D F
Notes: 2 3 4 5 8 9 10 12

FAYETTE

Red Brick Inn

206 W. Main St., Fayette, OH 43521
(419) 237-2276

Guests will enjoy a visit to our 130-year-old Victorian home filled with antique furnishings, including many family heirlooms. Four bedrooms are available, each with private bath. Three rooms have a private porch and one is handicapped-accessible. We are located in northwest Ohio near Harrison Lake State Park and Fayette's Historic Opera House at the corner of Routes 66 and 20.

Hosts: Don and Jane Stiriz
Rooms: 4 (4PB) $55
Full Breakfast
Notes: 2 5 8 9 10

HAMILTON

Gregory Creek Inn

4972 Le Sourdsville West Chester Rd.
Hamilton, OH 45011
(513) 887-0725

"New log home in quiet country setting." Located in SW Ohio, 5 miles west of I-75, between Cincinnati and Dayton. Close to state parks, amusement parks, golf courses, Paintball Country, antique centers, universities, or spend a quiet day on our farm enjoying the beautiful outdoors. Each guest unit in our home has a living/kitchen combination, private bath, and two queen-size beds. Hosts have lived and farmed these farms for over fifty years. Reservations required.

Gregory Creek Inn

Hosts: Bob and Janet Niederman
Rooms: 2 (2PB) $80
Full Breakfast
Notes: 2 5 7 10

HOCKING COUNTY

Painted Valley Farm

17232 Curtis Rd., Laurelville, OH 43135-9579
(740) 887-4446; (888) 887-4446
E-mail: paintedvalley@earthlink.net
Web site: www.hockinghills.com/paintedvalley

---

6 Pets welcome; 7 Children welcome; 8 Tennis nearby; 9 Swimming nearby; 10 Golf nearby; 11 Skiing nearby; 12 May be booked through travel agent

Enjoy a real horse farm and stay in our log home. We are close to all the state parks in the beautiful Hocking Hills, plus the famous outdoor drama "Tecumseh," in Chillicothe. We love to pamper our guests with candlelight breakfasts, relaxing in our hot tub, and homemade cookies in their rooms. The cookie jar is always full with Luanne's famous oatmeal cookies, and most of the breakfasts feature Larry's real maple syrup. God has loaned us this valley to share with others. Resident pets for petting.

Hosts: Larry and Luanne Guffey
Rooms: 2 (2PB) $80
Full Breakfast
Notes: 2 5 7 9 10

HOLMES COUNTY

"Back in Tyme" Lodging

U. S. 62, Wilmot, OH 44689
(330) 359-4080; (800) 520-0091
E-mail: victyme@sssnet.com
Web site: www.backntyme.com

Welcome to Back in Tyme. Let us be your home away from home! We offer total private lodging in Wilmot, Ohio. Gateway to Amish Country. We are available to only 1 party at a time, couple, family, or groups. Accommodations for 8 persons. Complete kitchen, full-size living room, cable TV, VCR, AC. Located just 10 minutes from Kidron, Berlin, Walnut Creek.

Rooms: 5 (5SB) $79–109
Full Breakfast
Credit Cards: A B D
Notes: 2 5 7 9 10

MAGNOLIA

Elson Inn B & B

225 N. Main St., Rte. 183, Magnolia, OH 44643
(330) 866-9242; Fax (330) 866-3398
E-mail: jelson@neo.rr.com
Web site: www.elsoninn.com

This 1879 Victorian Italianate's common rooms include a parlor, library, sitting room, dining room, large wraparound porch with swings, rockers, and an outdoor garden room. Close to Amish country, Football Hall of Fame, historical sites, fishing, hiking the Sandy-Beaver Canal, tennis, Atwood Lake golf courses, and fine dining. King, queen, and a dorm room with two double beds, private shower/baths, all individually controlled heating and air-conditioning. Original family antiques abound; visited by President William McKinley. Listed on the National Register of Historical Places. Located in a quaint canal village. Come relax with us; 24-hour reservations required but 1 week preferred. Closed on Christmas.

Elson Inn

Hosts: Jolane and Gus Elson
Rooms: 5 (5PB) $100–120
Full Breakfast
Credit Cards: A B D
Notes: 2 5 8 9 10

NOTES: Credit cards accepted: A Master Card; B Visa; C American Express; D Discover; E Diners Club; F Other; 2 Personal checks accepted; 3 Lunch available; 4 Dinner available; 5 Open all year;

MILLERSBURG

Fields of Home Guest House

7278 Cty. Rd. 201, Millersburg, OH 44654
(330) 674-7152
Web site: www.bbonline.com/oh/fieldsofhome/

Fields of Home

In the heart of Amish country. Beautiful log cabin B & B with five luxury rooms. Private entrances and baths, whirlpool tubs, fireplaces, kitchenettes, wrap-around porch with panoramic view, spring-fed pond, fishing, paddleboat, large family room common area, perennial gardens, and spacious lawn. Radios with CD players and telephones in rooms. We also have private individual cabins available with fireplaces and Jacuzzi tubs.

Hosts: Mervin and Ruth Yoder
Rooms: 5 (5PB) $65–155
Continental Breakfast
Credit Cards: A B D F
Notes: 2 5 7

Red Fox Country Inn

26367 Danville Amity Rd., P. O. Box 717
Danville, OH 43014-9769
(740) 599-7369; (877) 600-7310
Fax (740) 599-7369
E-mail: sudsimp@aol.com
Web site: www.redfoxcountryinn.com

Red Fox Country Inn is located on 15 rolling acres in scenic central Ohio,

near Amish country. It was originally built in the 1830s to house travelers. In 1994 the farm home was renovated into a Country-style B & B. We have four guest rooms, all with private baths and showers. We also serve a full-course country breakfast.

Hosts: Sue and Denny Simpkins
Rooms: 4 (4PB) $65–95
Full Breakfast
Credit Cards: A B D
Notes: 2 5 7 8 9 10 11

NAPOLEON

The Augusta Rose Bed and Breakfast

345 W. Main St., Napoleon, OH 43545
(419) 592-5852; (877) 590-1960
E-mail: augrose@bright.net
Web site: www.augustarose.com

The Augusta Rose

Restored Queen Anne-style Victorian located approximately three blocks from downtown Napoleon. The second floor is dedicated completely to our guests and includes AC and two sitting rooms, one with TV. The neighborhood is beautiful, quiet, architecturally interesting. Antique shops located in Napoleon and all surrounding communities, along with many historic attractions and fun festivals.

Hosts: Ed and Mary Hoeffel
Rooms: 4 (4PB) $65–85
Full Breakfast
Credit Cards: A B C
Notes: 2 5 7 8 9 10 12

NEW BEDFORD

A Valley View Inn of New Bedford

32327 State Rte. 643, New Bedford, OH 43824
(330) 897-3232; (800) 331-VIEW
    Fax (330) 897-0636
E-mail: valleyvu@bright.net
Web site: www.avalleyviewinn.com

Located in the midst of Amish country with a ministry to God's people, this 10-room inn is the perfect place to relax and be refreshed in body and spirit. The panoramic view is nothing short of breathtaking. Whether with a group or as a couple, you can enjoy the scenery, stroll down paths in our woods, fish in our pond, or offer an apple to the resident draft horses. Handicapped accessible and nonsmoking. (2 Corinthians 9:12,13) Sunday, a continental breakfast is served.

A Valley View Inn

Hosts: Dan and Nancy Lembke
Rooms: 10 (10PB) $80–150

No Breakfast Served
Credit Cards: A B
Notes: 2 5 7 10

OXFORD

The Duck Pond Bed and Breakfast LLC

6391 Morning Sun Rd.; P. O. Box 407
    Oxford, OH 45056-0504
(513) 523-8914; (877) 912-0490
E-mail: duckpond@juno.com
Web site: www.duckpondbb.com

The Duck Pond

An 1863 farmhouse situated 3 miles north of Miami University and uptown Oxford, 2 miles south of Hueston Woods State Park, which has an eighteen-hole golf course, nature trails, boating, swimming, and fishing. Antiquing awaits 15 miles away. Come and enjoy the quaintness that only a bed and breakfast can offer. Be our guest and enjoy our famous Hawaiian French toast. Reservations are required, so please call in advance. The Duck Pond is a member of the Ohio Bed and Breakfast Association and has met OBBA inspection standards.

Host: Marge Pendleton
Rooms: 4 (2PB;2SB) $70–90
Full Breakfast
Notes: 2 5 7 8 9 10

PLAIN CITY

Yoder's Bed and Breakfast

8144 Cemetery Pike, Plain City, OH 43064-9123
(614) 873-4489

Located on a 107-acre farm northwest
of Columbus. Big Darby Creek runs
along the front yard. Excellent bird-
watching. Within minutes of Amish
restaurants, gift shops, cheese house,
Amish furniture store, bookstores, and
antique shops. King and queen beds,
air-conditioning. No smoking or pets.

Host: Claribel Yoder
Rooms: 4 (1PB;3SB) $55–68
Full Breakfast
Notes: 2 5

PUT-IN-BAY

Trenton Guest House

511 Trenton Ave.; P.O. Box 607
   Put-in-Bay, OH 43456
(419) 285-2306
Web site: www.trenton.put-in-bay.com

Nestled on 3 wooded acres, this beautifully landscaped Cape Cod-style
home is the perfect couples' getaway.
Along with king-size beds and private
baths, each spacious room includes
TV/VCR, central air, and deluxe continental breakfast. Whether you're
enjoying quiet time in the hammock
or relaxing on the porch overlooking
the vineyards, you'll know you're on
island time.

Hosts: Michael and Susan Byrnes
Rooms: 3 (3PB) $80–150
Continental Breakfast
Credit Cards: A B
Notes: 2 9

RIPLEY

The Baird House B & B

201 N. 2nd St., Ripley, OH 45167-1002
(937) 392-4918

The Baird House

Original area built in 1825—additions
built 1849 and 1867—on Historic
Register. Walking distance to museums, restaurants, variety and antique
stores, and library. Four museums,
John Rankin House, John Parker
Museum, Ripley Museum, and
Tobacco Museum. 35' parlor with two
marble fireplaces and chandelier from
France (marble from Italy). Lots of
history. King, queen, or twin beds,
gourmet breakfast. Lots of music
available; professional saxophone
player. Unbelievable sunsets over the
Ohio River! You won't want to leave!

Hosts: Glenn and Patricia Kittles
Rooms: 3 (2PB;2SB) $125–150
Gourmet Breakfast
Notes: 2 8 10

---

6 Pets welcome; 7 Children welcome; 8 Tennis nearby; 9 Swimming nearby; 10 Golf nearby; 11 Skiing nearby; 12 May be booked through travel agent

SUGAR GROVE

Hickory Bend B & B

7541 Dupler Rd., SE
   Sugar Grove, OH 43155-9751
(740) 746-8381
E-mail: ppeery@ohiohills.com
Web site: www.users.ohiohills.com

Nestled in the Hocking Hills of southeastern Ohio on 10 wooded acres. "So
peaceful, we go out to watch the car go
by on Sunday afternoon," says Pat.
Patty is a spinner and weaver. The
cozy, private room is outside the home
in the midst of dogwood, poplar, and
oak trees. Guests come for full breakfast and conversation. Heated on the
cold days, cooled on the hot days. Call,
write, or e-mail for brochure.

Hickory Bend

Hosts: Pat and Patty Peery
Rooms: 1 (1PB) $50
Full Breakfast
Notes: 2 8 10

SUGARCREEK

Breitenbach B & B

307 Dover Rd., Sugarcreek, OH 44681
(330) 343-3603; (800) THE WINE
   Fax (330) 343-8290
Web site: www.breitenbachwine.com

Breitenbach

Splendid accommodations in a quaint
Swiss village in the heart of Amish
country. This home is artistically furnished with a mixture of antiques,
ethnic treasures, and local arts and
crafts. We can provide you with an
itinerary and maps for places that
might pique your interest. Nearby
Amish restaurants, cheese houses, flea
markets, antique malls, and quilt and
craft shops. Evening refreshments and
a full gourmet breakfast. All rooms are
individually decorated and have air-
conditioning and private baths.

Host: Deanna Bear
Rooms: 4 (4PB) $75–85
Full Breakfast
Credit Cards: A B
Notes: 2 5 10

WAKEMAN

Melrose Farm
Bed and Breakfast

727 Vesta Rd., Wakeman, OH 44889-9392
(419) 929-1867; (877) 929-1867
E-mail: melrose@accnorwalk.com
Web site: www.accnorwalk.com/~melrose

Melrose Farm is a peaceful country
retreat halfway between Oberlin and
Ashland. Each of the three lovely guest

rooms in the 125-year-old brick house has a private bath. Guests enjoy the tennis court, stocked pond, perennial gardens, and quiet, rural setting. Thirty miles from Cedar Point, an hour's drive from Cleveland or Toledo, 2 hours from Columbus. Air-conditioned comfort with old-fashioned, relaxed hospitality. Special Monday–Thursday rates for a multinight stay.

Hosts: Abe and Eleanor Klassen
Rooms: 3 (3PB) $75–85
Full Breakfast
Credit Cards: A B C D
Notes: 2 3 4 5 7 8 9 10

WALNUT CREEK

Indiantree Farm B & B

5488 State Rte. # 515, Millersburg, OH 44654
(330) 893-2497; (888) 267-5607
E-mail: indiantree@valkyrie.net

Indiantree Farm

Peaceful lodging in a guest house on a picturesque hilltop farm in the heart of Amish country, a mile from Walnut Creek. Large front porch, farming with horses, hiking trails. Apartments with kitchen and bath for the price of a room. An oasis where time slows and the mood is conversation, not television.

Hosts: Larry and Nola Miller
Rooms: 3 (3PB) $75–90
Continental Breakfast
Notes: 2 5 10

Marbeyo B & B

2370 Cty. Rd. 144, Sugarcreek, OH 44681-9662
(330) 852-4533
E-mail: marbeyo1@juno.com
Web site: www.marbeyo.com

Hosted by an Amish/Mennonite family, nestled in the heart of the Amish country in eastern Holmes County. Three bedrooms, private baths, AC. Relax in the quiet country; take leisurely walks on the farm; see the animals. Enjoy a delicious breakfast at your convenience.

Hosts: Mark and Betty Yoder
Rooms: 3 (3PB) $60–70
Full Breakfast
Credit Cards: A B D
Notes: 2 5 7 10

WAYNESVILLE

The Lark's Nest Bed 'n' Breakfast at Caesar's Creek

619 Ward Rd., Wilmington, OH 45177
(937) 382-4788
Web site: www.ohiobba.com/larksnest.htm

The Lark's Nest

The Lark's Nest is a new log cabin home located on a country road. It is surrounded by the woods of Caesar's Creek State Park in Waynesville-Harveysburg, Ohio. There are moun-

---

6 Pets welcome; 7 Children welcome; 8 Tennis nearby; 9 Swimming nearby; 10 Golf nearby; 11 Skiing nearby; 12 May be booked through travel agent

tain bike trails, boating, and antique shopping all nearby. Each guest room is individually theme decorated with king-size beds. (Futons on request.) Enjoy a backyard bonfire or grill out on our deck. Close to Blue Jacket, Ohio Renaissance Festival, and Kings Island. Prices are subject to change.

Rooms: 3 (3PB) $95–110
Full Breakfast
Credit Cards: A B C
Notes: 2 5 7 8 9 10 11

WEST ALEXANDRIA

Twin Creek Country B & B

5353 Enterprise Rd.
   West Alexandria, OH 45381-9518
(937) 787-3990; Fax (937) 787-3990
E-mail: drulrich@infinet.com

Twin Creek Country

This 1830s farmhouse is remodeled to offer a quiet getaway for families and couples. The entire house, upper or lower level, or individual rooms are available. There is a 2-room suite and bathroom upstairs and a 1-room suite and bathroom downstairs including a large parlor room. Furnished kitchen available to all guests. Owners live 100 yards away. Guests can roam the 170 acres, including 70 acres of woods. Restaurants nearby. Suitable for 2 families at once. Close to the I-70, I-75 interchange.

Hosts: Dr. Mark and Carolyn Ulrich
Rooms: 2 (2PB) $79
Full Breakfast
Credit Cards: A B C D E
Notes: 2 3 4 5 7 9 10

WILLSHIRE

Hillside Bed and Breakfast

2751 Vanwert Mercer Co. Line Rd.
   Willshire, OH 45898
(419) 495-2845
E-mail: dmgamble@webtv.net

Relax in a tranquil country setting overlooking the fields on a working grain farm. Watch the birds, squirrels, and rabbits, or enjoy the nature trails, antiques, and Oliver Tractor collection. Hot tub, central air, bikes, pool table, foosball table, satellite TV, or surf the web for your entertainment. Can also accommodate groups. Easy access off of US 33 and State Route 49. Restaurants and antique shops nearby. Children must be supervised.

Host: Dean Gamble
Rooms: 3 (1PB;2SB) $55–60 whole house $200
Continental Breakfast
Notes: 2 5 7 9 10

NOTES: Credit cards accepted: A Master Card; B Visa; C American Express; D Discover; E Diners Club; F Other; 2 Personal checks accepted; 3 Lunch available; 4 Dinner available; 5 Open all year;

WILMOT

Raber's Tri-County View

1004 State Rte. 62, P. O. Box 155
   Wilmot, OH 44689-0155
(330) 359-5189; (877) 722-3772
E-mail: rabersbnb@msn.com

Amid an Amish settlement, we have a peaceful and unique setting with scenery of three counties. Each room has an individual decor of Victorian, Country, or Amish; a private bath, queen-sized bed, central AC/heating, and are nonsmoking. A continual breakfast is served at your convenience, except on Sundays at 8 A.M. There are a variety of shops, restaurants, and antique shops within 5 miles. God be with you.

Hosts: Ed and Esther Raber
Rooms: 3 (3PB) $65–95
Continental Breakfast
Credit Cards: A B F
Notes: 2 5 7 9 10

ZOAR

The Cider Mill
Bed And Breakfast

198 E. 2nd St.; P. O. Box 438, Zoar, OH 44697
(330) 874-3240

The Cider Mill was built in 1863. It was and is the nation's most successful communal settlement. The Cider Mill served as a steam-operated mill and as the village cabinet shop. It was converted to living quarters in 1972. Rooms feature exposed ceiling beams and tastefully selected antiques. Clean and beautiful bathrooms provide modern comfort. Our three-story spiral staircase connects each level of the house. The fireplace with stone hearth in the gathering room is a perfect place to relax. To start your day, you'll be served a full breakfast from our country kitchen.

Hosts: Vernon and Dorothy Furbay
Rooms: 3 (2PB;2SB) $60–75
Full Breakfast
Notes: 2 5   9 10 11

---

6 Pets welcome; 7 Children welcome; 8 Tennis nearby; 9 Swimming nearby; 10 Golf nearby; 11 Skiing nearby; 12 May be booked through travel agent

OKLAHOMA

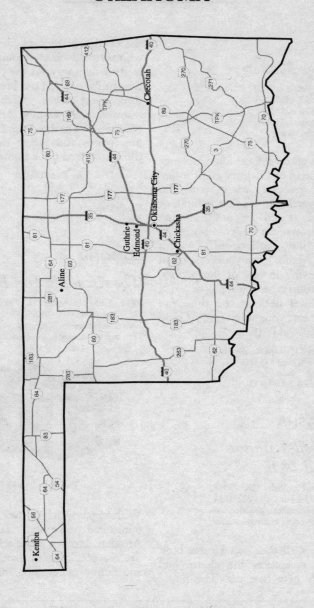

Oklahoma

ALINE

Heritage Manor

33 Heritage Rd., Aline, OK 73716-9118
(580) 463-2563; (800) 295-2563
  Fax (580) 463-2563
E-mail: heritage@pldi.net
Web site: www.1aj.org

Enjoy the vintage decor and ambience of a Victorian or Country guest room. Roam the peaceful gardens, wander 80 acres of watchable wildlife habitat, or read and search in 5000-volume library! Browse for hours viewing the museum-like collections within Heritage Manor. Enjoy a breakfast of your choosing in one of the parlors, gazebo, courtyard, gardens, or on a tree-top-level deck at the time you wish to eat your Heritage "Good Morning" breakfast!

Hosts: A.J. and Carolyn Rexroat
Rooms: 4 (2PB;2SB) $75–150
Full Breakfast
Notes: 2 3 4 5 6 7 8 9 10 11

CHICKASHA

Campbell-Richison House B & B

1428 Kansas, Chickasha, OK 73018
(405) 222-1754; Fax (405) 222-1754
E-mail: innkeeper@campbellrichison.com
Web site: www.campbellrichison.com

The Campbell-Richison House, built in 1909, recaptures the charm and hospitality of a past era. The house shares the history of three families who were all Grady County pioneers in their own way. At the present time the family-run bed and breakfast hosts three guest rooms, which have been restored and warmly decorated for your visit. Whether business or pleasure, come and enjoy this restored three-story red brick home.

Hosts: David and Kami Patcliff
Rooms: 3 (3PB) $50–70
Full Breakfast
Credit Cards: A B
Notes: 2 5 7 8 9 10

EDMOND

The Arcadian Inn B & B

328 E. 1st St., Edmond, OK 73034-4543
(405) 348-6347; (800) 299-6347
E-mail: arcadianinn@juno.com
Web site: www.arcadianinn.com

The Arcadian Inn

With angels watching over you, you are ministered peace and relaxation. The Arcadian Inn is a step back in time to the era of Christian love, hospitality, and family values. The Inn, historical

---

NOTES: Credit cards accepted: A Master Card; B Visa; C American Express; D Discover; E Diners Club; F Other; 2 Personal checks accepted; 3 Lunch available; 4 Dinner available; 5

home of Dr. Ruhl, has eight gue-strooms, all with double-size Jacuzzi tubs, most with fireplaces and breakfast parlors where your sumptuous morning meal is served with romantic candle-light. Perfect for getaways, birthdays, anniversaries, and wedding nights. Winner of prestigious "Reader's Choice Award" in Oklahoma for 3 years in a row, 9 years in the top 5.

Hosts: Gary and Martha Hall
Rooms: 8 (8PB) $119–219
Full Breakfast
Credit Cards: A B C D
Notes: 2 5 8 9 10 12

GUTHRIE

Victorian Rose B & B

415 E. Cleveland Ave., Guthrie, OK 73044-3308
(405) 282-3928

The 100-year-old Queen Anne home, built in 1894, mixes the charm of the past with the comforts of the present. Located on a brick street, it features a wrap-around porch with gingerbread accents, a porch swing, and garden area. Lovely restoration with quality workmanship: beautiful oak floors; exquisite, original beveled windows; gleaming brass light fixtures; and antiques. Three blocks from historic downtown (the largest urban historic district in the U.S.). Three beautiful Victorian guest rooms offer queen beds and private baths. Full, compli-mentary gourmet breakfast.

Hosts: Linda and Foy Shahan
Rooms: 3 (3PB) $79–99
Full Breakfast
Credit Cards: A B D
Notes: 2 5 8 9 10 12

Victorian Rose

KENTON

Black Mesa Bed and Breakfast

P. O. Box 81; (2 Miles N of Kenton)
Kenton, OK 73946-0081
(580) 261-7443; (800) 866-3009
E-mail: bmbb1@juno.com
Web site: www.ccccok.or/bmbb.html

Black Mesa

This 1910 ranch house, on a working ranch, located 2 miles north of Kenton, near the base of Black Mesa, boasts the best in country hospitality. Accommodations include a ground-floor double-occupancy room w/bath, a second-story family suite that sleeps 8 w/bath, and a two-bedroom guest cottage with bath house. We offer

days of adventure, spectacular sunsets,
and down home hospitality.

Hosts: Vicki and Monty Joe Roberts
Rooms: 4 (2PB;2SB) $60–80
Full Breakfast
Credit Cards: A B D
Notes: 2 3 4 5 6 7 10

OREGON

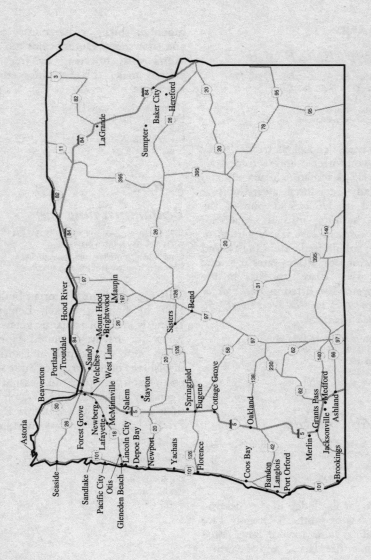

Oregon

ASHLAND

Cowslip's Belle B & B

159 N. Main St., Ashland, OR 97520-1729
(541) 488-2901; (800) 888-6819
    Fax (541) 488-2901
E-mail: stay@cowslip.com
Web site: www.cowslip.com

Teddy bears, chocolate truffles, cozy down comforters, and scrumptious breakfasts. A romantic luxury inn and nationally acclaimed award-winner featured in *McCall's* as one of the "most charming inns in America"; *Country Accents* says it's "a garden of many splendored delights"; and Northwest Best Places rates it as one of the Best Places to Kiss in the Northwest. Also listed in *Weekends for Two in the Pacific Northwest: 50 Romantic Getaways*.

Hosts: Jon and Carmen Reinhardt
Rooms: 5 (5PB) $115–195
Full Breakfast
Credit Cards: F
Notes: 2 8 9 10 11 12

Mt. Ashland Inn

550 Mt. Ashland Rd., Ashland, OR 97520-9745
(541) 482-8707; (800) 830-8707)
E-mail: stay@mtashlandinn.com
Web site: www.mtashlandinn.com

Spectacular log lodge in the Siskiyou Mountains of southern Oregon. Five very deluxe suites include large jetted tubs, gas fireplaces, and beautiful mountain views. Complimentary mountain bikes, cross-country skis, and snowshoes. Outdoor hot tub and sauna with towering fir trees all around make this an unforgettable adventure.

Hosts: Chuck and Laurel Biegert
Rooms: 5 (5PB) $160–200
Full Breakfast
Credit Cards: A B D
Notes: 2 5 11

ASTORIA

Benjamin Young Inn

3652 Duane St., Astoria, OR 97103-2421
(503) 325-6172; (800) 201-1286
E-mail: benjamin@benjaminyounginn.com
Web site: www.benjaminyounginn.com

This Queen Anne Victorian built in 1888 by Salmon Packer, Benjamin Young is ideal for romantic getaways. Enjoy the newly decorated Honeymoon Suite with cupola and antique furnishings or the Fireplace Suite with two-person whirlpool tub. Feast at our legendary breakfast table. Watch the ships go by on the Columbia River. Private baths, river views, weddings, and catering.

Host: Carolyn Hammer
Rooms: 5 (5PB) $85–145
Full Breakfast
Credit Cards: A B C D
Notes: 2 5 7 8 9 10 12

NOTES: Credit cards accepted: A Master Card; B Visa; C American Express; D Discover; E Diners Club; F Other; 2 Personal checks accepted; 3 Lunch available; 4 Dinner available; 5 Open all year;

Columbia River Inn
Bed and Breakfast

1681 Franklin Ave., Astoria, OR 97103-3616
(503) 325-5044; (800) 953-5044
Web site: www.columbiariverbb.com

Columbia River Inn is charming in
every way. Built in 1870, this beautiful
"painted lady" Victorian has a gazebo
for weddings and parties in the beautifully landscaped garden. Come see the
"stairway to the stars," a unique, terraced garden view of the celebrated
Columbia River. Brand-new aquatic
center and seafood lab nearby. A new
7-screen theater close by; also close to
museums. The inn offers four elegantly
furnished rooms, one with a working
fireplace and Jacuzzi. Beautiful side
garden added with cobblestone sidewalk. The innkeeper's specialty is hospitality—"Home is where the heart is."
Children 10 years and older welcome.
Guests may use off-street parking.
Gift certificates available.

Columbia River Inn

Host: Ms. Karen Nelson
Rooms: 4 (4PB) $80–130 plus tax
Full Breakfast
Credit Cards: A B C F
Notes: 2 5 7 9 10

Grandview
Bed and Breakfast

1574 Grand Ave., Astoria, OR 97103-3733
(503) 325-5555; (800) 488-3250
E-mail: grandviewbedandbreakfast@usa.net
Web site: www.pacifier.com/~grndview

Grandview

Features of this home are a ballet turret, inset balconies, open staircase, bay
windows, tower. Furnished with queen
beds, many canopy beds, bird borders,
some Victorian chairs, settees, some
wicker, birdhouses. Many rooms have
excellent views of the Columbia River.
One room has clouds, another butter-
flies. Two-bedroom units for family.
No liquor, no smoking in the home.
Golf 10 miles.

Host: Charleen Maxwell
Rooms: 9 (7PB;2SB) $75–101
Full Breakfast
Credit Cards: A B D
Notes: 5 7 8 9

BEND

Juniper Acres B & B

65220 Smokey Ridge Rd., Bend, OR 97701-9108
(541) 389-2193
E-mail: verndella@teleport.com
Web site: www.juniperacres.com

6 Pets welcome; 7 Children welcome; 8 Tennis nearby; 9 Swimming nearby; 10 Golf nearby; 11 Skiing
nearby; 12 May be booked through travel agent

This lodge-style log home sits on 9½ acres of wooded privacy. Our great room looks out to expansive mountain views. Each room has a private bath, queen bed, TV/VCR, and sitting area plus desk. The facility is air-conditioned for the comfort of our guests. A full breakfast is served, and the innkeepers enjoy company and visiting.

Hosts: Vern and Della Bjerk
Rooms: 2 (2PB) $89 plus tax
Full Breakfast
Credit Cards:
Notes: 2 5 10 11

BRIDGEPORT

Bruno Ranch B & B

19518 Bridgeport Ln.; P. O. Box 5051
    Bridgeport, OR 97819
(541) 446-3468; Fax (541) 446-3468

Bruno Ranch

Bruno Ranch B & B, set on ranchland adjoining the Wallowa Whitman National Forest, this is rural Oregon at its best. Just 25 miles south of Baker City, the surrounding land abounds with opportunities for fishing, birdwatching, hunting, biking, hiking, scenic drives, and squirrel hunting. Children, pets, and horses welcome; appointments appreciated.

Host: Maria Bruno
Rooms: 2 (2SB) $35–40
Full Breakfast
Credit Cards:
Notes: 4 5 6 7

BROOKINGS

Chetco River Inn
Lavender Bee Farm

21202 High Prairie Rd.
    Brookings, OR 97415-8200
(541) 670-1645; (800) 327-2688
E-mail: chetcoriverinn@starband.net
Web site: www.chetcoriverinn.com

Pristine river and modern inn await you a short distance from the coast. Big country breakfast, huge beds with down and handmade quilts, large indoor fireplace common room, and covered porch with rocking chairs for your comfort. To do: trails, fishing, star gazing, swimming, mushrooming, birding, and flower and herb gardens. New addition—Lavender Farm. Lavender fields now open for public. Lavender cutting during June through September.

Rooms: 6 (6PB) $125
Full Breakfast
Credit Cards: A B
Notes: 2 3 4 5 7 9 12

FOREST GROVE

Oak Tree B & B

2300 N. W. Thatcher Rd., Forest Grove, OR 97116
(503) 357-6939; Fax (503) 357-3297
E-mail: oaktreebnb@aol.com
Web site: www.moriah.com/oaktree

Our home is less than a mile from the quiet, rural, yet progressive community of Forest Grove. Forest Grove lies between the mountains and the ocean, 35 minutes to Portland and 90 minutes to the Pacific. Our comfortable accommodations include an acre of well-tended gardens, a view of rolling farmland from our guest living room, laundry facilities, robes and slippers; fax and data port available. Sorry, no smoking or pets.

Hosts: Bob and Donna McIntosh
Rooms: 2 (2PB) $60
Full Breakfast
Credit Cards: A B
Notes: 2 5 7

GRANTS PASS

Flery Manor Bed and Breakfast

2000 Jumpoff Joe Creek Rd.
    Grants Pass, OR 97526
(541) 476-3591; Fax (541) 471-2303
E-mail: flery@flerymanor.com
Web site: www.flerymanor.com

"Get away from the hurried world. . . retreat to the comfort and hospitality of Flery Manor." Elegant, romantic, secluded. On 7 mountain view acres near the Rouge River. Elegantly decorated bedrooms. Suites have king beds, fireplaces, Jacuzzi tub, and private balcony. Ponds, paths, waterfall, streams, and gazebo. Library, parlor w/piano, 2-story-high living room, huge balcony, and formal dining room. Three-course gourmet breakfast. Access to private health club/pool. Easy I-5 access. Open year-round. Featured in *Chef* magazine.

Hosts: John and Marla Vidrinskas
Rooms: 5 (4PB;1SB) $85–150
Full Breakfast

Credit Cards: A B   F
Notes: 2 4 5 8 9 10 11 12

HEREFORD

Fort Reading B & B

20588 Hwy. 245, Hereford, OR 97837-9601
(541) 446-3478; (800) 573-4285
    Fax (541) 446-3478
E-mail: ftreading@ortelco.net

Fort Reading

Come, enjoy a stay in the secluded, beautiful Burnt River Valley in Southeastern Oregon. We're a working cattle ranch with stables available and trails to ride. Relax in our two-bedroom cottage away from telephone and TV. There's a fully equipped kitchen to use or breakfast in the ranch house. Lake and stream fishing close by, historic cemeteries, mining town of Sumpter, and the Oregon Trail Interpretive Center in Baker City, all within 1 hour's drive.

Hosts: Daryl and Barbara Hawes
Rooms: 2 (2SB) $60–100
Full Breakfast
Credit Cards:
Notes: 2 3 4 6 7

6 Pets welcome; 7 Children welcome; 8 Tennis nearby; 9 Swimming nearby; 10 Golf nearby; 11 Skiing nearby; 12 May be booked through travel agent

JACKSONVILLE

The Touvelle House

P. O. Box 1891; 455 N. Oregon
  Jacksonville, OR 97530-1891
(541) 899-8938; (800) 846-8422
  Fax (541) 899-3992
E-mail: touvelle@wave.net
Web site: www.touvellehouse.com

The Touvelle House

Elegant 1916 three-story craftsman mansion located on over an acre of gardens and parklike grounds. Six rooms all with private baths. Two blocks from town and minutes from Ashland. Seasonal pool on site; AC in each room. Step back in time and enjoy our lovely home.

Rooms: 6 (6PB) $85–140
Full Breakfast
Credit Cards: A B C D F
Notes: 5 7 8 9 10 11 12

LINCOLN CITY

Brey House
Oceanview B & B Inn

3725 N. W. Keel Ave.
  Lincoln City, OR 97367-4867
(541) 994-7123; Fax (541) 994-5941
E-mail: breysinn@webtv.net
Web site: www.breyhouse.com

The ocean awaits you just across the street. Enjoy whale-watching, storm-watching, or just beachcombing. We are conveniently located a short walking distance from local restaurants and retail shops. Guests have four beautiful rooms to choose from, all with private baths and queen beds. Flannel sheets and electric blankets are in all the guest rooms. Enjoy Milt and Shirley's talked-about breakfast. Brey House is a three-story, Cape Cod–style home.

Hosts: Milt and Shirley Brey
Rooms: 4 (4PB) $80–150
Full Breakfast
Credit Cards: A B D F
Notes: 5 8 9 10 12

Pacific Rest Bed and Breakfast and Cottages

1611 N. E. 11th St.
  Lincoln City, OR 97367-3410
(541) 994-2337; (888) 405-7378
E-mail: jwaetjen@wcn.net
Web site: http://pacificrestbb.hypermart.net/

Pacific Rest

A special place where you'll find rest and respite for the spirit as well as for the body. Built with the B & B guest in mind, you'll find two spacious suites

---

NOTES: Credit cards accepted: A Master Card; B Visa; C American Express; D Discover; E Diners Club; F Other; 2 Personal checks accepted; 3 Lunch available; 4 Dinner available; 5 Open all year;

with private baths and decks and books for every interest. Located on a hillside within walking distance of shops, restaurants, lake and ocean. . . ideal for a romantic getaway or family retreat. Also available: two- and three-bedroom, two-bath, fully furnished, oceanview cottages with hot tubs, TV/VCR. Ideal for small retreats and family reunion. Gracious hospitality and personal service abound. We serve a full candlelight breakfast, gourmet coffee, teas, and homemade treats to our guests who soon become friends.

Hosts: Ray and Judy Waetjen
Rooms: 4 (4PB) $90–125
Full Breakfast
Credit Cards:
Notes: 2 5 7 8 9 10

MT. HOOD AREA

Falcon's Crest Inn

P. O. Box 185; 87287 Government Camp Loop
   Hwy., Government Camp, OR 97028-0185
(503) 272-3403; (800) 624-7384
   Fax (503) 272-3454
E-mail: info@falconscrest.com
Web site: www.falconscrest.com

Falcon's Crest Inn is a beautiful mountain lodge/chalet-style house, architecturally designed to fit into the quiet, natural forest and majestic setting of Oregon's Cascade Mountains. The inn is within walking distance of Ski Bowl, a year-round playground featuring downhill skiing in the winter and the Alpine Slide in the summer! Five suites, all with private baths. Each guest room is individually decorated with interesting and unique collectibles and offers beautiful views of

mountains and forests. Phones are available in each suite. Smoking restricted. A fine-dining restaurant is on the premises. Ski packages and special event specialists! Children 6 and older welcome.

Hosts: B J and Melody Johnson
Rooms: 5 (5PB) $125–179
Full Breakfast
Credit Cards: A B C D E
Notes: 2 4 5 8 9 10 11 12

Falcon's Crest

PORTLAND

Hostess House
Bed and Breakfast

5758 N. E. Emerson St., Portland, OR 97218
(503) 282-7892; (877) 4600 ext
   Fax (503) 282-7892
E-mail: hostess@hostesshouse.com
Web site: www.hostesshouse.com

Tranquil, affordable getaway that is city close and country quiet. Tastefully and simply refurbished contemporary inn is in a modest residential neighborhood. Near bus, light rail, airport. Within 10–15 minutes of Convention Center, Rose Garden Arena, Coliseum, and downtown. Comfy bathrobes provided. Guests served

---

6 Pets welcome; 7 Children welcome; 8 Tennis nearby; 9 Swimming nearby; 10 Golf nearby; 11 Skiing nearby; 12 May be booked through travel agent

delectable breakfast in a dining room overlooking a deep terraced backyard. Special menus by request. "Rest your head. . .rest your heart." Make Hostess House your "home" away from home while traveling.

Host: Milli Laughlin
Rooms: 2 (2SB) $60
Full Breakfast
Credit Cards: A B C D
Notes: 2 5 7 8 9 10 11

ROSEBURG

Hokanson's Guest House Bed and Breakfast

848 S. E. Jackson, Roseburg, OR 97470
(541) 672-2632
Web site: www.moriah.com/hokanson

Gracefully standing on land once owned by Roseburg's founding father, Aaron Rose, the Guest House was built in 1882 in the Gothic Revival style. The Guest House is Roseburg's only B & B on the National Register of Historic Places. Each of the two guest rooms, furnished in Victorian decor, has a private bath with a clawfoot tub. Breakfast is always a three-course affair. Conveniently located one block from downtown, the Guest House is beautifully landscaped with lovely lawns, flower gardens, and even a pond for your aesthetic pleasure.

Hosts: John and Victoria Hokanson
Rooms: 2 (2PB) $55–95
Full Breakfast
Credit Cards: A B C D E
Notes: 2 4 5 7 8 9 10

SALEM

A Creekside Inn, The Marquee House

333 Wyatt Court, NE, Salem, OR 97301
(503) 391-0837; (800) 949-0837
 Fax (503) 391-1713
E-mail: rickiemh@open.org
Web site: www.marqueehouse.com

Stunning garden setting on historic Mill Creek provides tranquility in the city. This 1930s Mt. Vernon Colonial has antiques, fireplaces, and a truly relaxing atmosphere served up with sumptuous breakfasts. Within walking distance of the Capitol, Willamette University, historic districts; convenient for wine country tours. Data ports available for business use. Nightly film showing with "bottomless" popcorn bowl; Murder Mystery Weekends available.

The Marquee House

Host: Rickie Hart
Rooms: 5 (3PB;2SB) $65–95
Full Breakfast
Credit Cards: A B D E
Notes: 2 5 7 8 9 10 11 12

SEASIDE

The Guest House B & B

486 Necanicum Dr., Seaside, OR 97138

NOTES: Credit cards accepted: A Master Card; B Visa; C American Express; D Discover; E Diners Club; F Other; 2 Personal checks accepted; 3 Lunch available; 4 Dinner available; 5 Open all year;

(503) 717-0495; (800) 340-8150
   Fax (503) 717-9385
E-mail: guest-house@obbg.org
Web site: www.obbg.org

Spacious, comfortable, casual B & B
with mix of antiques, new things, and
historical touches. View of river and
mountains. Two and one-half blocks
from ocean beach. One-half mile from
antique mall and factory outlet stores.
Common room with fireplace, piano,
and table for games. Delicious food.
Friendly hosts. Many recreational and
sightseeing opportunities nearby. Pets
allowed in attached garage or fenced
yard. Also, we have a rental cottage
and rental condo, which take pets.

Hosts: Nancy and Ken Bailey
Rooms: 4 (4PB) $60–95
Full Breakfast
Credit Cards: A B D
Notes: 2 5 6 7 8 9 10 12

10th Avenue Inn B & B

125 10th Ave., Seaside, OR 97138-6241
(503) 738-0643; (800) 745-BEST
   Fax (503) 738-0172
E-mail: 10aveinn@seasurf.net
Web site: www.10aveinn.com

Light cascades into this 1908 home,
once belonging to a circuit court
judge. Panoramic views of the ocean,
Seaside's famous Promenade, beach
homes, and the coast mountain range.
Casual elegance greets you in the parlor, complete with cozy fireplace and a
baby grand piano. Join us for evening
snacks, lively conversation, and a magnificent ocean sunset. The morning
brings breakfasts described as a feast
for the eye as well as the palate.

Children over 12 welcome. Please no
smokers or pets.

Hosts: Lesle and Jack Palmeri
Rooms: 3 (3PB) $89–129
Full Breakfast
Credit Cards: A B C D E
Notes: 5 9 10 12

SISTERS

Australian Outback Country Lodge B & B

68733 Junipine Ln. , P. O. Box 1993
   Sisters, OR 97759
(541) 549-4312; Fax (541) 549-4213
E-mail: scbb@outlawnet.com
Web site:
   www.australianoutback@sisterslodging.com

Australian Outback Country Lodge
B & B in Sisters, Oregon, offers a big
country breakfast and cozy beds in a
wooded setting perfect for retreats,
weddings, honeymoons, and getaways
close to Mt. Bachelor, skiing, golfing,
hiking, rafting, and fishing. Travel to
Sisters, Oregon, and vacation in a
comfortable, country bed and breakfast. Relax on our pine swing, feed our
many deer friends, or take a walk
along Squaw Creek. Our outdoor
Jacuzzi is sure to delight even the wea-
riest traveler—you'll be pampered as
you relax next to the fire and unwind
in the serene setting of our high desert
bed and breakfast inn. AAA rated.

Hosts: Richard and Margaret Mason
Rooms: 5 (5PB) $99–149
Full Breakfast
Credit Cards: A B
Notes: 2 5 6 7 8 9 10 11 12

6 Pets welcome; 7 Children welcome; 8 Tennis nearby; 9 Swimming nearby; 10 Golf nearby; 11 Skiing
nearby; 12 May be booked through travel agent

Conklin's Guest House

69013 Camp Polk Rd., Sisters, OR 97759-9705
(541) 549-0123; (800) 549-4262
   Fax (541) 549-4481
Web site: www.conklinsguesthouse.com

Conklin's Guest House

Conklin's Guest House is surrounded by a sprawling meadow with a panoramic backdrop of snowcapped peaks. Rich in history, near-century-old homesite gives evidence that early settlers chose the most beautiful sites first! Modern conveniences and attention to detail ensure a comfortable and restful stay. A truly peaceful environment within walking distance of Sisters' bustling shops and restaurants. Guests may use the barbecue, swimming pool, and laundry facilities, and otherwise be at home! The ponds are stocked with trout for catch-and-release fishing. The Sisters area has something for everyone, from rafting and rock climbing to dining and shopping and much more. Children 12 and over welcome.

Hosts: Marie and Frank Conklin
Rooms: 5 (5PB) $90–150
Full Breakfast
Credit Cards:
Notes: 2   5   8 9 10 11

NOTES: Credit cards accepted: A Master Card; B Visa; C American Express; D Discover; E Diners Club; F Other; 2 Personal checks accepted; 3 Lunch available; 4 Dinner available; 5 Open all year;

PENNSYLVANIA

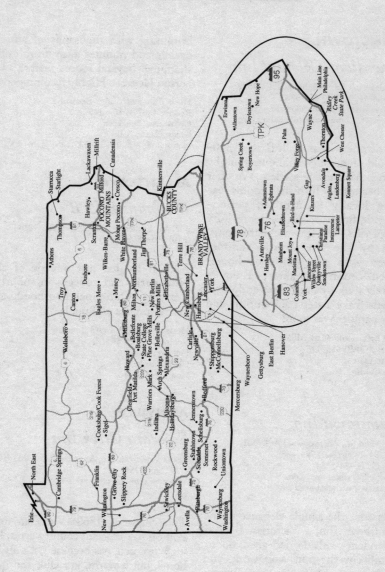

Pennsylvania

ADAMSTOWN

Brownstone Colonial Inn

590 Galen Hall Rd., Reinholds, PA 17569
(717) 484-4460; (877) 464-9862
E-mail: info@brownstonecolonialinn.com
Web site: www.brownstonecolonialinn.com

Brownstone Colonial Inn is a 210-year-old sandstone farmhouse built by German Mennonite settlers. We offer three beautifully furnished rooms featuring locally handcrafted period-authentic furniture, plank floors, lofty windowsills, and private bathrooms. Dine by the fire in the summer kitchen with a scrumptious home-cooked country breakfast. Enjoy a leisurely walk by our flower and water gardens. Take a step back in time and let us pamper you soon!

Hosts: Brenda and Mark Miller
Rooms: 3 (3PB) $85–115
Full Breakfast
Credit Cards:
Notes: 2 5 7 9 10 11

Adamstown Inn

62 W. Main St., Adamstown, PA 19501
(717) 484-0800; (800) 594-4808
    Fax (717) 484-1384
E-mail: info@adamstown.com
Web site: www.adamstown.com

Experience the simple elegance of the Adamstown Inn, a Victorian B & B resplendent with leaded-glass doors, magnificent chestnut woodwork, and Oriental rugs, located in a small town brimming with thousands of antique dealers and minutes away from outlet shopping. Several rooms feature two-person Jacuzzis. Highly recommended!

Hosts: Tom and Wanda Berman
Rooms: 4 (4PB) $69–149
Continental Breakfast
Credit Cards: A B C
Notes: 2 5 8 9 10 11 12

ALLENTOWN

Brennans B & B

3827 W. Linden St., Allentown, PA 18104
(610) 395-0869

B & B located just outside of city. Near parks and colleges in suburban Cetronia. Quiet neighborhood, also near churches and malls.

Hosts: Lois and Edward Brennan
Rooms: 2 (2PB) $45
Full Breakfast
Credit Cards:
Notes: 2 5 7 10

ANNVILLE

Swatara Creek Inn

10463 Jonestown Rd., Annville, PA 17003-8438
(717) 865-3259
Web site: www.swataracreekinn.com

This charming 1860s Victorian mansion on 4½ peaceful country acres, lovingly restored, has become not only our home, but a warm, graceful, and quiet

---

NOTES: Credit cards accepted: A Master Card; B Visa; C American Express; D Discover; E Diners Club; F Other; 2 Personal checks accepted; 3 Lunch available; 4 Dinner available; 5 Open all year;

retreat away from your home. Furnished in a comfortable style, all rooms feature quilted queen canopy beds, private baths, and air-conditioning. Awaken to a homemade breakfast. Located near Lebanon Valley College, Fort Indiantown Gap, Appalachian Trail, Hershey, Harrisburg, Reading, and Lancaster. Wheelchair accessible. Smoking outside home. AAA 3-diamond approved.

Swatara Creek Inn

Hosts: Dick and Susan Hess
Rooms: 6 (6PB) $60–80
Full Breakfast
Credit Cards: A B D
Notes: 2 5 7 10

BELLEVILLE

Twin Oaks B & B

73 S. Dryhouse Rd., Belleville, PA 17004-8633
(717) 935-2026

In the heart of the Kishacoquillas Valley, 30 minutes from Penn State. Norman and Sarah welcome guests to clean, spacious rooms. In a quiet country setting with a panoramic view of Stone and Jacks Mountain.

Hosts: Norman and Sarah Glick
Rooms: 4 (1PB;3SB) $50–70

Full Breakfast
Credit Cards:
Notes: 2 5

BOYERTOWN

Enchanted Cottage

22 Deer Run Rd., Boyertown, PA 19512-8312
(610) 845-8845
Web site: www.choice-guide.com/pa/enchanted/

Peace, quiet, and complete privacy await you in this romantic and secluded Cotswold-like cottage nestled in acres of woods. Double bed in air-conditioned bedroom adjoining Laura Ashley bathroom. Gourmet breakfast served in main house. Complimentary beverages and cheese. Fresh flowers, antiques. Near historic sites, cultural activities, Reading outlets, Amish country, churches. You—our only guests—will find our lifestyle informal but gracious.

Enchanted Cottage

Hosts: Peg and Richard Groff
Rooms: 1 (1PB) $85–90
Full Breakfast
Credit Cards:
Notes: 2 5 8 10 11 12

---

6 Pets welcome; 7 Children welcome; 8 Tennis nearby; 9 Swimming nearby; 10 Golf nearby; 11 Skiing nearby; 12 May be booked through travel agent

CANTON

M–Mm Good B & B

Rd. 1, Box 71, Canton, PA 17724
(570) 673-8153

Located along Route 414, 3 miles east of Canton in the quiet country center of the Endless Mountains. Clean, comfortable rooms and a breakfast including our homemade muffins or sticky buns. Picnic tables under shady maple trees. Hiking, fishing.

Hosts: Melvin and Irene Good
Rooms: 4 (1PB;3SB) $30–50
Full Breakfast
Credit Cards:
Notes: 2 5 7

CARLISLE

Homestay B & B

1022 Park Pl., Mechanicsburg, PA 17055
(717) 697-1864; Fax (717) 697-7335
E-mail: info@homestayfarm.com
Web site: www.homestayfarm.com

Homestay

An 1841 Pennsylvania Dutch farmhouse filled with family antiques and located on a 113-acre flower and vegetable farm, bordered by the Yellow Breeches Creek, a well-known eastern trout stream. Each room has its own AC, floor fan, TV, and phone. Also for guests are a screened flower porch, common TV room, and a sitting/reading room.

Host: Barbara Marbain
Rooms: 4 (2PB;2SB) $70–90
Full Breakfast
Credit Cards: A B F
Notes: 2 9 10

Line Limousin Farm House

2070 Ritner Hwy., Carlisle, PA 17013-9303
(717) 243-1281; Fax (717) 249-5537
E-mail: bline@planetcable.net
Web site: www.pafarmstay.com/line/index.html

Line Limousin Farm House

Step back in time and stay with us in our 1864 brick and stone farmhouse, which has always been owned by the Line family. French Limousin cattle are raised on our 100-acre farm. Cross over our stone fences to spot wildlife and a large variety of birds. After a large breakfast, join us for worship at our historic First Presbyterian Church. Two rooms have comfortable king beds, private baths, AC, and TV. Nonsmoking. Two-night minimum stay. Children over 8 welcome.

Hosts: Bob and Joan Line
Rooms: 3 (3PB) $80–95
Full Breakfast
Credit Cards:
Notes: 2 5 10

NOTES: Credit cards accepted: A Master Card; B Visa; C American Express; D Discover; E Diners Club; F Other; 2 Personal checks accepted; 3 Lunch available; 4 Dinner available; 5 Open all year;

Pheasant Field B & B

150 Hickorytown Rd., Carlisle, PA 17013-9732
(714) 258-0717; (877) 258-0717
    Fax (717) 258-0717
E-mail: stay@pheasantfield.com
Web site: www.pheasantfield.com

Stay in this lovely old brick farmhouse set in quiet country surroundings. Wake up to a full country breakfast including fresh bread or muffins, fresh fruit, a hot entrée, and plenty of hot coffee. After a game of tennis or a hike on the Appalachian Trail, relax in the family room or living room and help yourself to a homemade cookie (or two). Feel free to bring your horse—we offer overnight boarding, when space is available. Collector car shows, antiquing, and fly-fishing are nearby. Smoking is permitted outside. AAA 3-diamond rating. "Come home to the country." Two-night minimum stay.

Hosts:
Rooms: 5 (5PB) $90–150
Full Breakfast
Credit Cards: A B C D
Notes: 2 5 6 8 10 12

CHRISTIANA

Georgetown B & B

1222 Georgetown Rd.
    Christiana, PA 17509-9721
(717) 786-4570

Once a miller's home, the original structure was converted to a B & B for the enjoyment of guests in a relaxing home away from home. Entrance to the house is by a brick walkway. An herb garden lets guests smell the lavender and mint,

just two of the herbs used to garnish morning breakfasts. There is a choice of three bedrooms decorated with antiques and collectibles. Lancaster County Amish, a unique group of people who travel in horse-drawn carriages, pass in front of the Georgetown. Visit the local Strasburg Railroad and Train Museum.

Host: Doris W. Woerth
Rooms: 3 (1PB;2SB) $50–60
Full Breakfast
Credit Cards:
Notes: 2 5 9 10

CLEARFIELD

Christopher Kratzer House

101 E. Cherry St., Clearfield, PA 16830
(814) 765-5024; (888) 252-2632
E-mail: bbaggett@uplink.net
Web site:
    www.virtualcities.com/pa/kratzerhouse.htm

Graceful circa 1840 Classic Revival mansion in Old Town Historic District predates Victorian era and features antiques and objets d'art. Lovely views of river and park; children's playground. Three guest rooms; two air-conditioned suites with private baths. Wood-burning fireplace in common room. Gourmet breakfasts, afternoon tea, Sunday night candlelight suppers on request. Entertainment, art gallery, "attic flea market" on premises. State parks and Rails to Trails nearby. Just 3 miles off I-80.

Hosts: Bruce and Ginny Baggett
Rooms: 3 (2PB;1SB) $75–90
Gourmet Breakfast
Credit Cards: A B D
Notes: 2 5 7 8 9 10 12

---

6 Pets welcome; 7 Children welcome; 8 Tennis nearby; 9 Swimming nearby; 10 Golf nearby; 11 Skiing nearby; 12 May be booked through travel agent

Victorian Loft B & B

216 S. Front St., Clearfield, PA 16830-2218
(814) 765-4805; (800) 798-0456
 Fax (814) 765-9596
E-mail: pdurant@csrlink.net
Web site:
 www.virtualcities.com/pa/victorianloft.html

Elegant 1894 riverfront Victorian in the historic district. AC rooms with balcony or skylights. Suite has private kitchenette-dining area, living room w/entertainment center, and whirlpool bath. Family movies provided. Fiber studio. Hosts are Bible college graduates. Perfect stop on PA I-80—3 miles off Exit 19. Also completely equipped 3 BR cabin on 8 forested acres, located 2 miles from Parker Dam and Elliot State Parks. Or try our new "Second Street Suite," primarily designed and especially nice for longer stays.

Victorian Loft

Hosts: Tim and Peggy Durant
Rooms: 6 (4PB;2SB) $70–135
Full Breakfast
Credit Cards: A B C D
Notes: 2 5 6 7 8 9 10 11 12

COCHRANVILLE

Elver Valley B & B

432 Sawmill Rd., Cochranville, PA 19330

(717) 529-2803; (877) TO ELVER
 Fax (717) 529-2803
E-mail: evrohrer@webtv.net
Web site: www.pafarmstay.com/elvervalley

Quiet, country, overlooks water gardens. Ranch-style guest home. Queen beds, private baths, AC, dish TV, no stairs. Swing gazebo, stream for splashing, building dams, pond for boating, fishing, swimming. Spacious lawn, petting pasture in full view of seasonal cabin. Fully furnished with kitchen. Picnic tables, outside fireplace for campfires. Sleeps twelve. Families our specialty. Tour information for Lancaster County Dutch Country and Brandywine Valley. Visit Longwood Gardens, Brandywine River Museum. Amish wood crafts outlet shopping and antiques.

Hosts: Elvin and Vera Rohrer
Rooms: 2 (2PB) $55
Full Breakfast
Credit Cards:
Notes: 2 5 7 10

ELIZABETHVILLE

The Inn at Elizabethville

P. O. Box 236; 30 W. Main St.
 Elizabethville, PA 17023
(717) 362-3476; Fax (717) 362-1444
E-mail: theinnwench@adelphia.net

Built in 1883, this comfortable two-story house was owned by a Civil War veteran and founder of a local wagon company. The Confederate Room features an unusual fireplace with cabinets and painted decorations. A breezy comfortable porch invites guests to relax, drink lemonade, eat homemade cookies, and watch the world go by. Country auctions, antiques, local craft fairs, and outdoor activities entice guests.

Host: Heidi Milbrand
Rooms: 7 (7PB) $54–70
Full Breakfast
Credit Cards: A B
Notes: 2 5 8 9 10

EPHRATA

Historic Smithton Inn

900 W. Main St., Ephrata, PA 17522-1328
(717) 733-6094; (877) 755-4590
Web site: www.historicsmithtoninn.com

Historic romantic inn in picturesque Lancaster County. Home of the Penna. Dutch people. Museums, crafts, antiques, outlet centers. Rooms with some whirlpools, some canopy beds, all with fireplaces, full breakfasts included, and snacks at check-in time. No smoking allowed. Pets allowed only by arrangement.

Hosts: Dorothy Graybill
Rooms: 8 (8PB) $85–175
Full Breakfast
Credit Cards: A B
Notes: 2 5 6 7 9 10 12

The Inns at Doneckers

318–324 N. State St., Ephrata, PA 17522
(717) 738-9502; Fax (717) 738-9554
E-mail: donecker@doneckers.com
Web site: www.doneckers.com

Early American inns in the heart of PA Dutch Country, historic Lancaster County. Elegantly appointed rooms or suites with fireplace and Jacuzzi. Enjoy the entire Doneckers community: fine dining at our French/American restaurant; distinctive styles for women, men, children and the home in our upscale fashion store; fine furniture galleries wth complete collections from Baker, Hickory Chair, Century, Henredon, Kindel, MacKenzie-Childs, Harrods of London, Habersham, and more; local artists' studios and our Christopher Radko Gallery. Minutes away from the renowned antique markets of Adamstown, PA. Special rates and getaway packages available. View each room online at www.doneckers.com.

Hosts: Mr. and Mrs. H. William Donecker
Rooms: 40 (38PB;2SB) $69–210
Continental Breakfast
Credit Cards: A B C D
Notes: 2 3 4 5 7 10

Meadow Valley Farm Guest Home

221 Meadow Valley Rd.
  Ephrata, PA 17522-9574
(717) 733-8390; (877) 562-4530
  Fax (717) 733-9068
E-mail: walterhurst@juno.com

Meadow Valley Farm

Located in the heart of Lancaster County's beautiful farmland, this 88-

acre working farm provides peaceful relaxation of the rural countryside. Stay in a 150-year-old historic summer house that is situated near a quiet pond where swans swim gracefully. Watch the farm dog herd the cows into the barn at milking time. See or help us gather and pack the eggs. Experience life on a real farm. Enjoy local fresh produce, flea markets. Green Dragon. Cloisters Wildlife Preserve. Boating, fishing, picnicking, and play area. Bring the family. No breakfast, but kitchen provided. Air-conditioned. Phone. Farmers' markets.

Hosts: Marlene and Walter Hurst
Rooms: 3 (1PB;2SB) $35–45
No Breakfast Served
Credit Cards:
Notes: 2 5 6 7 8 9 10

GETTYSBURG

The Doubleday Inn

104 Doubleday Ave., Gettysburg, PA 17325
(717) 334-9119; Fax (717) 334-7907
E-mail: doubledayinn@blazenet.net
Web site: www.doubledayinn.com

The Doubleday Inn

Located directly on the Gettysburg battlefield, this beautifully restored Colonial country inn enjoys splendid views of historic Gettysburg and the battlefield. Guests enjoy candlelit country breakfasts, afternoon refreshments, and the cozy comfort of a centrally air-conditioned inn surrounded by lovely antiques and Civil War memorabilia. Free presentations by battlefield historians on selected evenings. Children over 8 welcome.

Hosts: Ruth Anne and Charles Wilcox
Rooms: 9 (7PB;2SB) $100–140
Full Breakfast
Credit Cards: A B D
Notes: 2 5 8 9 10 11 12

Hickory Bridge Farm

96 Hickory Bridge Rd., Orrtanna, PA 17353-9734
(717) 642-5261
E-mail: hickory@mail.cvn.net
Web site: www.hickorybridgefarm.com

Only 8 miles west of historic Gettysburg. Unique country dining and B & B. Cozy cottages with woodstoves and private baths are located in secluded, wooded settings along a stream. Lovely rooms are available in the farmhouse with antiques, private baths, and whirlpool tubs. Full, farm breakfast served at the farmhouse, which was built in the late 1700s. Country dining offered on Fridays, Saturdays, and Sundays in a 130-year-old barn with many antiques. Family-owned/operated for more than twenty years.

Hosts: Robert and Mary Lynn Martin
Rooms: 9 (9PB) $85–145
Full Breakfast
Credit Cards: A B D
Notes: 2 4 5 8 9 10 11

NOTES: Credit cards accepted: A Master Card; B Visa; C American Express; D Discover; E Diners Club; F Other; 2 Personal checks accepted; 3 Lunch available; 4 Dinner available; 5 Open all year;

Keystone Inn Bed and Breakfast

231 Hanover St., Gettysburg, PA 17325
(717) 337-3888
Web site:
www.virtualcities.com/ons/pa/pag6601.htm

The Keystone Inn is a large, brick Victorian home built in 1913. The high-ceilinged rooms are decorated in lace and flowers, and a handsome chestnut staircase rises to the third floor. The guest rooms are bright, cheerful, and air-conditioned. Each has a reading nook and writing desk. Choose your own breakfast from our full breakfast menu. One suite available.

Hosts: Wilmer and Doris Martin
Rooms: 5 (5PB) $79–119
Full Breakfast
Credit Cards: A B D
Notes: 2 5 7 8 9 10 11

GROVE CITY

Snow Goose Inn

112 E. Main St., Grove City, PA 16127-2213
(724) 458-4644; (800) 317-4644
Fax (724) 458-1686
E-mail: msgoose@stargate.net
Web site: www.bbonline.com/pa/snowgoose/

The Snow Goose Inn is a large house, circa 1895, formerly a doctor's home. It has a large, wrap-around front porch with an old-fashioned porch swing. Comfortable, air-conditioned guest rooms have private baths. Each is decorated with antiques and touches of country. A full breakfast is served, along with homemade muffins, home-baked breakfast rolls, etc.

Hosts: Orvil and Dorothy McMillen
Rooms: 4 (4PB) $70
Full Breakfast
Credit Cards: A B
Notes: 2 5 7 8 9 10 11 12

HERSHEY

Mottern's B & B

28 E. Main St., Hummelstown, PA 17036-1615
(717) 566-3840; Fax (717) 566-3780
E-mail: motternsbb@hotmail.com
Web site:
http://home.earthlink.net/~jmottern/lodging/
title.html

Mottern's

Enjoy small-town hospitality 5 minutes from Hersheypark. B & B is a private apartment on the first floor of our restored 1860s limestone home. Living room, dining room, or second bedroom, bedroom, bath, kitchen, laundry, central air, CCTV (2), and VCR. A pergola-covered patio overlooks our walled garden. Located at the town center. Discount Hersheypark tickets. No charge for children (accommodates family of 5). Internet and multiple-night discounts.

Hosts: Susan and Jeffrey Mottern
Rooms: 1 (1PB) $150
Continental Breakfast
Credit Cards: A B F
Notes: 2 5 7 8 9 10 11 12

Pets welcome; 7 Children welcome; 8 Tennis nearby; 9 Swimming nearby; 10 Golf nearby; 11 Skiing nearby; 12 May be booked through travel agent

Nancy's Guest House

235 Hershey Rd., Hummelstown, PA 17036-9245
(717) 566-9844
E-mail: marnan@paonline.com

Nancy's Guest House

Comfort, homeyness, and privacy are
what you find at our guest house. You
are our only guests. Located 2 miles
from Hershey Park, our second-floor,
one-unit, nonsmoking apartment has
a private entrance and a large deck.
There are two bedrooms, a living
room, a kitchen, and a bath with laundry. Color television and AC add to
the comfort. Eat in or go out, choosing from fast food or fine dining.
Travelers' checks or cash are accepted;
checks limited. A 10% discount for
five nights or more. Located 3 1/2
miles from I–81 on Route 39.

Hosts: Marlin and Nancy Geesaman
Rooms: 2 (2PB) $40–65 Winter; May–Sept $65–85
No Breakfast Served
Credit Cards:
Notes: 7 8 9 10 11

Pinehurst Inn
B & B Hershey

50 Northeast Dr., Hershey, PA 17033-2732
(717) 533-2603; (800) 743-9140
    Fax (717) 533-8616

E-mail: becky@pinehursthershey.com
Web site: www.pinehursthershey.com

The Pinehurst Inn B & B was built in
1931 by Milton Hershey, candy magnate and philanthropist, as a home for
orphaned boys. It became a B & B in
1986. The Pinehurst is ½ mile to most
Hershey attractions (e.g., Hershey
park, Chocolate World, outlets, zoo,
Hershey Gardens, concert and sport
arena). Full breakfast is served.
Family-friendly and a great spot for
reunions and meetings.

Pinehurst Inn

Hosts: Terry and Becky LaFountain
Rooms: 14 (6PB;8SB) $55–105
Full Breakfast
Credit Cards: A B
Notes: 2 5 7 9 10

Shepherd's Acres B & B

168 Bell Rd., Palmyra, PA 17078
(717) 838-3899
E-mail: shepherdsacres@juno.com
Web site: www.shepherdsacres.com

Friendships for a lifetime can be made
at Shepherd's Acres B & B. Come and
enjoy the beauty and tranquility of
country living. Our Cape Cod house
is situated on 18 acres of Lebanon
County farmland. A nature trail for

NOTES: Credit cards accepted: A Master Card; B Visa; C American Express; D Discover; E Diners
Club; F Other; 2 Personal checks accepted; 3 Lunch available; 4 Dinner available; 5 Open all year;

walking and viewing God's creation weaves its way through the property. Sheep grazing in the pasture can be seen by all who sit on the sunporch for breakfast. Every room is ample in size and is enhanced by Margy's wall hangings and quilts. Each room has a sitting area, TV, and is air-conditioned. See Hershey, Lancaster, or Gettysburg from here. We'll be looking for you!

Hosts: Jerry and Margy Allebach
Rooms: 3 (1PB;2SB) $60–70
Full Breakfast
Credit Cards:
Notes: 2 5 7 8 9 10 11

INTERCOURSE

Intercourse Village B & B Suites

Rte. 340, Main St., P. O. Box 340
    Intercourse, PA 17534
(717) 768-2626; (800) 664-0949
E-mail: ivbbs@aol.com
Web site: www.amishcountryinns.com

Intercourse Village B & B

AAA 4-diamond rated. Enjoy these new romantic B & B suites for couples. Located in the heart of Amish country. See our fully restored 1909 Victorian-style home. Then take a walk down the brick pathway to our new country homestead suites. All rooms have private baths, fireplaces, and include a gourmet candlelit breakfast. King/queen beds, honeymoon/anniversary suites. Walk to the craft, quilt, and antique shoppes. Come stay with us in this quaint Amish country village.

Host: Ruthann Thomas
Rooms: 8 (8PB) $119–199
Full Breakfast
Credit Cards: A B C
Notes: 5 10

JIM THORPE

The Inn at Jim Thorpe

24 Broadway, Jim Thorpe, PA 18229-2006
(570) 325-2599; (800) 329-2599
    Fax (570) 325-9145
E-mail: innjt@ptd.net
Web site: www.innjt.com

Nestled in the heart of a truly unique and historic village, the inn combines Victorian elegance with 21st-century comforts. Our grand hotel features charming guest rooms and world-class suites with whirlpools and fireplaces, classic cuisine, and an authentic Irish pub! Discover our rich history through tours of national historic landmarks and award-winning museums. Visit quaint shops and art galleries. For the adventurous, there's top-rated mountain biking and white-water rafting. You'll find all this and more in the enchanted village of Jim Thorpe.

Hosts: David Drury
Rooms: 45 (45PB) $89–279

6 Pets welcome; 7 Children welcome; 8 Tennis nearby; 9 Swimming nearby; 10 Golf nearby; 11 Skiing nearby; 12 May be booked through travel agent

Continental Breakfast
Credit Cards: A B C D E
Notes: 3 4 5 7 8 11 12

KINZERS

Sycamore Haven Farm

35 S. Kinzer Rd., Kinzers, PA 17535
(717) 442-4901

We have approximately forty milking
cows and many young cattle and cats
for children to enjoy. Our farmhouse
has three guest rooms, all with double
beds and one single. Cots and
playpen available. Fifteen miles east
of Lancaster city. Route 30 to Kinzer
Road; turn right at the first farm on
the left.

Hosts: Charles and Janet Groff
Rooms: 3 (3SB) $35–40
Continental Breakfast
Credit Cards: F
Notes: 2 5 6 7 8 9 10

LAMPETER

Australian Walkabout Inn

837 Village Rd.; P. O. Box 294
   Lampeter, PA 17537-0294
(717) 464-0707; Fax (717) 464-2501
Web site: www.walkaboutinn.com

The Walkabout is a 1925 brick,
Mennonite farmhouse featuring large
wrap-around porches, balconies, English
gardens with goldfish pools and fountains. The inn itself is filled with
antiques, and each room has a private
bath, cable TV, and fireplace; all rooms
have queen canopies, whirlpools, or hot
tubs. An elegant candlelight breakfast is

served. The honeymoon and anniversary
suites are beautiful and the fantasy cottage is fabulous! AAA 3-diamonds.
Winter getaway packages available
December through May.

Hosts: Jay and Val Petersheim
Rooms: 6 (6PB) $99–289
Full Breakfast
Credit Cards: A B C
Notes: 2 5 8 9 10 12

LANCASTER

Alden House B & B

62 E. Main St., Lititz, PA 17543-1947
(717) 627-3363; (800) 584-0753
   Fax (717) 627-5428
E-mail: inn@aldenhouse.com
Web site: www.aldenhouse.com

Step out our front door and into the
quaint town of Lititz, where art galleries, antique shops, country stores,
and soda fountain shops line the
street. The Alden House, an 1850s
brick Colonial home elegantly
restored and beautifully decorated, is
nestled in the historic district. With
lovely rooms and spacious suites, private baths, queen beds, and cable TV,
we offer a blend of old world charm
and new world comfort.

Hosts: Tom and Lillian Vazquez
Rooms: 5 (5PB) $90–120
Full Breakfast
Credit Cards: A B
Notes: 2 5 7 8 10

The Apple Bin Inn B & B

2835 Willow St. Pike, N
   Willow Street, PA 17584-9482
(717) 464-5881; (800) 338-4296
   Fax (717) 464-1818

NOTES: Credit cards accepted: A Master Card; B Visa; C American Express; D Discover; E Diners
Club; F Other; 2 Personal checks accepted; 3 Lunch available; 4 Dinner available; 5 Open all year;

E-mail: bininn@aol.com
Web site: www.applebininn.com

As a village bed and breakfast, the Apple Bin Inn offers distinctive, colonial charm with a country touch. Each of the four rooms and the carriage house is appointed in luxury and comfort, offering private baths, love seats, wing chairs, and comfortable Colonial or Country-style beds. After a full breakfast of homemade specialties, your adventure in Lancaster County begins. Visit historical sites, outlet malls, quilt shops, and antique stores.

Hosts: Dottie and Mike McLoughlin
Rooms: 5 (5PB) $95–155
Full Breakfast
Credit Cards: A B C
Notes: 2 5 8 10

The Artist's Inn and Gallery

117 E. Main St., P. O. Box 26
  Terre Hill, PA 17581
(717) 445-0219; (888) 999-4479
E-mail: stay@artistinn.com
Web site: www.artistinn.com

Spend the night in an art gallery! Antique-filled inn in the small town of Terre Hill, nestled among Amish farms, features colored pencil art gallery of the innkeeper. You'll feel like you've escaped to a simpler time as horse-drawn carriages clip-clop past the inn, and chimes play from a nearby church. Enjoy gourmet breakfasts, whirlpool tubs, Victorian porches, fireplaces in all guest rooms, and extensive gardens. Tennis, golf, hiking, major antique center, outlets all nearby.

Hosts: Jan and Bruce Garrabrandt
Rooms: 3 (3PB) $95–179
Full Breakfast
Credit Cards: A B C D
Notes: 2 5 8 10 11 12

The Artist's Inn

Ben Mar Farm B & B

5721 Old Philadelphia Pike
  Gap, PA 17527-9717
(717) 768-3309
Web site: www.pamall.net/benmar

Come stay on our working dairy farm. We are located in the heart of the famous Amish country. Experience quiet country life while staying in the large, beautifully decorated rooms of our 200-year-old farmhouse. Our efficiency apartment is a favorite; it includes a full kitchen and queen and double beds with private bath. Enjoy a full country breakfast brought to your room. Air-conditioned.

Hosts: Herb and Melanie Benner
Rooms: 2 (2PB) $70–80
Full Breakfast
Credit Cards: F
Notes: 2 5 7 8

Carriage Corner B & B

P. O. Box 371; 3705 E. Newport Rd.
  Intercourse, PA 17534-0371
(717) 768-3059; (800) 209-3059
  Fax (717) 768-0691
E-mail: gschuit@dejazzed.com
Web site: www.carriagecornerbandb.com

Central, peaceful, and comfortable. Carriage Corner offers traditional Christian hospitality amid the Amish farmland where the rest of the world falls away. Within walking distance of a quaint village from yesteryear with a myriad of local shops, where Amish buggies converge. Wake up and let the wafting aroma of freshly brewed coffee lure you to the dining room, where a hearty breakfast awaits you. Catering to couples who desire to fully explore the Pennsylvania Dutch country. Amish dinners arranged.

Hosts: Gordon and Gwen Schuit
Rooms: 5 (5PB) $68–89
Full Breakfast
Credit Cards: A B
Notes: 2 5 7 12

Cedar Hill Farm

305 Longenecker Rd., Mount Joy, PA 17552-8404
(717) 653-4655; Fax (717) 653-9242
E-mail: cedarhill@supernet.com
Web site: www.cedarhillfarm.com

This 1817 stone farmhouse overlooks a peaceful stream and was the birthplace of the host. Stroll the acreage or relax on wicker rockers on the large front porch. Enjoy the singing of the birds and serene countryside. A winding staircase leads to the comfortable rooms, each with a private bath, one

with a whirlpool tub. Central AC. A room for honeymooners offers a private balcony. Continental-plus breakfast is served beside a fireplace. Midway between the Lancaster and Hershey areas, where farmers' markets, antique shops, and good restaurants abound. Dinners arranged with Amish.

Hosts: Russel and Gladys Swarr
Rooms: 5 (5PB) $85–105
Continental Breakfast
Credit Cards: A B C D
Notes: 2 5 7 8 9 10 12

Cocalico Creek Bed and Breakfast

224 S. 4th St., Denver, PA 17517-1227
(717) 336-0271; (888) 208-7334
E-mail: cocalicocrk@dejazzd.com
Web site: www.cocalicocrk.com

Cocalico Creek

Nestled in the quaint town of Denver, surrounded by Amish and Mennonite farms, this 1920s classic stone inn offers casual elegance in a country setting, overlooking pastures and gardens. A tranquil retreat, blending with sounds of ducks splashing in ponds and creek or the occasional Amish buggy passing by. Tastefully decorated interiors and four guest rooms, each

---

NOTES: Credit cards accepted: A Master Card; B Visa; C American Express; D Discover; E Diners Club; F Other; 2 Personal checks accepted; 3 Lunch available; 4 Dinner available; 5 Open all year;

with private bath. Minutes from Antiques Capital USA–Adamstown, golf, hiking, farmers' markets, outlet shopping, and fine dining. Explore the history, culture, and rural scenic beauty. AAA-rated.

Host: Charlene Sweeney
Rooms: 4 (4PB) $92–110
Full Breakfast
Credit Cards: A B C D

The Columbian

360 Chestnut St., Columbia, PA 17512-1156
(717) 684-5869; (800) 422-5869
E-mail: inn@columbianinn.com
Web site: www.columbianinn.com

The Columbian

This circa 1897 inn is centrally located in the small historic river town of Columbia. The Colonial Revival mansion features an ornate stained-glass window and magnificent tiered staircase. Large, air-conditioned rooms offer queen/king beds, private baths, and cable TV. Suite with balcony and/or fireplaces available. Come relax and unwind in our lovely home and browse through the antique shops, art galleries, outlets, and museums only a brief stroll away. Getaway packages, gift certificates available.

Hosts: Chris and Becky Will
Rooms: 5 (5PB) $75–135

Full Breakfast
Credit Cards: A B D
Notes: 2 5 8 9 10 11
Notes: 2 5 7 9 10 11

Country Farmhouse B & B

1780 Donegal Springs Rd., Mt. Joy, PA 17552
(717) 653-0935; Fax (717) 653-0935
E-mail: brguest@wideworld.net

Circa 1834 homestead surrounded by cornfields and pastures. Antique-filled rooms with private baths; candlelight gourmet breakfasts, afternoon tea. Come relax, watch our beautiful sunsets, visit 1722 Donegal Church, walk by a trout stream, and renew your spirit. Antique shops, Hersheypark/Gardens/ Spa, Lancaster/Hershey retail outlets, Renaissance Faire, Mt. Hope/Nissley Winery/Concerts, farmers' markets, and the National Civil War Museum within 20 minutes. Private cottage with king-sized bed, fireplace, and whirlpool available.

Hosts: Terry and Barb Stephens
Rooms: 3 (3PB) $75–150
Full Breakfast
Credit Cards: A B
Notes: 2 5 10

Country Farmhouse

---

6 Pets welcome; 7 Children welcome; 8 Tennis nearby; 9 Swimming nearby; 10 Golf nearby; 11 Skiing nearby; 12 May be booked through travel agent

Dutch Pride Guest House B & B

1383 Lancaster Rd., Manheim, PA 17545
(717) 665-5083; (877) 665-5083
E-mail: dutchpridebnb@earthlink.net
Web site: www.bbonline.com/pa/dutchpride

Dutch Pride

Relax in the heart of Lancaster County tucked between Lancaster and Lebanon. Our stone ranch house is restful, with screened gazebo, flower gardens, and sunroom. Guest house suite, full kitchen, air-conditioning, television, telephone, office, private bath, and queen bed. Smoke-free. Located close to Hershey Chocolate World and the Gettysburg Battlefield. Harrisburg, farmers' markets, Amish farms, outlet shopping, antiques, covered bridges, restaurants, airports, and auctions are nearby. Country setting and easy to find. Children over eight welcome.

Hosts: Roy and Mary Jane Sauder
Rooms: 3 (2PB;1SB) $75–120
Full Breakfast
Credit Cards: A B
Notes: 2 5 7 9 10

Flowers & Thyme B & B

238 Strasburg Pike, Lancaster, PA 17602-1326
(717) 393-1460; Fax (717) 399-1986

E-mail: padutchbnb@aol.com
Web site: http://members.aol.com/padutchbnb

In the heart of PA Dutch Amish country, you'll find our B & B surrounded by English cottage gardens and a gazebo waiting for you. We are located in a country setting, overlooking a picturesque working farm. You'll find tastefully created interiors, genuine hospitality, and clean, comfortable rooms with queen beds. Your choice of a room with a canopy bed, fireplace, or Jacuzzi. Bountiful country breakfasts are served in the spacious gathering room. Close by are the outlets and music theaters. Enjoy the hospitality and warmth of a Lancaster County B & B. Nonsmoking.

Flowers and Thyme

Hosts: Don and Ruth Harnish
Rooms: 3 (3PB) $89–129
Full Breakfast
Credit Cards: A B
Notes: 2 5 8 9 10

The King's Cottage, a B & B Inn

1049 E. King St., Lancaster, PA 17602-3231
(717) 397-1017; (800) 747-8717
    Fax (717) 397-3447
E-mail: info@kingscottagebb.com
Web site: www.kingscottagebb.com

NOTES: Credit cards accepted: A Master Card; B Visa; C American Express; D Discover; E Diners Club; F Other; 2 Personal checks accepted; 3 Lunch available; 4 Dinner available; 5 Open all year;

Escape to romantic elegance at an award-winning Spanish-style mansion between historic Lancaster City and Amish farmland. Shop for antiques, enjoy farmers' markets and outlets, golf, and relax with tea and cordials in front of our fireplace. Pamper yourself with our warm hospitality, comfortable king and queen beds, private baths, whirlpool tubs, fireplaces, and sumptuous gourmet breakfasts. Our Carriage House offers breakfast delivered to your door. On National Register, AAA 3-diamond, Mobil-Excellent, Select Registry!

Hosts: Janis Kutterer and Ann Willets
Rooms: 8 (8PB) $155–260
Full Breakfast
Credit Cards: A B D
Notes: 2 5 10 12

Maytown Manor B & B

25 W. High St., P. O. Box 275
   Maytown, PA 17550
(717) 426-2116; (866) 426-2116
   Fax (717) 426-2116
E-mail: innkeepers@maytownmanorbandb.com
Web site: www.maytownmanorbandb.com

Maytown Manor

Built in 1880, this Federal-style brick house is located in Maytown,

Lancaster County, PA. Awaken to the smells of freshly brewed coffee and home-baked muffins. After enjoying your hearty breakfast in the formal dining room, explore nearby Amish country, visit historical Gettysburg, or take a ride on the wild side at Hersheypark. In the late afternoon, relax in our parlor while sipping a soothing cup of tea. Upon returning from dinner, read a favorite book from the library, enjoy a snack from the guest pantry, and then retire to your thoughtfully appointed guest room.

Hosts: Jeffrey and Julie Clouser
Rooms: 3 (3PB) $85–95
Full Breakfast
Credit Cards: A B
Notes: 2 5 8 10 11

Meadowview Guest House

2169 New Holland Pike, Lancaster, PA 17601
(717) 299-4017

This Dutch Colonial home is located in the heart of the Pennsylvania Dutch Amish area. Three guest rooms and kitchen on the second floor. There is a stove, refrigerator, sink, and dishes. A breakfast tray is put in the kitchen in the morning for each guest room. Close to many historic sites and to farmers' and antique markets. Excellent restaurants and many attractions help guests enjoy the beautiful country. Personalized maps are provided. Children over 6 welcome.

Hosts: Edward and Sheila Christie
Rooms: 3 (1PB;2SB) $40–55
Continental Breakfast
Credit Cards:
Notes: 2 5 8 9 10 12

---

6 Pets welcome; 7 Children welcome; 8 Tennis nearby; 9 Swimming nearby; 10 Golf nearby; 11 Skiing nearby; 12 May be booked through travel agent

New Life Homestead B & B

1400 E. King St., Lancaster, PA 17602-3240
(717) 396-8928; (888) 503-2987
    Fax (717) 396-0461
E-mail: wgiersch@redrose.net
Web site: www.newlifebnb.com

New Life Homestead

Located in the heart of Amish country, close to all attractions. If you ever
wanted to know about the Amish and
Mennonite people, this is where to
learn. The home features antiques and
heirlooms. Full breakfasts and evening
refreshments are served. Your hosts
are a Mennonite family with traditional family values. Private baths, air-
conditioning.

Hosts: Carol and Bill Giersch
Rooms: 3 (1PB;2SB) $75–95
Full Breakfast
Credit Cards:
Notes: 2 5 7 8 9 10

Penn's Valley Farm and Guest House

6182 Metzler Rd., Manheim, PA 17545-8629
(717) 898-7386; Fax (717) 898-8489
E-mail: pennsvbandb@cs.com
Web site: www.pennsvalleyfarm.com

Guest house and one pink Victorian
room available for guests. Located on

64 acres of farmland. Full breakfast
available and optional. Animals
include pigs and cats. Guest house
sleeps 7 people. Decorative, clean, air-
conditioned. Located halfway between
Hersheypark and Amish community,
close to a town named East Petersburg
on the map.

Hosts: Melvin and Gladys Metzler
Rooms: 2 (2PB) $60–70
Full Breakfast
Credit Cards: A B C
Notes: 2 5 7

Rock-a-Bye B & B / Antique Shop

138 W. Frederick St., Millersville, PA 17551
(717) 872-5990; (877) 872-5990
    Fax (717) 871-1027
E-mail: rockabyein@aol.com
Web site: www.rock-a-bye-bnb.com

A brick Victorian home in a college
town awaits your family visit. We love
children and do our best to accommodate all family needs. Close to
shopping, Amish restaurants, dinner
theaters, and recreation. A carriage
house antique shop is on the premises.

Hosts: Ann and Bill Marks
Rooms: 4 (3PB;1SB) $80–98
Full Breakfast
Credit Cards: A B
Notes: 2 5 7 8 9 10

1725 Historic Witmer's Tavern Inn and Museum

2014 Old Philadelphia Pike
    Lancaster, PA 17602-3413
(717) 299-5305
E-mail: witmerstavern@cs.com
Web site: www.witmerstavern.com

This pre-Revolutionary War Inn (circa 1725) is the oldest and most complete Pennsylvania inn still lodging travelers in its original building. Designated a National Landmark, the property has been restored to its original, simple pioneer style with hand-fashioned hardware, "bubbly" glass, and nine-over-six windows. There is even an Indian escape tunnel. Guest rooms feature antiques, fresh flowers, antique quilts, and original wood-burning fireplaces. Revolutionary and Colonial dignitaries like Washington, Lafayette, Jefferson, and Adams were entertained here. The Witmers provisioned hundreds of immigrants as they set up Conestoga Wagon trains and headed for western and southern homestead regions. Amish farmland adjacent to and in the rear of the inn. Lovely park located nearby. The innkeeper, native to the area, can provide an abundance of local information. He can also plan for any type of special occasion. Guests can make an appointment for a relaxing therapeutic massage. Recently opened is our American heritage and artifact museum. Inquire about children.

Host: Brant E. Hartung
Rooms: 7 (2PB;5SB) $70–110
Continental Breakfast
Credit Cards: F
Notes: 2 5 7 8 9 10 11 12

Smoketown Motor Lodge and Carriage House

190 E. Brook Rd., Smoketown, PA 17576
(717) 397-6944
Web site:
    www.smoketownmotorlodge@padutch.com

Nestled on 3 beautiful acres of an original Amish homestead in the heart of Lancaster County. The rooms are smoke-free, clean, and comfortable, each with refrigerator, cable TV, and air-conditioning. Ask about the Carriage House. The grounds are inviting, with two shaded patios and a gazebo. Relax in the shade of a small wooded area between the main lodge and the Carriage House. Near Sight & Sound Theater, Kitchen Kettle Village, and Bird-in-Hand.

Hosts: Mike and Linda Martin
Rooms: 17 (17PB) $46–85
Continental Breakfast
Credit Cards: A B C D F
Notes: 2 5 7 8 9 10

Vogt Farm B & B

1225 Colebrook Rd., Marietta, PA 17547-9101
(717) 653-4810; (800) 854-0399
    Fax (717) 653-5288
E-mail: cbb@vogtfarmbnb.com
Web site: www.vogtfarmbnb.com

Here on the farm you can enjoy the countryside and starlit nights. Our rooms are supplied with the amenities adults expect at the finest lodging. We give you a delicious breakfast and Kathy is your personal concierge. Our rooms have cable TV, AC, and fine furnishings. Our guests leave with a rested spirit, having had a wonderful time.

Hosts: Keith and Kathy Vogt
Rooms: 3 (3PB) $90–145
Full Breakfast
Credit Cards: A B C D F
Notes: 2 5

---

6 Pets welcome; 7 Children welcome; 8 Tennis nearby; 9 Swimming nearby; 10 Golf nearby; 11 Skiing nearby; 12 May be booked through travel agent

Walnut Lawn B & B

1027 Village Rd., Lancaster, PA 17602
(717) 464-1382
E-mail: walnutlawn@proclaim.net
Web site: http://walnutlawn.proclaim.net

Walnut Lawn

Our 1909 brick home with chestnut woodwork is "beautiful" and "peaceful." Local quilts, heirlooms, and family vocational artifacts of milling, gardening, quilting, and African missionary work define our guest rooms. Breakfasts feature our own nuts and fruits plus local milk, eggs, and meats. We are Mennonite and our acre is part of the tract of land purchased from William Penn in 1710 by the first Mennonite settlers in Lancaster County. Sight & Sound Theatre is nearby.

Hosts: Daniel and Erma Wenger
Rooms: 4 (4PB) $60–80 plus tax
Full Breakfast
Credit Cards:
Notes: 2 5 7 8 9 10

Wenger's B & B

571 Hossler Rd., Manheim, PA 17545-9294
(717) 665-3862

Relax and enjoy your stay in the quiet countryside of Lancaster County. Our ranch-style house is within walking distance of our son's 100-acre dairy farm. The spacious rooms will accommodate families. Take a guided tour through the Amish farmland. Hershey, Pennsylvania's state capital at Harrisburg, and the Gettysburg Battlefield are within 1 hour's drive.

Hosts: Arthur and Mary Wenger
Rooms: 2 (2PB) $60–65
Full Breakfast
Credit Cards:
Notes: 2 5 7

LANCASTER COUNTY

Amethyst Inn

144 W. Main St.; P. O. Box 938
    Adamstown, PA 19501
(717) 484-0800; (800) 594-4808
    Fax (717) 484-1384
E-mail: info@adamstown.com
Web site: www.amethystinn.com

Amethyst Inn

Situated high on a hill with a magnificent view of historic Main Street, the Amethyst Inn is a Victorian "Painted Lady" home built in the 1830s. Architectural elements have been painstakingly clad in seven colors— shades of amethyst, gold, lavender, and forest green. A magnificent 9-foot intricately carved front door welcomes guests into Victorian splendor and

---

NOTES: Credit cards accepted: A Master Card; B Visa; C American Express; D Discover; E Diners Club; F Other; 2 Personal checks accepted; 3 Lunch available; 4 Dinner available; 5 Open all year;

warm hospitality. Guest rooms feature period antique furnishings, queen-size beds, captivating two-person Jacuzzis, and charming gas log fireplaces; one room features a relaxing sauna.

Hosts: Tom and Wanda Berman
Rooms: 4 (4PB) $125–165
Continental Breakfast
Credit Cards: A B C F
Notes: 2 5 8 9 10 12

Crosskeys Countryside

158 Colonial Rd., Gordonville, PA 17529
(717) 768-7677
E-mail: glennandchris@wjtl.net

Nestled in a cluster of trees in the middle of Lancaster County farmland, you will enjoy a slower pace as you rest and observe the pasture across the way. Your private suite of hand-stenciled rooms will allow you to get away from the pressures of the world and enable God to minister restoration to you. If you feel like touring local shops, we are just three blocks outside of Intercourse, PA.

Hosts: Glenn and Christina Ricker
Rooms: 1 (1PB) $85
Continental Breakfast
Credit Cards:
Notes: 2 5 7 10

MC CLURE

Mountain Dale Farm

R. R. 2 Box 985, McClure, PA 17841-9638
(570) 658-3536
E-mail: mtndale@sunlink.net
Web site: www.pafarmstay.com

Our 175-acre general farm is secluded, yet very accessible. Many activities may be enjoyed on the farm and nearby state parks. Farm animals include sheep, goats, cattle, horses, geese, ducks, chickens, and a dog. Guests may help with barn chores. Accommodations: 5 efficiency cabins and 3 dormitory cabins, all with kitchen and bath. Three forest cabins with outdoor cooking and privies. Four rooms in farmhouse, two with private baths.

Hosts: Ken and Sally Hassinger
Rooms: 15 (10PB;5SB) $60–85
No Breakfast Served
Credit Cards:
Notes: 2 5 7 9 10

MILTON

Pau-Lyn's Country Bed and Breakfast

Box 676, Broadway Rd., Milton, PA 17847
(570) 742-4110
E-mail: paulyns@uplink.net
Web site: www.welcome.to/paulyns

Pau-Lyn's Country B & B

The beautiful Susquehanna Valley of central Pennsylvania is unique. Varied, pleasant experiences await

---

6 Pets welcome; 7 Children welcome; 8 Tennis nearby; 9 Swimming nearby; 10 Golf nearby; 11 Skiing nearby; 12 May be booked through travel agent

those who want to be in touch with God's handiwork. Observe agriculture, scenic mountains, rivers, and valleys. Recreation abounds—Underground Railroad stops and much more. The innkeepers provide nostalgic memories throughout the antique-furnished, 1850 Victorian brick house, 2 miles from I-80, 4 miles from Route 15. Air-conditioned. "A restful haven."

Hosts: Paul and Evelyn Landis
Rooms: 7 (4PB;3SB) $60-70
Full Breakfast
Credit Cards:
Notes: 2 5 7 8 9 10 11 12

MUNCY

The Bodine House

307 S. Main St., Muncy, PA 17756
(570) 546-8949; Fax (570) 546-0607
E-mail: bodine@pcspower.net
Web site: www.bodinehouse.com

The Bodine House

The Bodine House is located on a tree-lined street in historic Muncy, PA, in the Susquehanna River Valley 1 mile from I-180. Built circa 1805, it has been restored to its original architecture and is listed on the National Register of Historic Places. It is the area's oldest B & B (established in 1983) and has

been featured in several national publications. All guest rooms have private baths and individual heat and air-conditioning. Telephone, fax, and E-mail service is available on request.

Hosts: David and Marie Louise Smith
Rooms: 4 (4PB) $70-125
Full Breakfast
Credit Cards: A B C D E F
Notes: 2 5 7 8 9 10 11 12

NEW HOPE

Tattersall Inn

P. O. Box 569, Pt. Pleasant, PA 18950-0569
(215) 297-8233; (800) 297-4988
    Fax (215) 297-5023
Web site: www.tattersallinn.com

Circa 1750. This Bucks County plastered fieldstone house with its 18-inch-thick walls, broad porches, and wainscoted entry hall offers a peaceful place to relax, rebuild, and enjoy the bucolic surroundings in Olde Bucks. Breakfast is served in the dining room or brought to your room. All rooms have queen-sized beds, private baths, air-conditioning; some have fireplaces.

Hosts: Donna and Robert Trevorron
Rooms: 6 (6PB) $120–155
Full Breakfast
Credit Cards: A B
Notes: 5 9 11

Tattersall Inn

NEWVILLE

Nature's Nook Farm

740 Shed Rd., Newville, PA 17241-9763
(717) 776-5619; Fax (717) 776-5619
E-mail: donloisl@pa.net

Located in a quiet, peaceful setting along the Blue Mountains. Warm Mennonite hospitality and clean, comfortable lodging await you. Enjoy freshly brewed garden tea and fresh fruit, in season. Homemade cinnamon rolls, muffins, and coffee cakes. Perennial flower garden. Close to Colonel Denning State Park with hiking trails, fishing, and swimming. Two hours to Lancaster, 1 hour to Harrisburg, and 1½ hours to Gettysburg and Hershey. The home is wheelchair accessible. Rate listed includes one child also. No age limit for children.

Hosts: Don and Lois Leatherman
Rooms: 1 (1PB) $55
Continental Breakfast
Credit Cards:
Notes: 2 5 7 8 9 10

NORTH EAST

Vineyard Bed and Breakfast

10757 Sidehill Rd., North East, PA 16428-4961
(814) 725-5307; (888) 725-8998
E-mail: vinyrdbb@erie.net
Web site: www.lakeside.net/vineyardbb

Your hosts welcome you to the "Heart of Grape Country" on the shores of Lake Erie, surrounded by vineyards and orchards. Our turn-of-the-century home is quiet and peaceful with rooms

furnished with queen- or king-size beds and tastefully decorated to complement our home.

Hosts: Clyde and Judy Burnham
Rooms: 5 (5PB) $65–85
Full Breakfast
Credit Cards: A B C D
Notes: 2 5 6 7 9 10 11

PARADISE

Hershey Farm Home Lodging

73 Oak Hill Dr., Paradise, PA 17562
(717) 687-6037

Country life awaits you in our historic 1825 brick farmhouse. Experience the family-operated dairy farm. Quiet off-the-road setting, but close to attractions and restaurants, just minutes from everything. Close to Strasburg Railroad and Amish farm neighbors. Relax on the porch or lawn and listen to the birds sing, watch kittens play, or children swinging. Warm hospitality.

Hosts: Nevin and Ruth Hershey
Rooms: 3 (1PB;2SB) $36–48
Continental Breakfast
Notes: 2   5   7

Maple Lane Farm B & B

505 Paradise Ln., Paradise, PA 17562
(717) 687-7479

This 200-acre, family-owned dairy farm is situated in the heart of Amish country near Strasburg with craft shops, quilt shops, museums, farmers' markets, antique shops, outlets, and auctions nearby. The large front porch overlooks flowers, a spacious lawn, green meadows, and rolling hills with no busy highways. Pleasantly furnished rooms have quilts, crafts, canopy and poster beds, TVs, and air-conditioning. Victorian parlor with organ for guest use. Tasty breakfast served by candlelight. Dinner with an Amish family can be arranged.

Hosts: Edwin and Marion Rohrer
Rooms: 4 (2PB;2SB) $45–70
Continental Breakfast
Notes: 2 5 7 8 9 10

PITTSBURGH AREA

The Inn on Grandview

310 E. Grandview Ave.
   Zelienople, PA 16063-1101
(724) 452-0469; (888) 544-3481
   Fax (724) 452-0200
E-mail: grandinn@fyi.net
Web site: www.fyi.net/~grandinn

The Inn is located 30 minutes north of Pittsburgh in historic Zelienople/Harmony. Fine dining, quaint shops, and antique stores are within walking distance. This large Colonial began its days in the late 1800s as an overnight stop for travelers, now beautifully restored. One mile from I-79. Private baths, CTV, AC, fireplaces, and whirlpool. Wake up to a wonderful breakfast.

Hosts: Rich and Juanita Eppinger
Rooms: 4 (4PB) $85–130
Full Breakfast
Credit Cards: A B C D
Notes: 2 5 7 8 9 10 11 12

POCONO MOUNTAINS

La Anna Guest House

R. R. 2 Box 2801, Cresco, PA 18326-9303
(570) 676-4225; Fax (570) 676-4225
E-mail: missjill1@excite.com

La Anna

The 122-year-old Victorian home is furnished with Victorian and Empire antiques. It has spacious guest rooms, quiet surroundings, and a trout pond. You can walk to waterfalls and mountain views; deer and other wildlife are often seen nearby.

Host: Kay Swingle
Rooms: 4 (4SB) $25–55
Continental Breakfast
Credit Cards:
Notes: 2 5 7 8 9 10 11

SCRANTON

Weeping Willow Inn

308 N. Eaton Rd., Tunkhannock, PA 18657
(570) 836-7257
E-mail: weepingwillow@emcs.net

Our charming Colonial home has been lovingly restored, and we cordially invite you to experience its warmth and rich history. All rooms are furnished in antiques. A full breakast by candlelight is offered each morning. Beautiful mountains and the nearby roads of the Endless Mountains region of northeastern Pennsylvania offer many antique shops and craft stores. A relaxing bed and breakfast experience awaits you at the Weeping Willow Inn!

Weeping Willow Inn

Hosts: Patty and Randy Ehrenzeller
Rooms: 3 (3PB) $85–95
Full Breakfast
Credit Cards: A B C
Notes: 2 5 7 8 9 10 11

SEWICKLEY

Whistlestop Bed and Breakfast

95 Broad St., Leetsdale, PA 15056
(724) 251-0852
Web site: www.pittsburghbnb.com

A quaint brick Victorian home built in 1888 by the Harmonist Society, a Christian communal group similar to the Shakers. Four guest units, two with private baths, and two with shared baths. Kids stay free with parents. Your hostess is well known for her country cooking, specializing in breads, muffins, pastries, and jams. Leetsdale is located on the Ohio River, 12 miles west of Pittsburgh (the airport is 20 minutes away) and close to the classic American village of Sewickley, where fine examples of historic architecture are well maintained. The home is smoke-free.

Hosts: Steve and Joyce Smith
Rooms: 4 (2PB;2SB) $60–70
Full Breakfast
Credit Cards: A B C D
Notes: 2 5 7

SHIPPENSBURG

Field and Pine B & B

2155 Ritner Hwy.
   Shippensburg, PA 17257-9756
(717) 776-7179; Fax (717) 776-0076
E-mail: fieldpine@aol.com
Web site: www.virtualcities.com

Surrounded by stately pine trees, Field and Pine is a family-owned bed and breakfast with the charm of an Early American stone house on an 80-acre gentleman's farm. Built in 1790, the house has seven working fireplaces, original wide-pine floors, and stenciled walls. Bedrooms are furnished with antiques, quilts, and comforters. A gourmet breakfast is served in the formal dining room. Three miles from I-81, between Carlisle and Shippensburg. Children over 12 welcome.

Hosts: Allan and Mary Ellen Williams
Rooms: 3 (1PB;2SB) $70–85
Full Breakfast
Credit Cards: A B   F
Notes: 2 5 8 9 10 12

Pets welcome; 7 Children welcome; 8 Tennis nearby; 9 Swimming nearby; 10 Golf nearby; 11 Skiing nearby; 12 May be booked through travel agent

SMOKETOWN

Homestead Lodging

184 Eastbrook Rd., Smoketown, PA 17576-9701
(717) 393-6927; Fax (717) 393-1424
E-mail: lkepiro@juno.com
Web site: www.bbonline.com/pa/homestead/

Homestead Lodging

Warm Christian hospitality, personal attention, and knowledge of the area provide a delightful getaway to relax and "recharge." Our clean, comfortable rooms provide a "home away from home" atmosphere. Homestead Lodging is surrounded by lovely landscaping. Enjoy walking down the lane to the Amish farm or enjoy a quiet evening on our porch. We are within minutes of Christian theaters, dinner theaters, music theaters, restaurants, farmers' markets, quilt, antique, and craft shops, outlets, and museums.

Hosts: Robert and Lori Kepiro
Rooms: 5 (5PB) $44–69
Continental Breakfast
Credit Cards: A B D
Notes: 2 5 7 8 9 10 12

SOMERSET

Quill Haven Country Inn

1519 N. Center Ave., Somerset, PA 15501-7001
(814) 443-4514; Fax (814) 445-1376

E-mail: quill@quillhaven.com
Web site: www.quillhaven.com

A 1918 "gentleman's farmhouse" furnished with antiques and reproductions. Four uniquely decorated guest rooms with private baths, AC, and cable TV and VCRs. Common room with fireplace and mini-kitchenette, sunroom where breakfast is served, private deck with hot tub. AAA-rated 3 diamonds. Near Hidden Valley and Seven Springs ski resorts; Frank Lloyd Wright's Fallingwater; Youghioghen Reservoir; Ohiopyle for hiking, biking, and white-water sports; outlet mall; golf courses; and antique shops. Located 1.2 miles from the PA Turnpike, Exit 10.

Quill Haven

Hosts: Carol and Rowland Miller
Rooms: 4 (4PB) $85–110
Full Breakfast
Credit Cards: A B C D
Notes: 2 5 7 8 9 10 11 12

SOMERSET COUNTY

Laurel Echo Farm Vacation B & B

174 Crossroad, Rockwood, PA 15557
(814) 926-2760; (888) 655-5335
Web site: www.bbonline.com/pa/echofarm

NOTES: Credit cards accepted: A Master Card; B Visa; C American Express; D Discover; E Diners Club; F Other; 2 Personal checks accepted; 3 Lunch available; 4 Dinner available; 5 Open all year;

We are a century-old family farm raising beef and dairy calves on 100 acres. Since the children are gone, I pursued my dream of opening a bed and breakfast in our two-story farmhouse. We are in the Laurel Highlands of Somerset Co. with beautiful mountains and farmland. There are two ski resorts nearby, two state parks, and the popular Frank Lloyd Wright homes, Fallingwater and Kentucky Knob. We have two smaller rooms for kids plus an extra kitchen for your use.

Hosts: Paul and Carol Pyle
Rooms: 2 (2PB) $55–75
Full Breakfast
Notes: 2 5 6 7 8 9 10 11

Laurel Echo Farm

SPRUCE CREEK

The Marshall House B & B

HC -01, Box 10, Spruce Creek, PA 16683-9707
(814) 632-8319
E-mail: smdll@psu.edu

Our country home is located near the village of Spruce Creek. Spend time enjoying the central air-conditioning or spend time on the front porch listening to the sounds of the creek, reading, or just resting. Family activi-

ties available at Old Bedford Village, Raystown Lake, Horse Shoe Curve, Bland's Park, Lincoln and Indian Caverns, and Penn State University. Fishermen and hunters welcome.

Hosts: Sharon and Jim Dell
Rooms: 2 (2SB) $45–55
Full Breakfast
Credit Cards:
Notes: 2 5 7 10 11

STAHLSTOWN

Thorn's Cottage B & B

R. D. 1, Box 254, Stahlstown, PA 15687
(724) 593-6429

Located in the historic Ligonier Valley area of the Laurel Mountains, 7 miles from the PA Turnpike, 50 miles east of Pittsburgh, the cottage offers homey, woodland privacy. Relax on the sunporch or in the herb garden with its swing. Near Fallingwater, white-water rafting, biking and hiking trails, and the quaint town of Ligonier with shops, dining, amusement park. Breakfast includes home-baked muffins and scones. Full kitchen.

Hosts: Larry and Beth Thorn
Rooms: 1 (1PB) $85
Full Breakfast
Credit Cards:
Notes: 2 5 7 9 10 11

STARRUCCA

Nethercott Inn

6 Starrucca Creek Rd.
   Starrucca, PA 18462-0026
(570) 727-2211; Fax (570) 727-3811
E-mail: netheinn@nep.net

---

6 Pets welcome; 7 Children welcome; 8 Tennis nearby; 9 Swimming nearby; 10 Golf nearby; 11 Skiing nearby; 12 May be booked through travel agent

Web site: www.nethercottinn.com

This lovely 1893 Victorian home is nestled in a small village in the Endless Mountains and furnished in a pleasing combination of antique and country. All rooms have queen-size beds, AC, and private baths. Only 3 1/2 hours from New York City and Philadelphia, 8 hours from Toronto. Our "Winter Loft" sleeps eight and has full kitchen and two baths. Available for ski rentals, family reunions, etc.

Nethercott Inn

Hosts: Charlotte and John Keyser
Rooms: 7 (7PB) $80–125
Full Breakfast
Credit Cards: A B C D F
Notes: 2 5 7 9 10 11 12

STRASBURG

1786 The Limestone Inn

33 E. Main St., Strasburg, PA 17579
(717) 687-8392; (800) 278-8392
   Fax (717) 687-8366
E-mail: limestoneinn@yahoo.com
Web site: www.thelimestoneinn.com

Located in the heart of the Pennsylvania Dutch Country, this historic inn was built in 1786. Stop and enjoy life in the slow lane.

Hosts: Denise and Richard Waller
Rooms: 5 (5PB) $89–115
Full Breakfast
Credit Cards: A B C D
Notes: 2 5 10

VOLANT

Candleford Inn

225 Mercer St.; P. O. Box 212, Volant, PA 16156
(724) 533-4497
E-mail: candlefordinn@mail.com
Web site: www.candlefordinn.com

Nestled within a beautiful valley of western Pennsylvania is the quaint village of Volant, home of Candleford Inn, as well as many unique shops and the famous Volant Mills. A late 19th-century house, Candleford Inn combines a touch of class with the warmth of an old country home. The four guest rooms are each recently renovated and now all have private bathrooms, some with whirlpool tubs or steam shower. Full homemade hot breakfast varies daily.

Hosts: Howard and Carolyn Moss
Rooms: 4 (4PB) $80–120
Full Breakfast
Credit Cards: A B C D
Notes: 2 5 7 10

WAYNESBORO

The Shepherd and Ewe B & B

11205 Country Club Rd.
   Waynesboro, PA 17268-9273
(717) 762-8525; (888) 937-4393
   Fax (717) 762-5880
E-mail: rlrfintouch@pa.net

Set high atop lush acres of rolling farmland, this year-round getaway is a gracious, country retreat where guests find plenty of peace and rest, warm welcomes, and natural beauty. Our full country breakfasts start your day with down-home delights. Gettysburg, Washington, DC, and Lancaster are a short drive away.

Hosts: Twila and Robert Risser
Rooms: 5 (3PB;2SB) $79–89
Full Breakfast
Credit Cards: A B C D
Notes: 2 5 7 9 10

The Shepherd and Ewe

WELLSBORO

Kaltenbach's Bed and Breakfast

Stony Fork Rd. R. D. 6 # 106 A
  Wellsboro, PA 16901
(570) 724-4954; (800) 722-4954
Web site: www.kaltenbachsinn.com

Kaltenbach's

This sprawling, country home with room for thirty-two guests offers comfortable lodging, home-style breakfasts, and warm hospitality. Set on a 72-acre farm, Kaltenbach's provides opportunities for walks through meadows, pastures, and forests; picnicking; and watching the sheep, pigs, rabbits, and wildlife. All-you-can-eat country breakfasts. Honeymoon suites have tubs or Jacuzzis for two. Hunting and golf packages are available. Pennsylvania Grand Canyon nearby. Enjoy hiking and biking on Pine Creek's all-new "Rail Trails," built on the old Conrail bed. Kaltenbach's was awarded a 2-star rating in the Mobil Travel Guide for its accommodations and hospitality. Professional Association of Innkeepers International inn member.

Host: Lee Kaltenbach
Rooms: 11 (11PB) $70–150
Full Breakfast
Credit Cards: A B D
Notes: 2 3 4 5 7 8 9 10 11 12

YORK

Friendship House B & B

728 E. Philadelphia St., York, PA 17403-1609
(717) 843-8299
E-mail: friendshiphome@juno.com

An 1890s vintage townhouse located close to markets, shopping, and recreation. Spacious bedrooms with queen beds. Property has a beautiful private yard with quaint gardens. Also has a three-car garage. A country breakfast is served most mornings. New in 1999—gas log fireplace in living room.

Hosts: Becky Detwiler and Karen Maust
Rooms: 3 (2PB;1SB) $65
Full Breakfast
Credit Cards:
Notes: 2 5 7 8 9 10 11

---

6 Pets welcome; 7 Children welcome; 8 Tennis nearby; 9 Swimming nearby; 10 Golf nearby; 11 Skiing nearby; 12 May be booked through travel agent

RHODE ISLAND

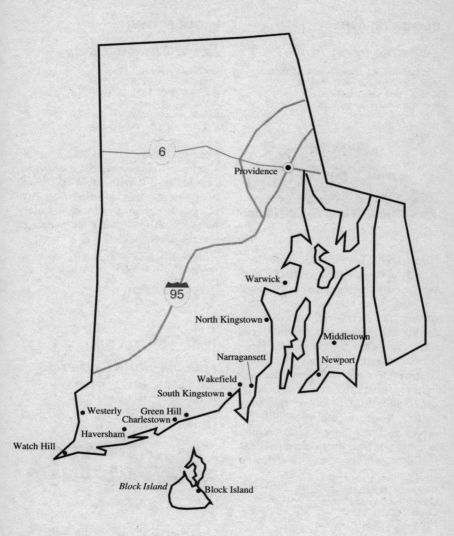

6

Providence

95

Warwick

North Kingstown

Narragansett

Wakefield

South Kingstown

Westerly · Green Hill
Charlestown

Haversham

Watch Hill

Middletown

Newport

Block Island · Block Island

Rhode Island

BLOCK ISLAND

The Rose Farm Inn

Box E, Roslyn Rd., Block Island, RI 02807
(401) 466-2034; Fax (401) 466-2053
E-mail: rosefarm@riconnect.com
Web site: www.rosefarminn.com

The Rose Farm Inn

Circa 1897. This romantic inn is comprised of two buildings, the turn-of-the-century farmhouse and the newer Captain Rose House. Canopy beds, sitting areas, and whirlpool tubs are among the elegant touches that grace the rooms at the Captain Rose House. Most rooms afford either an ocean or countryside view; and there's always a light sea breeze to be enjoyed from the decks and front porch of the farmhouse. A continental-plus buffet is served each morning on the enclosed sunporch, which overlooks the ocean. Children over the age of 12 welcome.

Host: Judith B. Rose
Rooms: 19 (17PB;2SB) $129–250
Continental Breakfast
Credit Cards: A B C D
Notes: 2 7 8 9

MIDDLETOWN

Inn at Shadow Lawn

120 Miantonomi Ave.
   Middletown, RI 02842-5450
(401) 847-0902; (800) 352-3750
   Fax (401) 848-6529
E-mail: randy@shadowlawn.com
Web site: www.shadowlawn.com

Shadow Lawn is a 142-year-old Victorian mansion. Eight rooms, private baths, TV with cable and VCR, telephones, air-conditioning, fireplaces, refrigerator, and complimentary wine. Also available for weddings, meetings, retreats, etc.

Hosts: Randy and Selma Fabricant
Rooms: 8 (8PB) $99–225
Full Breakfast
Credit Cards: A B C D E F
Notes: 5 7 8 9 10 12

NEWPORT

Halidon Hill Guest House

25 Halidon Ave., Newport, RI 02840
(401) 847-8318; (800) 448-5131
   Fax (401) 849-1347

Halidon Hill

Georgian Colonial home with spacious rooms. Convenient to shopping

---

NOTES: Credit cards accepted: A Master Card; B Visa; C American Express; D Discover; E Diners Club; F Other; 2 Personal checks accepted; 3 Lunch available; 4 Dinner available; 5 Open all year;

areas, local restaurants, mansions, and yacht clubs. In-ground pool and deck area. Full breakfast.

Hosts: Helen and Paul Burke
Rooms: 4 (2PB;2SB) $75–250
Full Breakfast
Credit Cards: C D E
Notes: 2 7 8 9 10 12

Polly's Place

349 Valley Rd., Newport, RI 02842-5236
(401) 847-2160; (877) 9-POLLYS
E-mail: pollysbnb@bigplanet.com
Web site: www.pollysbnb.com

A tranquil setting with gourmet breakfasts served overlooking fields of wildflowers, a lively brook, and colorful birds. Large comfortable rooms, moderately priced, just three minutes from the harbor and beaches. Private apartment available by the week. Children over 10 welcome.

Host: Polly Carning
Rooms: 3 (3PB) $85–160
Full Breakfast
Credit Cards:
Notes: 2 5 8 9 10 12

Samuel Durfee House

352 Spring St., Newport, RI 02840
(401) 847-1652; (877) 696-2374
E-mail: innkeeper@samueldurfeehouse.com
Web site: www.samueldurfeehouse.com

The Samuel Durfee House is an elegant 1803 Federal period inn. Conveniently located in Newport's Yachting Village, we are just a block away from the restaurants and shops on Thames Street and a block and a half from Bellevue Avenue, with its boutiques and mansions. Enjoy a delicious, gourmet full breakfast each morning in the parlor or patio. Our rooms have been uniquely decorated and have private bathrooms. Afternoon refreshments, air-conditioning, and private off-street parking are provided.

Samuel Durfee House

Hosts: Michael and Heather De Pinho
Rooms: 5 (5PB) $85–195
Full Breakfast
Credit Cards: A B
Notes: 2 5 8 9 10 12

Stella Maris Inn

91 Washington St., Newport, RI 02840-1531
(401) 849-2862
Web site: www.stellamarisinn.com

Early Newport mansion, 1861, redstone exterior, extensive gardens on 2 acres, on-site parking, wrap-around porch. Some water view rooms, fireplaces, elevator, antique furnishings, French Victorian style, former convent converted to B & B in 1990. Fresh home-cooked muffins and breads daily.

Hosts: Dorothy and Ed Madden
Rooms: 9 (9PB) $95–225
Continental Breakfast
Notes: 2 5 8 9 10

---

6 Pets welcome; 7 Children welcome; 8 Tennis nearby; 9 Swimming nearby; 10 Golf nearby; 11 Skiing nearby; 12 May be booked through travel agent

Wayside Guest House

406 Bellevue Ave., Newport, RI 02840
(401) 847-0302; (800) 653-7678
    Fax (401) 848-9374
E-mail: wayside406@earthlink.net

Wayside Guest House

This lovely Georgian-style "summer cottage" sits among the famed mansions on Bellevue Avenue, in the very heart of historic Newport. Be our guest, and enjoy the comfort and the splendor of Newport's Gilded Age. . . in a warm, welcoming, and intimate way. Open year-round. Our summer season runs May 1–October 31. Off-season rates are available November 1–April 30. Begin your morning with a wholesome continental breakfast, then spend the day touring the city's many lovely attractions, returning home to enjoy a refreshing swim in our heated pool. Then, relax, read, or bird-watch on lawn chairs in a quiet garden spot or take a stroll along historic Cliffwalk, safe above the crashing surf.

Host: Donnie Post
Rooms: 10 (10PB) $135–175
Continental Breakfast
Credit Cards:
Notes: 2 5 7 8 9 10

PROVIDENCE

Old Court B & B

144 Benefit St., Providence, RI 02903-1208
(401) 454-4074; Fax (401) 274-4830
E-mail: reserve@oldcourt.com
Web site: www.oldcourt.com

The Old Court Bed and Breakfast is filled with antique furniture, chandeliers, and memorabilia from the 19th century, with each room designed to reflect period tastes. The antique, Victorian beds are comfortable and spacious. Just a 3-minute walk from the center of downtown Providence, near Brown University and Rhode Island School of Design.

Host: David M. Dolbashian
Rooms: 10 (10PB) $145–165
Full Breakfast
Credit Cards: A B C D
Notes: 2 5 12

WAKEFIELD

Larchwood Inn

521 Main St., Wakefield, RI 02879
(401) 783-5454; (800) 275-5450
    Fax (401) 783-1800
Web site: www.larchwoodinn.com

The Larchwood Inn is conveniently located near Newport and Block Island, RI, as well as Mystic, CT. Local attractions include beautiful surf and sheltered beaches, boating, hiking, bike and horseback riding, and skiing.

Hosts: Francis and Diann Browning
Rooms: 18 (11PB;7SB) $35–150
No Breakfast Served
Credit Cards: A B C D E
Notes: 2 3 4 5 6 7 8 9 10 11 12

NOTES: Credit cards accepted: A Master Card; B Visa; C American Express; D Discover; E Diners Club; F Other; 2 Personal checks accepted; 3 Lunch available; 4 Dinner available; 5 Open all year;

WESTERLY

Woody Hill Bed and Breakfast

149 S. Woody Hill Rd., Westerly, RI 02891-5918
(401) 322-0452
E-mail: woodyhill@riconnect.com
Web site: www.woodyhill.com

Relaxed 18th-century ambience on 20
acres with in-ground pool, antiques,
perennial gardens. Minutes from
ocean beaches, Mystic, Newport, and
Foxwoods. Availability calendar and
pictures on web site.

Host: Ellen L. Madison
Rooms: 4 (4PB) $95–150
Full Breakfast
Credit Cards: F
Notes: 2 5 7 8 9 10 12

---

6 Pets welcome; 7 Children welcome; 8 Tennis nearby; 9 Swimming nearby; 10 Golf nearby; 11 Skiing
nearby; 12 May be booked through travel agent

SOUTH CAROLINA

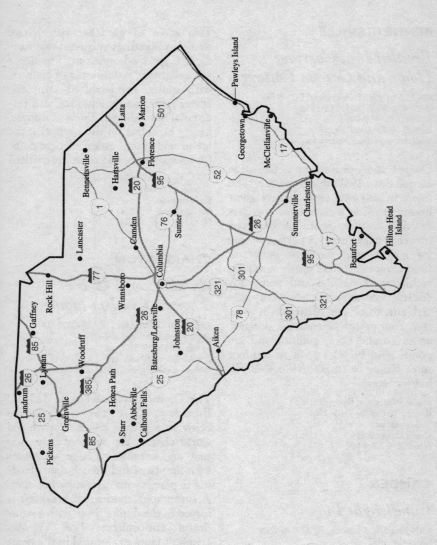

South Carolina

BENNETTSVILLE

Breeden Inn, Carriage House and Garden Cottage

404 E. Main St., Bennettsville, SC 29512
(843) 479-3665; (888) 335-2996
    Fax (843) 479-7998
E-mail: breedeninn@att.net
Web site: www.breedeninn.com

Owned and operated by a Christian couple since 1988, this romantic 1886 mansion and two 19th-century guest houses provide a haven for travelers desiring a true Southern bed and breakfast experience. A perfect setting for retreats and romantic getaways. Guest rooms offer plush comfort, architectural details, and seemingly endless decorative touches. Many special amenities are included in your stay. Four pretty-as-a-picture porches, an in-ground pool, goldfish and koi ponds, and bicycles lend to outdoor fun. Enjoy a memorable NY/FL halfway stay!

Hosts: Wesley and Bonnie Park
Rooms: 10 (10PB) $105–150
Full Breakfast
Credit Cards: A B C
Notes: 2 5 7 8 9 10

CAMDEN

Candlelight Inn

1904 Broad St., Camden, SC 29020-2606
(803) 424-1057
E-mail: candlelightinncamden@yahoo.com
Web site: www.candlelightinn.org

Two acres of gardens with native southern plantings surround this candlelit Cape Cod-style inn. The decor is a delightful, tasteful mix of country, with quilts, hand-crafted samplers, poster beds, family antiques, and traditional furnishings. Enjoy a unique, hearty breakfast on the sunporch; the menu and place setting change daily. Or how about breakfast in the garden?

Hosts: Jo Ann and George Celani
Rooms: 3 (3PB) $90–105
Full Breakfast
Credit Cards: A B C D
Notes: 2 5 8 10 12

CHARLESTON

Antebellum B & B at Thomas Lamboll House

19 King St., Charleston, SC 29401-2734
(843) 723-3212; (888) 874-0793
    Fax (843) 723-5420
E-mail: lamboll@aol.com
Web site: www.lambollhouse.com/home.htm

The Thomas Lamboll House Bed and Breakfast. Enjoy the ambience of being in a private residence with old world charm. You will have the privacy and comfort of large bedrooms with fireplaces and French doors leading to piazza with distant harbor view. A sumptuous continental breakfast is served in the dining room with a wonderful atmosphere. The Thomas Lamboll House is located in the heart

---

NOTES: Credit cards accepted: A Master Card; B Visa; C American Express; D Discover; E Diners Club; F Other; 2 Personal checks accepted; 3 Lunch available; 4 Dinner available; 5

of the historic district, and off-street parking is provided at no charge.

Hosts: Marie and Emerson Read
Rooms: 2 (2PB) $125–175
Continental Breakfast
Credit Cards: A B
Notes: 2 5 7 8 9 10

Belvedere B & B

40 Rutledge Ave., Charleston, SC 29401-1702
(843) 722-0973; (800) 816-1664
Web site: www.belvedereinn.com

Belvedere

A Colonial Revival mansion built in 1900 with an exquisite Adamesque interior taken from the circa 1800 Belvedere Plantation house. In downtown historic district on Colonial Lake, walking distance from historical points of interest, restaurants, and shopping. Guests may use the public areas and piazzas in this romantic, beautifully restored mansion. Children over 8 welcome.

Hosts: David Spell, Innkeeper
     Joanne Kuhn, Mgr.
Rooms: 3 (3PB) $135-195
Continental Breakfast
Credit Cards:
Notes: 2 5 8 9 10 12

Country Victorian B & B

105 Tradd St., Charleston, SC 29401-2422
(843) 577-0682

Come relive the charm of the past. Relax in a rocker on the piazza of this historic home and watch the carriages go by. Walk to antique shops, churches, restaurants, art galleries, museums, and all historic points of interest. The house, built in 1820, is located in the historic district south of Broad. Rooms have private entrances and contain antique iron and brass beds, old quilts, antique oak and wicker furniture, and braided rugs over heart-of-pine floors. Homemade cookies will be waiting. Many extras! Featured in *Country Quilts Magazine*. Children over 10 welcome.

Host: Diane Deardurff Weed
Rooms: 2 (2PB) $95–195
Continental Breakfast
Credit Cards:
Notes: 2 5 8 9 10

Country Victorian

1837 Bed and Breakfast

126 Wentworth St., Charleston, SC 29401-1737
(843) 723-7166; (877) 723-1837
     Fax (843) 722-7179
Web site: www.1837bb.com

Enjoy accommodations in a wealthy cotton planter's home and brick carriage house centrally located in Charleston's historic district. Canopied, poster, rice

6 Pets welcome; 7 Children welcome; 8 Tennis nearby; 9 Swimming nearby; 10 Golf nearby; 11 Skiing nearby; 12 May be booked through travel agent

beds. Walk to boat tours, the old market, antique shops, restaurants, and main attractions. Near the Charleston Place (convention center) and College of Charleston. Gourmet breakfast is served in the formal dining room and includes raspberry french toast, ham frittata with Mornay sauce, and home-baked breads such as pecan sticky buns and blueberry muffins. The 1837 Tea Room serves afternoon tea to guests. Off-street parking available. Special winter rates.

1837

Hosts: Sherri Weaver and Richard Dunn
Rooms: 9 (9PB) $79–165
Full Breakfast
Credit Cards: A B C D
Notes: 2 5 7 8 9 10 12

King George IV Inn

32 George St., Charleston, SC 29401-1416
(843) 723-9339; (888) 723-1667
    Fax (843) 723-7749
E-mail: info@kinggeorgeiv.com
Web site: www.kinggeorgeiv.com

A 200-year-old house in the heart of the historic district. The inn is Federal style, with three levels of Charleston side porches. The house has 10-foot ceilings with decorative plaster moldings, wide-planked hard-wood floors, old furnishings, and antiques. Private baths, off-street parking, air-conditioning, TVs. One-minute walk to King Street, 5 minutes to the market.

Hosts: Debra, Terry, and Debbie
Rooms: 10 (8PB;2SB) $89–185
Continental Breakfast
Credit Cards: A B C
Notes: 2 5 8 9 10 12

The Kitchen House (circa 1732)

126 Tradd St., Charleston, SC 29401-2420
(843) 577-6362; Fax (843) 965-5615
E-mail: loisevans@worldnet.att.net
Web site: www.thekitchenhouse.net

Nestled in the heart of the historic district, the Kitchen House is a totally restored 18th-century dwelling. Dr. Peter Fayssoux, surgeon general to the Continental Army, called it home. You'll enjoy the Southern hospitality, absolute privacy, fireplaces, and antiques. Outside, experience your own private patio, colonial herb garden, fishpond, and fountain. Concierge service. Honeymoon packages. Featured in *Colonial Homes Magazine*, *The New York Times*, and *Best Places to Stay in the South*.

The Kitchen House

NOTES: Credit cards accepted: A Master Card; B Visa; C American Express; D Discover; E Diners Club; F Other; 2 Personal checks accepted; 3 Lunch available; 4 Dinner available; 5

Hosts: Lois Evans
Rooms: 3 (3PB) $150–300
Full Breakfast
Credit Cards: A B
Notes: 2 5 7 8 9 10 12

Linwood Historic Home and Gardens B & B

200 S. Palmetto St., Summerville, SC 29483-6042
(843) 871-2620; Fax (843) 875-2515
E-mail: linwoodbb@aol.com
Web site: www.bbonline.com/sc/linwood

Once the home of a 19th-century plantation owner. Gracious hospitality abounds at Linwood, a beautifully restored Victorian home featuring high ceilings, chandeliers, period antiques, and wide porches. Surrounded by 2 acres of lush gardens, Linwood is in the center of the charming village of Summerville, near shops and restaurants. Linwood has a lovely, large in-ground pool. Famous plantations, golf courses, beaches, and historic Charleston are nearby. Recreation or retreat—we are here to serve you.

Hosts: Peter and Linda Shelbourne
Rooms: 4 (4PB) $85–150
Continental Breakfast
Credit Cards: A B
Notes: 2 5 8 9 10 12

Rutledge Victorian Guest House

114 Rutledge Ave, Charleston, SC 29401-1333
(843) 722-7551; (888) 722-7553
   Fax (843) 727-0065
Web site: www.bbonline.com/sc/rutledge

Elegant Charleston home in downtown historic district. Century-old

house with rare, decorative, Italianate architecture with beautiful ceiling moldings. Rooms have mahogany and oak fireplaces, 12-foot ceilings, hardwood floors, 10-foot doors and windows, and antiques. Lovely, 120-foot porch with rocking chairs and joggling board overlooking the park and Roman Columns, remains of the Confederate soldiers' reunion hall. Relaxed atmosphere, AC, parking, and TVs. Lovely formal dining rooms where complimentary continental plus breakfast is served. Short walk to historic sites. Our Kitchen House (#6 Ambrose Alley) also is available.

Hosts: Lyn, Dave, and Norm
Rooms: 11 (7PB;4SB) $150–280
Continental Breakfast
Credit Cards: A B
Notes: 2 5 7 8 9 10 12

Villa de la Fontaine

138 Wentworth St., Charleston, SC 29401-1734
(843) 577-7709
Web site:
   www.charleston.cityinformation.com/villa/

Villa de la Fontaine

Villa de la Fontaine is a columned Greek Revival mansion in the heart of the historic district. It was built in

1838 and boasts a ½-acre garden with fountain and terraces. Restored to impeccable condition, the mansion is furnished with museum-quality furniture and accessories. The hosts are retired ASID interior designers and have decorated the rooms with 18th-century American antiques. Several of the rooms feature canopy beds. Breakfast is prepared by a master chef who prides himself on serving a different menu every day. Parking on the property, with 7-foot brick wall and iron gates! It is in the safest part of Charleston, near the College of Charleston. Minimum-stay requirements for weekends and holidays. We have been featured in the *New York Times* travel section, *Best Places to Stay in the South, Southern Living,* and *Feinschmecker Magazine.*

Hosts: Bill Fontaine / Audrey Hancock
Rooms: 6 (6PB) $125–200
Full Breakfast
Credit Cards:
Notes: 2 5 8 9 10

FLORENCE

The Breeden Inn, Carriage House and Garden Cottage

404 E. Main St., Bennettsville, SC 29512-3112
(843) 479-3665; (888) 335-2996
    Fax (843) 479-7998
E-mail: breedeninn@att.net
Web site: www.breedeninn.com

Located 40 miles NW of Florence; 22 miles off I-95 at Exit 181 or 193. "Something more than the expected" is what you will experience in this villagelike setting. Three 19th-century houses offer ten beautiful guest rooms, including four suites, one with a sunken whirlpool. A great NY/FL halfway stay. Many amenities unusual to B & B's. Two fully equipped kitchens, laundry rooms, and an antique shop offer convenience. Six original outbuildings surround an in-ground pool, gardens, and goldfish/koi ponds. The inn is listed on the National Register of Historic Places and designated as a Backyard Wildlife Habitat. Enjoy antique shops, Lake Wallace, walking trails, and historic touring.

The Breeden Inn

Hosts: Wesley and Bonnie Park
Rooms: 10 (10PB) $105–150
Full Breakfast
Credit Cards: A B C
Notes: 2 5 7 8 9 10 12

GEORGETOWN

Live Oak Inn
Bed and Breakfast

515 Prince St., Georgetown, SC 29440
(843) 545-8658; (888) 730-6004
    Fax (843) 545-8948
E-mail: info@liveoakinn.com
Web site: www.liveoakinn.com

Enjoy the comforts of today as you are surrounded by the elegance of the past in this 1905 Victorian home, nestled between two massive 500-year-old live oak trees. The home has nine fireplaces, inlaid oak floors, and beautiful multipaned windows. Each room is tastefully decorated and has your comfort in mind.

Live Oak Inn

Hosts: Jackie and Fred Hoelscher
Rooms: 5 (5PB) $85–135
Full Breakfast
Credit Cards: A B C D
Notes: 2 5 10 12

The Shaw House

613 Cypress Ct., Georgetown, SC 29440-3349
(843) 546-9663

The Shaw House is a spacious, two-story Colonial home in a natural setting with a beautiful view overlooking miles of marshland—perfect for bird-watchers. Within walking distance of downtown and great restaurants on the waterfront. Rooms are large, with many antiques and private baths. Breakfast is served at our guests' convenience. Also included are nighttime chocolates on each pillow, turn-backs, and some loving extras. Guests leave

with a little gift—prayers, recipes, and/or jellies. Approved by AAA, Mobil, and ABBA.

Hosts: Mary and Joe Shaw
Rooms: 3 (3PB) $65–85
Full Breakfast
Credit Cards:
Notes: 2 5 7 8 9 10

Ship Wrights B & B

609 Cypress Ct., Georgetown, SC 29440-3349
(843) 527-4475

Three thousand-plus square feet of beautiful, quiet, clean home is yours to use when you stay. It's nautically attired and tastefully laced with family heirlooms. Guests say they feel like they just stayed at their best friend's home. The bedrooms and baths are beautiful and very comfortable. You'll never get "Grandma Eicker's Pancakes" anywhere else. (The inn is famous for them; there's a great story behind the pancakes!) The view from the large porch is breathtaking, perfect for bird-watching. Five minutes from Ocean Beach. AAA-approved.

Ship Wrights

Host: Leatrice M. Wright
Rooms: 2 (2PB) $60
Full Breakfast
Notes: 2 5 7 8 9 10

6 Pets welcome; 7 Children welcome; 8 Tennis nearby; 9 Swimming nearby; 10 Golf nearby; 11 Skiing nearby; 12 May be booked through travel agent

LANDRUM

The Red Horse Inn

310 N. Campbell Rd., Landrum, SC 29356-9296
(864) 895-4968; Fax (864) 895-4968
E-mail: theredhorseinn@aol.com
Web site: www.theredhorseinn.com

Five charming cottages dot a hillside
of the 190 acres that comprise the Red
Horse Inn. The main inn sits majesti-
cally overlooking the cottages and the
expansive Blue Ridge Mountains.
Luxury inn rooms provide king-size
beds, fireplaces, whirlpools, color TV,
and AC. The cottages offer kitchens,
fireplaces, queen-size beds, whirlpools,
color TV, and AC. Massage available.
Deposit needed for children and pets.

Hosts: Mary and Roger Wolters
Rooms: 9 (9PB) $110–195
Continental Breakfast
Credit Cards: A B D F
Notes: 2 5 6 8 9 10 12

SUMMERVILLE

Linwood Historic Home and Gardens B & B

200 S. Palmetto St.
   Summerville, SC 29483-6042
(843) 871-2620; Fax (843) 875-2515
E-mail: linwoodbb@aol.com
Web site: www.bbonline.com/sc/linwood

Once the home of a 19th-century plantation owner. Gracious hospitality
abounds at Linwood, a beautifully
restored Victorian home featuring high
ceilings, chandeliers, period antiques,
and wide porches. Surrounded by 2
acres of lush gardens, Linwood is in the
center of the charming village of
Summerville, near shops and restaurants. Linwood has a lovely, large in-
ground pool. Famous plantations, golf
courses,   beaches,   and   historic
Charleston are nearby. Recreation or
retreat—we are here to serve you.

Hosts: Peter and Linda Shelbourne
Rooms: 4 (4PB) $85–150
Continental Breakfast
Credit Cards: A B
Notes: 2 5 8 9 10 12

SOUTH DAKOTA

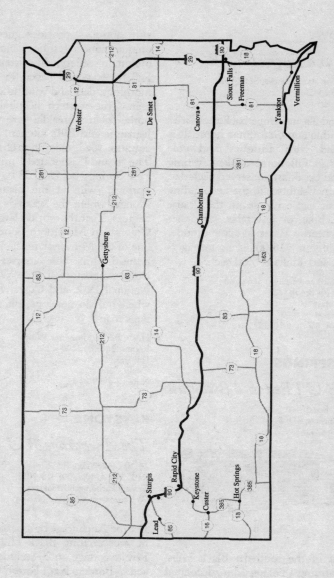

South Dakota

CANOVA

Skoglund Farm B & B

24375 438th Ave., Canova, SD 57321
(605) 247-3445

Skoglund Farm brings back memories of Grandpa and Grandma's home. It is furnished with antiques and collectibles. A full, home-cooked evening meal and breakfast are served each day. Guests may sightsee in the surrounding area, visit Little House on the Prairie Village, hike, or just relax. Churches located nearby. Rates: age 5 and under free, children $15.00 each, teenagers $20.00, and adults $35.00 each.

Hosts: Alden and Delores Skoglund
Rooms: 4 (0PB;4SB) $35
Full Breakfast
Credit Cards:
Notes: 2 4 6 7 8 9 10 12

HOT SPRINGS

The B & J Bed and Breakfast

HCR 52, Box 101-B
  Hot Springs, SD 57747-9701
(605) 745-4243

The B & J

Nestled in the southern Black Hills, this charming 1890 log cabin, decorated with antiques, provides guests with a unique pioneer setting. Enjoy peaceful mountain scenery while listening to the Fall River, which never freezes. Early mornings, deer and wild turkey may be seen. True western hospitality and a home-cooked breakfast are waiting in Jeananne and Bill's kitchen. Down the entrance road, enjoy horseback riding. The "B and J" is located 1 mile south of Hot Springs on U.S. 385/18. In Hot Springs, swim at the historic Evans Plunge, where the water is always 87 degrees. Visit the world's largest find of Columbian Mammoth bones. Golf at one of the Midwest's most challenging, beautiful nine-hole courses. Minutes from Angostura Lake, Wind Cave National Park, and Custer State Park, where buffalo, antelope, elk, and prairie dogs roam.

Hosts: Bill and Jeananne Wintz
Rooms: 1 (1PB) $100–125
Full Breakfast
Credit Cards:
Notes: 2 7 8 9 10 11

KEYSTONE

The Anchorage B & B

24110 Leaky Valley Rd., Keystone, SD 57751-6626
(605) 574-4740; (800) 318-7018
E-mail: anchoragebb@aol.com
Web site: www.anchoragebb.com

Let the Anchorage be a peaceful harbor in your exciting Black Hills vacation. Private cottage on 20 secluded, forested acres. Borders Nat'l Forest, Centennial

---

NOTES: Credit cards accepted: A Master Card; B Visa; C American Express; D Discover; E Diners Club; F Other; 2 Personal checks accepted; 3 Lunch available; 4 Dinner available; 5 Open all year;

Trail. Hike to Mt. Rushmore! Minutes from lakes, Custer State Park, Crazy Horse, Keystone, and Hill City. Satisfying full breakfast with hosts. Hot tub in the pines. Member BBISD.

Hosts: Jim and Lin Gogolin
Rooms: 1 (1PB) $95
Full Breakfast
Credit Cards: A B D
Notes: 2 5 7 8 10 11 12

PRESHO

Sweeney's B & B

103 S. Main Ave., Presho, SD 57568
(605) 895-2586

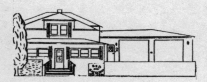

Sweeney's

Historic, large, early 1900s home. Redone with family heirlooms and antiques. In the Pheasant Capital of South Dakota. Halfway between Sioux Falls and Rapid City on I-90. No smoking allowed.

Hosts: Paul and Wanda Sweeney
Rooms: 3 (0PB;3SB) $50–60
Full Breakfast
Credit Cards:
Notes: 2 5 7 8 9 10

RAPID CITY

Abend Haus Cottages and Audrie's B & B

23029 Thunderhead Falls Rd., Rapid City, SD
    57702-8524
(605) 342-7788
Web site: www.audriesbb.com

The ultimate in charm and old world hospitality. Area's first B & B family owned since 1985. Our creekside log cottages/grand lodges are reminiscent of Germany and furnished with comfortable European antiques. All feature a private entrance, private bath, king bed, patio, hot tub, gas fireplace, and full breakfast. If the past intrigues you, the Old Powerhouse is for you. It has two suites, each with private hot tub. Visit our entire B & B on the web, which has separate color photo page and description for each suite/cottage.

Hosts: Hank and Audrie Kuhnhauser
Rooms: 9 (9PB) $115–175
Full Breakfast
Credit Cards:
Notes: 2 8 9 10 11

---

6 Pets welcome; 7 Children welcome; 8 Tennis nearby; 9 Swimming nearby; 10 Golf nearby; 11 Skiing nearby; 12 May be booked through travel agent

TENNESSEE

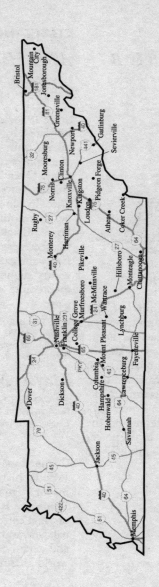

Bristol
Mountain City
Jonesborough
181
81
Greeneville
Newport
441
Gatlinburg
141
Sevierville
32
Mooresburg
Clinton
75
Norris
Knoxville
Kingston
Pigeon Forge
Loudon
70
Rugby
27
Harriman
Athens
Coker Creek
64
Monterey
40
Pikeville
Hillsboro
27
Monteagle
Chattanooga
McMinnville
24
Wartrace
Murfreesboro
College Grove
Lynchburg
31
Nashville
65
Franklin
231
65
Mount Pleasant
Fayetteville
24
PKY
Columbia
43
Lawrenceburg
Dover
Dickson
40
Hampshire
Hohenwald
Savannah
79
64
Jackson
45
45
51
422
40
64
51
Memphis

Tennessee

Majestic Mansion B & B

202 E. Washington Ave.
    Athens, TN 37303-3652
(423) 746-9041
E-mail: eden@usit.net
Web site: www.themansionbnb.com

Majestic Mansion

Nestled near the foothills of the Smokies, just off I-75 in southeastern Tennessee, this 1909 gracious home adds to historic downtown Athens. Stroll one block to the quaint town square filled with shops, from antiques to women's fashions. Relax in a rocking chair on the wooden porch with cool lemonade or play tennis on the nearby courts. Awake to a power breakfast or a light fitness meal. Three unique rooms available.

Hosts: Richard and Elaine Newman
Rooms: 3 (3PB) $85
Full Breakfast
Credit Cards: A B
Notes: 5 7 8 10

CHATTANOOGA

Alford House

5515 Alford Hill Drive, Chattanooga, TN 37419
(423) 821-7625; Fax (423) 821-7625

Since 1986. Chattanooga's first B & B. Bordered by the National Park with hiking trails and wildlife. A relaxing atmosphere filled with many collections. Over 100 glass baskets, steam engines, carousels, teddy bears, Rose & Lace. In winter over 150 snowmen will be found throughout this 15-room home. Breakfast on the upper deck weather permitting, after early coffee. Enjoy the gazebo or relax by the fire on wintry nights. Ask about our honeymoon suite and special discounts for pastors.

Host: Rhoda Alford Eaton
Rooms: 4 (4PB)
Continental Breakfast
Notes: 2 5 8 9 10 11 12

Mayor's Mansion Inn

801 Vine St., Chattanooga, TN 37403
(423) 265-5000; Fax (423) 265-5555
E-mail: info@innjoy.com
Web site: www.innjoy.com

Cornerstone to Chattanooga's Fort Wood historic district, formerly mayor's mansion in 1889. Rare Victorian Romanesque design with original coffered ceilings, hand-carved oak stairway, beveled-glass windows, and ceramic tile embellishments. Old world charm and hospitality in a set-

---

ting rich with Civil War history and turn-of-the-century architecture. This historic B & B has 11 exquisitely decorated guest rooms. Awarded National Trust Home Beautiful, 1997. Private baths, ornamental fireplaces, and a complimentary gourmet breakfast for guests. Fine dining at the inn available with reservations. Ballroom, meeting and reception areas, private dining and catering available to public.

Hosts: Gene and Carmen Fenn Drake
Rooms: 11 (11PB) $150–275
Full Breakfast
Credit Cards: A B C D
Notes: 2 4 5 10

CROSSVILLE

At Your Service

25 Overlook Terrace, Fairfield Glade, TN 38558
(931) 484-8059; Fax (931) 707-7798

Make your reservations now—come sit, relax, and refresh yourself in our casual atmosphere—two or three days would do you good. Fees are suggested amounts; your hosts are ordained in nonprofit Christian ministry, helping rekindle your spirit and refresh your soul. All meals are included and you can even help bake a pie and do crafts. Local activities also include fishing; major attractions within 1-2 hours. Call for brochure. Children 12 and older welcome.

Hosts: Chuck and Mary Pierce
Rooms: 2 (2SB) $45–60
Full Breakfast
Notes: 2 3 4 5 7 8 9 10

DICKSON

East Hills B & B Inn

100 E. Hill Terrace, Dickson, TN 37055
(615) 441-9428; Fax (615) 446-2181
E-mail: jaluther@dickson.net
Web site: www.easthillsbb.com

East Hills

A perfect place to relax, reflect, and strengthen body and soul or to renew relationships, celebrate anniversaries, or special events, friends, church and social functions, or for the business traveler with internet connections and phones. Built in the late '40s, restored in the early '90s, the inn has four bedrooms and two cottages, all with private baths and cable TV, and is furnished throughout with period antiques. There are rocking chairs and swings on the porches. Located on Highway 70 near Luther Lake and Greystone Golf Course, 6 miles from Montgomery Bell State Park, convenient to the Renissance Center, shopping, restaurants, downtown areas, historic Charlotte, and Cumberland Furnace. Rates include afternoon or evening refreshments and a full breakfast in the morning. No smoking, no alcohol.

Hosts: John and Anita Luther
Rooms: 7 (7PB) $75–135
Full Breakfast
Credit Cards: A B C D F
Notes: 2 5 8 9 10 12

---

6 Pets welcome; 7 Children welcome; 8 Tennis nearby; 9 Swimming nearby; 10 Golf nearby; 11 Skiing nearby; 12 May be booked through travel agent

FRANKLIN

Namaste Acres Barn B & B

5436 Leipers Creek Rd., Franklin, TN 37064-9208
(615) 791-0333; Fax (615) 591-0665
E-mail: namaste@aol.com
Web site: www.bbonline.com/tn/namaste

Quiet valley setting. Poolside deck and hot tub, hiking, horseback trails. Country inn offers four theme suites, including the Loft, Bunkhouse, Cabin, and Franklin. In-room coffee, phone, and refrigerator; TV/VCR (movies). Private entrance and bath. Featured in *Southern Living Magazine, Horse Illustrated,* and *Western Horseman.* One mile from Natchez Trace Parkway, 11 miles from historic Franklin, and 23 miles from Nashville. Established 1993. Reservation requested. AAA 3-diamond rating. Guided trail rides are available.

Hosts: Bill, Lisa, and Lindsay Winters
Rooms: 4 (4PB) $75–85
Continental Breakfast
Credit Cards: A B C D E
Notes: 2 5 7 9 10 12

GATLINBURG

Alpenhof Bed and Breakfast

1531 Providence Hill Rd., Sevierville, TN 37876
(865) 429-4771; (877) 429-4771
E-mail: alpenhofbb@aol.com
Web site: www.bbonline.com/tn/alpenhof

From I-40, Exit 407. Follow Hwy. 66 to Hwy. 338 N., turn right. Watch for left turn. 1 mile to Providence Hills, turn left. Take Providence Hills Rd. to Alpenhof sign.

Hosts: Joc and Heidi Mathews

Rooms: 4 (4PB) $89
Full Breakfast
Credit Cards: A B C
Notes: 2 4 5 7 10

Berry Springs Lodge

2149 Seaton Springs Rd., Sevierville, TN 37862
(865) 908-7935; (888) 760-8297
   Fax (865) 428-2814
E-mail: pseisert@aol.com
Web site: www.berrysprings.com

Berry Springs Lodge

In our newly built Lodge, you can expect relaxing luxury and first-class service. We constructed and opened the Lodge in the summer of 2000. We are the closest Lodge to Dollywood and only minutes to hiking trails and shopping. The Lodge offers 12 guest rooms, two large living room areas, a large dining room, spacious decks, and a view that will take your breath away. Imagine a quiet, tranquil mountaintop place where you can enjoy your vacation.

Hosts: Patrick and Susan Eisert
Rooms: 12 (12PB) $109–189
Full Breakfast
Credit Cards: A B C D
Notes: 5 8 9 10 11

Cornerstone Inn B & B

3966 Regal Ct., P. O. Box 1600
   Gatlinburg, TN 37738-1600
(865) 430-5064; (877) 877-5045
   Fax (865) 430-5064
E-mail: info@cornerstone-gatlinburg.com
Web site: www.cornerstone-gatlinburg.com

NOTES: Credit cards accepted: A Master Card; B Visa; C American Express; D Discover; E Diners Club; F Other; 2 Personal checks accepted; 3 Lunch available; 4 Dinner available; 5

Cornerstone Inn

A delightful country inn with a 50-foot front porch, surrounded by a panoramic mountain view. The inn is located within 5 miles of the Great Smoky Mountains National Park, the Great Smoky arts and crafts community, and very near Dollywood. Ideal for church groups, family reunions, anniversaries, and wedding parties. The inn offers full kitchen facilities, private baths, and a great room with wood-burning fireplace. A warm, serene, comfortable atmosphere.

Hosts: Kay and Don Cooper
Rooms: 4 (4PB) $85–95
Full Breakfast
Credit Cards: A B C D F
Notes: 2 5 7 8 9 10 12

GREENEVILLE

Nolichuckey Bluffs

295 Kinser Park Ln., Greeneville, TN 37743
(423) 787-7947; (800) 842-4690
Fax (423) 787-9247
E-mail: cabins@usit.net
Web site: www.tennessee-cabins.com

Private cabins—one- and two-bedroom on bluff of river overlooking the mountains. Kitchens, fireplaces, Jacuzzis. Large front porches with rocking chairs. Country store serves full break-fast, home-baked items, homemade ice cream. We love to pamper.

Host: Patricia Sadler
Rooms: 5 (5PB) $95–120
Full Breakfast
Credit Cards: A B C D
Notes: 2 5 6 7 8 9 10 12

HAMPSHIRE

Natchez Trace B & B Reservation Service

P. O. Box 193, Hampshire, TN 38461
(913) 285-2777; (800) 377-2770
E-mail: natcheztrace@worldnet.att.net
Web site: www.bbonline.com/natcheztrace

This reservation service is unusual in that all the homes listed are close to the Natchez Trace, the delightful National Parkway running from Nashville, Tennessee, to Natchez, Mississippi. Kay and Bill Jones can help you plan your trip along the Trace, with stays in interesting and historic homes along the way. Many locations of bed and breakfasts include the cities of Nashville, Franklin, Hohenwald, Linden, and Mt. Pleasant, Tennessee; Florence, Alabama; and Corinth, New Albany, Tupelo, Aberdeen, French Camp, Kosciusko, Canton, Raymond, Vicksburg, Port Gibson, Church Hill, and Natchez, Mississippi. $60–$190.

Host: Kay Jones

JACKSON

Boxwood Manor

P. O. Box 726, 311 E. Main St.
  Whiteville, TN 38075
(731) 254-0165; Fax (731) 254-8592

E-mail: boxwdmanor@aol.com
Web site: www.bedandbreakfast.com

Choose from four comfortable upstairs bedrooms. Relax w/friends on the upstairs screened porch. . .Enjoy small-town charm within proximity to city amenities. Full breakfast served in Manor's formal dining room. Reservations required.

Host: Jean Plaisance
Rooms: 4 (2PB;2SB) $75–85
Full Breakfast
Notes: 2 5 10

KINGSTON

Whitestone Country Inn

1200 Paint Rock Rd., Kingston, TN 37763-5843
(865) 376-0113; (888) 247-2464
    Fax (865) 376-4454
E-mail: moreinfo@whitestoneinn.com
Web site: www.whitestoneinn.com

A luxurious, AAA 4-diamond, secluded 360-acre estate on Watts Bar Lake provides a perfect environment for your next getaway. Surrounded by a wildlife and waterfowl refuge, Whitestone brings you close to all East Tennessee attractions, but far enough away to find sanctuary and relaxation in the tranquility of God's creation. Member, Select Registry. Recognized as one of the ten most romantic inns in America. Ideal location for weddings and retreats. Discounts to ministers.

Hosts: Paul and Jean Cowell
Rooms: 21 (21PB) $150–260
Full Breakfast
Credit Cards: A B C D
Notes: 2 3 4 5 7 8 9 10 12

Woodland Cove Bed and Breakfast

P. O. Box 791, Kingston, TN 37763
(865) 717-3719; (877) 700-2683
E-mail: woodlandcove@earthlink.net
Web site: www.woodlandcovebb.com

Woodland Cove

Come visit romantic, secluded Woodland Cove B & B on beautiful Watts Bar Lake in Kingston, Tennessee. Amenities include three guest rooms with private baths, piped-in music, and cable television provided in a smoke-free environment. Snacks and drinks in the Butler's Pantry are available 24 hours a day, plus a full gourmet breakfast. Canoes and paddleboats are provided for our guests on the lake. Fishing, swimming, and bird-watching are available for our visitors, as well. Experience a totally relaxing getaway!

Hosts: Bruce and Della Marshall
Rooms: 3 (3PB) $95–125
Full Breakfast
Credit Cards: A B D
Notes: 2 5 7 9 10 12

KNOXVILLE

Maplehurst Inn Bed and Breakfast

800 W. Hill Ave., Knoxville, TN 37920
(865) 523-7773; (800) 451-1562

E-mail: sonny@maplehurstinn.com
Web site: www.maplehurstinn.com

Maplehurst Inn

This lovely 84-year-old mansion is located right in downtown Knoxville in historic Maplehurst Park. Comfortable walking distance to over 30 restaurants, 3 museums, convention center, historic properties, etc. Our unique European-style B & B on the hill overlooking the Tennessee River blends 18th-century charm with modern amenities.

Hosts: Sonny and Becky Harben
Rooms: 11 (11PB) $69–149
Full Breakfast
Credit Cards: A B
Notes: 2 5 6 7 8 12

LYNCHBURG

Lynchburg B & B

P. O. Box 34, Lynchburg, TN 37352-0034
(931) 759-7158
E-mail: lynchburgbb@cafes.net
Web site: www.bbonline.com/tn/lynchburg/

Lynchburg

The atmosphere of this two-story home (circa 1877) provides relaxation and enjoyment in a small, historic town. Each room is decorated with antiques. Within walking distance to the Jack Daniels Distillery, shopping, restaurants, and downtown area. Big front porch for a quiet afternoon. View of beautiful hills.

Host: Virginia Tipps
Rooms: 3 (3PB) $68–78
Continental Breakfast
Credit Cards: A B
Notes: 2 5 7 9 10

MEMPHIS

The Bridgewater House

7015 Raleigh Lagrange Rd.
   Cordova, TN 38018-4223
(901) 384-0080; (800) 466-1001
   Fax (901) 72-3413
E-mail: mistilis@bellsouth.net
Web site: www.bbonline.com/tn/bridgewater

The Bridgewater House is a Greek Revival home converted from a schoolhouse that is more than 100 years old. It is a lovely, elegant dwelling filled with remembrances of travels, antiques, family heirlooms, and Oriental rugs. The Bridgewater House has original hardwood floors cut from trees on the property, enormous rooms, high ceilings, leaded-glass windows, and deep, hand-marbled moldings. There are two spacious bedrooms with private baths. The owners are a certified chef and executive chef and will serve a full gourmet breakfast and pamper guests with refreshments upon arriving. The house is located 1 mile from the largest city park in the United

---

6 Pets welcome; 7 Children welcome; 8 Tennis nearby; 9 Swimming nearby; 10 Golf nearby; 11 Skiing nearby; 12 May be booked through travel agent

States, which offers sailing, walking, and biking trails, horseback riding, fishing, canoeing, and more.

Hosts: Steve and Katherine Mistilis
Rooms: 2 (2PB) $110
Full Breakfast
Credit Cards: A B D
Notes: 2 5 8 10

MONTEAGLE

Adams Edgeworth Inn

Cottage 23, Monteagle Assembly
   Monteagle, TN 37403
(931) 924-4000; 1-87 RELAXINN
   Fax (931) 924-3236
E-mail: innjoy@blomand.com
Web site: www.relaxinn.com

Circa 1896, the Adams Edgeworth Inn celebrates a century of fine lodging and still is a leader in elegance and quality. Recently refurbished in country chintz decor, the inn is a comfortable refuge of fine antiques, original paintings, and quaint atmosphere. Historic Chautauqua Inn and Grounds with summer "season" of lectures, art, and music. Stroll through the 96-acre private Victorian village that surrounds the inn, or drive 6 miles to the Gothic campus of Sewanee, University of the South. Cultural activities year-round. Nearby are 150 miles of hiking trails, scenic vistas, and waterfalls, as well as tennis, swimming, golf, and riding. Fine candlelight dining. "One of the best inns I've ever visited anywhere. . ." (Sara Pitzer, recommended by "Country Inns" in *Country Inns Magazine*). Top 54 Inns of America—*National Geographic Traveler.*

Adams Edgeworth Inn

Rooms: 12 (12PB) $125–195
Full Breakfast
Credit Cards: A B C
Notes: 2 4 5 7 8 9 10 12

MOORESBURG

The Home Place B & B

132 Church Ln., Mooresburg, TN 37811-2208
(423) 921-8424; (800) 521-8424
   Fax (423) 921-8003
E-mail: prisrogers@charter.net
Web site: www.homeplacebb.com

Home Place

"Like going to Grandma's house," is how guests describe this B & B near Cherokee Lake in rural Tennessee. Built in the early 1800s by the host's ancestors, the house is furnished with family heirlooms but also has modern conveniences. All four guest rooms have a TV/VCR and a telephone. One suite features a Jacuzzi tub. A refriger-

---

NOTES: Credit cards accepted: A Master Card; B Visa; C American Express; D Discover; E Diners Club; F Other; 2 Personal checks accepted; 3 Lunch available; 4 Dinner available; 5

ator and microwave are available for guest use. Children are welcome. The first floor is accessible for guests with disabilities.

Host: Priscilla Rogers
Rooms: 4 (2PB;2SB) $45–65
Full Breakfast
Credit Cards: A B C D E
Notes: 2 5 7 10 12

MOUNTAIN CITY

Iron Mountain Inn B & B and Creekside Chalet

138 Moreland Dr., Butler, TN 37640
(423) 768-2446; (888) 781-2399
   Fax (423) 768-2451
E-mail: ironmtn@preferred.com
Web site: www.ironmountaininn.com

Iron Mountain Inn

Retreat to the mountains—lie back and stretch out in your private hot tub on the wrap-around decks of "The West Wing," a creekside chalet, or enjoy "Pampering Perfected" service atop the mountain at the inn.

Host: Vikki Woods
Rooms: 7 (5PB;2SB) $140–250
Full Breakfast
Credit Cards: A B C D
Notes: 2 3 4 5 6 7 9 10 11 12

Prospect Hill B & B Inn

801 W. Main St., Mountain City, TN 37683
(423) 727-0139; (800) 339-3084
E-mail: chtn@prospect-hill.com
Web site: www.prospect-hill.com

Hospitality and history set Prospect Hill apart. Huge rooms offer king and queen beds, whirlpool tubs for two, "traditional" furnishings that are never "stuffy." Enjoy robes, generous snack baskets, in-room TV, individual climate controls, and scented candles. Add a Celebration Package with a small cake, flowers, wine, and dinner for two at a fine local restaurant. Explore the Blue Ridge's many hidden treasures less than 1 hour away, or enjoy the three-state view from our porches.

Hosts: Robert and Judy Hotchkiss
Rooms: 5 (5PB) $79–200
Full Breakfast
Credit Cards: A B C D E F
Notes: 2 5 7 9 10 11 12

NASHVILLE

Carriage Lane Inn

411 N. Maney Ave., Murfreesboro, TN 37130
(615) 890-3630; (800) 357-2827
   Fax (615) 893-5707
E-mail: info@carriagelaneinn.com
Web site: www.carriagelaneinn.com

Treat your lover to a fanciful weekend full of romance, seclusion, and relaxation. After dining on a private four-course candlelit dinner, walk into your room full of roses, candles, the fireplace going, soft music, a whirlpool bathtub of scented water, massage oils, champagne, imported chocolates, and fresh fruit. A lovely home located in

---

6 Pets welcome; 7 Children welcome; 8 Tennis nearby; 9 Swimming nearby; 10 Golf nearby; 11 Skiing nearby; 12 May be booked through travel agent

the historic district close to shopping and restaurants downtown.

Carriage Lane Inn

Host: Sharon Petty
Rooms: 7 (7PB) $105–135
Full Breakfast
Credit Cards: A B C D
Notes: 2 4 5 10

Peacock Hill Country Inn

6994 Giles Hill Rd., College Grove, TN 37046
(615) 368-7727; (800) 327-6663
    Fax (615) 368-7933
Web site: www.peacockhillinn.com

Ten luxury accomodations on a 1000-acre working cattle farm, convenient to Franklin and Nashville. The complex includes a historic 1850s farmhouse, a two-story log cabin suite, a two-level granary suite, and the new/old McCaul House. All rooms and suites with king beds and private baths. Rooms available with whirlpools, European showers, and fireplaces. Candlelight dinners and box lunches available by reservation. Rated 4-diamond by AAA, Member Select Registry. Featured in *Country Inns Magazine, National Geographic Travel, Living Romantic Homes* and *Travel Holiday*. Nonsmoking facility. Pets welcome outside. Lunch and dinner available with advance reservations.

Hosts: Walter and Anita Ogilvie
Rooms: 10 (10PB) $135–245
Full Breakfast
Credit Cards: A B C D
Notes: 2 3 4 5 8 9 10 12

Rockhaven Cottage

147 Mires Rd., Mount Juliet, TN 37122-4210
(615) 449-5227; (866) 500-3802
E-mail: rockhavencabin@aol.com

Near Nashville, brand-new secluded cottage nestled among the trees on 10 private acres just off I-40 East. This one-bedroom, one-bath cottage has a whirlpool tub, queen bed, fully equipped kitchen, cable TV, porch swing, and a beautiful fishpond. Continental breakfast provided. Near lake, walking trails, restaurants, and shopping. Five minutes from 18-hole golf course. Open all year.

Hosts: Rhonda and Nate Powell
Rooms: 1 (1PB) $89
Continental Breakfast
Credit Cards:
Notes: 2 5 9 10 12

PIGEON FORGE

Huckleberry Inn

1754 Sandstone Way, Sevierville, TN 37876
(865) 428-2475; (800) 704-3278
E-mail: hberryinn@aol.com
Web site: www.bbonline.com/tn/huckleberry

Rustic, hand-built log inn secluded in the heart of the Great Smoky Mountains. Queen rooms with antiques, private baths, whirlpool tubs, and fireplaces. Screened porches with rocking chairs and mountain views! Full breakfast served each morning in the country kitchen by the stone fireplace or on the back porch listening to the birds sing. Let us help you relax, renew, and rejuvenate your spirit!

Host: Karan Bailey
Rooms: 3 (3PB) $89–109
Full Breakfast
Credit Cards: A B
Notes: 2 5 9 10 11

PIKEVILLE

Fall Creek Falls B & B Inn

R. R. 3, Box 298 B, Pikeville, TN 37367-9315
(423) 881-5494; Fax (423) 881-5040
E-mail: fcfbandb@bledsoe.net
Web site: www.fallcreekfalls.com

Fall Creek Falls

Elegant mountain inn featured in the August '94 *Tennessee* magazine and August '96 *Country* magazine. Seven guest rooms and one suite, all with private baths and air-conditioning. Some rooms have heart-shaped whirlpools and fireplaces. Victorian or country decor. One mile from nationally acclaimed Fall Creek Falls State Resort Park. Beautiful mountains, waterfalls, golfing, boating, fishing, tennis, hiking, horseback riding, and biking trails. AAA-rated. No smok-

ing. Full breakfast. Romantic, scenic, and quiet.

Hosts: Doug and Rita Pruett
Rooms: 8 (8PB) $79–143
Full Breakfast
Credit Cards: A B C D
Notes: 2 8 9 10 12

RED BOILING SPRINGS

Donoho Hotel

500 E. Main St., Red Boiling Springs, TN 37150
(615) 699-3141; (800) 799-1705
    Fax (615) 890-8289
E-mail: jefgapts@bellsouth.net
Web site: www.thedonohohotel.com

Steeped in tradition, the Donoho Hotel retains an atmosphere carried over from a century of entertaining guests in Red Boiling Springs, TN. Originally designed to cater to those drawn by the famous "healing powers of the springs," the Donoho has, over the years, evolved to the full-service hotel and restaurant status it enjoys today. The large, two-story wooden structure features wrap-around porches on both levels, with an abundance of antique rocking chairs.

Hosts: Robert and Pauline Stroop
Rooms: 36 (36PB) $62–95
Full Breakfast
Credit Cards: A
Notes: 3 4 7 9

SEVIERVILLE

Bonny Brook
Bed and Breakfast

2301 Wears Valley Rd., Sevierville, TN 37862
(865) 908-4745; Fax (865) 908-4745

---

6 Pets welcome; 7 Children welcome; 8 Tennis nearby; 9 Swimming nearby; 10 Golf nearby; 11 Skiing nearby; 12 May be booked through travel agent

E-mail: bonnybrookbb@msn.com
Web site: www.bonnybrook.net

"Rest and Be Thankful" at Bonny Brook Bed and Breakfast, a cozy inn tucked into the woods beside a cascading stream in the Smoky Mountains. Bonny Brook highlights the Scots-Irish heritage of the area as well as its natural beauty. Its peaceful location gives you privacy yet is highly convenient to the Great Smoky Mountains National Park, Gatlinburg, Pigeon Forge, Townsend, and Dollywood.

Host: A C Thomason
Rooms: 2 (2PB) $125–135
Full Breakfast
Credit Cards: A B
Notes: 2 5 10

Calico Inn

757 Ranch Way, Sevierville, TN 37862-4729
(865) 428-3833; (800) 235-1054
E-mail: calicoinn@aol.com
Web site: www.calico-inn.com

Calico Inn

Voted "Inn of the Year." The Calico Inn is located in the Smoky Mountains near Gatlinburg and Dollywood. It is an authentic log inn with touches of elegance. Decorated with antiques, collectibles, and country charm. Enjoy the spectacular mountain view, surrounded by 25 acres of peace and tranquility. Minutes from fine dining, live enter-

tainment shows, shopping, hiking, fishing, golf, horseback riding, and all other attractions the area has to offer, yet completely secluded.

Hosts: Lill and Jim Katzbeck
Rooms: 3 (3PB) $99–115
Full Breakfast
Credit Cards: A B
Notes: 2 5 7 8 9 10 11 12

Grandma's House

734 Pollard Rd., Kodak, TN 37764-0445
(865) 932-9942; (800) 676-3512
    Fax (865) 933-0748
E-mail: hildaimaj1@aol.com

Grandma's House

Grandma's House was built in 1989 at the base of the Great Smoky Mountains in beautiful Dumplin Valley. Owners Charlie and Hilda Hickman are native East Tennesseans. The area is alive with activity; however, peace and tranquility await at Grandma's House. Decorated with cozy quilts, heirloom antiques, and Hilda's artwork and crafts. As you walk up to the door of this Colonial-style home, childhood memories of visiting your own grandmother will come flooding back.

Hosts: Charlie and Hilda Hickman
Rooms: 3 (3PB) $75–90
Full Breakfast
Credit Cards:
Notes: 2 5   9 10 11

NOTES: Credit cards accepted: A Master Card; B Visa; C American Express; D Discover; E Diners Club; F Other; 2 Personal checks accepted; 3 Lunch available; 4 Dinner available; 5

Little Greenbrier Lodge

3685 Lyon Springs Rd.
  Sevierville, TN 37862-8257
(865) 429-2500; (800) 277-8100
  Fax (865) 429-4093
E-mail: littlegreenbrier@worldnet.att.net
Web site: www.littlegreenbrierlodge.com

Borders national park entrance.
Historic lodge on mountainside overlooks beautiful Wears Valley in the
Great Smoky Mountains. Antique
decor, very secluded and peaceful.
Great hiking. The aroma of hot pecan
pull-apart bread is mouthwatering.
Just 150 yards from hiking trails. Or
rock on the porch with a lemonade
and a great book.

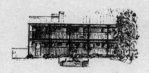

Little Greenbrier Lodge

Hosts: Susan and Charles Lebon
Rooms: 9 (9PB) $100–125
Full Breakfast
Credit Cards: A B D
Notes: 2   5   9   10   11   12

TOWNSEND

Gracehill

1169 Little Round Top Way, Townsend, TN 37882
(865) 448-3070; (866) 448-3070
  Fax (865) 448-3077
E-mail: visit@gracehillbandb.com
Web site: www.gracehillbandb.com

Welcome to Gracehill, two years in the
making, newly opened Thanksgiving

2000. Warm hospitality and attention
to detail are our trademark. The atmosphere is gracious and the amenities are
luxurious. Gracehill is the highest
home/accommodations in the county
at 2500 feet. It sits adjacent to the
Great Smoky Mountains National
Park, and the view is 360 degrees overlooking Blount and Sevier Counties
and the mountains of the national park.

Host: Kathleen Janke
Rooms: 4 (4PB) $200–300
Full Breakfast
Credit Cards: A B C
Notes: 2 3 4 5 9 10 11 12

---

6 Pets welcome; 7 Children welcome; 8 Tennis nearby; 9 Swimming nearby; 10 Golf nearby; 11
Skiing nearby; 12 May be booked through travel agent

TEXAS

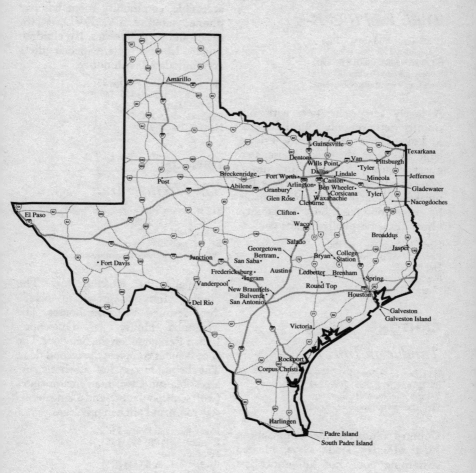

Amarillo

Gainesville
Denton
Wills Point · Van
Texarkana
Tyler · Pittsburgh
Breckenridge · Fort Worth Dallas Lindale
Jefferson
Post Abilene Arlington Canton Mineola
Gladewater
Granbury Ben Wheeler · Corsicana Tyler
Glen Rose Waxahachie
Nacogdoches
Cleburne

Clifton

El Paso Waco

Salado
Broaddus

Georgetown
Bertram · Jasper
Fort Davis Junction San Saba · Bryan College
Fredericksburg · Ingram Station
Vanderpool Austin · Ledbetter Brenham
New Braunfels Round Top Spring
Del Rio Bulverde · Houston
San Antonio
Galveston
Galveston Island

Victoria

Rockport
Corpus Christi

Harlingen
Padre Island
South Padre Island

Texas

AUSTIN

Trails End B & B

16708 Trails End Cove,
   Leander, TX 78641-9681
(512) 267-2901; (800) 850-2901
E-mail: jpjobnb@aol.com
Web site: www.trailsendbb.com

A lovely serene location with hill country views yet only a short distance to Lake Travis and the city. Private large rooms in the main house, two guest houses, a swimming pool, gazebo, and bicycles. We serve a full breakfast. Lunch and dinner available by reservation and host availability. Great Texas hospitality awaits you!

Hosts: Jo Ann and Tom Patty
Rooms: 5 (5PB) $85–125 plus tax
Full Breakfast
Credit Cards: A B C D E
Notes: 2 3 4 5 7 8 9 10 11 12

CANTON

Tumble on Inn

P. O. Box 1249, Van, TX 75790-1249
(903) 963-7669; (888) 707-3992
E-mail: info@tumbleoninn.com
Web site: www.tumbleoninn.com

Country comfort 8 miles from Canton First Monday Trade Days. Heated swimming pool, hot tub under the stars, game room with pool table and electronic darts. Perfect getaway for the urbanly overdosed. Bunkhouse for large groups sleeps 12 for $530 one night, $795 two nights. Handicapped accessible, community room has pay phone, satellite TV, DVD, VHS, music and book libraries. No children under 12, no pets. Special diets accommodated with notice.

Hosts: Gorden and Jean Jensen
Rooms: 6 (4PB;2SB) $75–140
Full Breakfast
Credit Cards: A B C D
Notes: 2 3 4 5 8 9 10

DENTON

The Heritage Inns

815 N. Locust St., Denton, TX 76201-2952
(940) 565-6414; (888) 565-6414
   Fax (940) 565-6515
E-mail: redbudbb@gte.net
Web site: www.theheritageinns.com

Originally the Redbud Inn. The Heritage Inns has grown to include three restored Victorian houses. The Magnolia House has Guiseppe's Italian Restaurant on the first floor. The B & B suites complete the second floor. The Pecan House has a wheelchair-accessible suite, two honeymoon suites (with whirlpool tubs), and a long-term-stay room and kitchen privileges.

Hosts: John and Donna Morris
Rooms: 11 (11PB) $65–135
Full Breakfast
Credit Cards: A B C D F
Notes: 2 3 4 5 7 9 10 12

NOTES: Credit cards accepted: A Master Card; B Visa; C American Express; D Discover; E Diners Club; F Other; 2 Personal checks accepted; 3 Lunch available; 4 Dinner available; 5 Open all year;

FORT WORTH

The Texas White House

1417 8th Ave., Fort Worth, TX 76104-4111
(817) 923-3597; (800) 279-6491
  Fax (817) 923-0410
E-mail: txwhitehou@aol.com
Web site: www.texaswhitehouse.com

Historically designated, award-winning, Country-style home has been restored to its original 1910 grandeur of simple, yet elegant decor. It is centrally located, within 5 minutes of downtown and Sundance Square, the Bass Performance Hall, TCU, and the Kimbell Art Museum. Each room contains a luxurious queen-sized bed with your choice of pillows. Three guest rooms in the house all have relaxing sitting areas and private baths with claw-footed tubs for shower or baths. The carriage house has two suites; the first floor sleeps up to 4 adults in two separate rooms, has a fireplace, hot tub, and is handicapped accessible; the second floor sleeps two and contains a hot tub and sauna. Breakfast, described by one of the guests as "fit for visiting royalty," may be served in either the dining room or to your room and will be a gourmet treat with fresh fruit or baked fruit in compote (seasonal), baked egg casseroles, and homemade breads and muffins, juices, coffee or tea.

Hosts: Jamie and Grover McMains
Rooms: 3 (3PB) $105–185
Full Breakfast
Credit Cards: A B C D E F
Notes: 2 5 10 12

FREDERICKSBURG

Magnolia House

101 E. Hackberry St.
  Fredericksburg, TX 78624-3915
(830) 997-0306; (800) 880-4374
  Fax (830) 997-0766
E-mail: magnolia@hetc.net
Web site: www.magnolia-house.com

Magnolia House

Built circa 1923, restored in 1991. Enjoy Southern hospitality in a grand and gracious manner. Outside are lovely magnolias and a bubbling fishpond. Inside, a beautiful living room and formal dining room provide areas for guests to mingle. There are two romantic suites with fireplaces and three rooms—all appointed with your comfort in mind. You'll find a relaxing patio and porches. The beautiful, bountiful breakfast makes this a truly memorable experience.

Hosts: Dee and David Lawford
Rooms: 5 (5PB) $95–140
Full Breakfast
Credit Cards: A B C D
Notes: 2 5 8 9 10

Schmidt Barn B & B

231 W. Main St., C/O Reservation Service
  Fredericksburg, TX 78624
(830) 997-5612; (866) 427-8374
  Fax (830) 997-8282
E-mail: schmidtbarn@fbg.net
Web site: www.schmidtbarn.com

---

6 Pets welcome; 7 Children welcome; 8 Tennis nearby; 9 Swimming nearby; 10 Golf nearby; 11 Skiing nearby; 12 May be booked through travel agent

Schmidt Barn

Schmidt Barn is located 1 1/2 miles outside historic Fredericksburg. The 1860s limestone structure has been turned into a charming guest house with a loft bedroom, living room, bath, and kitchen. Decorated with antiques. Hosts live next door. German-style breakfast is left in the guest house for you. The Barn has been featured in *Country Living, Travel and Leisure,* and *Country Accents* (cover story May–June 2000), also featured in *Country Almanac* (fall 2001). A member of Historic and Hospitality Accommodations of Texas. A B & B since 1980!

Hosts: Charles and Loretta Schmidt
Rooms: 1 (1PB) $95
Continental Breakfast
Credit Cards: A B D F
Notes: 2 5 6 7 8 9 10 12

A Way of the Wolf B & B / Retreat

458 Wolf Way, Fredericksburg, TX 78624
(830) 997-0711; (888) 929-9653
E-mail: wawolf@ktc.com
Web site: www.wayofthewolf.com

B & B/Retreat Center on restful 61 acres. Swimming pool. Accommodations: four-bedroom guest house with central living area and kitchen; romantic Civil War cabin with mini-kitchen, fireplace; reconstructed Amish barn with loft room and room at original crib level, both large bedrooms with mini-kitchens. All units have porches, heat and air-conditioning, furnished with antiques. Fredericksburg and Kerrville 15 minutes away. Assistance available for individual or group retreats. Log chapel on site.

Hosts: Ron and Karen Poidevin
Rooms: 7 (5PB;2SB) $85–160
Full Breakfast
Credit Cards:
Notes: 2 5 8 9 10

GAINESVILLE

Alexander B & B Acres, Inc.

3692 Cty. Rd. 201, Gainesville, TX 76240-8623
(903) 564-7440; (800) 887-8794
    Fax (903) 564-7440
E-mail: abba@texoma.net
Web site: www.alexanderbnb.com

Three-story Queen Anne country home and guest house nestled on 65 acres of woods and meadows just south of Whitesboro between Lakes Texoma and Ray Roberts; near antiques, large outlet mall, ranches, farms, and a zoo. A full breakfast is included for main house guests, where different themes decorate each bedroom; dinners are available by arrangement. Relax on large porches, the gazebo, the back deck with swimming pool and hot tub, or walk our wooded trails. A third-floor suite can be a bedroom, conference area, or extra lodging for groups and includes a bar sink, dorm fridge, and microwave. Two-story guest house offers three bedrooms sharing 1 1/2 baths, complete kitchen

---

NOTES: Credit cards accepted: A Master Card; B Visa; C American Express; D Discover; E Diners Club; F Other; 2 Personal checks accepted; 3 Lunch available; 4 Dinner available; 5 Open all year;

and laundry, living area, and large screened porch. Children are welcome in guest house. Both houses are available for small retreats.

Hosts: Jim and Pamela Alexander
Rooms: 8 (5PB;3SB) $60–125
Full Breakfast
Credit Cards: A B C D
Notes: 2 4 5 7 9 10 11 12

GALVESTON

Coppersmith Inn Bed and Breakfast

1914 Ave. M, Galveston, TX 77550-4707
(409) 763-7004; (800) 515-7444
E-mail: coppersmithinn@att.net
Web site: www.coppersmithinn.com

Coppersmith Inn

Queen Anne-style home built in 1887 with five rooms and private baths. Three are located in the house; one in a separate cottage, and one in the carriage house. The inn boasts gingerbread trim, a double veranda, turret tower, spectacular winding staircase of teak, walnut, and curly pine highlighted by stained glass and ornate newel post, large windows with original glass, exquisite heirloom antiques, Victorian decorations with romantic themes, and interesting faux painting. Also two fireplaces, a claw-foot porcelain tub, an antique tin tub used in a Kenny Rogers movie with three shower heads, whirlpool tub, lovely landscaped gardens, large wooden deck and brick sidewalks, and a full country breakfast served family style in our dining room.

Hosts: Karen and Patrick Geary
Rooms: 5 (5PB) $94–170
Full Breakfast
Credit Cards: A B C D F
Notes: 2 5 7 8 9 10 12

GLEN ROSE

Bussey's Something Special B & B

P. O. Box 1425; 202 Hereford
Glen Rose, TX 76043-1425
(254) 897-4843; (877) 426-2233
Fax (254) 897-9881
E-mail: msbussey@busseys.net
Web site: www.busseys.net

The cozy Victorian cottage has a king bed, jet tub/shower, and kitchenette. We pamper our guests, and we treasure your children. In the Cajun/Cowboy Bunkhouse you'll find a full bed handmade by host's grandfather, rustic garden/wood furniture, a shower, and kitchen. All nestled in the heart of Glen Rose. Relax on the porch swing; take a leisurely stroll to the historic town square for shopping and lunch. Historic buildings and museums are close by. Walk to the river or explore the countryside to experience the heart of Texas. Free fossil treasure maps for guests! Hosts on the premises. Private guest houses attached.

Hosts: Susan and Morris Bussey

Rooms: 2 (2PB) $80–95
Continental Breakfast
Credit Cards: A B C D F
Notes: 2 5 7 8 9 10 12

HARLINGEN

Vieh's Bed and Breakfast

18413 Landrum Park Rd., San Benito, TX 78586
(956) 425-4651
E-mail: viehbb@aol.com
Web site: www.vieh.com

Vieh's B & B is your home away from home. Ours is a south Texas, ranch-style home with a Mexican flavor in a 5-acre palm grove. There is approximately a mile of bird-watching trail around a large lake at the back of the property. The landscaping includes two large butterfly gardens along with a collection of exotic palm trees.

Let us help make your south Texas visit enjoyable. Mi casa es su casa.

Hosts: Charles and Lana Vieh
Rooms: 5 (3PB;2SB) $75–95
Full Breakfast
Notes: 2 5 6 7 10 12

JEFFERSON

Old Mulberry Inn B & B

209 Jefferson St., Jefferson, TX 75657
(903) 665-1945; (800) 263-5319
    Fax (903) 665-9123
E-mail: mulberry@jeffersontx.com
Web site: www.oldmulberryinn.com

Featured in *Southern Living*, this gracious inn is built in the style of Jefferson's finest antebellum homes. Relax in the Jacuzzi for two in the rustic but romantic Fishing Room, or choose from four other dramatically decorated rooms. Private baths feature footed tubs and showers. Linger by the library's fireplace or swing on the porch overlooking the garden and the oldest mulberry tree in town. Gourmet three-course breakfast. Homemade biscotti and cookies. Complimentary beverages. Cable TV/VCR. AAA 3-diamonds.

Old Mulberry Inn

Hosts: Donald and Gloria Degn
Rooms: 5 (5PB) $89–169
Full Breakfast
Credit Cards: A B C D
Notes: 2 5 9

Urquhart House of Eleven Gables

301 E. Walker St., Jefferson, TX 75657-1741
(903) 665-8442; (888) 922-8442
E-mail: joycejacks@aol.com
Web site: www.urquharthouse.com

The Urquhart House of Eleven Gables B & B is an experience of luxuries and historical elegance. Turn-of-the-century quality of life comes alive with period decor and antiques. Further creating the yesteryear ambience are equestrian carriages and wag-

NOTES: Credit cards accepted: A Master Card; B Visa; C American Express; D Discover; E Diners Club; F Other; 2 Personal checks accepted; 3 Lunch available; 4 Dinner available; 5 Open all year;

ons clip-clopping the street that fronts the wrap-around porch of this expansive 1890 Queen Anne house located in Jefferson, the "Most Visited Small Town in Texas." Relax with in-room TV, VCR, and a wide selection of vintage and late-release videos.

Host: Joyce Jackson
Rooms: 2 (2PB) $85–130
Full Breakfast
Credit Cards: A B C D E
Notes: 2 5 10 12

KERRVILLE

Mount Horeb House

140 Loma Vuelta, Kerrville, TX 78028
(830) 895-5515; (866) 895-5515
E-mail: gasthaus@ktc.com
Web site: www.fbglodging.com

Completely private cottage nestled beneath ancient oaks in a hill country garden setting just minutes from downtown Kerrville. Enjoy the screened front porch, the garden courtyard, or the walking paths.

Hosts: Dan and Ann Geroy
Rooms: 1 (1PB) $85
Continental Breakfast
Credit Cards: A B C D
Notes: 5   8 9 10

LEDBETTER

Ledbetter B & B

100 Hwy. 290, P. O. Box 212
   Ledbetter, TX 78946
(979) 249-3066; (800) 240-3066
   Fax (979) 249-3330
E-mail: jjervis@fais.net
Web site: www.ledbetter-tx.com

Ledbetter B & B, established in 1988, is a collection of multigeneration family. 1800–1900s homes within walking distance of the remaining 1870s downtown businesses. A full country breakfast buffet can serve 60 guests daily. Enjoy walks, fishing, birding, cookouts, games, indoor swimming, VCR/TV. A phone upon request. Ideal for reunions and retreats!

Hosts: Chris and Jay Jervis
Rooms: 16 (15PB;2SB) $75–105
Full Breakfast
Credit Cards: A B C
Notes: 2 3 4 5 7 8 9 10 11 12

MARBLE FALLS

The Coleman Garden Place

P. O. Box 695, Marble Falls, TX 78654
(830) 798-2911
Web site: www.colemangardenplace.com

Stroll leisurely around the gardens. Unwind on peaceful walking trails. Revel in the sunset from a porch or deck. Whatever relaxation means to you, you will find it at the Garden Place. Each morning at the Garden Place includes June's bountiful country breakfast, truly a feast for all the senses. "A delicious extravagance." (K.G., Dallas) The Carriage House: Offering best views. Two upstairs bedrooms, each w/queen-size bed and a private bath.

Hamilton House: A one-story building, wheelchair accessible. It accommodates up to 5 adult guests or a couple w/3 children; the living room sofa makes into a king-size bed or two

---

6 Pets welcome; 7 Children welcome; 8 Tennis nearby; 9 Swimming nearby; 10 Golf nearby; 11 Skiing nearby; 12 May be booked through travel agent

twins. The Murphy bed, when opened, sleeps 2 adults or 2 children.

Coleman Main House: If a group needs more space, we offer two rooms with private baths located upstairs in our home. These rooms are not available unless one group rents all our guest accommodations and still needs two more rooms. Each room has its own unique reading room.

Hosts: June and Carl Coleman
Rooms: 4 (4PB) $75–110
Full Breakfast
Credit Cards:
Notes: 2 8 9 10 11

MINEOLA

The Lott Home Bed and Breakfast

311 E. Kilpatrick St., Mineola, TX 75773
(903) 569-0341; (888) 232-5688
  Fax (903) 569-9805
E-mail: lotthomecottages@tyler.net
Web site: www.lotthomecottages.com

The Lott Home, circa 1918, is a beautiful example of Southern architecture. Innkeepers Mark and Sharon Chamblee purchased the home in 1992 and have painstakingly restored it. The Lott Home is only two blocks from historic downtown Mineola. Treat yourself to an unforgettable night in one of our large, comfortable suites. Relive a moment in time and take home wonderful memories.

Hosts: Mark and Sharon Chamblee
Rooms: 2 (2PB) $95–115
Full Breakfast
Credit Cards: A B C D
Notes: 2 5 8 10

NACOGDOCHES

Anderson Point B & B

29 East Lake Estates, Nacogdoches, TX 75964
(936) 569-7445
E-mail: anderpt@txucom.net
Web site: www.andersonpoint.com

Anderson Point

You won't want to leave this lovely, two-story, French-style home surrounded by 300 feet of lake frontage. Enjoy sweeping views of the water from every room and a double veranda for dining and dozing. You can stroll around the beautiful grounds or go fishing off the pier. Don't miss the glorious sunsets as you gather in the fireplace sitting room for coffee and conversation. A full breakfast is served every morning inside or out on the veranda. A private boat launch is available (excellent fishing). Enjoy a weekend on golden pond.

Host: Rachel Anderson
Rooms: 3 (1PB;2SB) $75–95
Full Breakfast
Credit Cards: A B
Notes: 2 5 6 9 12

Pine Creek Lodge

341 Pine Creek Rd., Nacogdoches, TX 75964-7017
(936) 560-6282; (888) 714-1414
  Fax (936) 560-1675
E-mail: pitts@lcc.net

NOTES: Credit cards accepted: A Master Card; B Visa; C American Express; D Discover; E Diners Club; F Other; 2 Personal checks accepted; 3 Lunch available; 4 Dinner available; 5 Open all year;

Web site: www.pinecreeklodge.com

Located on a beautifully wooded 140-acre property in the heart of east Texas, on the bend of a flowing creek. Pine Creek Lodge offers 19 lovely guest rooms. Most have king beds; all have private baths. Amenities include: AC, ceiling fans, TV/VCR, refrigerators, coffeepots, decks w/swings and rockers, monogrammed robes, delicious food, pool, hot tubs, fishing ponds, driving range, walking trail, common areas.

Hosts: The Pitts Family
Rooms: 19 (19PB) $65–150
Full Breakfast
Credit Cards: A B C D
Notes: 2 3 4 5 7 9 10

NEW BRAUNFELS

Hunter Road Stagecoach Stop

5541 F M 1102, New Braunfels, TX 78132
(830) 620-9453; (800) 201-2912
E-mail: stagecoach@satx.rr.com
Web site: www.stagecoachbedandbreakfast.com

This historic inn enchants you with an ambience of the past while maintaining today's comforts. The proprietors, one of whom is a landscape designer, personally welcome you to come and enjoy the picturesque grounds of antique roses, herbs, and native plants. The Log Pen Cabin and German Fachwerk barn, both erected in the mid-1800s, were once used as a stagecoach stop. The cabins have antique claw-foot tubs or a Jacuzzi and separate tile showers. Rooms are romantic, private retreats with queen-size bedding and porches

surrounded by herbs, flowers, trees, birds, and bees. Gourmet breakfast entrees include ripened fruit, homemade breads, eggs, potato pancakes, New Braunfels' sausage, or our specialty—cottage cheese lemon pancakes served with fresh raspberries.

Hosts: Bettina and Jeff Messinger
Rooms: 4 (4PB) $105–145
Full Breakfast
Credit Cards: A B C
Notes: 2 7 10 12

PITTSBURG

Carson House Inn and Grille and Mrs. B's Cottage

302 Mount Pleasant St.
  Pittsburg, TX 75686-1335
(903) 856-2468; (888) 302-1878
  Fax (903) 856-0709
E-mail: mailus@carsonhouse.com
Web site: www.carsonhouse.com

Carson House

Nestled in the piney woods of east Texas, this luxurious six-room Victorian inn built in 1878 takes you back in time while providing modern amenities and private baths. The Grille, located in the main house, has been acclaimed "one of East Texas's finest casually elegant restaurants."

Visitors to the inn enjoy a slower pace, friendly staff, gourmet restaurant, two hot tubs, and a small-town atmosphere, which revives the busiest people. Relaxation is assured!

Hosts: Eileen and Clark Jesmore
Rooms: 8 (6PB;2SB) $75–85
Full Breakfast
Credit Cards: A B C D E
Notes: 2 3 4 5 7 9 10

POST

Hotel Garza Historic Bed and Breakfast

302 E. Main St., Post, TX 79356-3339
(806) 495-3962
Web site: www.bbhost.com/hotelgarza

When you check into Hotel Garza, you'll experience the ambience of a 1915 western inn. More than 80 years later, with modern conveniences, this fine establishment offers overnight accommodations, wonderful home cooking, and Texas hospitality. Post is a Texas Main Street city founded by cereal king C.W. Post. Within walking distance of Hotel Garza, you'll find theaters, museums, fine gift shops, boutiques, and Old Mill Trade Days. A new guest cottage is now available. Come enjoy the waterfall garden.

Hosts: Jim and Janice Plummer
Rooms: 4 (4PB) $85–125
Full Breakfast
Credit Cards: A B
Notes: 2 5 7 8 9 10 12

SALADO

Inn at Salado

7 N. Main St., P. O. Box 320, Salado, TX 76571
(254) 947-0027; (800) 724-0027
  Fax (254) 947-3144
E-mail: rooms@inn-at-salado.com
Web site: www.inn-at-salado.com

Salado's first bed and breakfast is located in the heart of the historic district. Restored to its original 1872 splendor, the inn displays both a Texas historical marker and a National Register listing. The inn's ambience is enhanced by its antique furniture, porch swings, and live oak trees, all on 2 beautifully landscaped acres. A wedding chapel, meeting rooms, and catering complete the amenities offered by the inn.

Hosts: Rob and Suzanne Petro
Rooms: 8 (8PB) $70–160
Full Breakfast
Credit Cards: A B C D
Notes: 2 5 9 10

SAN ANTONIO

The Oge' House Inn on the Riverwalk

209 Washington St., San Antonio, TX 78204
(210) 223-2353; (800) 242-2770
  Fax (210) 226-5812
E-mail: ogeinn@swbell.net
Web site: www.ogeinn.com

This elegant, historic antebellum mansion is privately located on 1 1/2 landscaped acres along the famous Riverwalk. The inn is decorated in European antiques. A gourmet breakfast is served on Wedgwood china with

---

NOTES: Credit cards accepted: A Master Card; B Visa; C American Express; D Discover; E Diners Club; F Other; 2 Personal checks accepted; 3 Lunch available; 4 Dinner available; 5 Open all year;

silver and crystal. For business or pleasure, come enjoy quiet comfort and luxury. Mobil Select Registry Excellent.

Hosts: Sharrie and Patrick Magatagan
Rooms: 10 (10PB;0SB) $110–325
Full Breakfast
Credit Cards: A B C D E
Notes: 2 3 4 5 6 7 8 9 10 11 12

A Victorian Lady Inn

421 Howard St., San Antonio, TX 78212-5531
(210) 224-2524; (800) 879-7116
    Fax (210) 224-5123
E-mail: info@viclady.com
Web site: www.viclady.com

A Victorian Lady Inn

Elegant 1898 historic mansion offers some of the most spacious guest rooms in San Antonio! Well-appointed rooms include period antiques, high-back beds, sitting areas, porches, fireplaces, Jacuzzis, garden tubs, and wet bars. Full breakfast served daily in the grand dining room. Relax in the crystal blue pool surrounded by tropical palms. The Riverwalk, Alamo, Convention Center, and trolley are just blocks away. Free parking, free local calls, complimentary trolley passes.

Hosts: Joe and Kate Bowski
Rooms: 10 (10PB) $89–135
Full Breakfast
Credit Cards: A B C D
Notes: 2 5 8 9 10

SOUTH PADRE ISLAND

Brown Pelican Inn

P. O. Box 2667; 207 W. Aries
    South Padre Island, TX 78597-2667
(956) 761-2722; Fax (956) 761-8683
E-mail: innkeeper@brownpelican.com
Web site: www.brownpelican.com

The Brown Pelican offers some of the finest accommodations in south Texas. Situated on the quiet bay shoreline of this famed island, the inn boasts eight elegant and spotless guest rooms appointed with American and English antiques. Each with a private bath. Several rooms have spectacular bay views, and the covered porch is a favorite vantage point to experience a Texas sunset like you have never before seen.

Brown Pelican Inn

Hosts: Chris and Yves De Diesbach
Rooms: 8 (8PB) $100–150
Full Breakfast
Credit Cards: A B C D F
Notes: 2 5 9 10

---

6 Pets welcome; 7 Children welcome; 8 Tennis nearby; 9 Swimming nearby; 10 Golf nearby; 11 Skiing nearby; 12 May be booked through travel agent

SPRING

McLachlan Farm B & B

P. O. Box 538 / 24907 Hardy Rd.
  Spring, TX 77383-0538
(281) 350-2400; (800) 382-3988
  Fax (281) 288-1011
E-mail: stay@macfarm.com
Web site: www.macfarm.com

Beautiful 1911 farmhouse with porches and swings, nestled among 50 acres of shade trees and walking trails. Three guest rooms in main house with queen beds, sitting area, TV/VCR, private bath, and country gourmet breakfast. Two loft suites with separate entrances, balconies, king beds, Jacuzzi tub, fireplace, TV/VCR, and stereo. Two large private suites with queen-size bed, queen sleeper sofa, fireplace, TV/VCR, and stereo. Large bath with Jacuzzi tub and shower. Gourmet country breakfast served in main house. Near Old Town Spring, with over 200 shops.

Hosts: Jim and Joycelyn Clairmonte
Rooms: 5 (3PB;2SB) $90–165
Full Breakfast
Credit Cards: A B C D
Notes: 2 5 10 12

TYLER

Rosevine Inn B & B

415 S. Vine Ave., Tyler, TX 75702-7942
(903) 592-2221; Fax (903) 592-5522
E-mail: rosevine@iamerica.net
Web site: www.rosevine.com

Rosevine Inn is a quaint two-story home complete with a white picket fence, located in the Brick Street district of Tyler. The inn offers many amenities, including a covered outdoor hot tub and a courtyard with both a fountain and a fireplace. In the lodge-style game room, you may enjoy billiards, lots of board-type games, cards, darts, and horseshoes, as well as volleyball and badminton. Outdoor fires are a common nightly occurrence. A full, formal breakfast includes omelettes or quiches, coffee cakes, muffins, fresh fruit, coffee, teas—more than you can eat! The hosts can direct you to great restaurants, antique shops, museums, lakes, the zoo, the rose garden, and sites in Tyler and the surrounding area.

Hosts: Bert and Rebecca Powell
Rooms: 6 (6PB) $95–150
Full Breakfast
Credit Cards: A B C D E
Notes: 2 5 8 9 10 12

VARIOUS CITIES

Reservation Service: B & B Texas Style

701 Honeysuckle Ln., College Station, TX 77845
(979) 696-9222; (800) 899-4538
  Fax (979) 696-9444
E-mail: bnbtxstyle@aol.com
Web site: www.bnbtexasstyle.com

A reservation service for the state of Texas. In business since 1982. Nearly 100 listings, including Victorian mansions, private guest houses, cottages in the woods, and historic inns. Areas include Denton, Dallas, Waco, Bryan/College Station, Kemak, Rockport, Hill Country, Tyler, Jefferson, and Marshall. All personally inspected.

NOTES: Credit cards accepted: A Master Card; B Visa; C American Express; D Discover; E Diners Club; F Other; 2 Personal checks accepted; 3 Lunch available; 4 Dinner available; 5 Open all year;

WACO

The Lighthouse Bed and Breakfast

421 S. Harrison St., McGregor, TX 76657-1562
(254) 840-2589; (800) 616-0603
    Fax (254) 840-2589
E-mail: stay@thelighthousebandb.com
Web site: www.thelighthousebandb.com

The Lighthouse

Christian hospitality and Victorian charm await you at this quiet, small-town relaxation oasis. Whether you prefer to take quiet walks, swing peacefully on the porch, sip cold drinks or coffee in the gazebo, or take advantage of a tour to nearby Crawford and President Bush's ranch, you will find pampering and privacy appropriately combined. Several golf courses, lakes, and parks are nearby; and you are just minutes from numerous attractions like the Texas Ranger Hall of Fame, several museums like Dr. Pepper, Baylor and Mary Hardin-Baylor Universities, and Christian craftsmen at the Heritage Homestead. Enjoy romantic getaways, discounts for church groups and ministers, or be catered to as a business or corporate guest. Choose from eleven beautifully decorated rooms (each with a private bath) or ask about our honeymoon cottage at a separate private location. Children limited.

Hosts: Jerry and Jan Walters
Rooms: 13 (13PB) $45.50–150
Full Breakfast
Credit Cards: A B C D E
Notes: 2   5   7 8 9 10   12

WEATHERFORD

St. Botolph Inn B & B

808 S. Lamar St., Weatherford, TX 76086
(817) 594-1455; (800) 868-6520
    Fax (817) 599-3257
E-mail: info@stbotolphinn.com
Web site: www.stbotolphinn.com

Residential area. "Five guest rooms inside the mansion with baths, some with whirlpool tubs, and two outside cottages with spa/hot tubs in room." Afternoon tea.

Hosts: Dan and Shay Buttolph
Rooms: 7 (7PB) $85–215
Full Breakfast
Credit Cards: A B C D
Notes: 2   5   7 8 9 10

6 Pets welcome; 7 Children welcome; 8 Tennis nearby; 9 Swimming nearby; 10 Golf nearby; 11 Skiing nearby; 12 May be booked through travel agent

UTAH

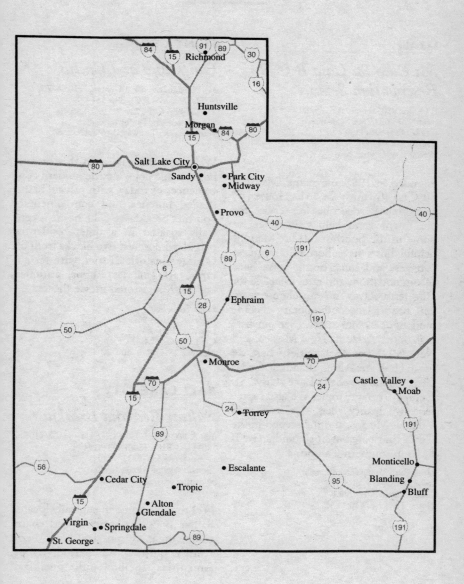

Utah

UTAH

Mi Casa Su Casa B & B Reservation Service

P. O. Box 950, Tempe, AZ 85280
(480) 990-0682; (800) 456-0682
    Fax (480) 990-3390
E-mail: micasa@azres.com
Web site: www.azres.com

Founded in 1981, our name, Mi Casa Su Casa (Spanish for "My House [is] Your House"), describes our service, for our intent is to help visitors feel at home in the Southwest. Our friendly, helpful hosts have host homes, guest cottages, and inns. Some hosts have accommodations and rates available for long-term stays. You can choose from 250 historic-to-contemporary accommodations in four states. (See our listings under Arizona, New Mexico, and Nevada.) A few of the cities where we list in Utah are: Alton, Blanding, Cedar City, Glendale, Salt Lake City, St. George, Torrey, Tropic. We also represent two luxury villas, one in Puerto Vallarta, Mexico, and the second in the Costa Brava area of Spain and a few B & Bs in southern California.

Host: Ruth Young (coordinator)
Rooms: $75–175
Credit Cards: A B C D E F
Notes: 2 5 6 7 8 9 10 11 12

SAINT GEORGE

Quicksand and Cactus

346 N. Main St., Saint George, UT 84770
(435) 674-1739; (800) 381-1654
    Fax (435) 674-1739
E-mail: quiksand@infowest.com
Web site: www.infowest.com/quicksand/

Walk into the past with this historic home while enjoying the modern conveniences of today, with private baths, shaded porches, and complimentary gourmet breakfasts. The home is centrally located in a quiet residential neighborhood just two blocks from St. George's historic district, with restaurants, art galleries, shops, antiques, and a 1927 restored movie theater.

Host: Carla Fox
Rooms: 3 (3PB) $55–85
Gourmet Breakfast
Credit Cards: A B D
Notes: 2 5 7 8 9 10 12

SALT LAKE CITY

Saltair Bed and Breakfast

164 S. 900 E, Salt Lake City, UT 84102-4103
(801) 533-8184; (800) 733-8184
    Fax (801) 595-0332
E-mail: saltair@saltlakebandb.com
Web site: www.saltlakebandb.com

Feel right at home in centrally located Saltair B & B. Antiques and charm complement queen-size brass beds, Amish quilts, and period lamps. Amenities include full breakfast,

---

NOTES: Credit cards accepted: A Master Card; B Visa; C American Express; D Discover; E Diners Club; F Other; 2 Personal checks accepted; 3 Lunch available; 4 Dinner available; 5 Open all year;

evening snacks, AC, hot tub, and goose down comforters. For extended stays, choose Alpine Cottages, built around 1870 next door to the B & B. Cottages sleep four and include fireplace, cable TV, full kitchen, sitting room, private bathroom, private phone line, and private entrance. Near Temple Square, the University of Utah, skiing, and canyons.

Hosts: Jan Bartlett and Nancy Saxton
Rooms: 5 (2PB;3SB) $79–109
Full Breakfast
Credit Cards: A B C D E
Notes: 2   5   8 9 10 11 12

Saltair

VERMONT

Vermont

ARLINGTON

Country Willows
B & B Inn C.1850

332 E. Arlington Rd., Arlington, VT 05250-9401
(802) 375-0019; (800) 796-2585
 Fax (802) 375-8054
E-mail: cw@sover.net
Web site: http://countrywillows.com

Intimate and romantic c.1850 gracious
Queen Anne Victorian, listed, National
Register of Historic Places. Welcoming
village retreat. Bountiful breakfasts, elegantly presented. Antiques, fireplaces,
spacious bed chambers, luxurious terry
velour bathrobes, en suite baths, queen
beds, handmade quilts, in-room cof-
fee/tea service, cable TV, and a wrap-
around porch invite relaxation amid spacious lawns and gardens with mountain
views. Minutes to Manchester, designer
outlets, antiquing, Battenkill River,
restaurants, concerts, theater, skiing.
Summer and winter activities nearby.

Country Willows

Hosts: Anne and Ron Weber
Rooms: 5 (5PB) $95–145
Full Breakfast
Credit Cards: A B C F
Notes: 2 5 7 8 9 10 11 12

Hill Farm Inn

458 Hill Farm Rd., Arlington, VT 05250-9311
(802) 375-2269; (800) 882-2545
 Fax (802) 375-9918
E-mail: hillfarm@vermontel.com
Web site: www.hillfarminn.com

Hill Farm Inn is one of Vermont's
original farmsteads granted from King
George III in 1775. Operated as an
inn since 1905, it still retains the character of an old farm vacation inn on 50
beautiful acres complete with farm
animals, huge red barn and silo, walking trails through the wetlands along
the Battenkill River, and spectacular
mountain and valley views in all directions. Minutes to Manchester and
Arlington. Hiking, biking, canoeing,
fishing, skiing, sleigh rides, and shopping nearby. Families are welcome.

Hosts: Craig and Kathleen Yanez
Rooms: 15 (15PB) $75–165
Full Breakfast
Credit Cards: A B D F
Notes: 2 5 7 8 9 10 11

Shenandoah Farm
Bed and Breakfast

4862 Rte. 313 W., Arlington, VT 05250
(802) 375-6372

Guests can enjoy quiet country lodging amid the glorious beauty of
Vermont. This lovely 1820 Colonial is
comfortably furnished with beautiful
antiques and colonial furniture. It
maintains the "at home" atmosphere

NOTES: Credit cards accepted: A Master Card; B Visa; C American Express; D Discover; E Diners
Club; F Other; 2 Personal checks accepted; 3 Lunch available; 4 Dinner available; 5 Open all year;

that was its hallmark when it was a roadhouse in 1930. The nearby Battenkill offers fishing, canoeing, tubing, and swimming. Many museums, recreational attractions, fine restaurants, and delightful craft shops are only minutes away.

Shenandoah Farm

Hosts: Woody and Donna Masterson
Rooms: 5 (1PB;4SB) $80–100
Full Breakfast
Credit Cards: A B
Notes: 2 5 7 8 9 10 11

BARNET

The Old Homestead B & B Inn

1573 U. S. Rte. 5 S., Barnet, VT 05821
(802) 633-4016; (877) 653-4663
   Fax (802) 633-4924
E-mail: reserve@theoldhomestead.com
Web site: www.theoldhomestead.com

Old Homestead

In the Connecticut River Valley, a warm, friendly, Colonial home blends 1850 elegance with 2002 amenities. Enjoy antiques, treasures, and collectibles, a cozy fire, warm sunporch, lovely gardens. Enclosed private porches enhance enjoyment of White Mountain sunrises and a clear Vermont night sky. Full breakfast and afternoon tea. Spaces available for conferences, family gatherings, and chamber music rehearsal retreats. Take Exit 18 off I-91, on US Route 5, in the quiet village of Barnet.

Host: Gail Warnaar
Rooms: 5 (3PB;2SB) $65–115
Full Breakfast
Credit Cards: A B D
Notes: 2 5 7 8 9 10 11 12

BRADFORD

Peach Brook Inn B & B

P. O. Box 122, Doe Hill Rd.
   Newbury, VT 05051-0122
(802) 866-3389

Our bed and breakfast is just off Vermont Route 5, which follows the Connecticut River. It is on a country lane with small farms and a variety of farm animals, plus a great farm stand. The house, Colonial-style with a carriage house and barn, is on a bluff, giving us a panoramic view of the river, mountains, a village, and farmland. Built in the 1780s, the house gives you a feeling of bygone years with its beams, fireplaces, and antiques. Guests describe the inn as "beautiful," "peaceful," and "home." Children over 10 welcome.

Host: Joyce Emery
Rooms: 3 (1PB;2SB) $50–75
Full Breakfast
Notes: 2 5 7 8 9 10 11

6 Pets welcome; 7 Children welcome; 8 Tennis nearby; 9 Swimming nearby; 10 Golf nearby; 11 Skiing nearby; 12 May be booked through travel agent

BRATTLEBORO

1868 Crosby House

175 Western Ave., Brattleboro, VT 05301
(802) 257-7145; (800) 528-1868
E-mail: lynn@crosbyhouse.com
Web site: www.crosbyhouse.com

1868 Crosby House

Built in 1868, this restored Italianate
Victorian beckons with historic architecture and a beguiling opportunity to
step back in time. Bedrooms offer fireplaces, whirlpool, air-conditioning,
TV/VCR, private-line phones, gourmet breakfasts, and other luxury amenities. Two beautifully decorated suites
with cathedral ceilings and garden
views or skylights are fully equipped
and furnished for self-catering stays.
Private, landscaped gardens offer the
perfect setting for quiet afternoons or
elegant celebrations.

Host: L. Kuralt
Rooms: 5 (5PB) $115–160
Full Breakfast
Credit Cards: A B D
Notes: 2 5 8 9 10 11 12

BURLINGTON

Black Bear Inn

4010 Bolton Access Rd.
  Bolton Valley, VT 05477-0026
(802) 434-2126; (800) 395-6335
  Fax (802) 434-5156
E-mail: blkbear@wcvt.com
Web site: www.blkbearinn.com

A true Vermont mountaintop country
inn with 25 rooms, private baths, many
with flowering balconies, great views,
private hot tubs, fireplaces or Vermont
firestoves. Over 5000 acres to explore
with waterfalls and swimming holes.
Minutes away from Ben & Jerry's,
Vermont Teddy Bear Factory,
Shelburne Museum. Burlington and
Stowe, golf, tennis, antiquing, canoeing, mountain hiking and biking just
minutes away. Dining room serves full
breakfast and dinner daily. For our
friends traveling with our furry
friends, the Bone and Bisquit Inn
awaits you and your best friend. Come,
relax, and enjoy the cool, clean, green
mountains of Vermont.

Host: Ken Richardson
Rooms: 25 (25PB) $79–215
Full Breakfast
Credit Cards: A B
Notes: 4 5 6 7 8 9 10 11 12

FAIRLEE

Silver Maple Lodge and Cottages

520 U. S. Rte. 5 S., Fairlee, VT 05045-9705
(802) 333-4326; (800) 666-1946
E-mail: scott@silvermaplelodge.com
Web site: www.silvermaplelodge.com

NOTES: Credit cards accepted: A Master Card; B Visa; C American Express; D Discover; E Diners
Club; F Other; 2 Personal checks accepted; 3 Lunch available; 4 Dinner available; 5 Open all year;

A historic bed and breakfast country inn located in a four-season recreational area. Enjoy canoeing, fishing, golf, tennis, and skiing within a few miles of the lodge. Visit nearby flea markets and country auctions. Choose a newly renovated room in our antique farmhouse or a handsome, pine-paneled cottage room. Three cottages with working fireplaces. Many fine restaurants nearby; Dartmouth College 17 miles away. Hot-air balloon packages, inn-to-inn bicycling, canoeing, and walking tours. Brochures available.

Silver Maple Lodge

Hosts: Scott and Sharon Wright
Rooms: 16 (14PB;2SB) $65–99
Continental Breakfast
Credit Cards: A B C D
Notes: 2 5 6 7 8 9 10 11 12

JAY

The 1893 House B & B

134 Highland Ave., North Troy, VT 05859
(802) 988-9614; (888) 988-9614
 Fax (802) 988-2684
E-mail: pshover@sover.net

Our Victorian B & B home in North Troy, VT; a quaint valley town surrounded by beautiful mountains. Located 8 miles from Jay Peak Ski Resort. Some of the nearby interests are skiing, golfing, bicycling, and hiking. We are 4 miles from the end of the long trail, and we do make arrangements for hikers. We serve a complete breakfast of eggs, bacon, toast, potatoes, juice, coffee, tea, milk, homemade breads, pancakes, or French toast.

Hosts: Pat and Rick Shover
Rooms: 4 (0PB;4SB) $50
Full Breakfast
Credit Cards:
Notes: 2 5 7 8 9 10 11

KILLINGTON

Cortina Inn and Resort

103 U. S. Rte. 4, Killington, VT 05751
(802) 773-3333; (800) 451-6108
 Fax (802) 775-6948
E-mail: cortina1@aol.com
Web site: www.cortinainn.com

Cortina Inn and Resort is located in the heart of the Green Mountains of central Vermont, near world-famous Killington Ski Resort. Situated on 32 manicured acres with extensive gardens, woods, a pond, and eight tennis courts. Conference and banquet facilities to accommodate up to 250. The beautiful gardens and landscaped grounds are perfect for outdoor weddings, receptions, and family reunions.

Hosts: Bob and Breda Harnish
Rooms: 96 (96PB) $124–199
Full Breakfast
Credit Cards: A B C D E
Notes: 2 4 5 6 7 8 9 10 11 12

6 Pets welcome; 7 Children welcome; 8 Tennis nearby; 9 Swimming nearby; 10 Golf nearby; 11 Skiing nearby; 12 May be booked through travel agent

Grey Bonnet Inn

831 Rte. 100, Killington, VT 05751
(802) 775-2537; (800) 342-2086
    Fax (802) 775-3371
E-mail: innkeep@together.net
Web site: www.greybonnetinn.com

Romantic 41-room antique-filled coun-try inn. Dining room seats 100, pub seats 25. Indoor/outdoor pools. Tennis court and hiking trail all on 25 acres. Located in central Vermont's highly recreational areas. Close to skiing, golf, fishing, boating, and antiquing. Large family rooms available. Both golf and skiing packages are available.

Hosts: Karen and Paul Steele
Rooms: 41 (41PB) $69–185
Full Breakfast
Credit Cards: A B C
Notes: 2 4 5 7 8 9 10 11 12

Swiss Farm Inn

4441 Rte. 100 N, P. O. Box 510
    Pittsfield, VT 05762
(802) 746-8341; (800) 245-5126
    Fax (802) 746-8908
E-mail: stevensfiv@aol.com
Web site: www.swissfarminn.com

A family tradition for fifty years now. Roger and Joyce Stevens will make you feel at home from the minute you arrive. Breakfast and dinner are pre-pared and served by your hosts and promise to be a true homemade coun-try delight. We are 12 miles from Killington Ski Resort, biking, hiking, snowmobiling, horseback riding, golf, tennis, and great swimming. Children are always welcome. Having lived in the Caribbean for some time, the Stevens family create a warm blend of Caribbean and country life.

Hosts: Roger and Joyce Stevens
Rooms: 15 (15PB) $60–100
Full Breakfast
Credit Cards: A B C   F
Notes: 2 4 5 7 8 9 10 11

LONDONDERRY

Blue Gentian Lodge

289 Magic Mountain Rd.
    Londonderry, VT 05148-9705
(802) 824-5908; (800) 456-2405
    Fax (802) 824-3531
E-mail: kenalberti@csi.com
Web site: www.bluegentian.com

A special place to stay, nestled at the foot of Magic Mountain. All rooms have private baths and cable color TV and include a full breakfast in the din-ing room. Enjoy seasonal activities on the grounds, the heated swimming pool, and walking trails. The recreation room offers Ping-Pong, bumper pool, board games, and library. Golf, tennis, fishing, outlet shopping, antiquing, horseback riding, and skiing (downhill and cross-country) are nearby.

Hosts: The Alberti Family
Rooms: 13 (13PB) $50–95
Full Breakfast
Credit Cards: A B
Notes: 2 4 5 7 8 9 10 11

LOWER WATERFORD

Rabbit Hill Inn

48 Lower Waterford Rd.
    Lower Waterford, VT 05848
(802) 748-5168; (800) 76-BUNNY
    Fax (802) 748-8342

NOTES: Credit cards accepted: A Master Card; B Visa; C American Express; D Discover; E Diners Club; F Other; 2 Personal checks accepted; 3 Lunch available; 4 Dinner available; 5 Open all year;

E-mail: info@rabbithillinn.com
Web site: www.rabbithillinn.com

Nestled between a river and the mountains, in a village untouched by time, sits the historic Rabbit Hill Inn. Escape to this tranquil place and experience the gentle comforts of enchanting guest rooms and suites, a Jacuzzi by candlelight, memorable gourmet dining, and pampering service. Enjoy a variety of activities or simply relax. We await you with truly heartfelt hospitality unlike any you've experienced. Meals included. Award-winning, nationally acclaimed inn, rated 4-stars by Mobil and 4-diamonds by AAA.

Hosts: Brian and Leslie Mulcahy
Rooms: 19 (19PB) $260–410
Full Breakfast
Credit Cards: A B C
Notes: 2 4 9 10 11

LUDLOW

Golden Stage Inn

399 Depot St., Proctorsville, VT 05153
(802) 226-7744; (800) 253-8226
E-mail: goldenstageinn@tds.net
Web site: www.goldenstageinn.com

Relaxed elegance in a historic antique-filled country inn. Eighteenth-century stagecoach stop, later home to Otis Skinner, famous theater performer, and his daughter, writer Cornelius Otis Skinner. Enjoy full breakfast and candlelight dinners in the solarium. Full-size pool, AC, wheelchair accessible. Antiques, golf, bike, summer theater, ski Okemo.

Hosts: Sandy and Peter Gregg
Rooms: 10 (8PB;2SB) $79–225

Full Breakfast
Credit Cards: A B C
Notes: 2 4 5 7 10 11 12

Hound's Folly

9 Dawley Rd., Mount Holly, VT 05758
(802) 259-2718
E-mail: durr2ofhf@aol.com

Colonial 1810 farmhouse situated on 20 acres of beautiful open meadowland. Here you will find sheep grazing. Three guest rooms individually decorated. Our dogs are an integral part of the setting. Hearty breakfasts. If you love animals, this is the place for you.

Hound's Folly

Hosts: Luise and Elise Durr
Rooms: 3 (3SB) 70–75
Full Breakfast
Credit Cards: A B
Notes: 2   7 8 9 10 11

LYNDON

Branch Brook B & B

36 Branch Brook Ln., P. O. Box 217
    Lyndon, VT 05849
(802) 626-8316; (800) 572-7712
E-mail: bbbb@together.net

Join us in our newly renovated Federal period home, dating from the 1830s.

6 Pets welcome; 7 Children welcome; 8 Tennis nearby; 9 Swimming nearby; 10 Golf nearby; 11 Skiing nearby; 12 May be booked through travel agent

Located in the village of Lyndon, in Vermont's North East Kingdom, Branch Brook offers you the best of country surroundings in a small village setting, with its naturally landscaped grounds overlooking a brook. There's easy access to lakes and rivers for boating or beautiful rural roads to drive, bike, or hike on, and Burke Mountain for skiing. We're just a few miles from Burke Mountain, Willoughby and Crystal Lakes, and minutes from Lyndon State College.

Branch Brook

Host: Ann Tolman
Rooms: 5 (3PB;2SB) $71.50–93.50 plus tax
Full Breakfast
Credit Cards: A B
Notes: 2 5 7 10 11

MIDDLEBURY

The Middlebury Inn

14 Courthouse Sq., Middlebury, VT 05753
(802) 388-4961; (800) 842-4666
   Fax (802) 388-4563
E-mail: midinnvt@sover.net
Web site: www.middleburyinn.com

Welcoming travelers since 1827. The inn is located in a lovely, lively college town enchanced by a legion of historical, cultural, and entertaining attractions. Forty-five elegantly restored rooms in the main house, 10 in Porter House Mansion, and 20 Contemporary Motel rooms. Cable color TVs, blow dryers, telephones, and AC/heaters in all rooms. The inn offers breakfast, lunch, dinner, seasonal porch dining, afternoon tea, and Sunday brunch. Recommended by AAA: Member of Historic Hotels of America. Pets limited.

Hosts: The Emanuel Family
Rooms: 75 (75PB) $88–365
Continental Breakfast
Credit Cards: A B C D E
Notes: 2 3 4 5 6 7 8 9 10 11 12

MONTGOMERY CENTER

The Inn on Trout River

241 Main St., P. O. Box 76
   Montgomery Center, VT 05471-0076
(802) 326-4391; (800) 338-7049
   Fax (802) 326-3194
E-mail: info@troutinn.com
Web site: www.troutinn.com

AAA-rated historic country inn and restaurant, ideally located in Montgomery Center—the Covered Bridge Town of the Green Mountains—for exploring the Jay Peak region. Guest rooms include a family suite and honeymoon suite and feature queen beds, private baths, down quilts, and feather pillows. Recreation: downhill and cross-country skiing, snowmobiling, hiking, biking, golfing, fishing. Activities: nature photography, museums, shopping, foliage and cultural heritage driving tours.

NOTES: Credit cards accepted: A Master Card; B Visa; C American Express; D Discover; E Diners Club; F Other; 2 Personal checks accepted; 3 Lunch available; 4 Dinner available; 5 Open all year;

The Inn on Trout River

Hosts: Michael and Lee Forman
Rooms: 10 (10PB) $86–125
Full Breakfast
Credit Cards: A B C D
Notes: 4 5 7 8 10 11 12

NORTH HERO

The North Hero House Inn and Restaurant

P. O. Box 207, Rte. 2
   North Hero, VT 05474-0106
(802) 372-4732; (888) 525-3644
   Fax (802) 372-3218
E-mail: nhhlake@aol.com
Web site: www.northherohouse.com

The North Hero House Inn

Whether you're drawn to the Lake Champlain islands of northern Vermont by the wide-open vistas or the lulling sound of water lapping at shore's edge, the North Hero House will warmly welcome you into the heart of the nation's "Sixth Great

Lake." The main inn, built in 1891, first provided a retreat for guests arriving by steamship. You'll be enchanted with the beautifully restored buildings, antiques, and collectibles. The area's rural charm, waterside farms, orchards, and sandy beaches are complemented by festivals, craft fairs, historical day trips, and plenty of outdoor activities to keep you busy exploring the string of islands.

Host: Walter Blasberg, Owner
Rooms: 26 (26PB) $75–255
Full Breakfast
Credit Cards: A B C
Notes: 2 4 5 7 8 9 10 12

PROCTORSVILLE

Whitney Brook Bed and Breakfast

2423 Twenty Mile Stream Rd.
   Proctorsville, VT 05153-9703
(802) 226-7460
E-mail: whitney_brook@yahoo.com
Web site: www.whitneybrook.com

Whitney Brook Bed and Breakfast is located in an 1870 Vermont farmhouse on a private and quiet 100 acres with stone walls, streams, meadows, and woods. The house has been renovated to provide a comfortable home atmosphere, while maintaining the old farmhouse charm. A large living room with fireplace and an upstairs sitting area with a selection of games are available for guests. Nearby are antique and specialty shops such as the well-known Vermont Country Store. For the sports-minded, our area provides downhill (Okemo) and cross-country

---

6 Pets welcome; 7 Children welcome; 8 Tennis nearby; 9 Swimming nearby; 10 Golf nearby; 11 Skiing nearby; 12 May be booked through travel agent

skiing within 10 minutes and great hiking, biking, golfing, fishing, and horseback riding. Our picnic table and Adirondack chairs are always ready for a pleasant afternoon of reading.

Rooms: 4 (2PB;2SB) $60–102
Full Breakfast
Credit Cards: A B C D
Notes: 2 5 8 9 10 11

RANDOLPH

Sweetserenity Bed and Breakfast

40 Randolph Ave., Randolph, VT 05060
(802) 728-9590; (888) 491-9590
  Fax (775) 414-9487
E-mail: reserveb@sover.net
Web site: www.sweet-serenity.com

In the geographic center of Vermont, an 1870 Victorian three-bedroom B & B is waiting for you. Enjoy good conversation, a comfortable bed, and a hearty breakfast. Our library has many quality books. Walk to the Montague Golf Course in a wee 2 minutes. The village center with the Chandler Music Hall is only a 5-minute walk. May the Lord bless you as you consider your vacation or brief getaway time for relaxation and refreshment.

Hosts: Don and Evelyn Sweetser
Rooms: 3 (1PB;2SB) $75–110
Full Breakfast
Credit Cards: A B C D
Notes: 2 5 7 8 9 10 11

RUTLAND

I. B. Munson House B & B Inn

37 S. Main St.; P. O. Box 427
  Wallingford, VT 05773-0427
(802) 446-2860; (888) 519-3771
  Fax (802) 446-3336
E-mail: stay@ibmunsoninn.com
Web site: www.ibmunsoninn.com

An 1856 Victorian mansion nestled in a quaint historic village. Tastefully restored and decorated with antique furnishings. Unique guest rooms feature private baths and many amenities; a pleasure for your senses. Deep clawfoot soaking tubs, air-conditioning, and fireplaces are available. Gourmet breakfast served in formal dining room. A special place to rest and be pampered.

I. B. Munson House

Hosts: Tom and Jo Ann Brem
Rooms: 7 (7PB) $105–165
Full Breakfast
Credit Cards: A B C
Notes: 2 3 4 5 8 9 10 11 12

Maplewood Inn

1108 S. Main St., Fair Haven, VT 05743
(802) 265-8039; (800) 253-7729
  Fax (802) 265-8210
E-mail: stay@maplewoodinn.net
Web site: www.maplewoodinn.net

NOTES: Credit cards accepted: A Master Card; B Visa; C American Express; D Discover; E Diners Club; F Other; 2 Personal checks accepted; 3 Lunch available; 4 Dinner available; 5 Open all year;

Elegant accommodations with romantic charm in a historic, 1843 Greek Revival. Lovely rooms and suites boast antiques, fireplaces, AC, CCTV—all with private baths. Relax and enjoy the sitting room or parlor, with a complimentary cordial. Near lakes, skiing, and many of Vermont's treasures and pleasures. Recommended by more than thirty guidebooks. A four-season inn.

Hosts: Lisa Ne Jame Osborne and Donald Osborne
Rooms: 5 (5PB) $89–150
Full Breakfast
Credit Cards: A B C
Notes: 5 6 7 8 9 10 11 12

STOWE

Brass Lantern Inn

717 Maple St., Stowe, VT 05672-4250
(802) 253-2229; (800) 729-2980
 Fax (802) 253-7425
E-mail: brasslntrn@aol.com
Web site: www.brasslanterninn.com

Brass Lantern Inn

An award-winning traditional bed and breakfast in the heart of Stowe, overlooking Mount Mansfield, Vermont's most prominent mountain. The inn features period antiques, handmade quilts, local artisan wares, and AC. Most rooms have views and whirlpool tubs; some also have fireplaces. A hint of romance abounds, an intimate inn for romantics. Special packages include honeymoon/anniversary, romance, golf, adventure, spa, ski, historic, and more. No smoking. "Vermont B & B Innkeeper of the Year, 2001."

Host: Andy Alrich
Rooms: 9 (9PB) $90–225
Full Breakfast
Credit Cards: A B C
Notes: 5 8 9 10 11 12

WAITSFIELD

The Mad River Inn

P. O. Box 75, Waitsfield, VT 05673-0075
(802) 496-7900; (800) 832-8278
 Fax (802) 496-5390
E-mail: madriverinn@madriver.com
Web site: www.madriverinn.com

An 1860s country Victorian charm with picturesque mountain views and distant barns. Ten romantic guest rooms have feather beds, antiques, and private baths. Gourmet breakfast. Afternoon tea with baked goods. Elegant living room with library and comfortable couches, sunporch, ski lounge with woodstove, TV/VCR, billiards, and games. Gazebo and outdoor Jacuzzi. Next to recreation path along Mad River. Spacious and wonderful for groups and families. Great midweek rates. Near Vermont Icelandic horse farm, Sugarbush, and Mad River Glen ski resorts and hiking.

Rooms: 9 (9PB) $89–135
Gourmet Breakfast
Credit Cards: A B C F
Notes: 2 5 7 8 9 10 11 12

---

6 Pets welcome; 7 Children welcome; 8 Tennis nearby; 9 Swimming nearby; 10 Golf nearby; 11 Skiing nearby; 12 May be booked through travel agent

WATERBURY

Inn at Blush Hill

784 Blush Hill Road
 Waterbury, VT 05676-9719
(802) 244-7529; (800) 736-7522
 Fax (802) 244-7314
E-mail: inn@blushhill.com
Web site: www.blushhill.com

A c. 1790 Cape Cod bed and breakfast, set high on a hilltop with 5 rolling acres and unsurpassed mountain views. 5 individually decorated rooms, feather beds, A/C, antiques, canopy, Jacuzzi bathtub, fireplace. Spacious common rooms. Full country breakfast and afternoon refreshments are served. Adjacent to Ben & Jerry's.

Host: Pamela Gosselin
Rooms: 5 (5PB) $89-160
Full Breakfast
Credit Cards: A B C D
Notes: 2   5   7 8 9 10 11 12

WESTON

The Colonial House

287 Rte 100, Weston, VT 05161-5402
(802) 824-6286; (800) 639-5033
 Fax (802) 824-3934
E-mail: cohoinn@sover.net
Web site: www.cohoinn.com

The Colonial House is a unique country inn and motel offering a full breakfast with its rooms. Dinner is available on Friday and Saturday nights year-round and midweek during the summer, fall, and winter holiday periods. Rooms are light and airy. The guest living room has an attached solarium where coffee, tea, and fresh-

baked goods are offered each afternoon. Convenient to all southern Vermont attractions.

Hosts: Kim and Jeff Seymour
Rooms: 15 (9PB;6SB) $59.20-108.00
Full Breakfast
Credit Cards: A B D
Notes: 2 4 5 7 9 10 11

WILMINGTON

Baked Apples at Shearer Hill Farm B & B

Shearer Hill Rd., P. O. Box 1453
 Wilmington, VT 05301-1453
(802) 464-3253; (800) 437-3104
E-mail: ppusey@shearerhillfarm.com
Web site: www.shearerhillfarm.com

Wake to the aroma of freshly brewed coffee, homemade muffins, and breads. Enjoy our small working farm located on a pristine country road. Large rooms with private baths. A delicious Vermont breakfast. Near Mount Snow ski areas, groomed cross-country skiing trails on property, sleigh rides nearby. Marlboro Music Festival 5 miles away. Outstanding golf courses, swimming, hiking, boating, horseback riding, mountain biking, and many fine restaurants nearby.

Hosts: Christian Innkeepers: Bill and Patti Pusey
Rooms: 6 (6PB) $90
Full Breakfast
Credit Cards: A B C D
Notes: 2 5 7 8 9 10 11

WOODSTOCK

Applebutter Inn

Happy Valley Rd., Taftsville, VT 05073
(802) 457-4158; Fax (802) 457-4158
E-mail: aplbtrn@aol.com

The Applebutter Inn is nestled in the
quiet and peaceful hamlet of Taftsville,
VT, 3 miles from the centers of
Woodstock and Quechee. Our guests
are pampered with delicious freshly
made baked goods and a full breakfast,
which may include omelettes, crepes,
pancakes, or waffles, puddings, and
many seasonal variations. The
Applebutter Inn is a perfect place to
refresh the soul and enliven the spirit.

Hosts: Barbara Barry and Michael Pacht
Rooms: 5 (5PB) $95–185
Full Breakfast
Credit Cards: A B
Notes: 2 9 10 11

Barr House

55 South St., Woodstock, VT 05091-1232
(802) 457-3334
Web site: www.woodstockvt.com/innsd-k.htm

We are a 19th-century saltbox situated
on 1½ acres in the village near the
green. Our bed and breakfast overlooks golf and cross-country ski
courses but is away from busy thor-
oughfares. Small and unique. Two
charming rooms are hosted by a sixth-
generation Vermont native. Full
Vermont breakfast. Public room. Gift
certificates. Children over 12 welcome. Nonsmoking. No pets.

Hosts: Katharine and Jim Paul
Rooms: 2 (2SB) $70–80

Full Breakfast
Notes: 2 5   8 9 10 11

The Maple Leaf Inn

P. O. Box 273, Barnard, VT 05031-0273
(802) 234-5342; (800) 51-MAPLE
Web site: www.mapleleafinn.com

The Maple Leaf Inn

The Maple Leaf is an elegant
Victorian-style inn resplendent with
gables, dormers, wrap-around porch,
gazebo, gingerbread trim, and soaring
chimneys, nestled within 16 acres of
maple and birch trees. All of our guest
rooms have a king-size bed, sitting
area, TV/VCR, telephone, and private
bath—most with whirlpool tubs.
Wood-burning fireplaces grace most
of our guest rooms, as well. Stenciling,
stitchery, and handmade quilts blend
with antique and reproduction furnishings to give each guest room a
warm and welcoming individuality.
The aroma of our gourmet breakfast
will entice you to our dining room,
where your candlelit table awaits. The
Maple Leaf Inn has been awarded the
AAA ◆ ◆ ◆ ◆.

Hosts: Gary and Janet Robison
Rooms: 7 (7PB) $120–230
Full Breakfast
Credit Cards: A B C D E
Notes: 2   5 8 9 10 11 12

---

6 Pets welcome; 7 Children welcome; 8 Tennis nearby; 9 Swimming nearby; 10 Golf nearby; 11 Skiing
nearby; 12 May be booked through travel agent

VIRGINIA

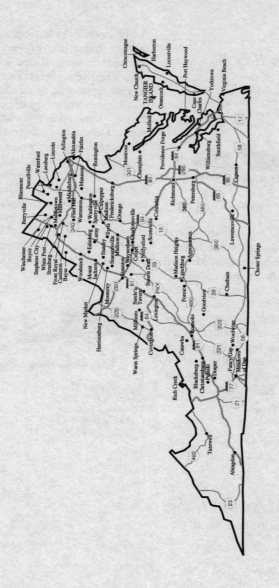

<u>Virginia</u>

ABINGDON

River Garden B & B

19080 N. Fork River Rd.
   Abingdon, VA 24210-4560
(540) 676-0335; (800) 952-4296
E-mail: wccrump@preferred.com
Web site: www.bbdirectory.com/inn/rivergarden

River Garden

Located in the country, the River Garden is 15 minutes from historic Abingdon, on the bank of the Holston River's North Fork. It is decorated in antique and period furniture and offers private entrances to all rooms and a covered deck outside, facing the river, as well as a deck at the water's edge. Rooms have queen and king beds with air-conditioning and central heat. A full breakfast is served. Enjoy the recreation room, fishing, and tubing.

Hosts: Carol and Bill Crump
Rooms: 4 (4PB) $75–80
Full Breakfast
Notes: 2 5 6 7 8 9 10 12

A Shenandoah Valley romantic, mountaintop hideaway. Property features spectacular views. Rustic, comfortable lodge open year-round. Treetop Lodge features bedrooms, private baths, living rooms, wood-burning stone fireplaces, decks, some kitchens/kitchenettes, books. Delivered continental breakfast. Welcome honeymooners, singles, couples, groups, retreats, children, pets (with advance notice). Restaurants, hiking, horseback riding, skiing, golfing, tennis, lake, caverns, vineyards, museums, antiques, crafts, creamery, corn maze, deer farm, Civil War history nearby. The "Mountain Lovers' Paradise" since 1937.

Sky Chalet Mountain Lodge

Hosts: Ken and Mona Seay
Rooms: 5 (5PB) $34–79
Continental Breakfast
Credit Cards: A B D E
Notes: 2   5 6 7 8 9 10 11 12

BASYE

Sky Chalet Mountain Lodges

Rte. 263 W., P. O. Box 300, Basye, VA 22810
(540) 856-2147; (877) 867-8439
   Fax (540) 856-2436
E-mail: skychalet@skychalet.com
Web site: www.skychalet.com

NOTES: Credit cards accepted: A Master Card; B Visa; C American Express; D Discover; E Diners Club; F Other; 2 Personal checks accepted; 3 Lunch available; 4 Dinner available; 5 Open all year;

BERRYVILLE

Blue Ridge B & B Reservation Service/ Rocks and Rills

2458 Castleman Rd., Berryville, VA 22611
(540) 955-1246; (800) 296-1246
Fax (540) 955-4240
E-mail: blurdgbb@shentel.net
Web site: www.blueridgebb.com

A lovely visit to the beautiful Rocks and Rills Farm Bed and Breakfast always includes a delicious full country breakfast each morning. Located on 11 rolling acres, complete with 5 acres of fragrant Christmas trees, we are at the top of the beautiful Shenandoah Valley. This antique-filled Colonial Williamsburg reproduction nestled in the foothills of the Blue Ridge Mountains is graced with a magnificent view of the mountains from a large deck suspended over a beautiful lawn and gardens. The Shenandoah River is located only 2 miles from this tranquil retreat on a lovely dirt road perfect for walking, hiking, or biking. Take a short drive to visit Harpers Ferry, WV, or the Skyline Drive to round out the day; then return to an evening in front of a roaring fire. Children, as well as pets, are always welcome. Indoor heated swimming pool w/hot tub. Massage can be arranged in-house. The host speaks seven different languages including fluent Spanish. The hostess can also help you with other accommodations, as we also own and operate the Blue Ridge B & B Reservation Service. We are located just 1 1/2 hours west of Washington, DC, 30 minutes from Dulles International Airport, and just 20 minutes east of I-81.

Hosts: Rita Z. Duncan and Rolando A. Amador
Rooms: 4 (2PB;2SB) $65–179
Full Breakfast
Credit Cards: A B C
Notes: 2 5 6 7 8 10 12

BLACKSBURG

Clay Corner Inn

401 Clay St. SW, Blacksburg, VA 24060-4708
(540) 953-2604; Fax (540) 951-0541
E-mail: claycorner@aol.com
Web site: www.claycorner.com

Clay Corner Inn is a casual B & B with the comforts of home, amenities of a hotel, and friendly atmosphere of a small inn. Each guest room has a private bath, cable TV, telephone, and king or queen bed. A full, healthy breakfast is served daily. The heated pool is open May–October, and the hot tub is open year round. The Huckleberry Trail, a 6-mile walking/jogging trail, begins 100 yards from the front door.

Hosts: John and Joanne Anderson
Rooms: 12 (12PB) $85–130
Full Breakfast
Credit Cards: A B C
Notes: 2 5 8 9 10

CAPE CHARLES

Chesapeake Charm Bed and Breakfast

202 Madison Ave., Cape Charles, VA 23310-2910
(757) 331-2676; (800) 546-9215; Fax ()
E-mail: info@chesapeakecharmbnb.com
Web site: www.chesapeakecharmbnb.com

Our family-friendly inn is located on the unspoiled eastern shore of Virginia. Enjoy all the modern conveniences of today enhanced by period antiques, individually controlled heat and AC. See spectacular Chesapeake Bay sunsets only 2 blocks from the B & B. Golf, tennis, fishing, history, and hiking all within short distances. Awake to a culinary breakfast delight each morning. A perfect way to celebrate a special birthday or anniversary or just to escape.

Host: Phyllis Tyndall
Rooms: 4 (4PB) $75–120
Full Breakfast
Credit Cards: A B C
Notes: 2 7 8 9 10 12

Sea Gate B & B

9 Tazewell Ave., Cape Charles, VA 23310-3127
(757) 331-2206; Fax (757) 331-2206
E-mail: seagate@pilot.infi.net
Web site: www.bbhost.com/seagate

Located in the sleepy town of Cape Charles, just three houses to the beach on Virginia's eastern shore. My home is your home! Day begins with a full breakfast served between 8-10 A.M., followed by leisure, hiking, birding, bathing, exploring, or golf at the Arnold Palmer Signature Course. Tea prepares you for the glorious sunsets over the bay. Sea Gate is the perfect place to rest, relax, and recharge away from the crush of modern America. Children over 7 welcome.

Sea Gate

Host: Chris Bannon
Rooms: 4 (2PB;2SB) $85–95
Full Breakfast
Credit Cards: A B
Notes: 2 5 7 8 9 10 12

CATAWBA

Down Home Bed and Breakfast

5209 Catawba Valley Dr., Catawba, VA 24070
(540) 384-6865
E-mail: dwnhmbb@rbnet.com
Web site: www.downhomebb.com

Down Home

Outstanding hiking and relaxed location. Between two great day hikes on the Appalachian Trail, McAfee's Knob and Dragon's Tooth. Minutes from the Jefferson National Forest and Craig County trout fishing. Also within walking distance of the

---

NOTES: Credit cards accepted: A Master Card; B Visa; C American Express; D Discover; E Diners Club; F Other; 2 Personal checks accepted; 3 Lunch available; 4 Dinner available; 5 Open all year;

Homeplace Restaurant. In-ground swimming pool (seasonal) and large deck for relaxing and watching birds. Private baths, guest living room, and full breakfast.

Hosts: Dave and Lucy Downs
Rooms: 2 (2PB) $75+ tax
Full Breakfast
Notes: 2 5 7 9 10

CHARLOTTESVILLE

The Inn at Monticello

1188 Scottsville Rd.
   Charlottesville, VA 22902-7102
(434) 979-3593; Fax (434) 296-1344
E-mail: stay@innatmonticello.com
Web site: www.innatmonticello.com

A charming country manor house built in 1850, the inn sits cradled in the valley at the foot of Thomas Jefferson's Monticello mountain. It looks out on landscaped grounds toward the mountains. Inside, we offer beautifully decorated rooms full of antique and period pieces. Some rooms have fireplaces, canopy beds, or a private porch. A gourmet breakfast is served.

Hosts: Norm and Becky Lindway
Rooms: 5 (5PB) $125–145
Full Breakfast
Credit Cards: A B
Notes: 2 5 8 9 10 11 12

CHINCOTEAGUE

Garden and Sea Inn

4188 Nelson Rd., P. O. Box 275
   New Church, VA 23415-0275
(757) 824-0672; (800) 824-0672
E-mail: innkeeper@gardenandseainn.com
Web site: www.gardenandseainn.com

Casual elegance and warm hospitality await you at this European-style country inn with its romantic, candlelit, fine dining restaurant. Near Chincoteague Wildlife Refuge and Assateague Island's beautiful beach, it offers large, luxurious guest rooms, beautifully designed; spacious private baths, some with whirlpools; Victorian detail and stained glass; Oriental rugs, antiques, bay windows; and patios and gardens. Mobil 3-star-rated. We are open mid-March to November 26.

Hosts: Tom and Sara Baker
Rooms: 8 (8PB) $75–195
Full Breakfast
Credit Cards: A B C D F
Notes: 2 3 4 5 6 8 9 10 12

The Watson House

4240 Main St., Chincoteague, VA 23336-2801
(757) 336-1564; (800) 336-6787
   Fax (757) 336-5776
Web site: www.watsonhouse.com

Watson House

Featured on the Learning Channel's "Romantic Escapes," the Watson House is a recently restored Victorian country home built in the late 1800s by David Robert Watson. Nestled in the heart of Chincoteague, it is within

---

6 Pets welcome; 7 Children welcome; 8 Tennis nearby; 9 Swimming nearby; 10 Golf nearby; 11 Skiing nearby; 12 May be booked through travel agent

walking distance of favorite shops and restaurants. We have six guest rooms furnished with antiques, private baths, and AC. A full breakfast is served in the dining room or on the veranda. We offer complimentary use of bicycles, beach chairs, and beach towels to enjoy our beautiful beach. Children over 10 welcome.

Hosts: Tom and Jacque Derrickson,
   David and Joanne Snead
Rooms: 6 (6PB) $79–129
Full Breakfast
Credit Cards: A B
Notes: 2   7 8 9 10

Inn at Poplar Corner

P. O. Box 905, Chincoteague, VA 23336-0905
(757) 336-6115; (800) 336-6787
   Fax (757) 336-5776
Web site: www.poplarcorner.com

Inn at Poplar Corner

The Inn at Poplar Corner is romantically decorated in Victorian style. Guest rooms are furnished with walnut beds, marble-top dressers, and wash stands; they have air-conditioning, ceiling fans, and large private baths with whirlpool tubs. Enjoy your full breakfast and afternoon tea on a wraparound veranda. The Chincoteague

National Wildlife Refuge and beach are only a few minutes away. Take advantage of our free use of bicycles to tour the refuge. This is a great way to appreciate the broad variety of wildlife. Children over 10 welcome.

Hosts: Tom and Jacque Derrickson,
   David and Joanne Snead
Rooms: 4 (4PB) $109–179
Full Breakfast
Credit Cards: A B
Notes: 2   7 8 9 10

CHRISTIANSBURG

Evergreen, The Bell-Capozzi House

201 E. Main St., Christiansburg, VA 24073-3007
(540) 382-7372; (800) 905-7372
   Fax (540) 382-0034
E-mail: evrgrninn@aol.com
Web site: www.evergreen-bnb.com

Victorian mansion in Virginia's Blue Ridge Highlands 1 1/2 miles from I-81. Private baths, traditional Southern breakfast, swimming pool, central air-conditioning, and tea-time or tee-time available by reservation. "The Cottage" is perfect for honeymoon, anniversary, or "special time."

Evergreen, The Bell-Capozzi House

NOTES: Credit cards accepted: A Master Card; B Visa; C American Express; D Discover; E Diners Club; F Other; 2 Personal checks accepted; 3 Lunch available; 4 Dinner available; 5 Open all year;

Hosts: Rocco and Barbara Bell-Cappozi
Rooms: 7 (7PB) $95–150
Full Breakfast
Credit Cards: A B C D
Notes: 2 5 9 10

CULPEPER

Fountain Hall

609 S. East St., Culpeper, VA 22701
(540) 825-8200; (800) 29-VISIT
E-mail: visit@fountainhall.com
Web site: www.fountainhall.com

This grand 1859 Colonial Revival home features tastefully restored and decorated rooms, some with private porch, whirlpool, or sitting room. Common rooms for reading, relaxing, TV, and conversation. Complimentary beverages. Gardens, stately trees, and mature boxwoods. Walk to the quaint historic district; visit antique and gift shops, restaurants, bookstores, and the museum. One mile from Highway 29 between Charlottesville, Washington, Richmond, and the Blue Ridge Mountains. Golf and dinner packages are available. AAA 3-diamonds, Mobil 3-stars.

Hosts: Steve and Kathi Walker
Rooms: 6 (6PB) $105–135
Continental Breakfast
Credit Cards: A B C D E
Notes: 2   10 12

FREDERICKSBURG

La Vista Plantation

4420 Guinea Station Rd.
  Fredericksburg, VA 22408-8850
(540) 898-8444; (800) 529-2823
E-mail: info@lavistaplantation.com
Web site: www.lavistaplantation.com

An 1838 Classical Revival country home nestled amid ancient tulip poplars, cedars, and hollies, surrounded by pastures, woods, and fields. The house retains its original charm, with intricate acorn-and-oak-leaf moldings, high ceilings, wide pine floors, and a two-story front portico. Choose a two-bedroom apartment (sleeps six) or huge formal room with mahogany, rice-carved, king poster bed. Both have AC, fireplaces, satellite TV/VCR, radios, and refrigerators. Brown-egg breakfast and stocked pond.

Hosts: Michele and Edward Schiesser
Rooms: 2 (2PB) $115
Full Breakfast
Credit Cards: A B
Notes: 2 5 7 8 10 12

La Vista Plantation

HARBORTON

Harborton House

28044 Harborton Rd., Harborton, VA 23389
(757) 442-6800; (800) 882-0922
E-mail: info@harbortonhouse.com
Web site: www.harbortonhouse.com

Guests enjoy casual luxury at Harborton House while relaxing on the wrap-around porches of the graceful Victorian home. Located in the

---

6 Pets welcome; 7 Children welcome; 8 Tennis nearby; 9 Swimming nearby; 10 Golf nearby; 11 Skiing nearby; 12 May be booked through travel agent

heart of a peaceful residential fishing village, Harborton House is centrally situated close to all eastern shore attractions. There is a public dock and boat ramp in town.

Hosts: Helen and Andy Glenn
Rooms: 3 (3PB) $79–109
Full Breakfast
Credit Cards: A B
Notes: 2 5 8 9 10 12

Harborton House

HARRISONBURG

Kingsway Bed and Breakfast

3955 Singers Glen Rd.
   Harrisonburg, VA 22802-0711
(540) 867-9696
E-mail: leamancg@juno.com

Your hosts make your comfort their priority. The home is in a quiet rural area with a view of the mountains in the beautiful Shenandoah Valley. Hosts' carpentry and homemaking skills, houseplants and outdoor flowers, a large lawn, and the in-ground pool help make your stay restful. Just 4 1/2 miles from downtown. Nearby is Skyline Drive, caverns, historic sites, antique shops, and flea markets.

Hosts: Chester and Verna Leaman
Rooms: 3 (1PB;2SB) $60–65
Full Breakfast
Credit Cards:
Notes: 2 5 7 9 10 11 12

LEESBURG

Norris House Inn and Stove House Tea Room

108 Loudoun St., SW, Leesburg, VA 20175
(703) 777-1806; (800) 644-1806
   Fax (703) 771-8051
E-mail: inn@norrishouse.com
Web site: www.norrishouse.com

Elegant accommodations in the heart of Leesburg's historic district. Six guest rooms furnished with antiques and three wood-burning fireplaces. Full country breakfast. Convenient location within walking distance of fine restaurants. An hour's drive from Washington, DC, in Virginia's hunt country, rich in colonial and Civil War history, antiquing, and quaint villages. Perfect for romantic getaways, small meetings, and weddings. Open daily by reservation. Stone House Tea Room located on the inn's right.

Hosts: Pam and Don McMurray
Rooms: 6 (6SB) $100–150
Full Breakfast
Credit Cards: A B C D E
Notes: 2 5 8 9 10 12

LEXINGTON

Stoneridge Bed and Breakfast

246 Stoneridge Ln., Glasgow, VA 24555
(540) 463-4090; (800) 491-2930
   Fax (540) 463-6078
Web site: www.webfeat-inc.com/stoneridge

Stoneridge B & B is a romantic, 1829 antebellum home on 36 secluded acres of fields, streams, and woodlands. Five guest rooms each have private baths, queen beds, and ceiling fans. Most

---

NOTES: Credit cards accepted: A Master Card; B Visa; C American Express; D Discover; E Diners Club; F Other; 2 Personal checks accepted; 3 Lunch available; 4 Dinner available; 5 Open all year;

feature private balconies or porches, double Jacuzzis, and fireplaces. The large front porch affords wonderful mountain views and spectacular sunsets. Virginia wines are available, and a full gourmet country breakfast is served in the candlelit dining room or on the patio. Central AC. Five minutes south of historic Lexington. Children over 12 welcome.

Hosts: Jim and Evelyn Stallard
Rooms: 5 (5PB) $115–160
Full Breakfast
Credit Cards: A B C
Notes: 2 5

Stoneridge

LURAY

White Fence B & B

275 Chapel Rd., Stanley, VA 22851
(540) 778-4680; (800) 211-9885
  Fax (540) 778-4773
E-mail: whifenbb@shentel.net
Web site: www.whitefencebb.com

An 1890 Victorian on 3 acres in the beautiful Shenandoah Valley. Near Skyline Drive, the famous Luray Caverns, and 90 minutes to DC. Two cottages and one B & B suite, all with queen bed, TV/VCR, fireplace, two-person whirlpool, breakfast area, plush robes, and CD/clock/radio. Enjoy a beautiful breakfast basket delivered to your suite or a gourmet breakfast at

the B & B. This is a romantic, private getaway for those who enjoy superior accommodations with impeccable attention to detail.

White Fence

Hosts: Tom and Gwen Paton
Rooms: 3 (3PB) $116–149
Full Breakfast
Credit Cards: A B D
Notes: 2 5 9 10 11 12

LYNCHBURG

Federal Crest Inn Bed and Breakfast

1101 Federal St., Lynchburg, VA 24504-3018
(434) 845-6155; (800) 818-6155
  Fax (434) 845-1445
E-mail: inn@federalcrest.com
Web site: www.federalcrest.com

Recharge your spirit at this 1909 mansion in the Federal Hill historic district. Enjoy unique woodwork, bedroom fireplaces, and private baths (some Jacuzzi), canopy queen beds, '50s cafe and gift shop, country gourmet breakfast, friendly hosts, and much more. Spend time rocking on our porch, strolling among the flowers, visiting Civil War and Thomas Jefferson historic sites or the new D-Day Memorial. Fine dining, golfing, and Blue Ridge Mountains nearby.

6 Pets welcome; 7 Children welcome; 8 Tennis nearby; 9 Swimming nearby; 10 Golf nearby; 11 Skiing nearby; 12 May be booked through travel agent

Hosts: Ann and Phil Ripley
Rooms: 4 (4PB) $125–155
Full Breakfast
Credit Cards: A B C D F
Notes: 2 5 7 8 9 10 11 12

Federal Crest Inn

MIDDLEBURG

Middle Grove Inn B & B

37175 Jeb Stuart Rd., Philomont, VA 20131
(540) 338-0918; Fax (540) 338-3947
E-mail: middlegroveinn@cswebmail.com
Web site: www.middlegroveinn.com

Bob and Vicki invite you to enjoy a
relaxing time with them at Middle
Grove—in a true country setting in
Virginia horse and hunt country. We
hope you use this time to rest, pray, play,
contemplate, etc., to renew your mind,
body, and spirit! Retreat weekends available as well as special packages.

Hosts: Bob and Vicki Moore
Rooms: 4 (2PB;2SB) $65–110
Full Breakfast
Credit Cards: A B C
Notes: 2 3 4 5 9 10

MONTROSS

Porterville B & B

14201 King's Hwy., Montross, VA 22520-9709
(804) 493-9394

You'll find this cozy former Baptist parsonage in historic rural Westmoreland
County, 45 miles east of Fredericksburg
on VA St. Rte. 3. Nearby is Stratford
Hall Plantation, George Washington's
birthplace, Westmoreland State Park,
the county courthouse and museum.
Our two comfortable guest quarters,
the Cornelia Room and the Juanita
Room, are both on ground level for easy
acccess. A full country breakfast is
served daily, along with a big helping of
Southern hospitality. Ask about our
rates for singles.

Host: Mary Hall
Rooms: 2 (2SB) $65–95
Full Breakfast
Notes: 2 5 7 8 9 10

MT. JACKSON

Widow Kip's Country Inn

355 Orchard Dr., Mt. Jackson, VA 22842-9753
(540) 477-2400; (800) 478-8714
   Fax (540) 477-2409
E-mail: widokips@shentel.net
Web site: www.widowkips.com

Widow Kip's

NOTES: Credit cards accepted: A Master Card; B Visa; C American Express; D Discover; E Diners
Club; F Other; 2 Personal checks accepted; 3 Lunch available; 4 Dinner available; 5 Open all year;

A stately 1830 Colonial on 7 rural acres in the Shenandoah Valley overlooks the Blue Ridge Mountains. A romantic getaway, it offers five rooms in the main inn with fireplaces and antiques, as well as two courtyard cottages. Locally crafted quilts adorn the four-poster, canopy, and sleigh beds. Attractions include Civil War battlefields and museums, caverns, canoeing, hiking, horseback riding, golf, fishing, skiing, and swimming. A comment by a recent guest: "You have set a standard of professional excellence; we will be back."

Hosts: Betty and Bob Luse
Rooms: 7 (7PB) $85–125
Full Breakfast
Credit Cards: A B
Notes: 2 3 5 6 7 8 9 10 11 12

ROANOKE

The Chocolate Moose B & B

P. O. Box 802, 117 E. Blue Ridge St.
  Stuart, VA 24171
(276) 694-3745
Web site: www.chocolatemoosebb.com

The Chocolate Moose

This warm and elegant Southern home stands on the site where Stuart Normal College was established in

1867. Inside, the house has been restored to pristine condition with a very detailed decor that gives it a classic ambience. Outside, there are many gardens and a hydro spa that beckons guests to sit awhile and relax. Innkeepers Darryl and Judith love gardening and cooking and share their good energy doing massage therapy. As a naturopathic physician, Judith provides consultations and stocks a full line of herbs and supplements that are surrounded by beautiful handcrafted dried flower arrangements. Judith offers a complete nutritional analysis to get you on the road toward better health through supplementation and lifestyle changes. This healthful B & B offers an Overnight Rejuvenation Package that includes massage, dinner, and overnight stay with complimentary breakfast for $250 per couple.

Hosts: Darryl Bobletz and Judith Toscano
Rooms: 3 (1PB;2SB) $65
Full Breakfast
Credit Cards: A B

STAUNTON

Thornrose House at Gypsy Hill

531 Thornrose Ave., Staunton, VA 24401-3161
(540) 885-7026; (800) 861-4338
  Fax (540) 885-6458
E-mail: innkeeper@thronrosehouse.com
Web site: www.thornrosehouse.com

Thornrose House is a turn-of-the-century Georgian Revival house with a wrap-around veranda and nearly 1 acre of beautiful landscaped gardens graced with two sets of pergolas with brick walkways. It is adjacent to the 300-acre Gypsy Hill Park with facilities for golf, tennis, swimming, and summer band concerts. We're conveniently located in the heart of the Shenandoah Valley, presenting opportunities for hiking, biking, antiquing, historical museums, theaters including Shenandoah Shakespeare, and numerous fine restaurants. Children 6 and over welcome.

Thornrose House at Gypsy Hill

Hosts: Otis and Suzanne Huston
Rooms: 5 (5PB) $75–95
Full Breakfast
Credit Cards: A B C
Notes: 2 5 7 8 9 10

STAUNTON

Frederick House

28 N. New St., Staunton, VA 24401
(540) 885-4220; Fax (540) 885-5180
E-mail: ejharman@frederickhouse.com
Web site: www.frederickhouse.com

Frederick House is a small historic hotel in the European tradition. Six restored homes are situated across from Mary Baldwin College in Staunton, the oldest city in the Shenandoah Valley. You can walk to

restaurants, antique shops, galleries, and museums.

Hosts: Joe and Evy Harman
Rooms: 23 (23PB) $85–175
Full Breakfast
Credit Cards: A B C D E

TANGIER

Shirley's Bay View Inn

16408 W. Ridge Rd., P. O. Box 183
    Tangier, VA 23440-0183
(757) 891-2396
Web site: www.tangierisland.net

Enjoy a pleasant and restful visit to one of the last quiet and remote fishing villages on the Chesapeake Bay. You will stay at one of the oldest homes on Tangier Island, filled with the beauty and charm of days gone by. The beautiful beaches, sunsets, and customs of Tangier Island will make your stay a memorable one, and your hostess will make you feel you are part of the family.

Hosts: Wallace and Shirley Pruitt
Rooms: 11 (9PB;2SB) $85
Full Breakfast
Notes: 2 5 7 9

Sunset Inn

16650 W. Ridge Rd., Tangier, VA 23440
(757) 891-2535
Web site: www.tangierislandsunset.com

As you stay overnight on Tangier Island, you'll enjoy the spectacular beauty of the Chesapeake Bay. Its sunsets and sunrises are as beautiful as you might ever imagine. Upon arriving on Tangier Island, you step back in time. No stoplights or highways, its small paved paths are for golf carts and bikes. Other than walking, this is the island's only transportation. The relaxing and peaceful atmosphere is enjoyed by all ages. We have swimming, clamming, fishing, crabbing, island tours and cruises, and shopping in our island shops. We have a variety of great restaurants on the island, which provide Chesapeake Bay blue crab meat entrees on their menus. Upon arriving on the island, Ms. Grace (Sunset Inn Bed and Breakfast host) updates all her guests as to things to do while on the island. Those who visit enjoy coming back whenever possible; for those who cannot, precious memories abound for a lifetime.

Sunset Inn

Host: Ms. Grace Brown
Rooms: 10 (10PB) $65–80
No Breakfast Served
Notes: 2 5 7 9

WARRENTON

Black Horse Inn

8393 Meetze Rd., Warrenton, VA 20187-4340
(540) 349-4020; Fax (540) 349-4020
E-mail: relax@blackhorseinn.com
Web site: www.blackhorseinn.com

Black Horse Inn

In the heart of Virginia's horse country and vineyards and less than 1 hour from Washington DC, is the majestic Black Horse Inn, circa 1850. The inn reflects the deep, rich history of Virginia, beautifully situated on a hill with thoroughbred horses galloping in the fields surrounding the inn. It has nine unique rooms, each appointed with period pieces and reproductions and all with private baths. Four rooms have fireplaces, four have whirlpool baths, one has a multispray, spa-style shower; the remainder have claw-foot tubs and showers, and most have four-poster canopy beds. Rates range from $125 to $295 per evening and include a full breakfast and a hunt country tea. Children over 12 years old welcome.

Host: Lynn A. Pirozzoli
Rooms: 9 (9PB) $125–295
Full Breakfast
Credit Cards: A B C D
Notes: 2 5 7 8 9 10 12

WASHINGTON

Caledonia Farm—1812

47 Dearing Rd., Flint Hill, VA 22627
(540) 675-3693; (800) 262-1812
    Fax (540) 675-3693
Web site: www.bnb-n-va.com/cale1812.htm

6 Pets welcome; 7 Children welcome; 8 Tennis nearby; 9 Swimming nearby; 10 Golf nearby; 11 Skiing nearby; 12 May be booked through travel agent

Enjoy ultimate hospitality, comfort, scenery, and recreation adjacent to Virginia's Shenandoah National Park. This romantic getaway to history and nature includes outstanding full breakfasts, fireplaces, air-conditioning, hayrides, bicycles, lawn games, VCR, and piano. Fine dining, caves, Skyline Drive, battlefields, stables, antiquing, hiking, and climbing are all nearby. Washington, DC, is 68 miles away; Washington, VA, just 4 miles. A Virginia historic landmark, the farm is listed on the National Register of Historic Places. Unwind in our new spa. Children over 12 welcome.

Host: Phil Irwin
Rooms: 2 (2PB) $140
Full Breakfast
Credit Cards: A B D
Notes: 2 5 7 8 9 10 11 12

WILLIAMSBURG

Colonial Capital B & B

501 Richmond Rd.
  Williamsburg, VA 23185-3537
(757) 229-0233; (800) 776-0570
  Fax (757) 253-7667
E-mail: ccbb@widomaker.com
Web site: www.ccbb.com

Walk three blocks to Colonial Williamsburg; just minutes away from Jamestown, Yorktown, Busch Gardens, and Water Country USA. Antique furnishings, cozy canopied beds, private baths, in-room phones, and TV/VCR create a rich blend of warmth, style, comfort, and convenience. Begin your day with a full cooked breakfast and in the afternoon enjoy tea, wine, and relax-

ing conversation with friends new and old in our guest parlor or on the screened porch, patio, and deck. Free off-street parking. Convenience packages, discount tickets, and gift certificates are available for any occasion. Airport and Amtrak pickup. Returning guest discounts.

Hosts: Barbara and Phil Craig
Rooms: 5 (5PB) $135–150
Full Breakfast
Credit Cards: A B C D F
Notes: 2 5 8 9 10 12

Fox and Grape
Bed and Breakfast

701 Monumental Ave., Williamsburg, VA 23185
(757) 229-6914; (800) 292-3699
  Fax (757) 229-0951
E-mail: info@foxandgrapebb.com
Web site: www.foxandgrapebb.com

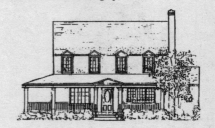

Fox and Grape

Here you'll find genteel accommodations 5 blocks north of Virginia's restored colonial capitol. This lovely two-story Colonial with its spacious wrap-around porch is a perfect place to enjoy your morning coffee, plan your day's activities in Williamsburg, or relax with your favorite book. Furnishings include antiques, counted cross-stitch, duck decoys, and folk-art Noah's arks made by your host. Pat enjoys doing counted cross-stitch; Bob carves walking sticks and makes nursery rhyme collectibles.

Hosts: Pat and Robert Orendorff
Rooms: 4 (4PB) $100–115
Full Breakfast
Credit Cards: A B D
Notes: 5 8 9 10

Hites Bed and Breakfast

704 Monumental Ave.
   Williamsburg, VA 23185-4505
(757) 229-4814

Charming Cape Cod—7-minute walk to Colonial Williamsburg. Spacious rooms furnished with antiques and collectibles. Each room has a TV, phone, coffeemaker, robes, and beautiful private baths with claw-foot tubs. The suite has a large sitting room with romantic setting, just what you want for a honeymoon, anniversary, etc. You can relax in a lovely garden with swings, goldfish pond.

Hites

Hosts: James and Faye Hite
Rooms: 2 (2PB) $95–110
Full Breakfast
Notes: 2 5 7 9 10 12

Liberty Rose B & B Inn

1022 Jamestown Rd.
   Williamsburg, VA 23185-3434
(757) 253-1260; (800) 545-1825
E-mail: reservations@libertyrose.com
Web site: www.libertyrose.com

Williamsburg's only 4-diamond bed and breakfast. Listed in the top ten most romantic by *American Historic Inns*. Beautiful hilltop setting 1 mile from Colonial Williamsburg historic village. Gardens, courtyards, century-old trees. Private luxurious baths and outstanding bed chambers! Breakfast is delicious, hosts are friendly, chocolate chip cookies are superb!

Hosts: Brad and Sandra Hirz
Rooms: 4 (4PB) $175–235
Full Breakfast
Credit Cards: A B C
Notes: 2 5 8 10 12

Newport House B & B

710 S. Henry St., Williamsburg, VA 23185-4113
(757) 229-1775

A reproduction of a 1756 home, Newport House has museum-standard period furnishings, including canopy beds. Only a 5-minute walk to the historic area. Breakfast with colonial recipes; colonial dancing in the ballroom Tuesday evenings (beginners welcome). The host is a historian/author (including a book on Christ) and former museum director. The hostess is a gardener, beekeeper, 18th-century seamstress, and former nurse. No smoking.

Hosts: John and Cathy Millar
Rooms: 2 (2PB) $140–160
Full Breakfast
Notes: 2 5 7 8 9 10 12

6 Pets welcome; 7 Children welcome; 8 Tennis nearby; 9 Swimming nearby; 10 Golf nearby; 11 Skiing nearby; 12 May be booked through travel agent

North Bend Plantation

12200 Weyanoke Rd.
  Charles City, VA 23030-3632
(804) 829-5176
Web site: www.northbendplantation.com

Circa 1819 National Register property, Greek Revival-style manor
house, 850-acre farm, owned and
operated by descendents of original
owner, Sarah Harrison—sister of 9th
U.S. president. Original antiques,
three porches, and pool. Lawn games,
bicycles, hammock, James River
Plantations, Colonial Williamsburg,
tennis, and golf nearby. Original Cross
and Open Bible doors, a Christian
home. Children over 6 welcome.

Hosts: George and Ridgely Copland
Rooms: 4 (4PB) $120–135
Full Breakfast
Credit Cards: A B
Notes: 2 5 7 8 9 10 12

Orange Hill B & B

18401 The Glebe Ln., Charles City, VA 23030
(804) 829-6988; (888) 501-8125
E-mail: orange-hill@juno.com
Web site: www.orangehillbb.com

Orange Hill

A cozy turn-of-the-century farmhouse, Orange Hill sits on 50 acres of
working farmland. It offers the peace-
fulness of the country in historic
Charles City County. It is only minutes from Colonial Williamsburg,
James River Plantations, Civil War
sites, shopping, fishing, golf, and
Colonial Downs racehorse track.
Features antiques. A Christian home.
Available for weddings. Children over
12 welcome.

Hosts: Mark and Kay Russo
Rooms: 3 (2PB;1SB) $80–105
Full Breakfast
Credit Cards: A B
Notes: 5 7 10

A Primrose Cottage

706 Richmond Rd.
  Williamsburg, VA 23185-3542
(757) 229-6421; (800) 522-1901
  Fax (757) 259-0717
Web site: www.primrose-cottage.com

A nature lover's delight. In the spring,
the front walkway is lined with prim-
roses. Thousands of tulips bloom in
April and May, and even in cooler
months something adds color to this
award-winning garden. There are four
rooms, all spacious, bright, and lovingly decorated with antiques. Three
rooms have fireplaces. Each has its
own TV and bath. Two of the bathrooms have Jacuzzis. You are invited to
play the harpsichord built by the
innkeeper. Wonderful hot breakfasts
are served every morning.

Host: Inge Curtis
Rooms: 4 (4PB) $95–125
Full Breakfast
Credit Cards: A B
Notes: 2 5 8 9 10 12

NOTES: Credit cards accepted: A Master Card; B Visa; C American Express; D Discover; E Diners
Club; F Other; 2 Personal checks accepted; 3 Lunch available; 4 Dinner available; 5 Open all year;

Williamsburg Sampler B & B Inn

922 Jamestown Rd.
  Williamsburg, VA 23185-3917
  (757) 253-0398; (800) 722-1169
    Fax (727) 253-2669
E-mail: wbgsamper@aol.com
Web site: www.williamsburgsampler.com

An 18th-century, plantation-style Colonial built during the bicentennial and in the heart of historic Colonial Williamsburg. Rich in warmth and atmosphere, so be prepared to be at "home" and relax in style. Chambers and suites with king-size pineapple-carved four-poster beds. View the Helen Marie Gallery of antiques and collectibles throughout the inn. Famous Skip Lunch® breakfast served each morning in the Rooster's Den. Proclaimed by Virginia's governor as Inn of the Year.

Williamsburg Sampler

Host: Ike Sisane
Rooms: 4 (4PB) $130–170
Full Breakfast
Credit Cards: A B
Notes: 2 5 8 9 10 12

WINCHESTER

Brownstone Cottage B & B

161 McCarty Ln., Winchester, VA 22602-4625
(540) 662-1962; Fax (540) 665-8948
E-mail: cs@brownstonecottage.com
Web site: www.brownstonecottage.com

Small, peaceful, quiet B & B in Shenandoah Valley. Five acres, only a short distance from interstate, restaurants, college, local theaters. Complimentary pass for guests to a local swim, racquet, and exercise club with sauna and whirlpool. We cater to private weddings—stress free! We make our guests feel very special and cared for. Garden with water fountain and swing, very relaxing. Afternoon tea available. Hostess ordained minister.

Brownstone Cottage

Hosts: Chuck and Sheila Brown
Rooms: 2 (2PB) $110
Full Breakfast
Credit Cards: A B
Notes: 2 5 8 9 10

Hotel Strasburg

213 S. Holliday St., Strasburg, VA 22657
(540) 465-9191; (800) 348-8327
    Fax (540) 465-4788
E-mail: thehotel@shentel.net
Web site: www.hotelstrasburg.com

Like stepping back in time to the 1890s, Hotel Strasburg combines

---

6 Pets welcome; 7 Children welcome; 8 Tennis nearby; 9 Swimming nearby; 10 Golf nearby; 11 Skiing nearby; 12 May be booked through travel agent

Victorian history and charm to make a special place for lodging, dining, and meeting. Our new conference/banquet facility will accommodate up to 100. Tastefully decorated with many antique period pieces of furniture and impressive collection of art. Guests are invited to wander through the inn's dining rooms and quaintly renovated sleeping rooms (Jacuzzi suites). Nestled at the foot of Massanutten Mountain near the entrance to the breathtaking Skyline Drive, Hotel Strasburg is your most romantic stop in the Romantic Era. Inquire about pets.

Hosts: Gary and Carol Rutherford
Rooms: 29 (29PB) $79–175
Continental Breakfast
Credit Cards: A B C D E
Notes: 3 4 5 7 9 10 11 12

WASHINGTON

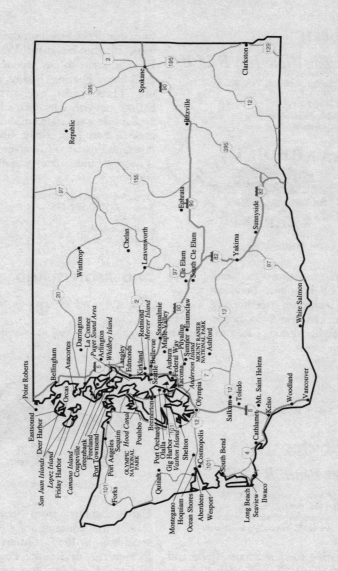

Washington

ABERDEEN

A Harbor View Inn B & B

111 W. 11th St., Aberdeen, WA 98520
(360) 533-7996; (877) 533-7996
   Fax (360) 533-0433
E-mail: harborview@olynet.com
Web site: www.aharborview.com

A Harbor View Inn

Every room with a water view, private baths, TV in rooms, breakfast served in the sunroom overlooking Grays Harbor. Historic 1905 home in historic neighborhood. Close to beaches and rain forest.

Host: Cindy Lonn
Rooms: 4 (4PB) $65–95
Full Breakfast
Credit Cards: A B
Notes: 5 7 8 9 10 12

ANACORTES

Sunset Beach B & B

2420 Puget Way, Anacortes, WA 98221
(360) 293-5428; (800) 359-3448
E-mail: sunsetbeach.bb@verizon.net
Web site: www.whidbey.com/sunsetbeach/

On exciting Rosario Straits. Relax and enjoy the view of seven major islands from our decks, stroll on the beach, or walk in the beautiful Washington Park, adjacent to our private gardens. Also enjoy boating, hiking, and fishing. Three bedrooms with private baths; one with a Jacuzzi; a hot tub is available in a separate building. 5 minutes to San Juan Ferry, fine restaurants, and marina. A convenient store is nearby. Sunsets are outstanding. No smoking.

Hosts: Joann and Hal Harker
Rooms: 3 (3PB) $89–125
Full Breakfast
Credit Cards: A B
Notes: 2 5 9 10 12

ANDERSON ISLAND

The Inn at Burg's Landing

8808 Villa Beach Rd.
   Anderson Island, WA 98303-9785
(253) 884-9185; (800) 431-5622
E-mail: innatburgslanding@mailexcite.com

The Inn at Burg's Landing

Catch the ferry from Steilacoom to stay at this contemporary log homestead built in 1987. It offers spectacular views of Mt. Rainier, Puget Sound, and the Cascade Mountains and is

---

NOTES: Credit cards accepted: A Master Card; B Visa; C American Express; D Discover; E Diners Club; F Other; 2 Personal checks accepted; 3 Lunch available; 4 Dinner available; 5 Open all year;

located south of Tacoma off I-5. Choose from three guest rooms, including the master bedroom with queen-size "log" bed, skylight above, and private whirlpool bath. The inn has a private beach. Collect seashells and agates, swim in two freshwater lakes nearby, and enjoy a game of tennis or golf. Tour the island by bicycle or on foot and watch for sailboats and deer. Hot tub. Full breakfast. Families welcome. No smoking.

Hosts: Ken and Annie Burg
Rooms: 4 (2PB;2SB) $80–125
Full Breakfast
Credit Cards: A B
Notes: 2 5 7 8 9 10 11

BELLINGHAM

South Bay B & B

4095 South Bay Dr. / Lake Whatcom
   Sedro Woolley, WA 98284
(360) 595-2086; (877) 595-2086
   Fax (360) 595-1043
E-mail: southbay@gte.net
Web site: www.southbaybb.com

Located on a hillside overlooking Lake Whatcom, South Bay is 15 miles SE of Bellingham, 15 miles NW of Sedro-Woolley. This Craftsman Retreat has guest rooms with queen beds, gas fireplaces, and private baths/oversize jetted whirlpool tubs for two. There are beautiful views from the patios, wrap-around porch, and decks. All guest rooms and common rooms have beautiful views of the lake and the forest. Come and rest at this quiet, peaceful, and romantic retreat.

Hosts: Dan and Sally Moore
Rooms: 4 (4PB) $135–150

Full Breakfast
Credit Cards: A B
Notes: 2 5 8 9 10 11 12

South Bay

CAMANO ISLAND

Inn at Barnum Point

464 S. Barnum Rd.
   Camano Island, WA 98282-8578
(360) 387-2256; (800) 910-2256
E-mail: barnum@camano.net
Web site: www.innatbarnumpoint.com

Spectacular view on a saltwater bay surrounded by mountains. Lights reflect on the water at night, and the moon shines a gold or silver path across it. Guest rooms are warm and cozy in winter and light and airy in summer. Try our luxury Shorebird Room with separate entrance, loft, soaking tub, and deck with grill. Breakfast provided. Sleeps 4–6. All rooms have a private bath, fireplace, and TV. Full breakfast.

Host: Carolin Barnum Dilorenzo
Rooms: 3 (3PB) $99–199
Full Breakfast
Credit Cards: A B D F
Notes: 2 5 7 8 9 10 12

---

6 Pets welcome; 7 Children welcome; 8 Tennis nearby; 9 Swimming nearby; 10 Golf nearby; 11 Skiing nearby; 12 May be booked through travel agent

CHELAN

Holden Village Bed and Breakfast

21081 S. Lakeshore Rd., Chelan, WA 98816
(509) 687-9695; Fax (509) 687-3375
Web site: www.holdenvillage.org

A quiet, comfortable country-style B & B with many handmade items including quilts, pottery, weavings, tables, and a delicious family-style breakfast. A large, covered porch overlooks beautiful Lake Chelan and the mountains beyond. Forest walking trails are nearby. Just 3 miles away, the Lady of the Lake boat heads uplake toward our parent community. Holden Village is a remote ecumenical retreat center that provides a place of healing, renewal, and refreshment for all of God's diverse people.

Rooms: 7 (7SB) $36–60
Full Breakfast
Credit Cards:
Notes: 2 5 7 9

A Quails Roost Inn

121 E. Highland Ave., Chelan, WA 98816-9625
(509) 682-2892; (800) 681-2892
Web site: www.aquailsroostinn.com

A Quails Roost Inn

Homesteaded in 1896, this Queen Anne-style Victorian was finished in 1902. The home is listed on the National Register of Historic Places. The mansion is situated on the north hill overlooking Lake Chelan and is a short walk from downtown or the lake. The view is breathtaking from the huge wrap-around veranda or the private porch off the Rose and Wicker Rooms. All rooms are theme-decorated and hand-stenciled. During the summer, enjoy your gourmet breakfast and fresh-ground coffee on the veranda.

Host: Marilee Stolzenburg
Rooms: 3 (3PB) $65–125
Full Breakfast
Credit Cards: A B F
Notes: 2 5 7 8 9 10 11 12

CLARKSTON

Cliff House Bed and Breakfast

1227 Westlake Dr.
  Clarkston, WA 99403-9755
(509) 758-1267
E-mail: cliffhouse@clarkston.com
Web site: www.cliffhouseclarkston.com

The Cliff House offers a quiet country atmosphere with an unsurpassed panoramic view of the Snake River 500 feet below, surrounded by majestic hills. There are many opportunities to observe a variety of wildlife. In this area, white-water rafting and jet-boat trips are taken into North America's deepest gorge, nearby Hell's Canyon. Relax in king beds and feast on a scrumptious breakfast. Pets welcome in pet carriers.

NOTES: Credit cards accepted: A Master Card; B Visa; C American Express; D Discover; E Diners Club; F Other; 2 Personal checks accepted; 3 Lunch available; 4 Dinner available; 5 Open all year;

Cliff House

Hosts: Yvonne and Everett Dickerson
Rooms: 2 (2PB) $80–85
Full Breakfast
Credit Cards:
Notes: 2 5 8 9 10 11

CLE ELUM

Iron Horse Inn
Bed and Breakfast

P. O. Box 629, South Cle Elum, WA 98943
(509) 674-5939; (800) 22TWAIN
   Fax (509) 674-1708
E-mail: maryp@cleelum.com
Web site: www.ironhorseinnbb.com

Former Milwaukee Railroad train crew bunkhouse, now offering eight bright and airy rooms on the second floor and two caboose car suites. The bridal suite has a double-size jetted tub. On the National Register of Historic Places, the inn has a museum-like atmosphere with an extensive collection of railroad memorabilia and artifacts. Nestled in the Cascade Mountain foothills, the inn is close to cross-country skiing, hiking, biking, rafting, horseback riding, fishing, and fine dining. Only 90 minutes east of Seattle.

Hosts: Mary and Doug Pittis
Rooms: 10 (6PB;4SB) $70–135

Full Breakfast
Credit Cards: A B
Notes: 2 5 7 10 11

COUPEVILLE

Anchorage Inn B & B

807 N. Main St., P. O. Box 673
   Coupeville, WA 98239
(360) 678-5811; (877) 230-1313
E-mail: anchorag@whidbey.net
Web site: www.anchorage-inn.com

Anchorage Inn

This Victorian has all the conveniences of the 21st century with private baths, TV/VCR, and phone. Sitting just 1 block above Penn Cove, sailboats and majestic Mt. Baker can be seen while enjoying coffee on our wrap-around porch. Full breakfasts are served every morning and refreshments all day long.

Hosts: Dave and Dianne Binder
Rooms: 7 (7PB) $80–130
Full Breakfast
Credit Cards: A B D F
Notes: 2 10

6 Pets welcome; 7 Children welcome; 8 Tennis nearby; 9 Swimming nearby; 10 Golf nearby; 11 Skiing nearby; 12 May be booked through travel agent

DEER HARBOR

Palmer's Chart House

P. O. Box 51, Orcas Island
  Deer Harbor, WA 98243
(360) 376-4231

The first bed and breakfast on Orcas Island (since 1975) with a magnificent water view. The 33-foot private yacht *Amante* is available for a minimal fee, with skipper Don. Low-key, personal attention makes this bed and breakfast unique and attractive. Well-traveled hosts speak Spanish. Children over 12 welcome.

Palmer's Chart House

Host: Don and Majean Palmer
Rooms: 2 (2PB) $60–80
Continental Breakfast
Notes: 2 8 9 10 11

LA CONNER

Benson Farmstead B & B

10113 Avon-Allen Rd., Bow, WA 98232
(360) 757-0578; (800) 441-9814
E-mail: bensonfarmstead@hotmail.com
Web site: www.bbhost.com/bensonbnb

Benson Farmstead is a lovely farmhouse filled with antiques and Scandinavian curios. It is surrounded by gardens and has a separate family cottage across the yard. After a delightful breakfast, take time to visit the historic town of LaConner, ferry to the San Juans, or go hiking and biking on the many nearby trails and parks. Have dinner at one of the excellent restaurants on Chuckanut Drive and return to the Bensons for homemade dessert and a soak in the hot tub.

Hosts: Jerry and Sharon Benson
Rooms: 5 (5PB) $80–99
Full Breakfast
Credit Cards: A B
Notes: 2 5 7 8 9 10 11 12

Rainbow Inn Bed and Breakfast

12757 Chilberg Rd., P. O. Box 15
  La Conner, WA 98257
(360) 466-4578; (888) 266-8879
  Fax (360) 466-3844
E-mail: rainbow@rainbowinnbandb.com
Web site: www.rainbowinnbandb.com

For a romantic, peaceful repose in a 1902–08 Craftsman home where Jesus' love flows, relax in a hammock or hot tub with a view of rich Skagit Valley farmlands and Mount Baker. Fine dining, antiques, quaint shops, kayaking, hot-air balloons, and bird- and whale-watching are available from La Conner. Miles of flat roads for biking and mountains for hiking and skiing. Grandma's cookies await you after your fun-filled day.

Hosts: Squires Family (Tom, Patsy, and Pam)
Rooms: 8 (5PB;3SB) $70–115
Full Breakfast
Credit Cards: A B C D E
Notes: 2 5 7 8 9 10 11 12

LEAVENWORTH

Bosch Garten B & B

9846 Dye Rd., Leavenworth, WA 98826-9312
(509) 548-6900; (800) 535-0069
    Fax (509) 548-3610
E-mail: innkeeper@boschgarten.com
Web site: www.boschgarten.com

Join your hosts for quiet elegance and
warm hospitality in this modern B & B
within walking distance of the unique
Bavarian Village. Spacious guest
rooms feature king beds, private baths,
and cable TV. Homemade breakfasts
feature local fruits with special dietary
needs considered. Enjoy cultural
events, festivals, and summer theater
productions in addition to the many
seasonal outdoor activities. Amenities
include hot tub, viewing decks, guest
living room, and library. Children over
12 welcome.

Hosts: Georgeanne and Denny Nichols
Rooms: 3 (3PB) $102–130
Full Breakfast
Credit Cards: A B
Notes: 2 5 8 9 10 11

Run of the River

9308 E. Leavenworth Rd., P. O. Box 285
    Leavenworth, WA 98826
(509) 548-7171; (800) 288-6491
    Fax (509) 548-7547
E-mail: info@runoftheriver.com
Web site: www.runoftheriver.com

This time, celebrate someplace special.
Run of the River, a nationally
acclaimed log inn on the Icicle River,
has been featured in *Country Living,*
Walking Magazine, Country Inns, and
Log Home Living. All suites feature

private decks with views of the river,
refuge, and mountains that surround
the inn. Each suite has a fireplace and
Jacuzzi tub surrounded by river rock,
spacious baths with luxurious features,
and hand-hewn log king beds.

Run of the River

Hosts: Monty and Karen Turner
Rooms: 6 (6PB) $205–245
Full Breakfast
Credit Cards: A B D
Notes: 2 5 8 9 10 11

OLYMPIA

Swantown Inn B & B

1431 11th Ave., SE, Olympia, WA 98501-2411
(360) 753-9123; Fax (360) 943-8047
E-mail: swantown@olywa.ne
Web site: www.swantowninn.us

Located in an elegant 1893 Victorian
mansion in the heart of Olympia surrounded by 3/4 acre of garden, the
Swantown Inn can be your headquarters to exploring the Puget Sound
region or your refuge for a quiet
retreat. Queen beds with cozy down
comforters, private baths, beautiful
views of the sunset over the capitol
dome, an inviting gazebo, and gourmet breakfasts are some of the ingre-
dients for a memorable visit.

---

6 Pets welcome; 7 Children welcome; 8 Tennis nearby; 9 Swimming nearby; 10 Golf nearby; 11 Skiing
nearby; 12 May be booked through travel agent

Hosts: Ed and Lillian Peeples
Rooms: 4 (4PB) $75–115
Full Breakfast
Credit Cards: A B
Notes: 2 5 12

ORCAS ISLAND

Massacre Bay Bed and Breakfast and Cottage

2098 Deer Harbor Rd., Eastbound, WA 98245
(360) 376-2766; (877) 248-7833
    Fax (360) 376-2766
E-mail: massacrebay@interisland.net
Web site: www.interisland.net/massacrebayb&b

Contemporary setting on 2 rural acres, Massacre Bay B & B provides spectacular marine views from upstairs bedrooms and studio cottage. Private view balconies. Living room and library with satellite TV/VCR, movies, books, games. Hearty breakfast served in your room, on your balcony, or main deck. Mooring buoy and bicycles available. On Orcas Island enjoy whale-watching cruises, kayaking, and hiking in Moran State Park. Sensible rates, seasonal discounts.

Hosts: Ray and Karen Brown
Rooms: 3 (3PB) $89–129
Full Breakfast
Notes: 2 5 7 10

Turtleback Farm Inn

1981 Crow Valley Rd.
    Eastbound, WA 98245-9704
(360) 376-4914; (800) 376-4914
    Fax (360) 376-5329
E-mail: info@turtlebackinn.com
Web site: www.turtlebackinn.com

Turtleback Farm Inn is noted for detail-perfect restoration, elegantly comfortable and spotless rooms, a glorious setting, and award-winning breakfasts. You will be made welcome and pampered by the warm hospitality of Bill and Susan Fletcher and their staff. Orcas Island is a haven for anyone who enjoys spectacular scenery, varied outdoor activities, unique shopping, and superb food. As spring turns to summer, the warm days encourage your enjoyment of nature at its best. Flowers are in full bloom; birds flutter; whales, seals, and porpoises coast lazily through the shimmering waters of the sound. After a day of hiking, fishing, bicycling, kayaking, sailing, windsurfing, or just reading by our pond, return to Turtleback for a relaxing soak in your private bath or a sherry on the deck overlooking the valley below. After a tasty dinner at one of the island's fine restaurants and perhaps a performance at the Orcas Center, guests can snuggle under a custom-made woolen comforter and doze off with visions of the delicious breakfast awaiting them in the morning.

Hosts: William and Susan C. Fletcher
Rooms: 11 (11PB) $90–225
Full Breakfast
Credit Cards: A B C D
Notes: 2 3 5 7 8 9 10 12

PORT ANGELES

Angeles Inn B & B

1203 E. 7th St.; P. O. Box 87
    Port Angeles, WA 98362
(360) 457-4269; (888) 552-4269
    Fax (360) 457-4269

NOTES: Credit cards accepted: A Master Card; B Visa; C American Express; D Discover; E Diners Club; F Other; 2 Personal checks accepted; 3 Lunch available; 4 Dinner available; 5 Open all year;

E-mail: info@angelesinn.com
Web site: www.angelesinn.com

Built by us in 1976, our house of 4,500 sq. ft. has almost 900 sq.ft. of common area. Our bedrooms are separated by at least two walls for quiet and privacy. The entire house has all the amenities you would expect in a 21st-century dwelling. *Better Homes and Gardens* featured, award-winning, contemporary dwelling. Centrally located on a quiet dead-end street with ground-level rooms. All king-size beds, private and shared baths, and CTV. Delicious, hearty breakfast served in our formal dining room between 7:00–9:00 A.M.

Hosts: Al and June James
Rooms: 4 (2PB;2SB) $65–115
Full Breakfast
Credit Cards: A B
Notes: 2 5 7 8 9 10 11 12

Five Seasuns Bed and Breakfast Inn

1006 S. Lincoln St., Port Angeles, WA 98362
(360) 452-8248; (800) 708-0777
   Fax (360) 452-8248
E-mail: info@seasuns.com
Web site: www.seasuns.com

Five Seasuns

Glorious gardens abound on estate grounds surrounding 1920s Dutch Colonial home with panoramic water and mountain views. Guest rooms are appointed for your comfort as you journey back to memories of time gone by.

Hosts: Jan and Bob
Rooms: 5 (5PB) $79–135
Full Breakfast
Credit Cards: A B C D
Notes: 2 3 8 9 11 12

PORT TOWNSEND

Ann Starrett Mansion B & B

744 Clay St., Port Townsend, WA 98368
(360) 385-3205; (800) 321-0644
   Fax (360) 385-2976
E-mail: info@starrettmansion.com
Web site: www.starrettmansion.com

A destination with a sense of history is a vacation with "romance." The 1889 mansion was built as a wedding gift. Authentic antiques and ambience will take you back to a gentler time. The inn won a National Trust for Historic Preservation "Great American Home Award." The lovely views and scrumptious breakfast will make you want to stay forever.

Hosts: Bob and Edel Sokol
Rooms: 11 (11PB) $110–190
Full Breakfast
Credit Cards: A B C D
Notes: 2 5 7 8 9 10 11 12

6 Pets welcome; 7 Children welcome; 8 Tennis nearby; 9 Swimming nearby; 10 Golf nearby; 11 Skiing nearby; 12 May be booked through travel agent

SEATTLE

Hill House
Bed and Breakfast

1113 E. John St., Seattle, WA 98102-5811
(206) 720-7161; (800) 720-7161
    Fax (206) 323-0772
E-mail: visitus@seattlebnb.com
Web site: www.seattlebnb.com

This 1903 Victorian is just a 15-minute
walk from downtown. It features superb
gourmet breakfasts served on china and
crystal and offers seven rooms, tastefully
appointed with antiques. All rooms
have queen beds with down comforters
and cotton sheets, fresh flowers, handmade soaps, and bathrobes. Walk to
numerous shops and restaurants.
Located 1/2 mile from downtown
attractions such as the Convention
Center and Pike Place Market. Close to
transportation and off-street parking.
AAA 3-diamond, Fodors, Seattle's
"Best Places, Best Places to Kiss
Northwest."

Hosts: Herman and Alea Foster
Rooms: 7 (5PB;2SB) $75–170
Gourmet Breakfast
Credit Cards: A B C D E F
Notes: 5 8 9 10

Hudgens Haven

9313 190, SW, Edmonds, WA 98020
(425) 776-2202
E-mail: booboona3@pol.net

Edmonds is a waterfront coummunity
on Puget Sound. Furnished in colonial
antiques with large guest room.
Queen-size bed, two chairs, one
rocker. Private bath and den with TV.

Large patio and garden. We are
located in a quiet neighborhood with a
striking view of Puget Sound and the
Olympic   Mountains.   Excellent
restaurants and shops.

Hosts: Edward and Lorna Hudgens
Rooms: 1 (1PB) $70–75
Full Breakfast
Notes: 2 5 6 9

SEQUIM

Glenna's Guthrie Cottage

10083 Old Olympic Hwy., Sequim, WA 98382
(360) 681-4341; (800) 930-4349
E-mail: glennas@olypen.com
Web site: www.olypen.com/glennas

Comfortable home setting in picturesque Sequim-Dungeness Valley, just
minutes from Highway 101, secluded
and peaceful. Some of the niceties at
Glenna's: a 32" TV in common room,
karaoke, cable TV in most rooms,
Olympic Mountain view, eagle watching, fax machine, on Olympic bike
trail, RV and boat parking, snack baskets in suites, 4-5 course breakfast, hot
tub under the stars, historic country
farm, we take children, old classics
VCR library, gift and antique shop,
suites have own entrance, guest Email
service, hot tub robes in rooms.

Hosts: Jack and Glenna O'Neil
Rooms: 4 (2PB;2SB) $69–135
Full Breakfast
Credit Cards: A B C
Notes: 2 7 8 9 10 11 12

NOTES: Credit cards accepted: A Master Card; B Visa; C American Express; D Discover; E Diners
Club; F Other; 2 Personal checks accepted; 3 Lunch available; 4 Dinner available; 5 Open all year;

SOUTH BEND

Maring's Courthouse Hill Bed and Breakfast

602 W. 2nd St., P. O. Box 34
    South Bend, WA 98586-0034
(360) 875-6519; (800) 875-6519
E-mail: maringbb@willapabay.org
Web site: www.willapabay.org/~maringbb

An 1892 church, this B & B is now a historic home with tasteful decor, offering river views, comfort, and warm hospitality in picturesque South Bend. Spacious guest rooms have queen/twin beds, cable television, and private baths. A full breakfast is served. Quiet location with wildlife. Situated 5 blocks off 101, a short walk from downtown. Well-behaved children welcome.

Hosts: Ed and Frances Maring
Rooms: 3 (2PB;1SB) $55–65
Full Breakfast
Credit Cards: A B C
Notes: 2   5   7   8   10

The Russell House Bed and Breakfast

902 E. Water St.; P. O. Box F
    South Bend, WA 98586
(360) 875-6487; (888) 484-6907
    Fax (360) 875-0025
E-mail: srowan@willipabay.org
Web site: www.willapabay.org/~srowan

Victorian home built in 1891 by John Russell. Overlooking the bay and surrounding territorial views. One hour to the beach and fishing area. Clam digging nearby, historical area. Celebrate your anniversary, birthday, or any special occasion. Business or just a night away from reality.

Hosts: Steve and Sylvia Rowan
Rooms: 4 (2PB;2SB) $70–90
Full Breakfast
Credit Cards: A B C D
Notes: 2 3 4 5 6 7   10 12

VANCOUVER

Vintage Inn Bed and Breakfast

310 W. 11th St., Vancouver, WA 98660-3146
(360) 693-6635; (888) 693-6635
E-mail: info@vintage-inn.com
Web site: www.vintage-inn.com

Hospitality plus! One of Vancouver's original mansions built in 1903 in the heart of downtown, with elegant antiques throughout. On the National Historic Register. Large rooms with comfortable queen beds. Bountiful breakfasts. Fine restaurants, antique shops, theaters, and art galleries—all within walking distance. Fort Vancouver national historic site 7 blocks away. Easy freeway access. Fifteen minutes from downtown Portland, Oregon, and airport. No smoking, pets, or alcohol.

Hosts: Mike and Doris Hale
Rooms: 4 (4SB) $89
Full Breakfast
Credit Cards: A B
Notes: 2   5   7

WHIDBEY ISLAND

Cliff House and Cottage

727 Windmill Dr., Freeland, WA 98249
(360) 321-1566; (800) 450-7142

---

6 Pets welcome; 7 Children welcome; 8 Tennis nearby; 9 Swimming nearby; 10 Golf nearby; 11 Skiing nearby; 12 May be booked through travel agent

E-mail: wink@whidbey.com
Web site: www.cliffhouse.net

Cliff House

Welcome to beautiful Whidbey Island and the stunning, amazing Cliff House or the "gnomelike" country cottage. Each is yours alone, graced by this natural coastal island setting with miles of beach. You will relax in seclusion with luxurious feather beds, fireplaces, kitchens, TV/VCR/CDs. Share your forest and sea retreat with deer, racoons, squirrels, blue heron, sea creatures, and our resident pair of nesting bald eagles! Dramatic views of mountains and sunsets over Puget Sound with world shipping lanes.

Hosts: Peggy Moore and Walter O'Toole
Rooms: 2 (2PB) $195–450
Continental Breakfast
Notes: 2 5 10 12

Guest House Cottages

24371 S. R. 525, Greenbank, WA 98253
(360) 678-3115; Fax (360) 678-3115
E-mail: guesthse@whidbey.net
Web site: www.guesthouselogcottages.com

Discover privacy, peace, and pampering in each of our six individually designed cottages in Greenbank, Whidbey Island. (Four of the cottages are log houses.) Each cottage has a private setting on 25 acres of island greenery and features personal Jacuzzis, fireplaces, kitchens, and TV/VCRs. More than 500 complimentary movies, an outdoor swimming pool, and a hot tub make for a relaxing retreat for two.

Hosts: Don and Maryjane Creger
Rooms: 6 (6PB) $125–295
Continental Breakfast
Credit Cards: A B D
Notes: 2 5 12

NOTES: Credit cards accepted: A Master Card; B Visa; C American Express; D Discover; E Diners Club; F Other; 2 Personal checks accepted; 3 Lunch available; 4 Dinner available; 5 Open all year;

WEST VIRGINIA

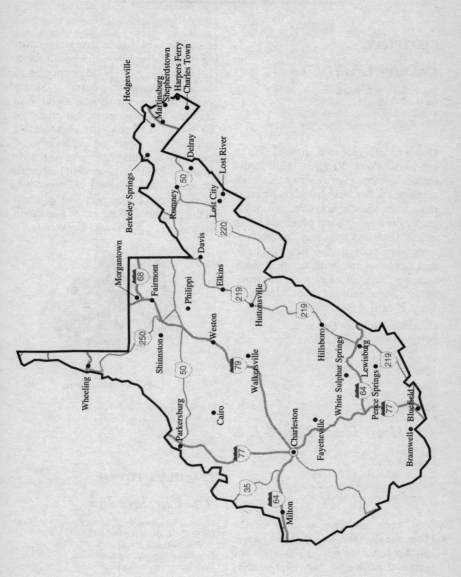

<u>West Virginia</u>

BLUEFIELD

Country Chalet B & B

Rte. 1, Box 176 B, Bluefield, WV 24701
(304) 487-2120; (866) 240-8455
E-mail: admin@countrychalet.com
Web site: www.countrychalet.com

Conveniently located near I-77 in southern West Virginia, this cedar shake A-frame provides a cozy, casual atmosphere for busy travelers or business folks. Stone fireplace, windows, sunny deck, or shaded porch for all to enjoy. Pets and children by permission. Free pass to the nearby health and fitness center with olympic pool. Smoke- and alcohol-free environment. Members of the Mountain State B & B Association.

Hosts: Max and Sharon Hudson
Rooms: 2 (1PB;1SB) $70
Full Breakfast
Credit Cards: A B
Notes: 2 4 5 6 7 8 9 10 11

CAIRO

Log House Homestead, L L C

Rte. 1, Box 223 B, Cairo, WV 26337
(304) 628-3249
E-mail: loghouse@ruralnet.org
Web site: www.members.ruralnet.org/
loghousehomestead/index.htm

Step back in time at Log House Homestead. We offer 2–5 people country seclusion with 1820s style and period furnishings, but 21st-century amenities. The whole two-story hewn log house is yours—sit in porch rockers overlooking the pond or cozy up to the stone fireplace. After a hearty breakfast, hike the North Bend Rail Trail just 1/4 mile away. No phone or TV but lots of books and games. It's a museum where you stay! Whole house rented as a unit; there are two bedrooms, 1/2 bath, and one full bath with Jacuzzi. Well-behaved children over 12 welcome. Innkeepers live adjacent to the property. Members of Mountain State Assoc. of Bed and Breakfasts.

Log House Homestead

Hosts: Martha and Dick Hartley
Rooms: 2 (2PB) $79–119
Full Breakfast
Notes: 2 5 8 9 10

CHARLES TOWN

The Carriage Inn

417 E. Washington St., Charles Town, WV 25414
(304) 728-8003; (800) 867-9830
   Fax (304) 728-2976
E-mail: carriage@intrepid.net
Web site: www.carriageinn.com

NOTES: Credit cards accepted: A Master Card; B Visa; C American Express; D Discover; E Diners Club; F Other; 2 Personal checks accepted; 3 Lunch available; 4 Dinner available; 5 Open all year;

Built in 1836, this Southern Colonial graces a tree-shaded acre. Spacious front porch with swing and rocker. Five large and airy main house bedrooms include private baths and queen-sized canopy beds. Working fireplaces. Adjacent Carriage House Suite features queen beds, private bath, and accommodates families with small children. All rooms are air-conditioned. Generals Grant and Sheridan met in the East Parlor. Listed in the National Register. Located on Washington Heritage National Scenic Byway. Five miles from Harpers Ferry. Member of Mountain State Assoc. of B & Bs.

Hosts: Al and Kay Standish
Rooms: 6 (6PB) $75–139
Full Breakfast
Credit Cards: A B C
Notes: 2 5 7 8 10 12

Washington House Inn Bed and Breakfast

216 S. George St., Charles Town, WV 25414-1632
(304) 725-7923; (800) 297-6957
    Fax (304) 728-5150
E-mail: emailus@washingtonhouseinnwv.com
Web site: www.washingtonhouseinnwv.com

Washington House Inn

In charming colonial Charles Town, nestled in the Blue Ridge Mountains where the Shenandoah and Potomac Rivers meet, the Washington House Inn is a magnificent 1899 Victorian built at the turn of the century by descendants of President George Washington. The inn welcomes and delights leisure and business travelers. "The Best of Everything." ". . .sets a benchmark for all other B & Bs." Come see us, you'll be glad you did! Member of the Mountain State Association of Bed and Breakfasts.

Hosts: Mel and Nina Vogel
Rooms: 7 (7PB) $99–150
Full Breakfast
Credit Cards: A B C D E
Notes: 2 5 7 8 9 10 12

CHARLESTON

Historic Charleston B & B

110 Elizabeth St., Charleston, WV 25311-2117
(304) 345-8156; (800) CALLWVA
    Fax (304) 342-1572
E-mail: bed2brkst@aol.com
Web site: www.bbonline.com/wv/charleston

This elegant 1907 French Country home located in walking distance of the state capitol and cultural center. Rooms with queen beds and private baths. Relax in the den by the fire, and when weather permits, enjoy the swing on the front porch. A full breakfast is served. We spoil our guests. Wedding couples are served breakfast in their suite. Close to hiking, biking, swimming, white-water rafting, and skiing. Come, enjoy the capital city with us!

---

6 Pets welcome; 7 Children welcome; 8 Tennis nearby; 9 Swimming nearby; 10 Golf nearby; 11 Skiing nearby; 12 May be booked through travel agent

Hosts: Bob and Jean Lambert
Rooms: 3 (3PB) $75–95
Full Breakfast
Credit Cards: A B C
Notes: 2 5 8 9 10

DELRAY

The Menagerie at Delray

P. O. Box 171; Lick Run Rd., Delray, WV 26714
(304) 496-8942
Web site: www.bedandbrunch.com

Private mountain getaway, 137 acres
and your choice of the farmhouse
(sleeps 8) or the Glasshouse (sleeps 4).
Good food, good beds, good people,
and your own good time. Campfire
ring and BBQ grill, peace and quiet.
Member of Mountain State Assoc. of
Bed and Breakfasts.

Host: Kim McCracken
Rooms: 2 (2PB) $65–95
Full Breakfast
Credit Cards: A B D
Notes: 2 3 4 5 7 9

ELKINS

The Post House
Bed and Breakfast

306 Robert E. Lee Ave., Elkins, WV 26241-3210
(304) 636-1792
E-mail: joanbarlow@aol.com
Web site: www.virtualcities.com

The Post House

Located in the heart of Elkins, we are
a bed and breakfast with three guest
rooms, one of which has an adjoining
children's room. Come visit with us,
and sit on our front porch or lounge in
our parklike backyard, which has a
children's playhouse. We are close to
Davis and Elkins College and other
cultural and scenic attractions, with
easy access to main roads. Certified
massage is available on premises.
Handmade quilts are on sale. Our
breakfast is continental.

Host: Jo Ann Post Barlow
Rooms: 5 (2PB;3SB) $60–65
Continental Breakfast
Credit Cards: F
Notes: 2 7 9 10 11

Rambling Rose
Bed and Breakfast

301 Marro Dr., Elkins, WV 26241
(304) 636-1790
E-mail: ramblingrosebb@neumedia.net
Web site: www.virtualcities.com

Get away from the noise and traffic of
daily life. Relax in the "homey" atmosphere of the Rambling Rose B & B and
join us for a full country breakfast.
Dine in the formal dining room or join
Rose in her country kitchen, central to
her home. There are four guest bedrooms, each share two full baths, one
featuring a whirlpool tub. Located only
2 blocks from downtown, guests can
take a walking tour of Elkins, enjoy festivals at the college and park, or go
sightseeing, biking, or antiquing in the
surrounding countryside. Member of
Mountain State Assoc. of B & Bs.

NOTES: Credit cards accepted: A Master Card; B Visa; C American Express; D Discover; E Diners
Club; F Other; 2 Personal checks accepted; 3 Lunch available; 4 Dinner available; 5 Open all year;

Hosts: Richard and Rose Trochlil
Rooms: 4 (4SB) $65–85
Full Breakfast
Notes: 2 3 5 7 8 9 10 11

Tunnel Mountain Bed and Breakfast

R. R. 1 Box 59-1, Elkins, WV 26241-9711
(304) 636-1684; (888) 211-9123
Web site: www.bbonline.com/wv/tunnel

Charming three-story fieldstone home nestled on 5 private, wooded acres surrounded by scenic peaks, lush forests, and sparkling rivers. Finished in pine and rare wormy chestnut woodwork. Tastefully decorated with antiques, collectibles, and crafts. Near Monongahela National Forest, Blackwater Falls, Seneca Rocks, Spruce Knob, Dolly Sods, Cass Railroad, Canaan Valley, Timberline, snowshoe, cross-country/downhill skiing, historic sites, festivals, and shops. M.A.B.B.

Hosts: Anne and Paul Beardslee
Rooms: 3 (3PB) $75–85
Full Breakfast
Notes: 2 5 8 9 10 11

FAIRMONT

Acacia House B & B

158 Locust Ave., Fairmont, WV 26554
(304) 367-1000; (888) 269-9541
E-mail: acacia@acaciahousewv.com
Web site: www.acaciahousewv.com

Shop on the premises with antiques and collectibles. Five minutes from Fairmont State College and Fairmont Hospital; 30 minutes from WVU sta-

dium and hospital. Location: I-79, Exit 137, Route 310 to Fairmont Avenue, right on Fourth Street, right to Locust Avenue, 1/4 mile on the right. Member of Mountain State Assoc. of Bed and Breakfasts.

Acacia House

Hosts: George and Kathy Sprowls
Rooms: 4 (2PB;2SB) $60–70
Full Breakfast
Credit Cards: A B C D
Notes: 5 12

HEDGESVILLE

The Farmhouse on Tomahawk Run

1828 Tomahawk Run Rd.
  Hedgesville, WV 25427-3527
(304) 754-7350; (888) 266-9516
  Fax (304) 754-7350
E-mail: farmhouse@tomahawkrun.com
Web site: www.tomahawkrun.com

The Civil War-era farmhouse, between Martinsburg and Berkeley Springs, stands near the foundation of the log cabin built by Judy's ancestors when they settled in the area in the 1740s. Nestled in a secluded valley by a meandering stream, the house is surrounded by 280 acres of peaceful countryside. A stone fireplace in the large gathering

---

6 Pets welcome; 7 Children welcome; 8 Tennis nearby; 9 Swimming nearby; 10 Golf nearby; 11 Skiing nearby; 12 May be booked through travel agent

room has a comforting log fire on cold evenings. A bountiful breakfast is served by candlelight in the dining room or with warm sunshine on the wrap-around porch. Small group retreats are welcomed, and the hosts are trained Marriage Enrichment event leaders. Member of Mountain State Assoc. of Bed and Breakfasts.

The Farmhouse on Tomahawk Run

Hosts: Judy and Hugh Erskine
Rooms: 5 (5PB) $85–140
Full Breakfast
Credit Cards: A B C D E
Notes: 2 5 7 10 12

LEWISBURG

Historic Pence Springs Grand Hotel

P. O. Box 90, Pence Springs, WV 24962
(304) 445-2606; (800) 826-1829
  Fax (304) 445-2204
E-mail: pencehotel@newwave.net
Web site: wvweb.com/pencespringshotel/

Located between Beckley and Lewisburg, Pence Springs is a place where time stands still. This National Registered Historic Inn is nestled in the mountains. Enjoy fishing on the Greenbrier, hiking our nature trails or just relaxing away the hours on the front porch. We offer a full service din-

ing room and host WV's largest flea market on Sundays April–October. The hotel has attracted national attention in *Southern Living, Gourmet,* and *AAA* magazine as well as *USA Today*. Member of Mountain State Assoc. of B & Bs.

Hosts: John and Wendy Lincoln
Rooms: 15 (15PB) $85–120
Full Breakfast
Credit Cards: A B C D
Notes: 2 3 4 5 6 7 10

MILTON

The Cedar House

92 Trenol Hts., Milton, WV 25541-9466
(304) 743-5516; (888) 743-5516
E-mail: vickersc@marshall.edu
Web site: www.bbonline.com/wv/cedarhouse

Enjoy the convenience of a contemporary home with old-fashioned hospitality. A spacious hilltop, AC, trilevel-style cedar house with a panoramic view of surrounding hills awaits visitors on 5 1/2 acres that provide quiet and privacy within 1 mile of I-64, Exit 28. Relax in front of the family room fireplace or play pool, games, or piano in the game room. Use the treadmill or roller traction table. Blenko Glass Company, antiques, crafts, flea market nearby. Hand-dipped chocolates a specialty. Member of Mountain State Assoc. of Bed and Breakfasts.

Host: Carole Vickers
Rooms: 3 (3PB) $80–90
Full Breakfast
Credit Cards: A B C D
Notes: 2 5 10

NOTES: Credit cards accepted: A Master Card; B Visa; C American Express; D Discover; E Diners Club; F Other; 2 Personal checks accepted; 3 Lunch available; 4 Dinner available; 5 Open all year;

PHILIPPI

Tygart Valley Star Bed and Breakfast

14 N. Walnut St., Philippi, WV 26416
(304) 457-1890; (877) 661-1890
E-mail: tvs@bcnetmail.org

Tygart Valley Star

Experience the town that celebrates the first land battle of the Civil War. Stay in a stately home or our carriage house. Full breakfasts are served each morning, and we accommodate special dietary needs. Located in central West Virginia off I-79, we are close to state and national parks, Civil War battlefields, and historic train rides. We welcome children and are eco-friendly. Member of the Mountain State B & B Association.

Hosts: Elizabeth and Andrew Gast-Bray
Rooms: 4 (2PB;2SB) $75–95
Full Breakfast
Credit Cards: A B
Notes: 2 4 5 7 8 9 10 11

SHINNSTON

Gillum House Bed and Breakfast

35 Walnut St., Shinnston, WV 26431-1154
(304) 592-0177; (888) 592-0177

Fax (304) 592-1882
E-mail: stayawhile@gillumhouse.com
Web site: www.gillumhouse.com

Welcome to our home. Six miles from I-79, 50 feet from West Fork River Rail-Trail, low-fat, low-cholesterol homemade full breakfasts. Bike/hike, visit only Chapel of Perpetual Adoration in WV, near two drive-in theaters, golf (regular or miniature), history, covered bridges, or just relax. Family friendly, smoke-free, pet-free inn offers three second-floor guest rooms with shared bath. Terry robes in closets. Dinner packages/gift certificates available. Member of Mountain State Association of B & Bs.

Host: Kathleen A. Panek
Rooms: 3 (0PB;3SB) $57–67
Full Breakfast
Credit Cards: A B
Notes: 2 3 4 5 7 9 10

WALKERSVILLE

Stone Farm

Rte. 1, Box 36, Walkersville, WV 26447
(304) 452-8477
E-mail: sfbb@msys.net
Web site: www.msys.net/sfbb/

This restored 1910 farmhouse situated on 140 acres in the Mountain Lakes region is a step back to a slower pace and time. A time of gardening, canning, farming, or swinging on the porch. A mix of antique, not so old, and new in a pleasant blend. Enjoy hiking, reading, Jacuzzi, watching wildlife, or nearby attractions and activities. Escape the hectic demands of today's life. Member of Mountain State Assoc. of Bed and Breakfasts.

Hosts: Lionel and Sandra Lilly
Rooms: 3 (3SB) $60 plus tax
Full Breakfast
Credit Cards: A B
Notes: 2 3 4 5 7 9 10

WESTON

Ingeberg Acres B & B

712 Left Millstone Rd., Weston, WV 26452
(304) 269-2834; (800) CALL WVA
   Fax (304) 269-2834
E-mail: mann@igebergacres.com
Web site: www.ingebergacres.com

Ingeberg Acres

A unique experience can be yours at this scenic, 450-acre horse and cattle farm. Ingeberg Acres is located in the heart of West Virginia, 7 miles from Weston, overlooking its own private valley. Hiking, swimming, hunting, and fishing—or just relaxing—can be the order of the day. Observe or participate in farm activities. Craft outlets and antique stores are nearby. Come enjoy the gardens, the pool, and the friendly atmosphere. German spoken. We also provide boarding for horses in transit. Member of Mountain State Assoc. of B & Bs.

Hosts: John and Inge Mann
Rooms: 4 (1PB;3SB) $59–80

Full Breakfast
Notes: 2   5 6 7 9 10

WHEELING

Bonnie Dwaine Bed and Breakfast

505 Wheeling Ave., Glen Dale, WV 26038
(304) 854-7250; (888) 507-4569
   Fax (304) 845-7256
E-mail: bonnie@bonnie-dwaine.com
Web site: www.bonnie-dwaine.com

This elegant, romantic Victorian B & B invites you to indulge yourself in quiet comfort and style in any one of its five tastefully appointed guest rooms. Each room features a private adjoining bath with whirlpool tub/shower. Relax to the music of the electric grand piano or share some quiet time in the library. A candlelight gourmet breakfast is served in the formal dining room on weekends. Breakfast offerings are extended continental Sunday-Thursday.

Hosts: Bonnie and Sid Grisell
Rooms: 5 (5PB) $79–125
Continental Breakfast
Credit Cards: A B C D E
Notes: 2   5   8   9   10   12

Bonnie Dwaine

NOTES: Credit cards accepted: A Master Card; B Visa; C American Express; D Discover; E Diners Club; F Other; 2 Personal checks accepted; 3 Lunch available; 4 Dinner available; 5 Open all year;

WISCONSIN

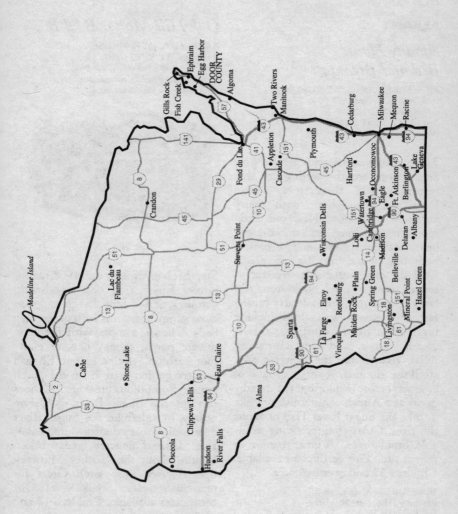

Wisconsin

ALBANY

Albany House Bed and Breakfast

405 S. Mill St., Albany, WI 53502-9502
(608) 862-3636; (866) 977-7000
   Fax (608) 862-1837
E-mail: innkeeper@albanyhouse.com
Web site: www.albanyhouse.com

Two parklike acres with flower gardens galore are the setting for this restored 1908 three-story home. Furnished throughout with many antiques and collectibles, our bedrooms feature king- and queen-sized beds, feather duvets, and a master bedroom wood-burning fireplace. Curl up on comfortable overstuffed seating with a good book from our large collection. After a hearty breakfast (homemade specialties include marmalade-filled muffins, classic cream scones, and iced cinnamon rolls), recover on the porch swing, stroll the grounds, or shoot a round of croquet before exploring the nearby Swiss and Amish communities. Hike or bike the Sugar River Trail or canoe the river. Cross-country skiing available. Smoke-free. A great reunion or retreat site. Gift certificates available. Children 12 and over welcome.

Hosts: Ken and Margie Stoup
Rooms: 6 (4PB;2SB) $65–105
Full Breakfast
Credit Cards: A B   F
Notes: 2   5   7 8 9 10 11

Oak Hill Manor B & B

P. O. Box 190; 401 E. Main St.
   Albany, WI 53502-0190
(608) 862-1400; Fax (608) 862-1403
E-mail: donna@oakhillmanor.com
Web site: www.oakhillmanor.com

Oak Hill Manor

Step back in time in our 1908 manor home. Enjoy rich oak woodwork, gasoliers, period furnishings, and spacious sunny bedrooms with queen-size beds. Choose a room with fireplace, private porch, canopy bed, or clawfoot bathtub. Relax in our English country garden or read on the porch swing. Sumptuous breakfast. Canoe/fish on the Sugar River, golf/shop nearby, or ride/hike the Sugar River bike trail. Cross-country skiing available. Complimentary guest bikes. Inquire about the "Ladies Midweek Special" (see Web site). Great for reunions/retreats. Smoke free. Gift certificates available. Children 12 and older welcome.

Hosts: Donna and Glen Rothe
Rooms: 4 (4PB) $80–110
Full Breakfast

NOTES: Credit cards accepted: A Master Card; B Visa; C American Express; D Discover; E Diners Club; F Other; 2 Personal checks accepted; 3 Lunch available; 4 Dinner available; 5 Open all year;

Credit Cards: A B   F
Notes: 2   5 7 8 9 10 11

ALGOMA

Amberwood Inn B & B

N. 7136 Hwy. 42, Algoma, WI 54201-9702
(920) 487-3471
E-mail: innkeeper@amberwoodinn.com
Web site: www.amberwoodinn.com

Amberwood Inn

Come to Amberwood, a romantic country inn with five large, luxury waterfront suites located 10 minutes from Door County. Enjoy our nearly 3 wooded acres, 300 feet of private Lake Michigan beach, sauna, in-room whirlpools, and spectacular breakfast. All suites offer individual lakefront deck, private bath, refrigerator, fireplace, fine antiques, and cable TV. Gift certificates available. Fall asleep to the sound of the waves; awaken to a sunrise over the water.

Hosts: Mark and Karen Rittle
Rooms: 6 (6PB) $89–127
Full Breakfast
Credit Cards: A B
Notes: 2   5   7   8   9   10

BARABOO

Pinehaven B & B

E13083 Hwy. 33, Baraboo, WI 53913
(608) 356-3489; Fax (608) 356-0818
E-mail: pinehaven@baraboo.com
Web site: www.pinehavenbnb.com

Located in a scenic valley with a small, private lake and Baraboo Bluffs in the background. The guest rooms are distinctly different, with wicker furniture and antiques, and queen and twin beds. Take a walk in this peaceful country setting. Area activities include Devil's Lake State Park, Circus World Museum, Wisconsin Dells, and ski resorts. Ask about our private guest cottage. No pets. No smoking. Gift certificates available. Closed in March. Children over 5 years welcome.

Hosts: Lyle and Marge Getschman
Rooms: 5 (5PB) $89–135
Full Breakfast
Credit Cards: A B   F
Notes: 2 5 7 8 9 10 11

BELLEVILLE

Abendruh B & B Swisstyle

7019 Gehin Dr., Belleville, WI 53508-9752
(608) 424-3808

Experience Bed and Breakfast Swisstyle. This highly acclaimed Wisconsin bed and breakfast offers true Swiss charm and hospitality. The serenity of this retreat is one of many treasures that keep guests coming back. Spacious guest rooms are adorned with beautiful family heirlooms. The sitting room has a high

---

6 Pets welcome; 7 Children welcome; 8 Tennis nearby; 9 Swimming nearby; 10 Golf nearby; 11 Skiing nearby; 12 May be booked through travel agent

cathedral ceiling and a cozy fireplace. An Abendruh breakfast is a perfect way to start a new day or end a peaceful stay.

Host: Mathilde Jaggi
Rooms: 2 (2PB) $65–70
Full Breakfast
Credit Cards:
Notes: 2 5 8 9 10 11 12

CAMBRIDGE

Country Comforts Bed and Breakfast

2722 Highland Dr., Cambridge, WI 53523
(608) 423-3097; (877) 771-1277
    Fax (608) 423-7743
E-mail: info@country-comforts.com
Web site: www.country-comforts.com

Country Comforts

Relax in the peace and quiet of the country, or wander a mile into town to shop Cambridge's historic Main Street. Renovated 100-year-old family farmhouse offers comfortable living space, quiet sleeping accommodations, and private baths. Wheelchair accessible. Four acres of lawn and gardens. Located 15 miles east of Madison, WI. Nearby attractions include: Rowe Pottery, Fireside Dinner Theatre, Glacial-Drumlin Bicycle Trail, Cam

Rock Park hiking and cross-country ski trails.

Hosts: Marian Korth and Mim Jacobson
Rooms: 4 (4PB) $99–169
Full Breakfast
Credit Cards: A B D
Notes: 2 5 9 11

CEDARBURG

Stagecoach Inn B & B

W. 61 N. 520 Washington, Cedarburg, WI 53012
(262) 375-0208; (888) 375-0208
    Fax (262) 375-6170
E-mail: info@stagecoach-inn-wi.com
Web site: www.stagecoach-inn-wi.com

Visit the Stagecoach Inn, a historically restored 1853 stone building. The inn features twelve comfortable guest rooms, some with oversized whirlpools, fireplaces, and antiques. A hearty breakfast is included. Relax in the pub and enjoy complimentary wine; visit the chocolate shop. Located in the downtown historic district within walking distance of galleries, restaurants, the winery, and specialty gift shops. The Stagecoach Inn: a destination for something special and a memorable getaway.

Hosts: Liz and Brook Brown
Rooms: 12 (12PB) $80–150
Continental Breakfast
Credit Cards: A B C D E
Notes: 2 5 8 9 10 11

Stagecoach Inn

NOTES: Credit cards accepted: A Master Card; B Visa; C American Express; D Discover; E Diners Club; F Other; 2 Personal checks accepted; 3 Lunch available; 4 Dinner available; 5 Open all year;

CHIPPEWA FALLS

Empty Nest Lakeside Tourist Suite

19194 52nd Ave., Chippewa Falls, WI 54729
(715) 720-1465
E-mail: zimmeremptynest@mymailstation.com

Empty Nest Lakeside

On beautiful Lake Wissota, our waterfront three-room suite exceeds your expectations with sunset views, lake breezes, privacy, and many special touches. Your suite includes queen bedroom, living room, dinette, and bath. The lakeside patio, hammock, and fire ring will give you hours of relaxation. TV/VCR/CD, phone, microwave, refrigerator, gas grill, pedal boat, and rowboat included, pontoon rental available. Bring your own boat to our dock. Short drive to all attractions. $75/night/2pp. $400/wk/2pp. $60/night/sgl./S–Th.

Hosts: Dave and Bev Zimmerman
Rooms: 1 (1PB) $75
Continental Breakfast
Notes: 2   7 8 9 10 11

McGilvray's Victorian B & B

312 W. Columbia St., Chippewa Falls, WI 54729-2321
(715) 720-1600; (888) 324-1893
E-mail: melanie@mcgilvraysbb.com
Web site: www.mcgilvraysbb.com

Experience the Midwest in this friendly, historic city. Once a booming lumber town, Chippewa Falls has many beautiful homes built at the turn of the century. Warm hospitality and a scrumptious breakfast are top priorities in this beautifully restored bed and breakfast. Relax by the fireplace on a chilly evening or enjoy one of the four porches on a summer day. There is much to do in the area: antiquing, biking, fishing, boating, skiing, and challenging golf courses. Children over 12 welcome.

Host: Melanie J. Berg
Rooms: 3 (3PB) $79–110
Full Breakfast
Credit Cards: A B
Notes: 2 5 8 9 10 11

CRANDON

Courthouse Square B & B

210 E. Polk St., Crandon, WI 54520-1436
(715) 478-2549; (888) 235-1665
    Fax (715) 478-2753
E-mail: chousebb@newnorth.net
Web site: www.courthousesquarebb.com

Guests frequently comment about the peace and tranquility of the setting. Enjoy birds and squirrels at the many benches placed throughout the flower and herb gardens, or stroll down the hill to the lake through the forget-me-nots and view the wildlife. The *Rhinelander Daily News* wrote: "Traditional hospitality is emphasized at Courthouse Square Bed and Breakfast, and it's evident from the moment you enter this delightful home where tranquility and peace abound. You will no doubt smell something delicious baking in Bess's kitchen as gourmet cooking is one of her specialties." Forty minutes from Northland Baptist Bible College. Churches are within walking distance. Inquire about children.

Courthouse Square

Hosts: Les and Bess Aho
Rooms: 3 (1PB;2SB) $62–70
Full Breakfast
Credit Cards: C
Notes: 2 5 8 9 10 11 12

DOOR COUNTY

Wagon Trail Resort

1041 Cty. Rd. 22, Ellison Bay, WI 54210
(920) 854-2385; (800) 999-2466
    Fax (920) 854-5278
E-mail: frontdesk@wagontrail.com
Web site: www.wagontrail.com

Take a drive to the quiet side of Door County. Wagon Trail Resort and Conference Center on Rowleys Bay.

Comfortable lodge rooms, secluded vacation homes, townhome, and cottages. Newly remodeled marina, indoor pool, whirlpool, and sauna. On-site restaurant, "Home of Grandma's Swedish Bakery." Perfect location for family vacations, weddings, or retreats.

Hosts:
Rooms: 78 (78PB) $69–239
No Breakfast Served
Credit Cards: A B D
Notes: 2 3 4 5 7 8 9 10 11 12

EAU CLAIRE

The Atrium B & B

5572 Prill Rd., Eau Claire, WI 54701-8121
(715) 833-9045; (888) 773-0094
    Fax (715) 831-9783
E-mail: info@atriumbb.com
Web site: www.atriumbb.com

The Atrium

Unwind in the best of both worlds; relaxed seclusion on 15 wooded, creekside acres only minutes from downtown, shopping, and dining. Enjoy magnificent antique stained-glass windows. Hike the woodland paths along Otter Creek, or relax in the Atrium with complimentary Wisconsin wine and cheeses. For your

---

comfort, all of our guest rooms have private baths, queen-sized beds, TVs, CD players, and phones. Two rooms have double whirlpools and fireplaces. Relax and renew!

Hosts: Celia and Dick Stoltz
Rooms: 4 (4PB) $85–179
Full Breakfast
Credit Cards: A B C D
Notes: 2 5 10 11

Otter Creek Inn

2536 Hwy. 12, P. O. Box 3183
  Eau Claire, WI 54702-6766
(715) 832-2945; (866) 832-2945
  Fax (715) 832-4607
E-mail: info@ottercreekinn.net
Web site: www.ottercreekinn.net

Each antique-filled guest room has a double whirlpool, private rest room, phone, air-conditioning, TV, and VCR. Many also have a fireplace and refrigerator. The breakfast menu allows a choice of entrees and breakfast in bed. This spacious inn (6500 square feet) is a three-story English Tudor with Country Victorian decor. Nestled on a wooded hill adjacent to, but high above, the creek, numerous restaurants and shops are less than 2 miles away. Outdoor in-ground heated swimming pool.

Hosts: Randy and Shelley Hansen
Rooms: 6 (6PB) $95–185
Full Breakfast
Credit Cards: A B C D E
Notes: 5 8 9 10 11

ELROY

East View
Bed and Breakfast

33620 Cty. P Rd., Elroy, WI 53929
(608) 463-7564
E-mail: eastview@elroynet.com
Web site: www.outspokinadventures.com/eastview

Spectacular country view, relaxing. Bike the Elroy-Sparta, 400, and Omaha bike trails. Near Wisconsin Dells, Amish community, Wildcat Mountain, canoeing. Breakfast served in upper sunroom with a fantastic view. Three rooms with bathrooms, common area, all with view of the countryside. Open year-round. Smoke free. Book two consecutive nights, second night one-half price. Gift certificates are available.

Hosts: Dom and Bev Puechner
Rooms: 3 (3PB) $70–75
Full Breakfast
Credit Cards: A B C
Notes: 2 5 9 10 11 12

EXELAND

Shepherd's Loft
Bed and Breakfast

166 N St. Rd. 40, Exeland, WI 54835
(715) 943-2317
E-mail: egschrock@juno.com

Quiet, lovely log home on a small sheep farm east of Wisconsin Blue Hills. Each guest room has a unique loft for reading, sleeping, or children's play. A full breakfast is served in the dining room or in the gazebo. In-house mini gift shop specializes in

---

6 Pets welcome; 7 Children welcome; 8 Tennis nearby; 9 Swimming nearby; 10 Golf nearby; 11 Skiing nearby; 12 May be booked through travel agent

sheepskin rugs and other sheep and wool-related gifts. "While you are with us may you find peace as you rest in the Shepherd's presence, and when you leave may you take with you a memory which will enrich your life."

Hosts: Lorene and Elwood Shrock
Rooms: 3 (1PB;2SB) $45–55
Full Breakfast
Credit Cards: A B
Notes: 2 5 7 9 10 11

FOND DU LAC

Dixon House
Bed and Breakfast

W7190 Forest Ave., Fond du Lac, WI 54937
(920) 923-3340
E-mail: rkuhls@execpc.com
Web site: www.dixonhouse.com

Dixon House

A 19th-century farmhouse updated to blend today's conveniences with the homey, nostalgic comfort of the past. A quiet resting place in the country, but conveniently close to town. Two guest rooms on the second floor share a large bathroom. Your hosts, Ron and Barb along with their son Iounut, will welcome you like family, treating you

to breakfast in the old-fashioned way of hospitality.

Hosts: Ronald and Barbara Kuhls
Rooms: 2 (0PB;2SB) $59–85
Full Breakfast
Notes: 2 5 7 9 10

FORT ATKINSON

The Lamp Post Inn

408 S. Main St., Fort Atkinson, WI 53538-2231
(920) 563-6561
Web site: www.thelamppostinn.com

We welcome you to the charm of our 126-year-old Victorian home filled with beautiful antiques. Five gramophones for your listening pleasure. For the modern, one of our baths features a large Jacuzzi. We are located 7 blocks from the famous Fireside Playhouse. You come a stranger, but leave here a friend. No smoking.

Hosts: Debbie and Mike Rusch
Rooms: 3 (2PB;1SB) $70–110
Full Breakfast
Notes: 2 5 7 8 9 10 11

GALENA, IL

Wisconsin House Stage
Coach Inn

2105 E. Main, Hazel Green, WI 53811
(608) 854-2233
E-mail: wishouse@mntc.net
Web site: www.wisconsinhouse.com

Built as a stagecoach inn in 1846, the inn now offers six rooms and two suites for your comfort. Join us for an evening's rest. Dine and be refreshed in the parlor, where General Grant

---

NOTES: Credit cards accepted: A Master Card; B Visa; C American Express; D Discover; E Diners Club; F Other; 2 Personal checks accepted; 3 Lunch available; 4 Dinner available; 5 Open all year;

spent many evenings with his friend Jefferson Crawford. Most conveniently located for all the attractions of the tristate area. Galena, IL, is 10 minutes away; Dubuque, IA, 15 miles away; and Platteville, only 20 miles away. Dinner is by reservation. Children must be well behaved.

Hosts: Ken and Pat Disch
Rooms: 8 (6PB;2SB) $65–125
Full Breakfast
Credit Cards: A B C D
Notes: 2 4 5 7 8 9 10 12

GILLS ROCK

Harbor House Inn

12666 State Hwy. 42, Ellison Bay, WI 54210-9784
(920) 854-5196
Web site: www.door-county-inn.com

Harbor House Inn

A 1904 Victorian bed and breakfast with a new Scandinavian wing, two cottages, and a newly built lighthouse overlooking quaint fishing harbor, within a short walk of ferry to islands, restaurants, and shops. Waterfront access, sauna, hot tub, bike rentals.

Hosts: David and Else Weborg
Rooms: 15 (15PB) $65–175
Continental Breakfast
Credit Cards: A B C
Notes: 6 7 8 9 10

HUDSON

Jefferson Day House

1109 Third St., Hudson, WI 54016
(715) 386-7111
E-mail: jeffersn@pressenter.com
Web site: www.jeffersondayhouse.com

This 1857 completely restored Italianate mansion has four guest rooms and one three-room suite. All rooms have double whirlpools, fireplaces, air-conditioning, queen beds, private bathrooms, and much more. Twenty minutes from the Twin Cities and 6 miles from Stillwater, MN. Arrive as a guest and leave as a friend.

Hosts: Tom and Sue Tyler
Rooms: 5 (5PB) $99–189
Full Breakfast
Credit Cards: A B C D
Notes: 2 5 6 8 9 10 11 12

JANESVILLE

Christine's Victorian Rose

603 E. Court St., Janesville, WI 53545
(608) 758-3819
E-mail: christinesbandb@aol.com
Web site: www.bbonline.com/wi/victorianrose/

The home is an 1888 Queen Anne Victorian featuring stained-glass windows, hardwood floors, and an open staircase highlighted by a newel post lamp. Amenities include central air, queen-size feather beds, a piano and fireplace in the parlor, and a wrap-around porch. Each guest room has a private bath. The Garden Room also has a daybed to accommodate an extra guest. Ask about our Victorian dress-up parties for celebrating special events.

---

6 Pets welcome; 7 Children welcome; 8 Tennis nearby; 9 Swimming nearby; 10 Golf nearby; 11 Skiing nearby; 12 May be booked through travel agent

Hosts: Christine and Paul Garchow
Rooms: 2 (2PB) $80
Full Breakfast
Notes: 2 5

LAKE GENEVA

Eleven Gables Inn on Lake Geneva

493 Wrigley Dr., Lake Geneva, WI 53147-2115
(262) 248-8393
E-mail: egielkgeneva.com
Web site: www.lkgeneva.com

Nestled in evergreen amid giant oaks in the Edgewater historical district, this quaint lakeside Carpenter's Gothic inn offers privacy and a prime location. Romantic bedrooms, bridal chamber, and unique country cottages all have fireplaces, down comforters, baths, TVs, wet bars, or cocktail refrigerators. Some have lattice courtyards, balconies, and private entrances. A private pier provides exclusive water activities. Bike rentals are available. This charming "Newport of the Midwest" community provides fine dining, boutiques, and entertainment year round.

Rooms: 8 (8PB) $109–274
Continental Breakfast
Credit Cards: A B C D E
Notes: 5 6 7 8 9 10 11

LIVINGSTON

Oak Hill Farm

9850 Hwy. 80, Livingston, WI 53554
(608) 943-6006

A comfortable country home with a warm, hospitable atmosphere that is enhanced with fireplaces, porches, and facilities for picnics, bird-watching, and hiking. In the area you will find state parks, museums, and lakes. Open May 1–Nov. 1.

Hosts: Elizabeth and Victor Johnson
Rooms: 4 (1PB;3SB) $50–60
Continental Breakfast
Notes: 2 6 7 8 9 10 11 12

LODI

Victorian Treasure Inn

115 Prairie St., Lodi, WI 53555-1240
(608) 592-5199; (800) 859-5199
  Fax (608) 592-7147
E-mail: innkeeper@victoriantreasure.com
Web site: www.victoriantreasure.com

Gracious hospitality and casual elegance in two National Historic Register Victorians featuring seven individually decorated guest rooms. Caring owner/innkeepers fuss over the details—meticulous rooms, thoughtful amenities, antique furnishings. Luxurious whirlpool suites with fireplaces, television/VCR, stereo/CD, coffeemaker, and more. Rates include a gourmet breakfast as featured on national PBS television, "Country Inn Cooking" with Gail Greco, and an evening wine and cheese reception. AAA 4-diamond award. Select Registry/IIA, 1999 Innkeeper of the Year.

Hosts: Todd and Kimberly Seidl
Rooms: 7 (7PB) $119–209
Full Breakfast
Credit Cards: A B D F
Notes: 2 5 8 9 10 11

NOTES: Credit cards accepted: A Master Card; B Visa; C American Express; D Discover; E Diners Club; F Other; 2 Personal checks accepted; 3 Lunch available; 4 Dinner available; 5 Open all year;

MADISON

Annie's Garden B & B

2117 Sheridan Dr., Madison, WI 53704-3844
(608) 244-2224; Fax (608) 244-2224
Web site: www.bbinternet.com/annies

When you want the world to go away, come to Annie's, the quiet inn on Warner Park with the beautiful view. Luxury accommodations—a full floor of space all to yourself, including a master bedroom; a smaller bedroom; connecting full bath; whirlpool room; pine-paneled library with fireplace; and dining room opening to lovely gardens, gazebo, and shaded terrace. Miles of nature trails to lake, marshes, and woods to enjoy wildlife and sports. Only 6 minutes from downtown Madison and the UW campus. Central AC. Two-night minimum. Meet our two cats. . .Sparkler and Firecracker.

Hosts: Anne and Larry Stuart
Rooms: 1 (1PB) $105–189
Full Breakfast
Credit Cards: A B C D
Notes: 2 5 7 8 9 10 11

Cameo Rose B & B

1090 Severson Rd., Belleville, WI 53508
(608) 424-6340
E-mail: innkeeper@cameorose.com
Web site: www.cameorose.com

Romantic Victorian B & B on 120 scenic acres of wooded hills and mowed hiking trails. Relax and be pampered. Enjoy immense peace and quiet on gazebo porch swing, by the fireplace in the living room, or in the wicker-filled tower sunroom. Complimentary full breakfast served on antique china and lace. Private baths, AC, smoke free, whirlpool, fireplaces.

Hosts: Dawn and Gary Bahr
Rooms: 5 (5PB) $115–169
Full Breakfast
Credit Cards: A B
Notes: 2 5 8 9 10 11

Mansion Hill Inn

424 N. Pinckney St., Madison, WI 53703
(608) 255-3999; (800) 798-9070
   Fax (608) 255-2217
elegant@mansionhillinn.com
Web site: www.mansionhillinn.com

The Mansion Hill Inn offers eleven luxurious rooms, each with a sumptuous bath. Whirlpool tubs with stereo headphones, hand-carved marble fireplaces, minibars, and elegant Victorian furnishings help make this restored mansion into a 4-diamond inn. A private wine cellar, VCRs, and access to private dining and athletic clubs are available on request. Guests are treated to turn-down service and evening refreshments in our parlor. The Mansion Hill Inn is ideal for honeymoons. It is listed on the National Register of Historic Places.

Host: Betty Blanchard
Rooms: 11 (11PB) $150–340
Continental Breakfast
Credit Cards: A B C
Notes: 2 7 8 9 10 12

MAIDEN ROCK

Harrisburg Inn

W 3334 Hwy. 35; P. O. Box 15
   Maiden Rock, WI 54750-0015

---

6 Pets welcome; 7 Children welcome; 8 Tennis nearby; 9 Swimming nearby; 10 Golf nearby; 11 Skiing nearby; 12 May be booked through travel agent

(715) 448-4500; Fax (715) 448-3908
E-mail: ccbern@cannon.net
Web site: www.harrisburginn.com

Harrisburg Inn

Nestled on a bluff-side overlooking the Mississippi River Valley, our inn truly has "a view with a room." Every room faces the river and surrounding blufflands where birds and flowers abound. Western Wisconsin's hills invite exploration where you'll find wonderful surprises in dining, antiquing, small-town festivals, and other delights. The Harrisburg offers relaxation, romance, and great breakfasts. Welcome! Inquire about children.

Hosts: Wayne and Di Gelhar
Rooms: 4 (4PB) $90–135
Full Breakfast
Credit Cards: A B C D
Notes: 2   5   7   8   9   10   11

MILWAUKEE

The Washington House Inn

W 62 N 573 Washington Ave.
Cedarburg, WI 53012
(262) 375-3550; (800) 554-4717
Fax (262) 375-9422
E-mail: whinn@execpc.com
Web site: www.washingtonhouseinn.com

The romance of Country Victorian comes alive as you enter the Washington House Inn, Cedarburg's historic bed and breakfast inn. A lovely collection of antique Victorian furniture, marble-trimmed fireplace, and fresh-cut flowers offer you a warm reception. Tastefully appointed in the romantic Country Victorian style, featuring antiques, cozy down quilts, flowers, and special touches for our guests' comfort. In late afternoon, relax in front of a cheery fire, sip wine, and socialize with other guests prior to dining at one of the excellent Cedarburg restaurants. Each morning enjoy a delicious continental breakfast in the warmth of the gathering room. Homemade muffins, cakes, and breads are baked in our own kitchen using recipes from an authentic, turn-of-the-century Cedarburg cookbook.

Host: Wendy Porterfield
Rooms: 34 (34PB) $89–219
Continental Breakfast
Credit Cards: A B C D E
Notes: 2   5   8   9   10   12

OCONTO

The Rose of Sharon B & B

1109 Superior Ave., Oconto, WI 54153
(920) 834-9885
E-mail: rose_bnb@yahoo.com
Web site: www.roseofsharonbnb.homestead.com

Built in the early 1900s, this lovely home provides a casual, cozy atmosphere where you can relax and enjoy your romantic retreat, family vacation, or even that business trip. Two bedrooms have king beds and double-size whirlpool tubs. All bedrooms are on the second floor. Our accommodations offer the perfect setting for small gath-

---

NOTES: Credit cards accepted: A Master Card; B Visa; C American Express; D Discover; E Diners Club; F Other; 2 Personal checks accepted; 3 Lunch available; 4 Dinner available; 5 Open all year;

erings. Five-minute drive to the bay and a short walk to a historical museum.

Hosts: Tom and Irma Majors
Rooms: 4 (4PB) $75–125
Full Breakfast
Notes: 2 5 7 8 9 10

OSCEOLA

Pleasant Lake B & B

2238 60th Ave., Osceola, WI 54020-4509
(715) 294-2545; (800) 294-2545
   Fax (715) 755-3163
E-mail: pllakebb@centurytel.net
Web site: www.pleasantlake.com

Romance, relaxation, and rejuvenation of your body and spirit. Walk leisurely in the woods, watch our wildlife neighbors, canoe the lake, sit around a crackling campfire with the stars reflecting on the moonlit lake, then relax in your own fireside whirlpool. Arise to the aromas of a full country breakfast and the songs of nature.

Hosts: Richard and Charlene Berg
Rooms: 8 (8PB) $99–159
Full Breakfast
Credit Cards: A B D F
Notes: 2 5 9 10 11

REEDSBURG

Parkview B & B

211 N. Park St., Reedsburg, WI 53959-1652
(608) 524-4333; Fax (608) 524-1172
E-mail: parkview@jvlnet.com
Web site: www.parkviewbb.com

Our 1895 Queen Anne Victorian home overlooks City Park in the historic district. Many of the original features of the home remain, such as hardware, hardwood floors, intricate woodwork, leaded and etched windows, plus a suitor's window. Wake-up coffee is followed by a full, homemade breakfast. Central air and ceiling fans add to guests' comfort. Located 1 block from downtown. Close to Wisconsin Dells, Baraboo, and Spring Green. Just 3 blocks from 400 Bike Trail.

Hosts: Tom and Donna Hofmann
Rooms: 4 (2PB;2SB) $75–95
Full Breakfast
Credit Cards: A B C
Notes: 2 5 7 10 11

SPRING GREEN

Bettinger House B & B

P. O. Box 243; 855 Wachter Ave. (Hwy. 23)
   Plain, WI 53577-0243
(608) 546-2951; Fax (608) 546-2951
E-mail: bhbb@charter.net
Web site: www.bettingerbnb.com

The Bettinger House is the hostess's grandparents' 1904 Victorian farmhouse; Grandma was a midwife who delivered 300 babies in this house. Choose from five spacious bedrooms that blend the old with the new, each named after noteworthy persons of Plain. The home is centrally air-conditioned. Start your day with one of the old-fashioned, full-course breakfasts for which we are famous. The Bettinger House is located near "House on the Rock," Frank Lloyd Wright's original Taliesen, American Players Theater, White Mound Park, and many more attractions.

Host: Marie Neider
Rooms: 5 (2PB;2SB) $60–80
Full Breakfast

---

6 Pets welcome; 7 Children welcome; 8 Tennis nearby; 9 Swimming nearby; 10 Golf nearby; 11 Skiing nearby; 12 May be booked through travel agent

Credit Cards: F
Notes: 2   5   8 9 10 11 12

Lamb's Inn B & B

23761 Misslich Rd.
  Richland Ctr., WI 53581-9626
(608) 585-4301; Fax (608) 585-2242
E-mail: lambsinn@mwt.net
Web site: www.lambs-inn.com

Lamb's Inn

Added, a new 1600 sq. ft. cabin, oak logs, pine ceilings, ash floors, hickory cabinets, and a fireplace woodstove gives a coziness to your visit. Set high on the side of the hill, looking down our valley, a wall of glass shows off the beautiful hills surrounding the cabin. Three bedrooms, two baths with tub/shower, a kitchen with a dishwasher, and sliding glass doors opening onto the deck make for a very special stay. Continental breakfast served in the cottage.

Hosts: Dick and Donna Messerschmidt
Rooms: 10 (8PB;2SB) $90–275
Full Breakfast
Credit Cards: A B D F
Notes: 2 5 8 9 10 12

ST. CROIX FALLS

Wissahickon Farms Country Inn

2263 Maple Dr., St. Croix Falls, WI 54024
(715) 483-3986
E-mail: wissainn@yahoo.com
Web site: www.wissainn.com

"Rustic country lodging with a touch of class." Located on a 30-acre hobby farm secluded by God's creative handiwork, our country inn portrays an old country store from a bygone era. Relax on the porch, enjoy the two-person whirlpool, or hike the many surrounding trails, including an ice age trail. The "Gandy Dancer" bicycle/snowmobile trail runs right through the farm. Furnishings include queen-size camelback bed, hide-a-bed sofa for two ($15 per extra person), and glider rocker. The small efficiency kitchen contains a refrigerator, microwave, etc. Guests have a TV with VCR. The inn is air-conditioned. No smoking, no pets. Bicycles are provided to ride the trail in summer and snowshoe in winter. With a donation to the "hay fund," Amish buggy rides are now available. Come see what the St. Croix River Valley has to offer!

Hosts: Steve and Sherilyn Litzkow
Rooms: 1 (1PB) $125
Continental Breakfast
Credit Cards: A B
Notes: 2 5 9 10 11

STEVENS POINT

Dreams of Yesteryear Bed and Breakfast

1100 Brawley St., Stevens Point, WI 54481-3536
(715) 341-4525; Fax (715) 341-4248
E-mail: bonnie@dreamsofyesteryear.com
Web site: www.dreamsofyesteryear.com

Dreams of Yesteryear

Featured in *Victorian Homes Magazine* and listed on the National Register of Historic Places. Your hosts are from Stevens Point and enjoy talking about the restoration of their turn-of-the-century home, which has been in the same family for three generations. All rooms are furnished in antiques. Guests enjoy the use of parlors, porches, and gardens. Two blocks from the historic downtown, antique and specialty shops, picturesque Green Circle Trails, the university, and more. Truly "a Victorian dream come true." Children over 12 welcome.

Hosts: Bonnie and Bill Maher
Rooms: 6 (4PB;2SB) $62–149
Full Breakfast
Credit Cards: A B C D
Notes: 2 5 7 8 9 10 11 12

A Victorian Swan on Water

1716 Water St., Stevens Point, WI 54481
(715) 345-0595; (800) 454-9886
   Fax (715) 345-0569
E-mail: victorian@g2a.net
Web site: www.bbinternet.com/victorian-swan

Our mission is to provide guests with a setting that is comfortable, clean, and beautiful. An 1889 Victorian home provides all that and more. Private baths with showers, tubs, or whirlpool suite, rooms furnished with antiques, fireplaces, and AC. Enjoy the flower gardens or the walking, biking, or ski trails. Share good food, good conversation, and a great atmosphere in this lovely university town. Special bike tours and gift certificates available.

Host: Joan Ouellette
Rooms: 4 (4PB) $65–140
Full Breakfast
Credit Cards: A B C D
Notes: 2 5 8 9 10 11 12

STURGEON BAY

Scofield House

908 Michigan St., Sturgeon Bay, WI 54235-0761
(920) 743-7727; (888) 463-0204
   Fax (920) 743-7727
E-mail: cpietrek@doorpi.net
Web site: www.scofieldhouse.com

Scofield House

---

6 Pets welcome; 7 Children welcome; 8 Tennis nearby; 9 Swimming nearby; 10 Golf nearby; 11 Skiing nearby; 12 May be booked through travel agent

"Door County's most elegant bed and breakfast." This 1902 multicolored, three-story Victorian was restored in 1987 by the present hosts. Guests keep coming back for the wonderful gourmet breakfasts and homemade "sweet treats" served fresh daily. The Scofield House has six guest rooms, all have private baths, color television/VCRs, and a video library of over 500. Double whirlpools, fireplaces, and central AC. Smoke free.

Hosts: Mike and Carolyn Pietrek
Rooms: 6 (6PB) $112–220
Full Breakfast
Credit Cards: A B
Notes: 2 5 9 10 11

White Lace Inn

16 N. 5th Ave., Sturgeon Bay, WI 54235
(920) 743-1105; (877) 948-5223
E-mail: romance@whitelaceinn.com
Web site: www.whitelaceinn.com

White Lace Inn

Our four historic homes are nestled in a friendly old neighborhood, bordered by a white picket fence, and surrounded by gardens. The White Lace is a romantic Victorian inn with eighteen wonderfully inviting guest rooms furnished in fine antiques, queen- or king-size four-poster or ornate Victorian beds, oversized whirlpool tub, an inviting fireplace, down comforters, and white lace. A warm welcome awaits as guests are greeted with lemonade or hot chocolate and cookies. Open year-round. Nonsmoking.

Hosts: Bonnie and Dennis Statz
Rooms: 18 (18PB) $68–239
Full Breakfast
Credit Cards: A B C D
Notes: 2 5 8 9 10 11

WISCONSIN DELLS

Historic Bennett House

825 Oak St., Wisconsin Dells, WI 53965
(608) 254-2500
Web site: www.historicbennetthouse.com

The 1863 home of pioneer photographer H. H. Bennett is warm and inviting in its casual elegance and welcoming atmosphere. Traveling with another couple? We have the ideal situation for you. Two lovely bedrooms, one with queen canopy bed and English armoire and the other with queen brass bed with wicker accents. Share a carpeted bedroom-size bath with Italian sinks and Bennett's claw-foot tub. You may, of course, reserve just one room. The library has become part of a two-room suite with private bath. View a favorite movie from our 100-plus collection. Savor a delicious gourmet breakfast, and visit Dells attractions: state parks; Bennett, Rockwell, Circus, and Railroad museums; riverboat tours; skiing; and the Crane Foundation.

NOTES: Credit cards accepted: A Master Card; B Visa; C American Express; D Discover; E Diners Club; F Other; 2 Personal checks accepted; 3 Lunch available; 4 Dinner available; 5 Open all year;

Hosts: Gail and Rich Obermeyer
Rooms: 3 (2PB;2SB) $80–99
Full Breakfast
Credit Cards:
Notes: 2 5 8 9 10 11

Historic Bennett House

Terrace Hill B & B

922 River Rd., Wisconsin Dells, WI 53965-1423
(608) 253-9363
E-mail: info@terracehillbb.com
Web site: www.terracehillbb.com

Our 100-year-old Victorian home is located atop a small bluff, a park bordering along one edge, and Wisconsin River across the street. Guests are treated to pleasant surroundings both inside and out. Newly remodeled rooms include canopy beds, whirlpools, claw-foot tub, and offer views and cozy surroundings. Just 1½ blocks from downtown Wisconsin Dells. Parking in rear. AC. Browse our eclectic library; experience serendipity.

Hosts: Len, Cookie, Lenard and Lynn Novak
Rooms: 4 (4PB) $85–140
Full Breakfast
Credit Cards: A B
Notes: 2 5 7 9 10 11

The White Rose Bed and Breakfast Inn

910 River Road, Wisconsin Dells, WI 53965
(608) 254-4724; (800) 482-4724
     Fax (608) 254-4585
E-mail: whiterose@jvlnet.com
Web site: www.thewhiterose.com

The White Rose B & B and The Sherman House Inn offer two enchanting turn-of-the-century mansions, with uniquely decorated, comfortable rooms all with private baths, cable TV, 7 with whirlpool baths, fireplaces, lavish gardens, and heated outdoor pool. Full breakfast served every morning of your stay in our Secret Garden Café. Weddings, receptions, business meetings, and family reunions are our specialty. Special packages are available year-round. We promise you an unforgettable experience!

Hosts: Marty and Shionagh Stuehler
Rooms: 15 (15PB) $80–165
Full Breakfast
Credit Cards: A B C D
Notes: 2 3 4 5 7 8 9 10 11

---

6 Pets welcome; 7 Children welcome; 8 Tennis nearby; 9 Swimming nearby; 10 Golf nearby; 11 Skiing nearby; 12 May be booked through travel agent

WYOMING

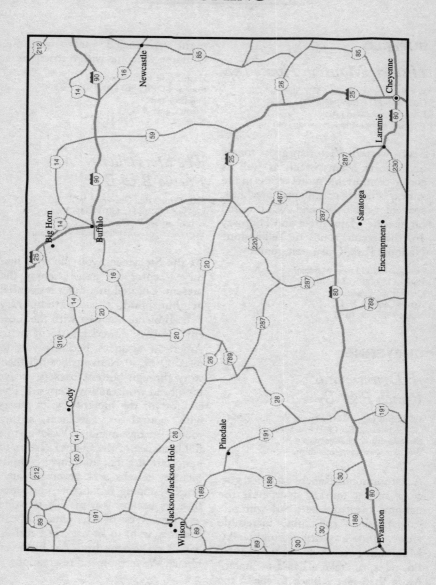

Wyoming

BUFFALO

Historic Mansion House Inn

313 N. Main St., Buffalo, WY 82834-1730
(307) 684-2218; (888) 455-9202
E-mail: dianem@trib.com
Web site: www.mansionhouseinn.com

Seven western Victorian guest rooms on historic Main Street, as well as eleven comfortable motel rooms in the annex, offering continental breakfast, spa, color cable TV, and AC. Located on historic Main Street and Highway 16, the scenic route to Yellowstone National Park. Open year-round.

Hosts: Phil and Diane Mehlhaff
Rooms: 18 (18PB) $45–70
Continental Breakfast
Credit Cards: A B D
Notes:5 7 8 9 10 11

CHEYENNE

A. Drummonds Ranch B & B

399 Happy Jack Rd., Cheyenne, WY 82007-9543
(307) 634-6042; Fax (307) 634-6042
E-mail: adrummond@juno.com
Web site: www.adrummond.com

A. Drummonds Ranch is a quiet, gracious retreat on 120 acres near the national forest and state park with private outdoor hot tubs, incredible views, and a glorious night sky. Mountain-bike, hike, cross-country ski, relax, or "take a llama to lunch." More than just a place to spend the night! Kenneled pets welcome. Children welcome with restrictions.

Host: Taydie Drummond
Rooms: 4 (2PB;2SB) $70–150
Full Breakfast
Credit Cards: A B
Notes: 2 3 4 5 6 7 10 11 12

The Storyteller Pueblo B & B

5201 Ogden Rd., Cheyenne, WY 82009-4925
(307) 634-7036; Fax (307) 634-7036
E-mail: stpbandb2@sisna.com
Web site: www.storyteller-pueblo-bnb.com

At the Storyteller, you slip into history. . .enter the past. . .enjoy the present. Located in a quiet residential neighborhood, this contemporary B & B blends the past with the present. Native American decor with American antiques beckons you to relax. Over 50 Native tribes tell their story through pottery, baskets, weavings, bead work, and western art. The comfort of the present awaits guests with central air, fireplaces, sitting rooms—many amenities. Wake up to a full breakfast of the Ojibwa Nation to jumpstart the day, and enjoy complimentary snacks and beverages anytime! Shopping, restaurants, museums, theaters beckon you to visit the Old and New West of Cheyenne. Or, you just may want to sit back and curl up with a good book from our historical library. We recommend reservations.

Hosts: Howard and Peggy Hutchings
Rooms: 4 (2PB;2SB) $65–100
Full Breakfast
Notes: 2   5   7 8 9 10 11 12

CODY

Aka Grandma's House
The Lockhart B & B Inn

109 W. Yellowstone Ave., Cody, WY 82435
(307) 587-6074; (800) 377-7255
    Fax (307) 587-8644
E-mail: lockhart@cowboystate.net
Web site: www.codyvacationproperties.com

The Lockhart

The historic Lockhart Inn is located overlooking the Shoshone River with spectacular mountain views. Once the home of famous American novelist Caroline Lockhart, and also one of Cody's first bars where Buffalo Bill Cody played cards in the dining room. A full all-you-can-eat country breakfast awaits you in the morning with hot and cold beverages on during the length of your stay. All rooms have queen beds, private baths, television, and telephones. Gather in the parlor for good conversation with other guests around the wood-burning stove, or play a tune or two on the piano. Located within walking distance of all major attractions, Old

Trail Town, Cody Nite Rodeo, and Buffalo Bill Historical Center (home to five museums under one roof). Come see what *AAA Today*, *Glamour*, and *HGTV* had to say about the Lockhart. Your home away from home out west.

Hosts: Don Kramer and Cindy Baldwin-Kramer
Rooms: 7 (7PB) $95–115
Full Breakfast
Credit Cards: A B   F
Notes: 2   7 8 9 10 11 12

Parson's Pillow

1202 14th St., Cody, WY 82414-3720
(307) 587-2382; (800) 377-2348
    Fax (307) 527-8908
E-mail: ppbb@trib.com
Web site: www.cruising-america.com/
    parsonspillow

Parson's Pillow

Our bed and breakfast is 100 years old. The first church in Cody, WY. There are five "theme" rooms. The common areas and each room have various touches of nature, the West, Elegance, and Christianity. We combine service and good food to make this time of fellowship comfortable and memorable, even inspiring. The area has diverse activities available including the Cody Museum, rodeo, and national parks. A place to worship, witness, and meet God.

Hosts: Paul and Dorothy Olson
Rooms: 5 (5PB) $85–95
Full Breakfast
Credit Cards: A B C
Notes: 2　5 6 7 8 9 10 11 12

ENCAMPMENT

Rustic Mountain Lodge and Cabin

Star Route Box 49, Encampment, WY　82325
(307) 327-5539; Fax (307) 327-5539
E-mail: maplatt@union-tel.com
Web site: www.plattsbedandbreakfast.com

Located on working ranch, with wonderful views of the Sierra Madre mountain range. Comfortable custom log structure, 3 bedrooms with 2 shared baths and one bedroom with private bath. Fishing, horseback riding and tours available. Family home staeded in 1886, 4th generation, plus 1000 sq. ft. cabin, 2 large bedrooms. All modern.

Hosts: Mayvon and Ron Platt
Rooms: 4 (1PB;3SB) $65
Full Breakfast
Notes: 2 3 4 5 6 7 8 9 10 11

EVANSTON

Pine Gables Inn Bed and Breakfast

1049 Center St., Evanston, WY　82930-3432
(307) 789-2069
E-mail: pinegabl@allwest.net
Web site: www.cruising-america.com/pinegables

Lovely inn on National Historic Register, built 1883. You will enjoy a hearty homemade breakfast in the antique-filled dining room. Beautiful murals and decorated bed chambers with private baths will capture your attention. Memories of a bygone time will bring you back again!

Pine Gables Inn

Hosts: Nephi and Ruby Jensen
Rooms: 6 (6PB) $60–135
Full Breakfast
Credit Cards: A B D
Notes: 2　5　8　9　10　11　12

NEWCASTLE

E V A—Great Spirit Ranch Bed and Breakfast

1262 Beaver Creek Rd.
　Newcastle, WY　82701-9772
(307) 746-2537
Web site: www.wyomingbnb-
　ranchrec.com/eva.html

Amid spectacular scenery of mountains and woods lies this secluded but modern log home bed and breakfast. Located on the historic Cheyenne/Deadwood stagecoach route and 526 acres of scenic grounds. Four roomy bedrooms, private baths, full country breakfast. Great room with fireplace, movie and reading libraries, board games and puzzles. An outdoor grill and kitchen available to guests. Hiking, exploring, cross-country skiing, wildlife, serenity! Hunting packages available. Fishing, rock climbing, snowmobile trails within minutes. Sports/sightseeing nearby. Handicapped accessible. No smoking. Reservations requested. Open year-round.

Host: Irene Spillaine
Rooms: 4 (2PB;2SB) $55–74
Full Breakfast
Credit Cards: A B
Notes: 2   5   7   9   10   11   12

PINEDALE

Pole Creek Ranch B & B

P. O. Box 278, Pinedale, WY 82941-0278
(307) 367-4433
E-mail: polecreekranch@wyoming.com
Web site: www.bbonline.com/wy/polecreek/

Come stay in our log bed and breakfast overlooking the majestic Wind River Mountains. Learn to ride horses on the ranch, relax on the cool front porch or in the outdoor hot tub. Let us plan your activities after a full ranch breakfast. The peace and beauty of Pole Creek Ranch is unsurpassed!

Hosts: Dexter and Carole Smith
Rooms: 3 (1PB;2SB) $55
Full Breakfast
Notes: 2 3 4 5 6 7 8 9 10 11

ALBERTA

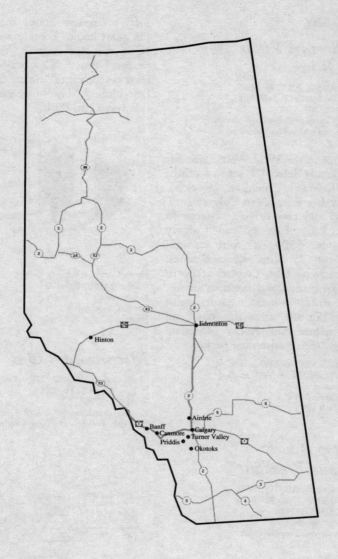

Alberta

CALGARY

Big Springs Estate B & B Inn

R. R. 1, Airdrie, AB T4B 2A3
(403) 948-5264; (888) 948-5851
 Fax (403) 948-5851
E-mail: bigsprings@bigsprings-bb.com
Web site: www.bigsprings-bb.com

Elegance in the Wild West! Gracious inn, Canada Select **** set in foothills of Alberta's Canadian Rockies. Twenty-five minutes to Calgary Int'l. Airport and easy driving distance to Banff, Lake Louise, and Calgary Stampede; 5500 sq. foot tranquil retreat on 35 acres. Elegant suites, ultra-masseur tubs, fireplaces, superb breakfast cuisine, and attentive service. Other amenities include garden guest lounge, hot tub "under the stars," and valley nature trail. Rocky Mountain and sightseeing adventure packages.

Hosts: Earle and Carol Whittaker
Rooms: 5 (5PB) $129–169 Canadian
Full Breakfast
Credit Cards: A B C F
Notes: 5 8 9 10 11 12

Hilltop Ranch Bed and Breakfast

Box 54, Calgary, AB T0L 1W0
(403) 931-2639; (800) 801-0451
 Fax (403) 931-3426
E-mail: gary@hilltopranch.net
Web site: www.hilltopranch.net

Fifty-seven-acre hobby ranch. From the guest book: "Food was awesome," "Can we live here?" "Very quiet, peaceful time," "Our stay here was icing on the cake," "Better than any 5-Star Hotel," "The horse and carriage ride was a real thrill!"

Hilltop Ranch

Hosts: Gary and Barbara Zorn
Rooms: 3 (3PB) $80–120
Full Breakfast
Credit Cards: A B F
Notes: 5 6 7 8 9 10 11 12

Merrywood B & B

23 Newton St., P O Box 377
 Langdon, AB T0J 1X2
(403) 936-5796
E-mail: underhiswing@look.ca
Web site: www.twics.ca/merrywoodbb

Merrywood

Relaxed accommodation in a quiet hamlet east of Calgary. Easy access to airport, downtown, Calgary Stampede, Calgary Zoo, the Canadian Rockies, rockhounding, dinosaur park, Rosebud Dinner Theatre, etc. One room with queen-size bed. One room with single bed. Cot available. Enjoy crafts, summer fresh garden produce and flowers. Fenced area for visiting small dogs.

Host: G. M. Chappell
Rooms: 2 (2SB) $45–60 Canadian
Full Breakfast
Notes: 5

ting room are on the ground floor, with separate entrance for guests. This is real cowboy country with city amenities easily accessible. Welcome!

Hosts: Sam and Rosemary Squire
Rooms: 2 (2SB) $50–65 Canadian
Full Breakfast
Credit Cards: F
Notes: 5 7 9 10

NANTON

Hearts Ease B & B

Box 460, Nanton, AB T0L 1R0
(403) 646-5789
E-mail: roseptl@telusplanet.net

Hearts Ease

We are a gracious older home in an attractive small town between Calgary and Fort Macleod, near the Rockies. Nanton is home to the Lancaster Bomber Air Museum, antique shops, restaurants, and is a 3-hour beautiful drive to Banff, Wateron, and the Tyrrel Museum. Guest rooms and bathroom are upstairs, dining and sit-

---

6 Pets welcome; 7 Children welcome; 8 Tennis nearby; 9 Swimming nearby; 10 Golf nearby; 11 Skiing nearby; 12 May be booked through travel agent

BRITISH COLUMBIA

Campbell River

Qualicum Beach

Nanoose Bay
Nanaimo
Chemainus

Tofino

Parksville
Duncan
Mill Bay

Sooke

Sidney
Metchosin
Brentwood Bay

Victoria

Pender Island

Halfmoon Bay

North Vancouver

Whistler
Vancouver
West Vancouver
New Westminster

Abbotsford
White Rock

Mayne Island

Pemberton
Heffley Creek

Vernon
Kamloops

Kelowna

Penticton

Nelson

Fernie

Fort Steele

Prince George

British Columbia

ABBOTSFORD

Everett House Bed and Breakfast

1990 Everett Rd., Abbotsford, BC V2S 7S3
(604) 859-2944; Fax (604) 859-9180
E-mail: everettbb@telus.net
Web site: www.vancouverbc.com/evertthousebb

We invite you to join us in our Victorian-style home. Easily accessible to the freeway and overlooking the Fraser Valley, our home is the perfect retreat, removed from the hustle of the city. It is also that "someplace special" for you while you conduct your business in the Fraser Valley. A stay at our home will provide you with a refreshing break from ordinary life.

Hosts: David and Cindy Sahlstrom
Rooms: 2 (2PB) $85–135
Full Breakfast
Credit Cards: A B
Notes: 5 7 9 10 11 12

NORTH VANCOUVER

Grand Manor Guest House B & B

1617 Grand Blvd.
    North Vancouver, BC V7L 3Y2
(604) 988-6082; (866) 988-6082
    Fax (604) 988-4596
E-mail: donna@grandmanor.net
Web site: www.grandmanor.net

Built in 1912, this four-story Edwardian home is one of the original mansions on the Grand Boulevard, built for the mayor. Rooms are clean, comfortable, and have city and mountain views. Centrally located to Lansdale, Lions Gate Hospital, and Rel. Centre; 15 minutes to downtown Vancouver, 1½ hours to Whistler. Decorated in antiques. Grand Manor is a great place to relax and enjoy new friends in a warm, comfortable atmosphere.

Grand Manor

Host: Donna Patrick
Rooms: 3 (2PB;1SB) $80–150
Gourmet Breakfast
Credit Cards: B
Notes: 5 7 8 9 10 11

PRINCE GEORGE

Beaverly B & B

12725 Miles Rd., Prince George, BC V2N 5C1
(250) 560-5255; (888) 522-2298
    Fax (250) 560-5211
E-mail: beaverlybandb@bcgroup.net
Web site: http://beaverlybandb.hypermart.net

Beaverly Bed and Breakfast is located 18 kilometers west of Prince George on 10 acres of beautiful British

---

NOTES: Credit cards accepted: A Master Card; B Visa; C American Express; D Discover; E Diners Club; F Other; 2 Personal checks accepted; 3 Lunch available; 4 Dinner available; 5 Open all year;

Columbia wilderness. You will feel very welcome and comfortable in our new home. Many trees surround us, and it is a birder's paradise. We serve a healthy, full breakfast in our country kitchen or on the deck weather permitting. Pick-up service from airport, train, or bus is available for a small fee. Follow blue B & B signs. Friendly service with a Dutch touch.

Hosts: Anneke and Adrian Van Peenen
Rooms: 2 (2SB) $65–75
Full Breakfast
Credit Cards: A B
Notes: 3 5 6 7 8 9 10 11 12

SOOKE

Ocean Wilderness Country Inn

109 W. Coast Rd., Sooke, BC V0S 1N0
(250) 646-2116; (800) 323-2116
   Fax (250) 646-2317
E-mail: ocean@sookenet.com
Web site: www.oceanwildernessinn.com

The inn offers nine guest rooms on 5 forested acres of oceanfront with breathtaking views. Large, beautifully decorated rooms have private baths and canopied beds. A silver service of coffee is delivered to your door as a gentle wake-up. Country breakfast from local produce is a wonderful treat. The ocean water hot tub is popular with weary travelers. There are several in-room soaker tubs for two, overlooking the ocean. Arrange a stress-relieving massage, mud facial, or seaweed/herb wrap in our on-site spa. Perfect for small seminars, family reunions, and weddings.

Host: Marion Rolston
Rooms: 9 (9PB) $99–175 Canadian
   (May–October)
Full Breakfast
Credit Cards: A B C
Notes: 2 5 6 7 9 12

UCLUELET

Burley's Lodge B & B

1078 Helen Rd # 550, Ucluelet, BC V0R 3A0
(250) 726-4444
E-mail: burleys@telus.net
Web site: www.uclueletaccommodations.com

Two large condos. Two bedrooms, 1 bath, each with full kitchen and bathroom, dining room, living room, TV with VCR. Close to beaches, lighthouse and lake. Kayaking, whale, bear, seals and bald eagle-watching. Complimentary tea and coffee.

Hosts: Ron and Micheline Burley
Rooms: 2 (2PB) $140–190 Canadian
No Breakfast Served
Credit Cards: A B
Notes: 5 7 8 9 10

VANCOUVER

Beachside B & B

4208 Evergreen Ave.
   West Vancouver, BC V7V 1H1
(604) 922-7773; (800) 563-3311
   Fax (604) 926-8073
E-mail: info@beach.bc.ca
Web site: www.beach.bc.ca

Experience oceanfront luxury in a quiet, secluded setting. Magnificent views of city and English Bay. Perfect romantic getaway or honeymoon. Enjoy the Jacuzzi on the beach. Watch seals, sea otter, eagles, waterfowl, and

6 Pets welcome; 7 Children welcome; 8 Tennis nearby; 9 Swimming nearby; 10 Golf nearby; 11 Skiing nearby; 12 May be booked through travel agent

cruise ships from giant driftwood logs at water's edge. Newly tiled private *baths and Jacuzzis*. Fireplaces, TV/VCR, queen *beds*, *refrigerators*, and microwaves in-room. Each has a private patio. Friendly attention to detail, parking; AAA, Canada Select 4 stars. Twenty minutes to downtown.

Host: Joan F. Gibbs
Rooms: 4 (4PB) $60–160 US
Full Breakfast
Credit Cards: A B
Notes: 2 5 7 9 10 11 12

Beautiful B & B Inn

428 W. 40th Ave., Vancouver, BC V5Y 2R4
(604) 327-1102; Fax (604) 327-2299
E-mail: sandbbb@portal.ca
Web site: www.beautifulbandb.bc.ca

Gorgeous Colonial accommodation with antiques, fresh flowers, views. Great central location from which guests may walk to Queen Elizabeth Park, Van Dusen Gardens, shopping, restaurants. Bus at the end of our street runs frequently and directly to downtown Vancouver (15 min.), Seattle (3 hrs.), Victoria (3 hrs.), and UBC (20 min.). Reach the Vancouver Airport by taxi in 12 minutes. Friendly, helpful host will assist you with your plans while in Vancouver.

Hosts: Corinne and Ian Sanderson
Rooms: 6 (2PB;4SB) $85–150
Full Breakfast
Credit Cards: F
Notes: 2 8 9 10 11 12

Lavender Walk

4858 8 A Ave., Tsawwassen, BC V4M 1S9
(604) 943-2230; Fax (604) 943-2231
E-mail: info@lavenderwalk.com
Web site: www.lavenderwalk.com

Lovely, spacious room with French doors opening to a large, private garden. This is your own private entrance to come and go as you choose. Accommodations include a queen bed plus two twins, en suite bath with shower. Coffee/tea in room. Color TV/VCR in room. Full breakfast in dining room overlooking the garden or on the patio. Afternoon tea or sherry is also provided. Enjoy our garden of wildflowers, lavender, fragrant herbs, and stream. We are located in Tsawwassen, just minutes to the ferries to Vancouver Island, the beach, waterslides, birding, golf courses. Walk or jog the shoreline dikes with the locals. Shops and restaurants nearby. Come, enjoy our hospitality.

Lavender Walk

Hosts: Shirley and Les Shields
Rooms: 1 (1PB) $85 Canadian no tax
Full Breakfast
Credit Cards: B C F
Notes: 8 9 10 11

Tall Cedars B & B

720 Robinson St., Vancouver, BC V3J 4G1
(604) 936-6016
E-mail: tallcedars@shaw.ca
Web site: www.tallcedarsvancouver.com

A B & B that offers comfortable, affordable accommodation with "country hospitality in the city." Close to downtown, great restaurants, lakes, and mountains. Come and enjoy our "Christian hospitality." (Hebrews 13:2)

Hosts: Dwyla and Ed Beglaw
Rooms: 4 (1PB;2SB) $75–95 Canadian
Continental Breakfast
Credit Cards: B
Notes: 4 5 7 8 9

VANCOUVER ISLAND

At the Sea-Breeze

2912 Esplanade St. , Box 1362
   Chemainus, BC V0R 1K0
(250) 246-4593; Fax (250) 246-4593
E-mail: c-breeze@shaw.ca
Web site: www.virtualcities.com

Turn-of-the-century home, beautifully appointed. Steps from the beach and boat ramp. Almost waterfront. Beautiful views from every room. One complete suite including kitchen. Enjoy watching sails and seals from an old-fashioned veranda. The Sea-Breeze is surrounded by clean, fresh breezes and sparkling water. Wir sprechen Deutsch! Picturesque town of Chemainus on Vancouver Island.

Hosts: John and Christa Stegemann
Rooms: 3 (3PB) $65–75 Canadian
Full Breakfast
Notes: 5 7 8 9 10

VICTORIA

Abigail's Hotel

906 McClure St., Victoria, BC V8V 3E7
(250) 388-5363; (800) 561-6565
   Fax (250) 388-7787
E-mail: innkeeper@abigailshotel.com
Web site: www.abigailshotel.com

Experience the charm and hospitality of our unique bed and breakfast inn. Located just three blocks from downtown shopping. Abigail's Hotel is rated "5 Stars" by Canada Select. We have twenty-three beautiful rooms pleasantly and elegantly decorated in warm, soft colors, and all rooms feature private en suite bathrooms. Each one has its own special romantic atmosphere. Hors d'ouevres are served every evening in our library. Our famous three-course gourmet breakfast is included in every stay.

Rooms: 23 (23PB) $219–389
Full Breakfast
Credit Cards: A B C
Notes: 5 8 9 10 12

Craigmyle B & B Inn Ltd.

1037 Craigdarroch Rd., Victoria, BC V8S 2A5
(888) 595-5411; (888) 595-5411
   Fax (250) 370-5276
E-mail: craigmyle@shaw.ca
Web site: www.bctravel.com/craigmyle

Craigmyle B & B was built in 1913 by the famous architect Samuel McClure. Craigmyle sits on what was once the Craigdarroch Castle tennis courts, and the step from the castle can still be seen coming down into the guest house garden. Craigmyle is a

---

6 Pets welcome; 7 Children welcome; 8 Tennis nearby; 9 Swimming nearby; 10 Golf nearby; 11 Skiing nearby; 12 May be booked through travel agent

Enjoy our world-class, year-round resort just 2 hours from Vancouver. Surround yourself with nature's beauty and allow us to pamper you with a wholesome breakfast, homemade jams, and fresh breads. Unique theme rooms feature cozy duvets and sherry decanters. Relax in the outdoor hot tub with mountain views! Family room with wood fireplace. Full guest kitchen. Located just 1 mile from village express gondolas. Valley trail system and bus route at our doorstep. Bike rentals on-site. Many seasonal activities. Now in two locations! Whistler Town Plaza is within walking distance of express ski lifts, fabulous restaurants, and new shops. These new condos feature gas fireplaces, entertainment centers, full kitchens, spa access, and underground parking.

Host: Ann Spence
Rooms: 5 (0PB) $85–145 Canadian
Full Breakfast
Credit Cards: A B
Notes: 2 5 7 8 9 10 11

Golden Dreams

6 Pets welcome; 7 Children welcome; 8 Tennis nearby; 9 Swimming nearby; 10 Golf nearby; 11 Skiing nearby; 12 May be booked through travel agent

MANITOBA

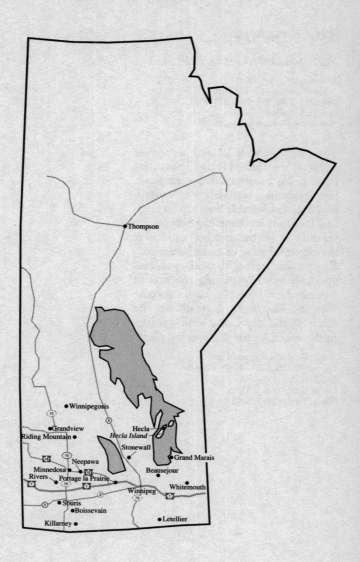

Thompson

Winnipegosis

Grandview
Riding Mountain ●
Hecla
Hecla Island
Neepawa
Stonewall
Minnedosa
Rivers ● Portage la Prairie
Grand Marais
Beausejour
Winnipeg
Whitemouth
Souris
Boissevain
Letellier
Killarney

Manitoba

HECLA ISLAND

Solmundson Gesta Hus

Riverton, P. O. Box 76
   Hecla Island, MB R0C 2R0
(204) 279-2088; Fax (204) 279-2088
E-mail: holtz@mb.sympatico.ca
Web site: www.heclatourism.mb.ca

The guest house is located on private property within Hecla Provincial Park. Enjoy luxurious, European-style hospitality in a completely renovated, modern, comfortable home in an original Icelandic settlement. Relax on the veranda or in the gazebo, and enjoy the beautiful view of Lake Winnipeg. Enjoy the tranquil and peaceful atmosphere while petting the cats or feeding the ducks. The host is a commercial fisherman, so feast on the catch of the day along with garden-fresh vegetables for the evening meal.

Hosts: Dave and Sharon Holtz
Rooms: 4 (1PB;3SB) $50–75 Canadian
Full Breakfast
Credit Cards: A B C D
Notes: 2 4 5 6 7 8 9 10 11 12

NOTES: Credit cards accepted: A Master Card; B Visa; C American Express; D Discover; E Diners Club; F Other; 2 Personal checks accepted; 3 Lunch available; 4 Dinner available; 5 Open all year;

NEW BRUNSWICK

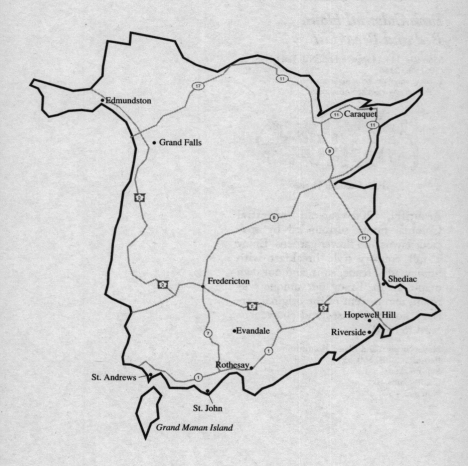

New Brunswick

HOPEWELL HILL

Peck Colonial House Bed and Breakfast

5566 Rte. 114, Hopewell Hill, NB E4H 3N5
(506) 882-2114
E-mail: stay@peckcolonial.com
Web site: www.peckcolonial.com

Peck Colonial House

Beautiful, 200-year-old ancestral Colonial home surrounded by spacious lawns and flower gardens. Enjoy a full country-style breakfast with homemade breads, jams, and our own maple syrup. Enjoy our unique tearoom, reminiscent of the original carriage house. Our seafood chowder is hard to beat!

Hosts: Stephen and Elaine Holmstrom
Rooms: 3 (3SB) $60–65
Full Breakfast
Credit Cards: B
Notes: 3 4 5 7

NOVA SCOTIA

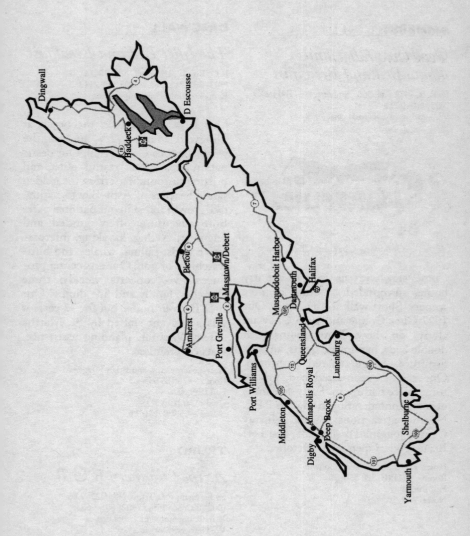

Nova Scotia

AMHERST

Goodwin's Chat and Chew Bed and Breakfast

R. R. 2, 5472 Rte. 366, Amherst, NS B4H 3X9
(902) 661-0282
Web site: www.bbcanada.com

Goodwin's Chat and Chew

Come stay with us in our country home, surrounded by rural country scenery. Short walk to the beach. Our 1927 Chev Coupe and 1955 Chev are always on show. Three rooms with double beds, handmade quilts, antique furniture. Large, shared bathroom. One room, queen-sized bed, private three-piece bathroom. Forty-five minutes to Confederation Bridge to P.E.I. Nearby attractions; Anne Murray Center, Joggin's Fossil Cliffs, and Fort Beausegour. Open May–October.

Hosts: Fraser and Arleen Goodwin
Rooms: 4 (1PB;3SB) $50–70
Full Breakfast
Notes: 7 9 10

DINGWALL

The Inlet Bed and Breakfast

P. O. Box 18, Dingwall, NS B0C 1G0
(902) 383-2112; Fax (902) 383-2112
E-mail: theinlet@ns.sympatico.ca

Our B & B is set on the beach at Dingwall Harbor, 2.5 km off the world-famous Cabot Trail. Our destination area offers restful quiet and pristine surroundings; from the golden sandy beaches of Aspy Bay to natural old-growth forest in our national park. Soft adventure offers guided and unguided cycling, kayaking, interpretative trails, sailing, whale- and bird-watching, or golf. Our arts center produces two concerts weekly, three churches, family and fine dining. Our B & B is our home, but for 37 years it was a convent staffed by St. Martha sisters. Vacation planning assistance. Cats on premises.

Hosts: Merne Ann and Brian Fitzgerald
Rooms: 3 (3SB) $55–65
Full Breakfast
Credit Cards: A B
Notes: 4 5 7 8 9 10 11

TRURO

At the Organery B & B

53 Farnham Rd., Truro, NS B2N 2X6
(902) 895-6653; Fax (902) 895-6653
E-mail: organery@ns.sympatico.ca
Web site: www.organery.ca

NOTES: Credit cards accepted: A Master Card; B Visa; C American Express; D Discover; E Diners Club; F Other; 2 Personal checks accepted; 3 Lunch available; 4 Dinner available; 5 Open all year;

Experience Nova Scotian hospitality in our charming country home. Relax in the beautiful inviting gardens. One of Nova Scotia's best-kept secrets awaits our guests at the Organery; a museum of 117 reed (pump) organs. Jan gives a fascinating evening tour of the collection. Guests can play too!! Our guests love our breakfast with Nova Scotia flavors and service. Dietary on request. English, Dutch, German, French spoken. Close to Tidal Bore, Agricultural College, restaurants. Forty-five minutes from Halifax International Airport.

rooms (8) have queen beds, two have two double beds. All have phone, AC, cable TV, heated outdoor pool, gardens. Walking distance to downtown, Acadia University. Nonsmoking. Dining room features fine country dining evenings 5:30–9:00 P.M.

Host: Betsey Harwood
Rooms: 10 (10PB) $105–195
Full Breakfast
Credit Cards: A B C
Notes: 3 9 12

At the Organery

Hosts: Jan van der Leest and Carolyn Matthews
Rooms: 3 (1PB;2SB) $50–75
Full Breakfast
Credit Cards: B
Notes: 2 5 7 8 9 10 11

WOLFVILLE

Tattingstone Inn

434 Main St., Wolfville, NS B0P 1X0
(902) 542-7696; (800) 565-7696
  Fax (902) 542-4427

Registered Historic home (1874). Ten beautifully furnished rooms with private baths, some with Jacuzzis. Most

---

6 Pets welcome; 7 Children welcome; 8 Tennis nearby; 9 Swimming nearby; 10 Golf nearby; 11 Skiing nearby; 12 May be booked through travel agent

ONTARIO

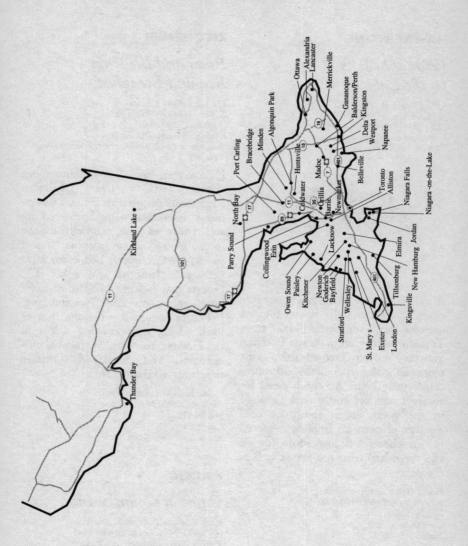

Ontario

HAWKESTONE

Verandahs B & B by the Lake

4 Palm Beach Rd., R. R. #2
Hawkestone, ON L0L 1T0
(705) 487-1910; (800) 841-1019
E-mail: jeankanty@sympatico.ca
Web site: www.verandahs.com

Verandahs

A warm welcome awaits you at our gracious Victorian-style home located between Barrie and Orillia (1 hour from Toronto) across from beautiful Lake Simcoe. We have three attractive guest rooms all with private baths and super-comfortable beds. Air-conditioned for summer comfort and a cozy fireplace in the guest sitting room for cool weather enjoyment. Breakfasts served in our cheerful dining room (or on the verandah) treat the eye as well as the palate.

Hosts: Henry and Jean Kanty
Rooms: 3 (3PB) $90–100 Canadian
Full Breakfast
Credit Cards: A B
Notes: 5 9 10 11

KITCHENER

Roses and Blessings Bed and Breakfast

112 High Acres Crescent
Kitchener, ON N2N 2Z9
(519) 742-1280; Fax (519) 742-8428
E-mail: nmwarren@golden.net
Web site: www.bbcanada.com/rosesandblessings

Discover an "oasis"! We pamper our guests with warm Christian Mennonite hospitality. Enjoy a sumptuous breakfast with home-baking and fruits in our candlelit dining room, as well as an evening dessert snack. Double/queen bedrooms have private bathrooms and cable TV. Guests may use our hot tub or exercise equipment. AC. Nonsmoking. Packages available—theater, horseback riding, and canoeing. Close to the farmers' markets, St. Jacobs, universities, and Stratford. Ontario superhost accreditation.

Hosts: Marg and Norm Warren
Rooms: 2 (2PB) $75 Canadian
Full Breakfast
Credit Cards: B F
Notes: 2 5 7 8 9 10

MADOC

Camelot Country Inn

R. R. 5, Madoc, ON K0K 2K0
(613) 473-0441; Fax (613) 473-0441
E-mail: marianifoster@hotmail.com
Web site: www.countryhosts.on.ca.;
    www.bbcanada.com

NOTES: Credit cards accepted: A Master Card; B Visa; C American Express; D Discover; E Diners Club; F Other; 2 Personal checks accepted; 3 Lunch available; 4 Dinner available; 5 Open all year;

Relax in the quiet, country setting of our 1853 brick-and-stone home. It is surrounded by plantings of red-and-white pine on 25 acres of land in the heart of Hastings County. Original woodwork and oak floors have been lovingly preserved. There are three guest rooms, two with double beds, and one with twins. Breakfast may be chosen from the country breakfast or one of two gourmet breakfasts. Dinner available upon request.

Camelot Country Inn

Host: Marian Foster
Rooms: 3 (0PB;1SB) $50–60
Full Breakfast
Notes: 4 5

MIDLAND

Inn the Woods Country Inn

4240-6th Line North, Oro-Medonte; R. R. #4
   Coldwater, ON L0K 1E0
(705) 835-6193; (800) 289-6295
   Fax (705) 835-0061
E-mail: info@inn-the-woods.com
Web site: www.inn-the-woods.com

A three-level, Colonial-style home on a ravine sitting on the fringe of the 5000-acre Copeland Forest. Located in the heart of the Medonte Hills ski country. Inn the Woods was built as a bed and breakfast and was designed for the comfort, privacy, and relaxation of our guests. It combines a peaceful scenic ambience with nearby availability of quaint shops, fine restaurants, hiking trails, scenic country roads, and fishing streams.

Hosts: Betty and Bob Shannon
Rooms: 5 (0PB;5SB) $75–85
Full Breakfast
Credit Cards: A B C E
Notes: 2 3 4 5 6 7 9 10 11

A Wymbolwood Beach House B & B

533 Tiny Beaches Rd. S.
   Wymbolwood Beach, ON L0L 2T0
(705) 361-3649; Fax (705) 361-3649
E-mail: lippert@primus.ca
Web site: www.wymbolwood.com

Discover Huronia's best-kept secret—A Wymbolwood Beach House, "A secluded haven, nestled in the evergreens overlooking Georgian Bay" (The new VR television). Centrally located to Midland, Penetanguishene, and Barrie, we offer a memorable getaway with all the comforts of home, including a delicious breakfast. Enjoy beautifully decorated guest rooms with cable TV, private baths, and a charming two-bedroom suite, complete with Jacuzzi tub. Experience area attractions, historic sites, boat cruises, sandy beaches. Hike, bike, cross-country ski through surrounding forest trails. Other features: central air, fireplace, games room, VCR, decks, spectacular sunsets. Open all year. Groups welcome. Weekly rates. Inquire about our seasonal packages.

---

6 Pets welcome; 7 Children welcome; 8 Tennis nearby; 9 Swimming nearby; 10 Golf nearby; 11 Skiing nearby; 12 May be booked through travel agent

Hosts: Jane and Bob
Rooms: 3 (3PB) $80–135
Full Breakfast
Credit Cards: B E
Notes: 5 8 9 10 11 12

NIAGARA FALLS

Pillar and Post Inn, Spa and Conference Centre

48 John St., P. O. Box 1011
    Niagara-On-The-Lake, ON L0S 1J0
(905) 468-2123; (888) 669-5566
    Fax (905) 468-1472
E-mail: reservations@vintageinns.com
Web site: www.vintageinns.com

Named Top Country Inn for Canada
1999 and 4-diamond for accommodation. World-class hotel and spa:
123 elegant guest rooms, spectacular
cuisine, in/outdoor pools, sauna,
health club. Five-minute walk to
shopping, free shuttle to theater.
Guest rooms from $150 winter, and
from $225 summer.

Host: Vincent Cotte, General Mgr.
Rooms: 123 (123PB) from $150
No Breakfast Served
Credit Cards: A B C D E
Notes: 3 4 5 7 8 9 10 12

Queen's Landing Inn and Conference Resort

155 Byron St., P. O. Box 1180
    Niagara-on-the-Lake, ON L0S 1J0
(905) 468-2195; (888) 669-5566
    Fax (905) 468-1472
E-mail: reservations@vintageinns.com
Web site: www.vintageinns.com

A Georgian-style mansion close to
the scenic Niagara River. Rated 4-

diamond by CAA/AAA in both dining and accommodation. Indoor pool,
whirlpool, saunas, award-winning gardens, and outdoor patio. Experience
incomparable quality and service.
Luxurious guest rooms from $150
winter and from $225 summer.

Host: Richard Dusome, General Mgr.
Rooms: 144 (144PB) from $150
No Breakfast Served
Credit Cards: A B C D E
Notes: 3 4 5 7 8 9 10 12

NIAGARA-ON-THE-LAKE

Willowcreek House B & B

P. O. Box 1028; 288 Dorchester St.
    Niagara-on-the-Lake, ON L0S 1J0
(905) 468-9060; (877) 589-9001
    Fax (905) 468-9061
E-mail: willowcreekhouse@sympatico.ca
Web site: www.niagaraonthelakebb.org

Visit our elegant Georgian home
located in Old Town. Walk to shops,
theaters, dining, the golf course. All
rooms have en suite baths; for that
romantic   getaway,   enjoy   our
Willowcreek Room with fireplace, and
Jacuzzi. We have central air and a
smoke- and pet-free environment.

Hosts: Margaret and Jake Janzen
Rooms: 3 (3PB) $120–140 Canadian
Full Breakfast
Credit Cards: A B C
Notes: 2 5 8 9 10

OTTAWA

Australis Guest House

35 Marlborough Ave., Ottawa, ON K1N 8E6
(613) 235-8461; Fax (613) 235-8461
E-mail: waters@magma.ca
Web site: www.bbcanada.com/1463.html

NOTES: Credit cards accepted: A Master Card; B Visa; C American Express; D Discover; E Diners
Club; F Other; 2 Personal checks accepted; 3 Lunch available; 4 Dinner available; 5 Open all year;

Australis Guest House

Oldest established bed and breakfast in Ottawa. Located on a quiet, tree-lined street in an embassy area and one block from the ducks and swans on Rideau River and Strathcona Park; 20-minute walk from Parliament. This period house has leaded-glass windows, fireplaces, oak floors, and unique stained-glass windows in the hall. Hearty, wholesome breakfasts created by Carol who is coauthor of "The Breakfast Companion" cookbook. Recipient of Gold Award for Star of City for Tourism. Recommended by *National Geographic Traveler*. Carol is a Rotarian.

Hosts: Carol and Brian Waters
Rooms: 3 (1PB;2SB) $75–95
Full Breakfast
Notes: 5

ST. MARYS

Eagleview Manor B & B

178 Widder St., E, Box 3183
    St. Marys, ON N4X 1A8
(519) 284-1811; (866) 294-0014
Web site: www.stohetown.net/eagleview

St. Marys is a quaint, peaceful town time forgot, nestled between the Thames River and Trout Creek. Home of Canadian Baseball Hall of Fame. Just minutes from Stratford and London. Amtrak stops here. Beautiful trails. Gracious smoke-free century Victorian home. Sweeping staircase. Stained-glass windows, Jacuzzi, quilts, fireplaces, antiques, three large guest rooms, three guest bathrooms, formal oak dining room. Menu breakfast, tea table, guest parlor, in-ground pool, veranda, open year-round. Retreat.

Hosts: Bob and Pat Young
Rooms: 3 (3SB) $60–85
Full Breakfast
Credit Cards: A B
Notes: 2 5 7 8 9 10 11

TORONTO

The Homewood Inn

65 Homewood Ave., Toronto, ON M4K 1C2
(416) 920-7944; Fax (416) 920-4091
E-mail: reservations@homewoodinn.com
Web site: www.homewoodinn.com

English-style bed and breakfast. Includes cable television, maid service, small fridge, and air-conditioned. On-site parking available. Full breakfast served daily from 7:00–9:30 A.M. Feel free to visit our website.

Host: Dolores Thompson-Wood
Rooms: 40 (8PB;32SB) $70–110
Full Breakfast
Credit Cards: A B C
Notes: 5 7

PRINCE EDWARD ISLAND

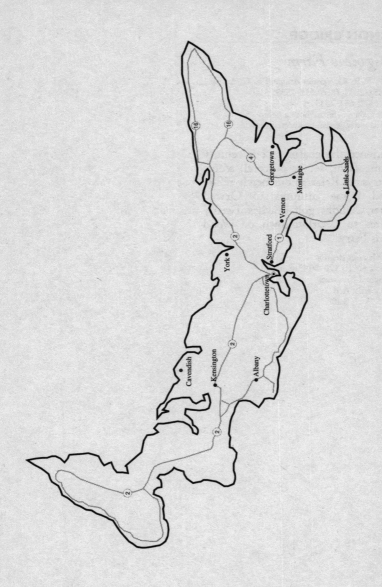

Prince Edward Island

VERNON BRIDGE

Craigview Farm

UIGG , R. R. #2, Vernon Bridge, PE C0A 2E0
(902) 651-2833; (866) 651-2833
   Fax (902) 651-2833
E-mail: craigviewfarm@hotmail.com
Web site: www.peisland.com/craigview

Experience the charm of our century working farm, set in peaceful, scenic countryside. Relax in our newly refurbished home minutes to Orwell Corner, Ceilidhs, golf, beaches. Twenty minutes to Charlottetown or Wood Islands Ferry.

Host: Magaret Beattie
Rooms: 2 (2PB) $70–80 Canadian
Continental Breakfast
Credit Cards: A B
Notes: 5 7 9 10

QUEBEC

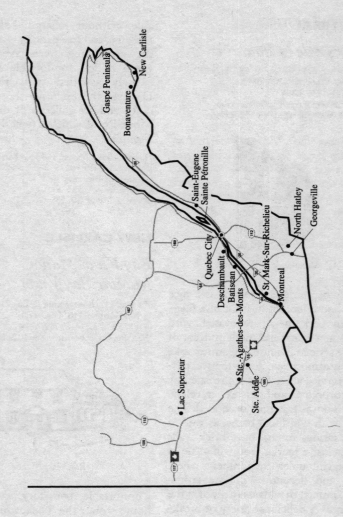

Quebec

MONTREAL

Auberge de la Fontaine

1301 Rachel St. E., Montreal, QB H2J 2K1
(514) 597-0166; (800) 597-0597
    Fax (514) 597-0496
E-mail: info@aubergedelafontaine.com
Web site: www.aubergedelafontaine.com

Auberge de la Fontaine

The Auberge de la Fontaine is a nice stone house located in front of a magnificent park, newly renovated, with rooms in a warm and modern decor of unique style in Montreal. Comfortable, friendly atmosphere and attentive, personal service are greatly appreciated by our corporate and leisure travelers. Each room is tastefully decorated. The suites with whirlpool baths, as well as the luxurious rooms, have brick walls and exclusive fabrics. You will settle in an elegant, quiet environment where duvet and decorative pillows ensure cozy comfort. Breakfast is a given at the Auberge. A delicious variety of breakfast foods is set out each morning, and you have access to the kitchen for snacks. A few parking spaces are available without charge behind the Auberge, and free parking is allowed on the surrounding streets. We want our guests to feel comfortable and to be entirely satisfied with their stay. Discover the exclusive shops, restaurants, and art galleries of the Plateau Mont-Royal, which is typical of French Montreal.

Hosts: Celine Boudeau and Jean Lamothe
Rooms: 21 (21PB) $115–277 Canadian
Continental Breakfast
Credit Cards: A B C E
Notes: 5 7 8 9 10 12

NEW CARLISLE

Bay View Manor / Manoir Bay View

395 Rte. 132, Bonaventure E, Box 21
    New Carlisle, QB G0C 1Z0
(418) 752-2725; (418) 752-6718
Web site: www.bbcanada.com/1012.html

Bay View Manor

Comfortable, two-story, wood frame home on the beautiful Gaspé Peninsula across the highway from the beach and beside an eighteen-hole golf course. The building was once a coun-

---

NOTES: Credit cards accepted: A Master Card; B Visa; C American Express; D Discover; E Diners Club; F Other; 2 Personal checks accepted; 3 Lunch available; 4 Dinner available; 5 Open all year;

try store and rural post office. Stroll our quiet, natural beach; see nesting seabirds along the rocky cliffs; watch fishermen tend their nets and lobster traps; enjoy beautiful sunrises and sunsets; view the lighthouse beacon on the nearby point; and fall asleep to the sound of waves on the shore. Explore museums, archaeological caves, fossil site, bird sanctuary, and British Heritage Village. Hike, fish, canoe, horseback ride, or bird-watch.

Host: Helen Sawyer
Rooms: 5 (1PB;4SB) $40–50
Full Breakfast
Notes: 5 7 8 9 10 11

QUEBEC

Hotel Manoir des Remparts

3 ½ des Remparts, Quebec, QB G1R 3R4
(418) 692-2056; Fax (418) 692-1125

Located minutes from the train/bus terminal and the famed Chateau Frontenac. With some rooms overlooking the majestic St. Lawrence River, the Manoir des Remparts boasts one of the most coveted locations available in the old city of Quebec. Newly renovated, it can offer its guests a vast choice of rooms, ranging from a budget room with shared washrooms to an all-inclusive room with private terrace.

Host: Mrs. Sitherary Ngor
Rooms: 34 (23PB;11SB) $45–70
Continental Breakfast
Credit Cards: A B C E
Notes: 5 7 11 12

6 Pets welcome; 7 Children welcome; 8 Tennis nearby; 9 Swimming nearby; 10 Golf nearby; 11 Skiing nearby; 12 May be booked through travel agent

PUERTO RICO

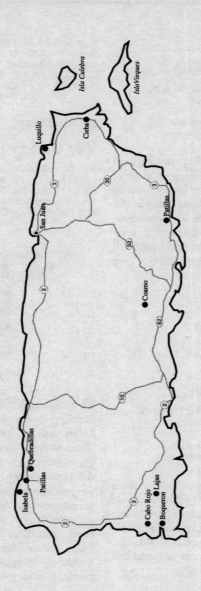

Puerto Rico

ISABELA

Costa Dorada Beach Resort

Emilio Gonzalez #900, Isabela, PR 00662
(787) 872-7595; (877) 975-0101
Fax (787) 872-7595
E-mail: info@costadoradabeach.com
Web site: www.costadoradabeach.com

Hotel in a tropical setting covered with palm trees on a mile-long stretch of white sand beach in the lovely town of Isabela, next to a fishing village. All oceanview rooms with air-conditioning, color cable TV, direct-dial telephone, two pools, tennis and basketball courts, Jacuzzi, restaurant, and bar. Live music on Saturdays.

Rooms: 52 (52PB) $122–150
Continental Breakfast
Credit Cards: A B C D
Notes: 3 4 5 7 8 9 10 12

QUEBRADILLAS

Parador Vistamar

Rd. 113 N #6205, Quebradillas, PR 00678
(787) 895-2065; (888) 391-0606
Fax (787) 895-2294
E-mail: info@paradorvistamar.com
Web site: www.paradorvistamar.com

This hilltop inn has a breathtaking view of Puerto Rico's northwest Gold Coast. Most of the rooms have ocean views, air-conditioning, color cable TV, private bath; some have balconies. Two pools, tennis, restaurant, and bar. Live music on Saturdays.

Host: Mrs. Iris M. Cancel
Rooms: 55 (55PB) $71–105
Continental Breakfast
Credit Cards: A B C F
Notes: 3 4 5 7 8 9 12

SAN JUAN

The Gallery Inn

204–206 Calle Norzagaray
  Old San Juan, PR 00901-1122
(787) 722-1808; Fax (787) 977-3929
E-mail: reservations@thegalleryinn.com
Web site: www.thegalleryinn.com

The Gallery Inn

This wonderful 300-year-old rambling building overlooks the sea atop the north wall of 500-year-old San Juan. Twenty-two beautifully appointed guest rooms are snuggled throughout the 18th-century historic home. Each is air-conditioned, with private bath and telephone, and will delight you with antiques, books, and whimsical trompe l'oeil walls. Our guests have access to many interesting rooms and spaces, including interior courtyards, patios, porticos, and gardens, punctuated by

---

NOTES: Credit cards accepted: A Master Card; B Visa; C American Express; D Discover; E Diners Club; F Other; 2 Personal checks accepted; 3 Lunch available; 4 Dinner available; 5 Open all year;

tropical flowering plants, trickling fountains, and colorful exotic birds. We are only a short walking distance to forts, museums, galleries, boutiques, and a fine selection of restaurants.

Hosts: Jan D'Esopo and Manuco Gandia
Rooms: 22 (22PB) $145–350
Continental Breakfast
Credit Cards: A B C E
Notes: 5 6 7 12

El Canario Inn

1317 Ashford Ave., San Juan, PR 00907
(787) 722-3861; (800) 533-2649
    Fax (787) 722-0391
E-mail: canariopr@aol.com
Web site: www.canariohotels.com

A historic and unique bed and breakfast inn. All guest rooms are air-conditioned with private baths, cable TVs, and telephones and come with a complimentary continental breakfast. Our tropical patios and sundeck provide a friendly and informal atmosphere. Centrally located near the beach, casinos, restaurants, boutiques, and public transportation.

Rooms: 25 (25PB) $75–129
Continental Breakfast
Credit Cards: A B C D E
Notes: 5 7 9 12

U.S. VIRGIN ISLANDS

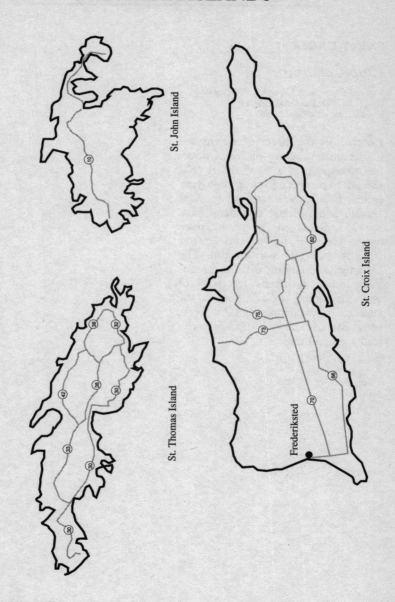

U.S. Virgin Islands

SAINT CROIX

Club Comanche

1 Strand Street, Saint Croix, VI 00820-5002
(800) 524-2066; Fax (340) 713-9145
E-mail: comanche@islands.net

Located in the heart of downtown
Christiansted, in the center of duty-
free shopping is a small hotel "old
enough to please and young enough to
tease." Enjoy the charm of an Old
Danish Main House that dates back
to 1735. Relax on the pool terrace
overlooking the harbor and let our
friendly staff take care of you. The
Comanche restaurant with its famous
West Indian cuisine and the charm of
open-air dining. In addition to the
expected tropical amenities, St. Croix
offers Buck Island with its underwater
trail reefs and trails.

Rooms: 30 (30PB) $50.00
No Breakfast Served
Credit Cards: A B C E
Notes: 3 4

NOTES: Credit cards accepted: A Master Card; B Visa; C American Express; D Discover; E Diners
Club; F Other; 2 Personal checks accepted; 3 Lunch available; 4 Dinner available; 5 Open all year;